Norton Menzies Fletcher

**Transactions Of The Highland and Agricultural Society Of Scotland**

Vol. XIV - Forth Series

Norton Menzies Fletcher

**Transactions Of The Highland and Agricultural Society Of Scotland**
*Vol. XIV - Forth Series*

ISBN/EAN: 9783348010313

Printed in Europe, USA, Canada, Australia, Japan

Cover: Foto ©ninafisch / pixelio.de

More available books at **www.hansebooks.com**

# TRANSACTIONS

OF THE

# HIGHLAND AND AGRICULTURAL SOCIETY OF SCOTLAND

WITH

AN ABSTRACT OF THE PROCEEDINGS AND THE PREMIUMS
OFFERED BY THE SOCIETY IN 1882.

### PUBLISHED ANNUALLY.

SEMPER ARMIS
NUNC ET INDUSTRIA

FOURTH SERIES.

VOL. XIV.

EDITED UNDER THE SUPERINTENDENCE OF FLETCHER NORTON MENZIES,
SECRETARY TO THE SOCIETY.

EDINBURGH:

WILLIAM BLACKWOOD & SONS, 45 GEORGE STREET.
AND 37 PATERNOSTER ROW, LONDON.
1882.

# WORKS ON AGRICULTURE, &c.

---

JOURNAL OF AGRICULTURE, AND TRANSACTIONS OF
THE HIGHLAND AND AGRICULTURAL SOCIETY OF SCOTLAND.
Second Series, 1828 to 1843, 21 vols., bound in cloth, £3, 3s.
Third Series, 1843 to 1865, 22 vols., bound in cloth, £4, 4s.

INDEX TO THE FIRST, SECOND, AND THIRD SERIES OF
THE TRANSACTIONS OF THE HIGHLAND AND AGRICULTURAL
SOCIETY OF SCOTLAND FROM 1799 TO 1865. Cloth, 5s.

TRANSACTIONS OF THE HIGHLAND AND AGRICUL-
TURAL SOCIETY OF SCOTLAND. Fourth Series, 1866–71, 6 numbers,
sewed, 4s. each; 1872–82, 11 volumes, cloth, 5s. each, published annually.

REPORT ON THE PRESENT STATE OF THE AGRICULTURE
OF SCOTLAND, arranged under the auspices of the Highland and Agricultural Society. Presented at the International Agricultural Congress
at Paris in June 1878. Cloth, 5s.

DICTIONARIUM SCOTO-CELTICUM: A Dictionary of the Gaelic
Language, in two volumes. Compiled and published under the direction of
the Highland Society of Scotland, 1828. Bound in cloth, £7, 7s.; 6 copies
on extra paper, £10, 10s.

PRACTICAL REMARKS ON AGRICULTURAL DRAINAGE.
By WILLIAM W. Hozier of Tannochside. Prize Report, published under
the auspices of the Society, 1870. Cloth, 1s.

HUMANITY TO ANIMALS, being Extracts from Prize Essays on
the most effectual method of inculcating that duty in Elementary Schools.
Published under the auspices of the Society. Sewed, 3d.

HISTORY OF THE HIGHLAND AND AGRICULTURAL
SOCIETY OF SCOTLAND, with Notices of Anterior Societies for the
Promotion of Agriculture in Scotland. By ALEXANDER RAMSAY. Demy
8vo. Cloth, 16s.

---

*The above Works can be had on application to* WILLIAM BLACKWOOD & SONS,
*45 George Street, Edinburgh; and 37 Paternoster Row, London.*

# CONTENTS.

# TRANSACTIONS

OF

# THE HIGHLAND AND AGRICULTURAL SOCIETY OF SCOTLAND.

## THE FIRST AND FUNDAMENTAL PRINCIPLE IN AGRICULTURE.

By George Bruce, Pennan Farm, Fraserburgh.

*[Premium—Ten Sovereigns.]*

To explain and solve this problem, I propose first to look at the negative side of the question, under the following headings :—

I. Artificial Manures used as Auxiliaries, and what effect have they had upon the cultivated area of this country?

II. Artificial Manures used in large quantities to continuous cropping, and have they upheld the fertility of the soil at a paying cost?

III. Our Rotation System, and has it fulfilled its mission in upholding the fertility of the soil?

IV. To prove the affirmative under the heading "Vegetable Matter."

### I. *Artificial Manures used as Auxiliaries, and what Effect have they had upon the Cultivated Area of this Country?*

Until about fifty years ago, I believe there were but little artificial manures applied to the soil. Then, the first thing that presents itself is, upon what did the crops in former ages feed? The Creator of the earth simply told Adam to till the ground. The needful fertility was evidently ready at hand in shape of vegetable matter, and we have every reason to believe that little else had been used as a fertiliser in this country until a recent period. In its natural state, vegetable matter varies exceedingly, both in quantity and quality. What is generally called the surface-soil is composed chiefly of the remains of the vegetable matter accumulated on the surface of the earth before tillage began, with the exception of what man has removed from one place to another, and this has been done to a certain extent all over Scotland. There is on almost every farm of long standing a superior field or two, or, perhaps, several parts of different fields, unmistakably pointing out the site of the ancient townships, to which the vegetable matter had been carried, and the adjacent land of higher altitude bears the marks of robbery to this day. With these exceptions, almost invariably the lowest lying lands and hollows are of the best quality. The low-lying lands having been formerly overrun by water from that of a higher altitude, the vegetable matter accumulated there was of the finest quality and of greatest depth; but these, no doubt, having borne more than a fair share of cropping, and the produce carried to other parts, the land is now more equalised. As the demand for farm produce increased, and the cultivated area extended, and tenant farmers meantime having been prohibited from carrying vegetable matter to make good the deficiency caused by cropping, the rotation system was evidently resorted to, in order to obtain a further supply of vegetable matter. But when specially-prepared manures were brought within convenient reach of farmers a power was put into their hands, either for good or evil, that they never had before, and during the last thirty years large quantities of these manures have been applied to the soil by farmers—not generally with the view of keeping up the fertility of the soil, but as auxiliaries, and to act upon the vegetable matter in the soil, in order to raise larger crops, and so long as the soil contained a certain quantity of vegetable matter these manures served the purpose, and paid the farmer. From twenty to thirty years ago three hundredweight of these manures applied to the acre along with half dung would have produced from twenty-five to thirty tons of turnips per acre. The same quantity of these manures applied to the same land now will scarcely produce fifteen tons per acre. Let us look also at our corn crops. Do they produce as much per acre as they did thirty-five years ago? From a pamphlet published by Mr. Horne, banker, Rhynie, Aberdeenshire, I learn that the average return per acre for that county at present is scarcely four quarters per acre, whereas forty years ago it was five quarters four bushels, or twelve bushels more. This seems a very important statement, when to this deficiency there has to be added to profit and loss account the amount of large bills for manures and feeding stuffs that was not then in existence, even though there have been added to the cultivated area a few thousand acres of inferior land. Startling as it will, no doubt, appear to many, yet we must inquire more particularly into this matter. If land is reduced in vegetable matter so that the produce is diminished by twelve bushels an acre of oats, what does it amount to? One quarter four bushels at twenty shillings per quarter is equal to thirty shillings per acre, and on a farm of 200 acres on a five-course rotation, say on eighty acres of oats, there would be a deficiency of 120 quarters, and at twenty shillings amounts to £120 a year. But this does not represent all the diminished return to the farmer, for the crops of turnips and grass are more dependent upon a good supply of vegetable matter in the soil than grain crops. Barring exceptions, I think it will be conceded that our special manures—as they have been applied to the *bare soil*—have failed to keep up the fertility of the land. I am inclined to go further, and say that along with certain conditions they have been the means of diminishing the fertility and value of the cultivated area of this country to an extent not yet fully admitted by the few nor thought of by the many. And I am astonished that this point has escaped the notice of our men of science, because several of these gentlemen have frequently written about a certain *fertility* being in the soil, and of its being extracted from the soil, but have always alluded to it in vague terms; never stating what it was composed of. I would like to ask those who are acquainted with chemistry, what the natural sap of a soil rich in vegetable matter is composed of. It is not water, for every practical farmer knows that it does not dry so soon as rain-water; this substance in rich land has a wonderful faculty in defending drought when not unduly exposed.

Seeing that the land had lost that healthy condition to produce the fine strong clover as of yore, and the sound turnips of thirty years ago, it was surely time for our men of science to have inquired into the cause of this unhealthy condition of the soil. A really skilful doctor would have endeavoured to have found out the disorder before attempting a cure. This has not been done by our men of science, consequently failure and disappointment have been the rule at our experimental stations. I may fairly ask, what is an unmanured plot? I answer Nature half-stripped of her natural fertility, a standard of poverty set up to test the value of different kinds of manures. I cannot discern any principle in such a mode of procedure, and one thing is certain, that no farmer can follow such a practice long with profit; and what is not profitable in agriculture must be set down as wrong in principle, and consequently sooner or later abandoned. Have the value of these manures been tested upon a sound basis at our experimental stations? I answer, No. Before this can be done the whole surface-soil containing vegetable matter—living and dead—would require to be removed, and the subsoil trenched up for the purpose, or these stations removed to an altitude 500 feet above sea-level, and to the poorest soil there that can be found.' Experiments in these two cases would be more truthful in telling the value of the manures alone. Would these manures leave a profit without the vegetable matter in the soil? My experience tells me that it is nothing short of a delusion to think of such a thing, and how such a line of action has ever been adopted at our experimental stations is beyond my conjecture. Vegetable matter cannot be displaced with profit, because it is the cheapest source from whence to supply nitrogen to all the crops of the farm. It was the first manure. It may be said to be the manure of the Creator. And there are instances, where, *by application*, it has stood the test of continuous cropping throughout the history of agriculture. Therefore, to preserve it in paying quantity in the soil is the first principle in agriculture, and will, undoubtedly, direct the future of land management; for it is indisputable that dead vegetable matter of good quality contains every ingredient necessary for the production of all the crops of the farm. If our men of science wish to test the value of vegetable matter as a fertiliser against these special manures, then let them break up a piece of rich grass land full of vegetable matter, and apply these special manures in any quantity they please to land containing no vegetable matter whatever. Let this be done both to root crops and grain crops, and publish the results and profit and loss in both cases, when, I am sure, the mind of the agricultural community will be directed into a new channel.

A theory has gone abroad that if a certain field is rich in any particular manure, farmers need only apply such other manures as the field is deficient in to secure good results; but to make this practicable it would require an army of chemists continually about the country to analyse not only every field, but different parts of every field, which cannot be carried out. But supposing there were no hindrances to farmers putting down their land to grass, would they not have at their command a much surer and better way of knowing what kind of manure every spot of the farm would require than by analysis of the soil; for there is nothing that will show the condition of the land better than three and four-years-old grass,—and this is the time to supply deficiencies, which a practical farmer would not have much difficulty in doing. And I think it is good practice not to plough up any grass land until it has first been made sufficiently rich in vegetable matter so as to support, at least, two paying grain crops and one turnip crop without any manure, excepting a moderate quantity of byre dung applied to the turnip crop. I believe it will be necessary here to explain that by adopting this system the whole of the present method of farming would be revolutionised. The object being to increase the quantity and quality of vegetable matter in the soil,— and rye grass by cultivation, having become a kind of cereal,

with few root leaves, and on its attaining the second or third
year becomes so weak, or dies altogether, that it will not pay to
top-dress it alone. It would, therefore, be necessary to sow along
with one bushel of rye-grass and ten pounds of clover per acre,
the following grasses, namely, four pounds meadow fescue, two
pounds hard fescue, four pounds cocks'-foot, two pounds Timothy,
and one pound crested dog's-tail. Top-dressing grass land with
artificial manures will then pay better than when applied to grain
crops or turnips. And I may mention that I have found bone meal
and sheep-feeding with corn and cake, &c., to answer well. It will
be seen, however, that the rotation system, as at present arranged,
puts a complete stop to this kind of farming by preventing the
proper use of natural grasses. Dr. Lawes has informed us that
*under tillage* there is a loss of nitrogen passing down through
the subsoil beyond the reach of plants, and away by the drains;
and is it not the fact that the great bulk of the manures used in
this country have been applied to the *bare soil?* Taking the
country, then, as a whole, the loss must be very great. Why
not apply the bulk of our purchased manures to our grass land?
The nitrogen derived from these manures would then not only
be saved, but the most valuable fertiliser to all the other crops
of the farm would be improved in quantity and quality, in
accordance with the kinds and quantities of the manures applied
This branch of agriculture is completely under the control of
the farmer; and, being so, it can be made to control all the
other crops of the farm. It is nature restored in an improved
condition. And, fortunately, there is no discord on this point
between our scientific gentlemen and the farming community.

Dr. Aitken says, at page 246 of the *Transactions of the Highland and Agricultural Society* for 1880:—" It would seem, then,
by judicious manuring alone the herbage of pasture land is,
within certain limits, capable of being controlled;" and at bottom
of page 244 of same *Transactions* he says:—" It has been observed that nitrates find their way more rapidly through the
soil, and come sooner in contact with the rootlets of deep rooting
plants such as *grasses*, and also that they effect a marked change
in the character of the lower soil and subsoil, rendering it more
porous and pulverulent." Both these quotations are of the
highest value. It is an unerring truth that all land out of
condition is hard and bad to labour, and that land in high condition is soft and mouldy and easy to labour. But the change in
the soil and subsoil, strictly speaking, is not effected by the nitrogenous manures, but by the rootlets of the grasses and clovers
forcing their way down through the soil and subsoil. This causes
this marvellous change, for marvellous it is. Therefore, whatever fertilising agents are made use of to improve the quantity
and quality of grass land effects this change in the soil. Thus,
the surface-soil is deepened and improved; and, when such

land is again brought under cultivation, the rootlets of the various crops follow the dead vegetable matter deep down into the soil, extracting nitrogen therefrom as required,  For the same reason all crops thrive well after a crop of beans; they leave a large quantity of vegetable matter in the soil, by their rootlets, when in vigorous growth the previous year, having penetrated deep into the soil, bringing nitrogen from afar to be made use of by the following crops.

Before leaving this part of the subject I would point out some of the results of the use of special manures.  In the first place, they were the means of raising larger crops, which paid the farmer. Next in order, they raised the value of land by farmers outbidding each other.  And lastly, they have been the means, along with the rotation system and other conditions in leases, of reducing the vegetable matter in the soil to a state below which profitable cultivation cannot now be carried on.

II. *Artificial Manures used in Large Quantities to Continuous Cropping; and have they upheld the Fertility of the Soil at a Paying Cost?*

I can only refer to the experiments at Rothamsted for proof under this heading, as published in the *Transactions of the Highland and Agricultural Society* for 1880, being a description of a visit to this experimental station by Dr. Andrew P. Aitken.  It is unfortunate, however, for these experiments that Dr. Aitken did not give us some idea of the composition of the soil at Rothamsted, and of the profit and loss attending these experiments.  On these all-important points we are left to judge from the produce of the unmanured plot, and from the expense of the manures applied.  Twenty-four years ago the produce of barley from the unmanured plot would have been about three quarters per acre.  This of itself shows that the soil at Rothamsted was then fairly rich in vegetable matter; and from the fact that this plot, after twenty-four years of continuous cropping, is still giving nearly two quarters of barley per acre, the belief is forced upon one that the soil at Rothamsted must contain a depth of vegetable matter becoming gradually available for the use of crops.  Our scientific gentlemen have obviously overlooked this fundamental element in the soil, and drawn conclusions from the use of certain manures at Rothamsted that can never be attained to upon a soil devoid of vegetable matter.  This appears to explain why so many different opinions are held with regard to Dr. Lawes' experiments. Favourable as such a soil is for the application of special manures, yet these experiments afford strong proof on the negative side of the problem I have on hand.

On examining the barley experiments at page 249, we find

the experiments extend over twenty-four years, in two periods of twelve years each. At the top of the last period stands the unmanured plot with a diminished produce of six bushels per acre below the first period; the next experiment is with 400 lbs. superphosphate *continuously*, and the diminished produce is over seven bushels per acre; next 400 lbs. mixed minerals, and the produce has diminished seven bushels; next 800 lbs. superphosphate and mixed minerals, and the produce has diminished nine bushels; next 200 lbs. ammonia salts and 400 lbs. superphosphate = 600 lbs., and the produce has diminished two bushels; next 600 lbs. ammonia salts and mixed minerals, and the diminished produce is four bushels; next 200 lbs. ammonia salts and 800 lbs. superphosphate and mixed minerals = 1000 lbs., diminished produce three bushels; next 275 lbs. nitrate of soda, diminished produce seven bushels; and farther down the list of these experiments there are larger applications of these manures; but all show that the crops have diminished more or less, with the single exception of the farm-yard dung, which is of course wholly made up of vegetable matter in a forward state of decomposition, and thereby the fertility and value of the land has been upheld.

But, were these experiments tested by profit and loss, as they must be before they can establish a right or wrong principle, I fear that no farmer could then follow the example. But the diminished produce, as shown by this table, does not show the full diminution over the twenty-four years. This table only shows the *average* of the second twelve years compared with the *average* of the first twelve years. Were we in a position to deduct the produce of the *twenty-fourth* year from the produce of the *first* year, probably the diminution over the whole experiments in this table would average about eight bushels per acre. The diminished value of the land in this instance in twenty-four years by continuous cropping would thus be the value of eight bushels barley per acre; and, valued at thirty-five shillings per acre, capitalised at twenty-five years' purchase, is equal to £43, 15s. per acre. This looks like a good reason for the distress in the agricultural districts of England. At all events it shows that, as vegetable matter decreases in the soil, so does the produce per acre; and on an average the unmanured plot has not diminished so much as the manured plots. This table of experiments is specially valuable in demonstrating that no other manure will uphold the fertility of the soil under continuous cropping but vegetable matter; and that the produce of the manured plots have been largely fed off the lost fertility of the soil, namely at the rate of 36s. 6d. annually at twenty-five years' purchase, or if taken at thirty years' purchase, the annual loss would be 43s. 6d. Therefore, if the value of the lost fertility drawn from the soil was added to the cost of the manures employed, I fear the result would not show this to be a profitable method of farming.

### III. *Our Rotation System; and has it fulfilled its Mission in Upholding the Fertility of the Soil?*

The principle here adopted is right so far as a new supply of vegetable matter can be obtained by putting down land two or three years to grass; for without doubt the origin of this *make-shift* was to obtain such a supply; but now that land in general has become so reduced in vegetable matter, three years in grass, with rye-grass alone, are quite insufficient to bring it up to a paying condition.

The fact that a tenant-farmer is bound to cultivate under any given rotation is wrong in principle, because farms and districts differ from each other so very widely that no prescribed rule can be laid down to suit all. I shall here mention a few circumstances under which enforced tillage becomes a disheartening and unprofitable business, namely, a farm may be too steep, or surrounded with bad roads, and far from markets. Under these circumstances tillage is too expensive to pay, even though the land be good. The elevation may be too high for profitable tillage. The vegetable matter may be of poor quality, or reduced below a paying quantity; and the tenant being bound to plough it up at a fixed age, renders him powerless in restoring the fertility of the soil. The rotation system also prevents a tenant from putting down any of the farm to permanent pasture. Another condition that goes hand in hand with the rotation system on many properties is that value for grass left by a tenant is restricted to three months' growth, or, at farthest, to what is called the season. This has a lowering effect towards the end of a lease, and tends to the withholding of the seeds necessary to the production of good grass. Professedly, the rotation system is intended to prevent farmers from reducing the fertility of the soil; but here proprietors restrict to a minimum the value of that very fertility when a farmer has it to dispose of. Surely it is possible to let out land to farmers under more reasonable conditions, and protect at the same time the interests of proprietors. A provision in agreements that a certain proportion of the arable land should always be under grass, and that none should be ploughed up under a specified age, would, in my opinion, secure good farming, and at the same time leave farmers at liberty to select the system best adapted to the holding. And if there were a certainty of receiving full value for all grass land of any age at a tenant's removal, this would go far to prevent the exhausted state of farms at the expiry of leases. Under conditions like the foregoing, farmers would learn how to manage grass land, which is the first step in the ladder to profitable farming. As at present enforced, the rotation system is gradually but surely diminishing the produce from the cultivated area of this country. It is surely one of the greatest blunders in modern agriculture to prevent farmers from improving grass land, or from putting it down to permanent pasture, which all rotations do. I know that there is such a thing as a six-course rotation, with three crops of grass, and only one crop of oats following; but this does not encourage a farmer in the use of natural grasses, and without these grasses top-dressing grass land is not done to the best advantage. To put land into a *highly-paying condition* (and why not attain to this?) less than seven years in grass comes short of the desired end. A five, six, or seven shift is a neatly-calculated, schoolboy-like transaction, without giving a farmer scope for his skill or a chance to better his circumstances. It is different when you break up a seven-year-old grass park: a vegetable manure is then obtained that will last longer than byre dung. Supposing a farmer enters to an exhausted farm, where vegetable matter, living and dead, is very meagre, and at the expiry of his lease leaves the land full of vegetable matter, both living and dead. Query—How is this vegetable matter to be valued, so that the farmer may receive compensation for it? If he is not to receive *full* value for fine old grass, he will certainly plough it up; and if he is not to receive value for dead vegetable matter left in excess, he will certainly use it up. This, in my opinion, is a more important question than compensation for unexhausted manures, because it is from vegetable matter that the bulk and weight of all the crops of the farm are derived. It is essential, therefore, to profitable farming that it be in the soil in large quantity; consequently, it is of prior importance and of more value to any holding than special manures. These manures have never been known to supply the place of vegetable matter. They have never been known to add fertility to the soil when applied to raise a turnip crop or a grain crop; they have only been known as the means of raising larger crops to be carried away. Let me ask, then, upon what grounds is it proposed to value these manures to an ingoing tenant?

From experience and observation I have come to be of opinion that cultivation more than 500 feet above sea-level is not profitable on an average of seasons in the north of Aberdeenshire, and that the same land would pay better under improved pasture. In Shetland there is very little cultivation more than 100 feet above sea-level, and the greater part is under 50 feet. The consequence is that almost invariably the harvest commences in August, and is finished before the crops in the high-lying districts of Aberdeenshire and Banffshire are cut.

### IV. *Vegetable Matter.*

I shall now endeavour to show the value of vegetable matter as a fertiliser. Having farmed in three different counties in Scotland, and having expended perhaps as much money on manures and feeding stuffs as any other farmer to a like extent of land, I shall in the first place give a brief sketch of my own experience.

The first two farms occupied by me in different counties were both low-lying farms, with a fair supply of vegetable matter in the soil. The first about an average of 120 feet above sea-level; the second varying from only ten to twenty feet above the sea. On both these farms I had little difficulty in raising full crops, and on the latter, after having it down to grass seven years, and after two crops of oats, I have had thirty tons an acre of turnips, with a moderate quantity of byre dung alone, and the grain crops were too much to stand. Having already referred to the luxuriance of the grass on this farm in a former essay, I pass on to the third farm, bordering the Moray Frith. The height above sea-level varies from 250 feet to 550 feet, and upon the old red sandstone and red conglomerate rocks. This farm had been worked on a five course rotation previous to my entry, and so completely exhausted of vegetable matter, that I found with heavy top-dressings of nitrogenous and phosphatic manures mixed, I could not pass three and a half quarters oats per acre on an average, and eight hundredweight of Peruvian guano and bone meal of best quality mixed, along with half dung, would only give me about an average of fifteen tons of turnips per acre, and the grass was miserable. The farm being naturally dry, with considerable fall, no doubt tended to lessen the quantity of vegetable-matter in the soil. It was a losing concern, and to have pursued the former course of management was evidently to lose a deal of money. Having had my attention drawn to the virtue of vegetable matter as a fertiliser long before, although never put to the test in such a fashion as this, I soon came to the conclusion that I should plough up no grass land until I had first enriched it in vegetable matter. First of all I sowed natural grasses on all the grass land, and commenced top-dressing it with bone meal and shell sand, and having continued to feed sheep on it, with cake, oats, and turnips, &c., ever since, the change is very great. The numbers of both cattle and sheep that can now be maintained on the farm are quite doubled. But there is one part of the farm deserving particular notice, namely, that part bounded by rocks, 400 feet high. Adjoining these rocks the surface soil appears to be deeper than any other part of the farm, and of a pretty reddish colour, and farmers are ready to exclaim, "Oh, what fine land!" If colour and depth of soil would make fine land they would have been right, but unfortunately it does not;

this soil had been blown from the rocks by strong gales of wind, consequently devoid of vegetable matter, and is much the worst paying land on the farm; indeed, it appears as if it were impossible to bring it up to a paying condition, the effect of byre dung and other manures on it only lasts about four years when it is clean gone. Such land would make a capital experimental station for trying the capabilities of different kinds of manures.

I would now direct attention to the American system of cultivation. I learn that when vegetable matter becomes reduced below a paying quantity in the soil they do not resort to purchased manures for a supply of nitrogen, but remove the establishment to a new supply of this fertiliser in shape of vegetable matter from virgin soil, showing clearly which of the two they consider the cheapest source of supply. The principle of cheap nitrogen is here brought to the front, and the problem solved by the selection of vegetable matter as against purchased manures. No doubt much of the vegetable matter in America could be improved in quality, but the quantity at their command is so overflowing that quality has not yet come to be a consideration. The Shetland people have also solved this problem in their practice in favour of vegetable matter, but by a different method from that of the Americans. They carry on to a portion of their arable land yearly a certain quantity of vegetable matter of the best quality they can find; and I have been a witness for nineteen years to see crops raised by neighbours, by the application of vegetable matter alone, that would astonish farmers in any part of the country. I speak within bounds when I say that twenty-five tons an acre of turnips is not above an average crop, and this, be it noticed, is produced without manure of any kind having been applied to the turnip crop. The manure was applied the previous year to the corn crops, and farther, this land never at any time received sixpence worth of purchased manures; not even lime. And what is still more remarkable, this land has been under continuous cropping for an unknown period of time. We have here the clearest proof of the value of vegetable matter as a fertiliser, and proof also that rest is not essential to the production of full crops of both turnips and grain, and that vegetable matter alone, if supplied in proper quantity and quality, will uphold land in the highest state of fertility under continuous cropping for an unknown period. Thus I claim to have solved the problem, the title of this essay, that the first and fundamental principle in agriculture is to preserve and uphold a paying quantity of vegetable matter in the soil. It must have been the misunderstanding of this great principle that caused our rotation system to be indiscriminately enforced under all circumstances. And this system, combined with the use of special manures, the effects of which has also been misunderstood, has had a baneful effect upon the agriculture of this country.

It cannot be too clearly put before landed proprietors and farmers that it is the effects left behind the use of these manures, *i.e.*, the removal or non-removal from the land of the crops to which they are applied, that constitutes them either fertilisers or exhausters of fertility. When applied to the bare soil, to raise a turnip crop or a grain crop, they reduce vegetable matter, and thus allow a larger quantity of it to be carried off the land, leaving the soil so much the poorer; but when applied to grass land, and the produce consumed thereon, they add fertility abundantly; and I cannot see that ground bones form any exception to this rule, but, being less soluble than other manures of this class, they reserve their strength for the grass period of the rotation, and so come in as a fertiliser, and, consequently, have always been a favourite manure with all good farmers under any circumstances.

A few words more about Shetland farming might be interesting. Almost without exception farmers have a right to pasture cattle and ponies on the adjacent hills. This allows them to carry a large stock in comparison to the extent of their arable land. The quantity of corn and fodder produced from the arable land to supply food for their animals during a stormy winter rules the number of animals that can be maintained upon the pasture at their command. This induces the Shetland farmer to have every foot of his arable land under continuous cropping, and the crops of oats and bere are considered of more importance than turnips; hence the byre dung is applied to the corn crops. And what kind of manure is it? In summer a large quantity of thin green turf is cut from the side of a hill outside the town dykes and dried, then carried home and built into stacks. This vegetable matter is alone used for litter, and the whole of the fodder, and a considerable quantity of the corn as well, is used for food. The byres are not cleaned out perhaps from harvest until seedtime, but the cattle bindings are raised up as the manure accumulates, and the cattle are moved from one side of the byre to the other. We have here the principle of covered court-yards in a primitive fashion. There is nothing new under the sun. In good weather the cattle are pastured on the hills outside the town dykes bringing their droppings to the townships. In spring this home-made nitrogen, *i.e.*, vegetable matter, is applied to the land, and ploughed, or dug down, and some very fine crops are raised by this method, and where they are not good it is generally the result of bad tillage, probably performed by Shetland ponies. Where these townships have been put down to permanent pasture, they have invariably become the finest of grass land, and form a very interesting study. In the Island of Unst, where the rotation system has lately been introduced, I have seen the strongest crops of clover on these townships that ever I remember having seen in my experience. The fact is here again established that vegetable matter reproduces itself in all the ordinary crops of the farm, just in accordance with the quantity and quality of it contained in the soil; this truth, despised as it has been during the past thirty years, defies contradiction.

For as much as was written last year in the *North British Agriculturist* newspaper and other places about the green lands or old townships of Sutherlandshire, no one explained how these lands at first became enriched. The present wealthy farmers of Sutherlandshire have told us that it is next to impossible for them to restore these lands to the high prestige at which they stood eighty years ago. Notwithstanding that they have first-class roads, railways, and abundance of manures and feeding stuffs at their command, none of which the men of old, who improved these lands, had in their day, need I say that these lands were improved by the application of vegetable matter alone, and by the same method that the farming in Shetland is being conducted at the present day. And we may judge of its lasting properties from the fact that it has stood a process of carrying away of this fertility by the sheep to the tops of the hills for a period of eighty years. This is another proof that vegetable matter is entitled to the first place in agriculture. Tillage added nothing to the improvement of this land. Tillage is never resorted to but to take something out of the land. Those who write about ploughing up grass land to renew it do not understand the subject. There are not a few farmers who tell us that they have better crops of oats after two-year-old grass than after three-year-old grass, and use this as an argument in favour of the five course rotation. Their averment may be true, but where it is true it shows that any former supply of vegetable matter in the soil is nearly exhausted, and that now they are confined to the byre dung for a supply of this fertiliser, which, when applied to the turnip crop, becomes also exhausted by the time it reaches the third year's grass. And as common rye grass and common red clover die out about the same time, or get weak, there may really be less vegetable matter in the soil in three-year-old grass than in two-year-old,—so the belief that the crop following it would not be so good is not without foundation, but the argument is in favour of the principle treated of in this essay, and strikes peculiarly hard against the six shift with three grasses; but the fact that nine-tenths of farmers in Scotland do not sow the proper seeds necessary to supply good grass all the year round, nor of a permanent character, is fatal to really high farming. True, manures and time will bring in these grasses, but it takes seven or eight years to do so, which is a serious loss. How can rye grass, a plant that dies when two or three years old, and almost destitute of root leaves, be expected to restore fertility to an exhausted soil? It is a mistake to expend money in top-dressing rye-grass alone, but it is one of the greatest mistakes in modern agriculture to place farmers in a position where they cannot profitably make use of natural grasses for enriching the soil. It may be asked if land is valued upon a sound basis at the present time? I leave this question for the consideration of those more immediately concerned, and shall conclude this essay by giving it as my opinion that the most urgent thing for those connected with the management of arable land is that those acquainted with chemistry should come to an early understanding as to what the first and fundamental principle in agriculture is. If this were clearly defined, the different opinions at present prevailing about carrying out of details would lose much of their present importance, and more attention would be given to the profitable application of capital to the soil.

Since this essay was put into the hands of The Highland and Agricultural Society last year, and subsequent to several allusions made to the subject of the essay in the public prints, Dr. Lawes issued a pamphlet which contained the following paragraph, namely :—

"Instead of regarding the operations of draining, fallows, liming, tillage, and the use of *mineral manures* as so many ways of increasing the stock of fertility, they would be more correctly described as processes for turning to account the existing but dormant elements of fertility contained in the land. They increase the produce, but at the expense of the stock of fertility in the soil."

---

## INOCULATION AS A PREVENTION OF PLEURO-PNEUMONIA.

### By R. RUTHERFORD, V.S., Edinburgh.

[*Premium—Ten Sovereigns.*]

IN considering the value of the practice of inoculation for the prevention of that malady in cattle known as "Contagious Pleuropneumonia," it would seem to me to be advisable to do so from two points of view, a scientific and an economic, the latter especially,—for it is not only necessary that the operation be sound in principle, it must be practicable to be of value at all, and must in results, favourable or otherwise, be able to bear the crucial test of comparison between it and any other mode of dealing with the disease. How far inoculation can answer these requirements I shall endeavour to show.

The practice of inoculation for the prevention of pleuropneumonia is now about thirty years old. It is based upon the now generally accepted theory of the disease being an eruptive fever, one of a group, some of which are common to man and some to the lower animals. Or to put it more plainly, pleuro-pneumonia is not from a pathologist's point of view, what at first sight it would appear to be, and what for a long time it really was considered, viz., "a disease of the lungs simply," analogous for instance to pleuro-pneumonia in the horse, or to the same disease sporadically occurring in cattle, diseases which have their origin in causes which are ordinary and quite remote from the causes of the epizootic malady; but a contagious eruptive fever, of which the changes that take place in the lungs, are a symptomatic feature.

The fever is the disease, the lung-changes a result, in the same way that in variola, or smallpox, there is firstly the variolous fever, then the succeeding eruption on the skin. In the former Nature does her best to throw the disease off through the lungs, in the latter through the skin.

Perhaps the greatest triumph of medicine (vaccination excepted), was the discovery of inoculation, which, prior to its introduction into this country by Lady Montagu, had long been known and successfully practised in the East. Applied to man the operation technically means the imparting of smallpox to a previously healthy person, by introducing the specific virus of the disease into the system through an incision or puncture in the skin, the result being variola or smallpox of a type milder, and the occurrence of which practically gives exemption from an attack of the true disease. Applied to cattle, the operation of inoculation means the introduction into the system through an opening of the skin of the specific virus of contagious pleuro-pneumonia, the result being a mild degree of fever, with certain phenomena of an eruptive character at the seat of the operation, the occurrence of which also gives exemption from the true disease.

So far the operation in man bears a resemblance to that in cattle, but no further, for between the two there is this great distinguishing difference, the artificially induced disease in man is contagious, whereas it has been clearly and indisputably shown, and placed beyond all doubt, that the conditions, the disease, produced by inoculating healthy cattle with the virus of pleuro-pneumonia are non-contagious. Having in view the fact that the contagium of pleuro-pneumonia is given off, I would say almost solely by the lungs, the reason for such difference is not far to seek, and rests in the fact that inoculation never produces lung-disease. As already hinted, and as I shall show further on, the eruptive phenomena, which next to the fever, are the leading features of inoculation, occur at the seat of operation.

It is fortunate that this is so, had it been otherwise, had the lungs as a result of the operation become affected in the same way that they do when an animal contracts the disease, the operation would be inexpedient, dangerous, and so valueless, since each animal which chanced to be operated upon would become a contagious centre, capable of disseminating the disease, quite as much as an ordinarily affected one. I believe myself correct in affirming, that this fact, which is really one of the most important in connection with our subject, is not generally known. In a paper like this, however, the matter must be placed beyond all doubt, and I am glad to be able to do so, not only from my own experience, but by the testimony of those who have made inoculation the subject of their investigation.

Dr. Willems of Hasselt in Belgium, who was the first to be successful with the operation, thus puts it:—"By inoculating pleuro-pneumonia a new disease is produced, the affection of the lungs, with all its peculiar characters being localised on some part of the exterior." *vide* Williams' *Veterinary Medicine*, p. 152, and again on page 153 of the same volume, we find the Belgian commission arrived at the conclusion, that the "Inoculation of the liquid extracted from the lungs of an animal affected with pleuro-pneumonia does not transmit to healthy animals of the same species, the same disease—at all events so far as its seat is concerned."

During my visits to Australia, I learned from Mr. Graham Mitchell, F.R.C.V.S., and from Mr. Alexander Bruce, chief inspector of stock for New South Wales, both of whom have had a long and extensive experience of inoculation, that their observations had led them conclusively to the same opinion.

Better than all, however, is the evidence which I can offer myself. During the last two or three years I have effectively inoculated between 2000 and 3000 head of cattle, milkers chiefly, of which number at least 2500 have since been slaughtered for public consumption. Most of them have been killed at the abattoirs of Edinburgh and Leith, and have always been found to have perfectly unaffected healthy lungs, so far at least as pleuro has been concerned. I do not in the whole course of my experience know of a single instance to the contrary, and have no hesitation in saying it may be taken as a well-ascertained fact, that "An inoculated animal, healthy at the time of operation, cannot possibly communicate pleuro-pneumonia to another one." I have frequently been asked the question, "Will an inoculated animal contract pleuro-pneumonia?" To such question as the result of my experience I can with confidence reply, No. I do not know of a single instance of such, but I would draw attention to the fact that I emphasise the word inoculated. In unskilful or careless hands, or from other causes, an animal may have been put through the form of the operation and still not have been inoculated, such a one may undoubtedly contract the disease; but I say that no animal will contract it that, after having been operated upon, has exhibited the characteristic features of inoculation, in proof of which I can give innumerable instances.

Over and over again I have seen inoculated cattle subjected to the test of standing the onset of not only one, but two or three outbreaks of the disease. It has been quite a common thing in my experience for inoculated cattle to stand exposed to the contagium of dying ones around them for days and for weeks, and to remain uninjured in other cases, where freshly brought in ones, not inoculated, have at once fallen victims. There can be no manner of doubt about it,—"an inoculated animal, healthy at the time of operation, will not afterwards contract pleuro-pneumonia."

Out of many instances in support of such a statement, I may be allowed to give the following one:—A client, who has a large town dairy, as also a farm some two miles or so from town, had pleuro-pneumonia very badly in his town byres; the disease had been running its course for some weeks, so that at the time of my inspection of them, more than half of his large stock were affected. I inoculated all that I could make at all sure about not being affected, the others being left to the care and, of course, at the disposition of the local authorities' inspector. On the same day I inoculated about a dozen calves, also in the town byres, and up at the farm ten head of freshly bought in, and very fine shorthorn milkers. Well, in a few weeks, all but two or three of the uninoculated ones were condemned and slaughtered, one or two at a time. Of course this was to be expected, as I said we knew them to be affected. What I wish to point out is, that they actually stood dying under the same roof with those I had inoculated, but without injuring them. Thus far the occurrence is a common one in my experience; but, fortunately, to illustrate still more the value of the protective power of inoculation, the history of this outbreak and its arrest does not end just yet. The byres were quarantined for two months, during which time they were thoroughly cleansed, the only inmates being the few I had inoculated, as also the calves—all of which were quite healthy. At the end of the two months, six fresh cows were bought in; they were not inoculated, for what reason I do not know, unless it be that my client wished to test the matter thoroughly. In less than three months the whole six were one by one put down for pleuro, the inoculated ones being still well. The same process of quarantine and cleansing had to be gone over, and then the premises being held clean by the local authority, the cows which I had inoculated at the farm about eight months previously, were brought in, and housed in the byres so many had been sent out of. To the stock were added four fresh ones, which again were not inoculated. It will be seen that at this time there were in the byres, subjected to the influence of any existing contagium—

1. The cows originally inoculated in them.
2. The calves originally inoculated in them

3. The cows inoculated at the farm, but which had never till now been exposed to the risk of contagium.

4. The four freshly bought in cows.

The result was the disease appeared again, and carried off three out of the four fresh cows which had not been inoculated, all the others remaining in the most perfect health. The history of this outbreak is not by any means the only one of its kind I have had to deal with. I have quoted it from amongst a number; because to my mind it shows out so strongly the value and the protective power of inoculation, not only in these few remaining exempt, that had been exposed all along to the contagium, but in those which had been brought in from the farm, and exposed to the influence of a contagium eight months after they were inoculated, and which, to prove its presence, carried off three out of the four not done. The calves were sent to the farm and were there mixed with some other stock, with no bad result in the way of conveying the disease, and I finally eradicated the disease from the town byres, by systematically inoculating all fresh stock, as bought in, and until such time as I judged the contagium would have died out.

One may reasonably here ask, Why in the face of such facts has the operation been kept so much in the background? The reason is not far to seek, and bears rather heavily on the veterinary profession.

When inoculation was first declared to be a success by Dr. Willems already quoted, various Government commissions, composed largely if not entirely of veterinary surgeons, were appointed to investigate the subject and report thereon. Some reported favourably, others did not, and there can be no doubt that their difference of opinion arose from the incompleteness of the experiments witnessed, and above all, from faults in the mode of performing the operation.

In this country I believe I am correct in affirming, that the then heads of the veterinary profession entirely condemned it. Professor John Gamgee did certainly for a time extol the operation, but he did so solely from his having fallen in with the views of some successful exponents of the operation on the Continent. When he began to practise it, his views as a result of his practice entirely changed, and we find him in his *Domestic Animals in Health and Disease* in the article on Pleuro-pneumonia, saying that "the operation was one which he had to condemn from experience." He does not say why, but we know it was because his mortality average was as high, and in some one or two instances, worse than from the disease itself. I have made considerable inquiry into his work in Edinburgh, and from what I have learned, I am not surprised he had such losses, his mode of performing the operation from beginning to end was a most objectionable one. Had Mr Gamgee exercised more

care and more perseverance he would have had no reason to
pen the above opinion, and there can be no doubt thousands and
thousands of cattle would have been, and much useless legisla-
tion in the matter, might have been saved to the country.

When the heads of the profession condemned the operation,
it is not to be wondered at if the rank and file followed suit,
and no doubt many did so, without knowing anything about it.
Blindly they believed what they were told, and I am very much
afraid they will continue to do so, till some one else in authority
tells them otherwise. As Fleming says:—"The persistency
with which the value of inoculation has been ignored in this
country would be astonishing did we not know how stubbornly
some people shut their eyes to the light, and close their minds
to the reception of facts which are not in harmony with precon-
ceived notions, or are adverse to opinions hastily promulgated,
and based on very imperfect knowledge."

On the Continent, however, the operation has not been so
cavalierly treated; from the first its value has been more or less
acknowledged, in proportion to the degree of success achieved
by the operation, and in one kingdom at least (Holland), compulsory inoculation of the healthy is now and has been for a
long time bracketed with the slaughter of the deceased. In
South Africa the value of inoculation has been recognised for
years, and, indeed, only a few months ago, I received a letter
from Natal, in which the writer says:—"It may be interesting
for you to know, that our colony of Natal has suffered severely
for years from pleuro-pneumonia, or lung sickness, and that the
only means of prevention found to be of any use is inoculation."

In Australia the operation has also been long known and
successfully practised, and to my mind, it speaks volumes in
favour of its value, when one considers how long its prestige has
not only lived, but that it has actually grown in favour, under
the most adverse conditions. In a report by Mr. Bruce, chief
inspector of stock, New South Wales, he says:—"Inoculation
is now generally practised throughout Australia, and as the stock
owners report, with decided success. There have certainly been
frequent instances of its failure, but these could always be
traced to one or other of the following causes:—

1. The cattle being diseased when operated upon.
2. To the use of improper virus.
3. To a wrong mode of operating.
4. To unfavourable weather.

He says, farther, that notwithstanding that the first attempts
at inoculation were made under the most unfavourable circumstances, a very large majority of the stock owners in all the
colonies expressed themselves strongly in favour of the operation,
and that majority has since gone on steadily increasing. In a
later report (1875), the same gentleman impresses upon his

government the desirability of making inoculation a compulsory measure, the whole of his subordinate inspectors, and the vast majority of the stock-owners, being thoroughly satisfied that it was the only preventive, and the only measure short of wholesale slaughter, which would eradicate the disease.

Perhaps, however, the most convincing evidence of its value, certainly the strongest yet afforded in this country, is in the history of my own work among the dairies of Edinburgh, Leith, and elsewhere, both in the county and out of it, where in the two former especially, pleuro-pneumonia had been rampant for years. From information personally gathered, I believe myself quite within the mark when I state, that with few exceptions, all the dairies in and around Edinburgh were more or less infected, and seldom free from the disease for any length of time. I have been credibly informed that it was no uncommon occurrence for a man's stock to be cleaned out twice within one year.

Such then was the state of matters when I began to urge the dairymen to inoculate. Unfortunately, the bad results which had been obtained by Mr. Gamgee was still fresh in the memory of my clients, so that it was a year or two before I could be allowed to demonstrate that the fault did not lie in the inoculation, but in the mode of carrying it out.

At length, however, on the 1st February 1878, I was permitted to inoculate some newly bought in poor Irish milkers for a much respected client (Mrs. Cairns), under conditions, which, considering the trial was to be decisive for or against the operation, were by me considered crucial.

The byres were and had been for a long time more or less infected, and in spite of alterations, and every other precaution, they had got into that state that it seemed impossible to carry on much longer. There were at the time I operated cows standing in the byres that were affected with pleuro-pneumonia; these were allowed to remain, tied up, I may say, alongside of my inoculated ones. The result, however, I am glad to say, proved at once the value of inoculation when properly done. All of them did well; more were inoculated, and also did well, and as in a few weeks it was seen they were remaining well, I soon had the gratification of knowing that inoculation was in a fair way of establishing itself.

The story of the following months is one of incessant labour. Byre after byre was placed in my hands for the one purpose, and in all of them I arrested the ravages of the disease, and by continuing in each case the inoculation of all fresh stock as they were bought in, finally eradicated it. Of course there is always the danger of buying it in. I have frequent instances of such. No great harm, however, results. Those inoculated are not infected, and those uninoculated, if any, are at once protected by the operation.

Since the day upon which I commenced publicly inoculating (1st Feb. 1878) down to the present time I have inoculated in ninety-six different places and byres. Of these, at the time of operation, eighty-nine were infected, the remaining seven being clean—the number of cattle inoculated being within a few of 2700. The mortality during the first year was five per cent., but owing to the greater precautions taken, arising out of a better knowledge of what is required, my mortality since has barely averaged two per cent.—a very low average considering that the vast majority of the cattle have been milkers, the class with which there is most risk. Let any one possessing any knowledge of the disease ask himself how many of those cattle would have been saved under the old *régime*. I assert that inoculation drove the disease out of every place where it was put in force—starved it out, in fact, and in point of comparison, in a way superior to any mode of doing so under the working of the Contagious Diseases (Animals) Act. If proof of this be required, it can be abundantly obtained from my clients, the dairymen of Edinburgh and elsewhere, and from many others, some of whom were not clients, but witnesses of the work.

I cannot leave this part of the subject without expressing a hope (I do so modestly) that if at any time the Government of this country desires to obtain reliable information as to the value of inoculation, they may come here for it. I can promise they will not go away empty-handed.

*Precautions to be observed in carrying out the Operation.*

In whatever way the operation be performed, its success and value depends largely upon the amount of painstaking intelligence and care which is brought to bear in the working out of detail, and in the amount of attention which is paid to the conditions and circumstances surrounding each outbreak. These conditions I have found may, for convenience, be divided into two sets—

1. Those existing outside the animal.
2. Those existing within the animal.

In the case of the first of these, the most important is the temperature and kind of weather prevalent and likely to be at the time of operation. In this country, from the month of April to the month of September, the operation may be proceeded with very little risk indeed, either outside or inside. Bullocks, and young stock especially, need never be housed, unless under sudden and unusual circumstances of very severe and wet weather. Cows, however, in my experience, are always better housed, especially if they are milkers. During the cold winter months there should be in the case of cows no exception to this rule; they should always be housed under inoculation, and every care taken to ensure the thorough comfort and genial warmth of the byres. They must be kept absolutely free from draughts of cold air; there should be no open doors, holes, nor broken windows behind them; and I have made it a practice, while allowing free breathing room over their heads, to keep them well protected over the back by packing the space between the rafters and roof with plenty of straw. In extreme cold weather I have successfully several times arrested very severe outbreaks without casuality by adding to these precautions clothing the body, especially the back part of it, with bags, or any coverings handy and warm enough, and by keeping lights burning in the byres day and night, so as to modify the temperature of the surrounding air. In short, in the case of cows, give them air at their heads above, but in other directions they cannot be kept too comfortably warm. So in the case of bullocks that may have to be inoculated during the cold months, I consider it necessary, and always have taken steps to ensure them more protection and comfort than is afforded them in the fields or in open cattle courts.

During last winter, and during cold raw weather, I arrested without loss an outbreak, the precautions taken to ensure comfort being, putting the animals (three-year-old bullocks) in sufficient number into different sheds, so that their very numbers ensured a degree of heat; the roofs of the sheds were covered thickly with straw, and the openings in front of the sheds were filled in with flakes outside and inside, with bundles of straw between. The result was that, as the grieve said, they were sometimes almost too warm. All did well, however. I stopped the disease without loss. I mention the case to show that, even if an outbreak occurs in the depth of winter, and it be decided to inoculate, the danger from cold need be no bar to the operation, seeing that the animals can be made warm enough by the exercise of a little ingenuity.

As I have already said, the operation is attended with little or no risk during mild and warm weather. Grazing stock and calves may be done with the greatest impunity. Cows, however, I must repeat, are better housed, so that they may be kept quieter and more under observation.

Attention to the second set of conditions, or those existing within the animal, is even more important than to the first.

The object of inoculating being generally to arrest an outbreak quite as much as to prevent it, it is of the greatest importance to determine accurately those that are already affected. It is hardly within the province of this paper to enumerate the various symtoms by which pleuro is known. They are sufficiently well known; but I would point out the immense value of and assistance that may be derived from the intelligent use of the clinical thermometer on all such occasions. Cattle affected with pleuro-pneumonia have been, and no doubt often are, inoculated in ignorance of the fact that they are affected; and although the same may happen even where the thermometer is employed in the detection of the disease, it is, in my experience, not so likely to happen, as the reading of the instrument will in most cases indicate pleuro long before the animal exhibits any of the ordinary symptoms of it.

In health the temperature averages in grazing stock 101°, or thereabouts; in housed milk cows the average obtained from some thousands is 101$\frac{4}{5}$°. In pleuro-pneumonia the temperature ranges from 103° to 107° (in some cases falling as low as 100° before death), and as inoculation does not pretend to cure the disease, it is advisable that due care be taken, and that none affected be inoculated. I advise the temperature being taken in every case if possible. I am aware that this is easier spoken about than done in the case of bullocks and young stock, but in cows that are housed, and in very young stock, it always can be done. All those that indicate health—that is, those whose temperature ranges from 101° to 102$\frac{2}{3}$°—may be done. Those ranging from 103° to 107° should not be done. True, there are cases in which the temperature may range at and above 103° from causes other than pleuro. No matter, do not inoculate such; rather delay the operation for a day or two until the temperature declines, or until satisfied one way or the other. Those whose temperature ranges about 103° are the ones the operator requires to be most guarded about. I have done lots of them that have come well through, but from the mild local results obtained I have judged such cases to be slightly affected ones, although probably only to the extent of the primary fever. It is right to mention that, even in cases where the thermometer has been most carefully used, animals have turned out in a day or two to be badly affected that at the time of trial showed no signs of it. Such cases, however, are rare, and do not affect the generally great value of the instrument intelligently used.

No animal should be inoculated, unless under very urgent circumstances, that has any condition about it of an inflammatory nature, or tendency that way—any strain, wound, or bruise, for instance. Internally and externally they should be in normal health and condition, or as nearly approaching to it as possible. In particular, no cow should be done that is within two months of calving, or that has just calved. I have inoculated without casualty cows eight days after calving. I consider the practice to be dangerous, however, and never unless forced to do so inoculate any until they are about three weeks calved, until such time, in fact, as the second cleansing is over, and the womb and other parts engaged in the process of parturition have recovered their normal tone and condition.

In the matter of feeding I have not found that any change or special precaution is necessary, provided always the food in quality and condition be non-injurious in itself.

The necessity for the precautions quoted rests in the circumstance that the peculiar inflammatory action set up by inoculation is apt to localise itself in any part, not the seat of the operation that is inflamed, weakened, or deficient in tone and vigour. And it is curious that, however benign and easily managed inoculation may be, confined to the ordinary seat of operation, it is highly dangerous and frequently fatal if set up in any other part of the body. When I commenced inoculating I was in ignorance of all that I have here cautioned others about; the path I was treading was a perfectly new one, and it has indeed since often been matter of surprise to me that I did not lose more than I did.

### Mode of Operation.

In proceeding to arrest an outbreak of pleuro, the first thing required is the lymph, or specific virus of the disease, with which to inoculate. This is always attainable in the case of an outbreak by simply slaughtering a beast judged to be in the early stages of the disease. Lymph, or virus, is the amber or sherry-coloured liquid exudate found occasionally on the free surfaces of the pleuro, under that membrane, between it and the lung, and nearly always in the interlobular tissues of the lungs; in consistence it is somewhat viscid, of a not unpleasant odour; it coagulates readily upon removal from the lungs, but again assumes a liquid condition. In selection of the lympth too much care cannot be taken; if possible let it be taken from a freshly-killed beast—one in fair condition, and free as far as can be ascertained from other disease, but especially from tuberculosis. My mode of collecting it cannot, I think, be improved upon for simplicity. I open up and pull apart with my fingers the tissues containing it, taking care not to tear or break down their substance; a pouch is thus formed into which the lymph gravitates, and from which it is spooned out into a clean vessel, a plate or saucer, if for immediate use, or into a clean glass bottle if to be kept, in which case it should be tightly corked up and buried in a few inches of soil until required. The very greatest care must be taken that only lymph as here described be collected, free from all impurities, blood, frothy serum, and other extraneous matter. Good lymph is only to be obtained in the salmon and brick red-coloured portions of the diseased lung, never from the hepatised dark-coloured portions. I mention this particularly, for not only have portions of the hepatised lung been used, but the fluid which follows an incision made through its substance, practices which, in their day, led largely to some of the bad results obtained. Lymph may be kept in cold weather fit for use, if excluded from the air for from three to five days, but in warm weather it cannot well be kept quite fit for use beyond the second or third day. There are ways of preserving it for two or three months; but, as my experiences have been rather unfavourable to using lymph in any way but in its pure state, I do not mention them, since I cannot recommend their adoption. In my hands, as in those of others, the use of preserved lymph, which is frequently weakened or in some way changed, has been attended with uncertain results; as, however, in inoculating we wish to have perfect exemption, I long ago gave up its use.

Having obtained the lymph, the operator next procures fully as many pieces of white Alloa worsted, eight inches long or so, as there are cattle to inoculate. These threads he saturates with the lymph ready for use, the threads in the meantime being the means of retaining the virus until insertion beneath the skin of the animal, after which, from their presence there, they help to localise the inoculative action.

In the actual performance of the operation various methods have been adopted. Most of them, however, are open to grave objections, not only as regards the material employed, but in the spot selected and manner of doing it. I have to condemn as dangerous the practice of making deep and cruel incisions in the head of the tail and of inserting therein pieces of diseased lung ; as also the modes recommended and carried out lately at the Brown Institution in London by Dr. Burdon Sanderson, viz., by subcutaneous and intravenous injection of the virus. Both are in their nature unreliable, and the latter is in my opinion not only a mode fraught with danger to the lives of the animals, but with the great bulk of them, and in most hands impracticable. Others again, in imitation of vaccination, merely scratch or scarify or incise the skin of the tail, and rub in a little virus. This mode is not attended with danger, but in my experience many of such so-called inoculations fail from being incomplete and too mild. The mode adopted by myself, and I think my results have proved it a good plan, is the insertion at the tip of the tail of a woollen thread saturated with the virus or lymph in a manner similar to the insertion of a small seton. The advantages claimed are—

1. The minimum of danger, as a result of the inoculative action, spreading from the seat of operation.
2. In the event of the inoculation spreading it can be arrested by amputation, which cannot be done in any other part of the body.
3. The operation is simple and easily performed.

The instruments required are a pair of strong scissors, a pair of rowelling scissors and a needle, which latter has to be made specially for the purpose. The one I use is provided with a handle, and is four inches long, three-sixteenths of an inch broad, thin, flexible, slightly curved, and with a lancet-shaped point, furnished with a slit or eye half an inch long, and about a quarter of an inch from the point. Across the eye it is slightly broader than at any other part, so as to facilitate its being easily inserted and withdrawn.

To perform the operation quickly, and with as little disturbance and pain as possible, the operator requires assistance, two men and a lad at least, one of the former to hold the animal by the nose, the other one to directly assist the operator by holding the tail with his left hand, while with his right he steadies the haunch. The lad is required to hold in readiness the saucer or vessel containing the threads, which are now supposed all arranged ready for use, saturated with the virus and doubled into lengths of about four inches.

All being now ready, lay hold of the end of the tail, and clip the hair close off from its under surface from the tip to about four or five inches upwards, then turning the tail round, so that its under surface is lying upwards and firmly held in the palm of the hand, the first incision is made with the rowelling scissors, about an inch from the tip, then another about two inches or so higher up. The incision should be only through the skin, and there should be little or no bleeding. The needle is then inserted at the lower incision, and passed quickly upwards and out at the upper incision, care being taken not to go too deep with it. One of the doubled threads is then inserted into the eye at the point of the needle, and the latter is carefully withdrawn and in such a way as not to strip the lymph off the thread, which latter of course is left in. The operation requires about two minutes time only, and the first step towards inoculation is complete.

In the case of all inoculated cattle, but especially when these are milk cows, the operator must not forget that the well-being of the animal and consequent success of the operation, irrespective of arresting the disease, is now largely dependent upon the care which he is now prepared to bestow on them. He should caution the attendants and milkers to be very careful in their handling of the animals, until out of his hands, they must not be kicked or struck, especially about the rump; without thinking anything of it I know people are very apt to do so, if a cow is lying when they think she should be standing, or if troublesome to milk or muck out. Now is the time also to see that the precautions in respect to the comfort of the animal, which I have pointed out as necessary, are in force. The continental inoculators give a doze of purgative medicine; I have seen no need for it, but I always recommend a little sulphur daily in the food from about the fifth or sixth day. A table spoonful to each animal daily is enough, continued till the decline of the inoculation.

### Favourable and Unfavourable Results.

After the operation the animals are generally a little restless, and to a close observer, some in a few days are evidently out of sorts. They do not, however, go off their food, not in the slightest degree, and in the case of milkers, there is no falling off in the milk given. About the third or fourth day and from that on to the sixth or seventh day, the tail, at the seat of operation, begins to swell, the hair stumps stand straight out, it is hot, painful on pressure, and of a reddish glazed appearance. There is, however, no discharge from the incision. Following close upon the above, the skin assumes a yellowish tint, and is covered with bran-like scales of desquamating cuticle. About the ninth day, occasionally earlier, but more often later, the animal loses the power of raising the tail, and examination will show that beads of amber-coloured lymph are exuding from the skin around the seat of operation. This lympth is identical in character and properties with that obtained from the lung, good and successful inoculation being obtained from its use. The appearance of this exudate is the most satisfactory evidence we can get that inoculation has taken place, and there can be no doubt, that when an animal exhibits it, such a one becomes exempt from pleuro. If an animal fails in exhibiting any of the foregoing signs of inoculation it is generally owing to one of the following causes:—Having had the disease before operation; having it at the time of operation, or from non-susceptibility, instances of which I have frequently come across. Succeeding the appearance of the eruption of lymph, the most favourable course which the inoculation can now take is the occurrence of a mild degree of fever, followed by gradual diminution of the local action, drying of the eruption, and scabbing over of the incision. The animal gradually recovers the use of the tail, and the whole process is practically over in from three to four weeks. A good many cases terminate in this the very mildest way, compatible with protection, especially in the case of bullocks, young stock, and calves.

The majority, however, especially in the case of milk cows, do not end so mildly. In those, following the appearance of the eruption, we get changes of the following description:—The end of the tail swells more, it becomes quite moist from coalescence of the vesicles from which the lymph escapes. There is a tendency for it to become dark hued and low in temperature towards the tip. Nature terminates such cases when able to do so, in one of two ways, either by the formation of an offensive sloughing sore, which after a time dries up, leaving the tip of

the tail crooked and denuded of hair at this part, or death of
the tip takes place and a line of demarcation being formed,
between the living part above and the dead tip below, the latter
is finally thrown off. My experience, however, is that the great
majority of milk cows do not seem to have the power of carrying
through this latter process favourably. Left to themselves, the
line of demarcation alluded to is never perfectly formed. The
death which has taken place at the tip spreads upwards, and
although I have seen it finally thrown off at a point higher up,
I have in view of the fact, that it may not be thrown off, but
may lead to further mischief, made the following my practice:—
After the appearance of the eruption I watch each case very
closely, and the earlier the eruption appears the closer it must
be watched. By experience I know if an inoculation is going to
spread, just as one can tell if it is going to decline. The time
to watch is about the ninth day, when, if the inoculative action
is severe, I at once amputate the tip of the tail an inch or so
above the upper incision. The stump should bleed freely, if it
does not, then remove a small portion more, or until it does
bleed freely. Cauterise the bleeding stump with a red-hot iron,
so as to stop the bleeding and form at once a surface impervious
to the air. The great majority of cases so treated require
nothing more, and in process of time a really very good imitation of a tuft makes its appearance to hide any apparent dis-
figurement. The shortening of the tail is the only objection I
have ever heard to inoculation. The objection is, however, a
purely sentimental one; better, I say, have no tail than no
beast.

In some cases we find that the eruption and the swelling
extends all the way up the tail. This looks very alarming, but as
long as the tail retains its normal temperature throughout the
extent of the swollen portion and a degree of movement, there
is nothing to be feared. Keep such cases well protected from
cold, and dress the swelling and eruption twice or three times a
day with flour; than which I have found nothing better, not
only for reducing the intensity of the local inoculative action,
but to prevent its spreading and assist in the drying up of the
exudate. Such cases are always accompanied by a marked
degree of fever, and in the case of cows for a few days they go
a little off their food and milk. They generally end by the
diminution of the swelling, drying of the exudate, and by the
formation of sloughs in one or more places, which after a time
heal up, requiring in the meantime no treatment beyond
occasional irrigation with carbolised water, or dusting with any
drying disinfecting powder to keep down smell. These are the
ordinary and favourable terminations of inoculation. The average
time required for the completion of the process being from the
day of operation to that of dismissal as follows:—

Period of development,    .    .    9 to 14 days.
   „    „ maturation,    .    .    .    4 to  7 days.
   „    „ decline and healing up,  .    14 to 21 days.

Calves and young stock have never in my experience required any attention after the operation; they get over it very easily, and very often without the loss of any portion of the tail. Bullock's come next in point of ease with which they pass through it, so that it may be taken that it is milking cows chiefly that require watchfulness and careful treatment from the hands of the operator; but I would here remark, if I have not already done so, that it is surprising how well they do in most cases from beginning to end of the process. They rarely, as I have said, miss a feed, are rarely affected in their milking, and they always feed and milk even better, after it is all over, than they did before the operation.

The unfavourable conditions, where the operation is in the hands of a careful person, should be very few, and consist in the inoculative action locating itself in some organ or part of the body where its presence and consequences arising therefrom, often proves fatal. They arise chiefly from neglect of some of the necessary precautions I have pointed out, and frequently as a result of injury after the operation. We have sometimes spreading of the inoculative action up the tail, in so rapid a manner, that before the operator can arrest its progress by amputation, the mischief is done and the process has spread from the head of the tail to the parts adjacent. The symptoms of this condition are a swollen, cold, deadened, limp condition of more or less of the tail. This is sphacelus, or death of the tail, arising from the intensity of the local action, leading to plugging of the blood-vessels. It may be known by its coldness, loss of sensation, and the bluish black colour of the skin. It may be arrested, and prevented from spreading to the rump, by free amputation and the application of the hot iron to the stump. There must be no false delicacy in handling such cases, and let there be no mistake about the portion removed—better remove two or three inches of good sound tail, than leave the smallest portion whose life has begun to go. I have saved lots of such cases, and have never scrupled about removing the whole tail even if I thought it necessary to do so. Better no tail (again) than no beast, and its loss does not seem to put them much about.

In other cases a circumscribed swelling occurs in some part of the body, but most usually on the point of the ischium, on either side of the head of the tail. These swellings are always the result of a blow received just before or after the operation, and depend upon the localisation of the inoculative action in the part. A hard swelling, hot and painful, and frequently productive of lameness, is formed, which, if it is going to run a favourable course, does not spread, but in process of time gradually softens. The mass inside liquefies beneath the skin, which latter finally breaking at a point, the contents gradually escape, and the parts healing up the animal is left none the worse. During the formation of the abcess some go off their food and milk, others don't.

The really most unfavourable termination to inoculation is where the inoculative action spreads to the muscles of the haunch or back, or to any other part of the body that has been severely bruised or injured in any way; or what is worse, when it spreads from the tail to the anus and vulva, and from those parts inside to the bowel and urino-genital organs. Many cases of the latter get better if the swelling extends no further than the vulva, but if the process does spread and extend inside they end fatally. The symptoms are, more or less, loss of appetite, symptomatic fever, inability to remain for any length of time in a standing posture, swelling of the external parts, discoloration of the skin, difficulty in passing fæces and making water and straining. Such cases should be destroyed, as they are hopeless, in fact they are the only hopeless ones I have met with. I think they are very apt to happen in the case of animals recently calved, especially if the calving has been difficult—hence my reason for advising the delay of inoculation in the case of newly calved cows to at least three weeks afterwards, or even longer if the parts be considered weak.

In those cases mentioned where the inoculation extends to the haunch, there is danger of a fatal end from the beast losing the use of the limb, and so getting down; where, however, they retain their ability to move about, rise easily, and take their food, they generally come all right, and are best assisted to this end by being turned into a comfortable loose box. I have not found that any application to the swellings is of any benefit, I am on the contrary of opinion that interference with them frequently makes them worse. Such are the unfavourable terminations; formidable as they, however, appear on paper, it must be borne in mind they are not really so in practice, and that the worst of them, those ending fatally, are of comparative infrequent occurrence.

Where care is taken in undertaking and carrying out the inoculation, the mortality need not exceed two per cent.; such at any rate is mine, and I see no reason why any one should have a higher rate, providing they go about the work carefully. In my early days my mortality was certainly higher (five per cent.), but I have explained that this arose from the fact that I had everything to learn, and was absolutely ignorant of a great many things, the knowledge and observance of which has since led to better results.

In the foregoing pages I have endeavoured to explain and illustrate the theory and value of inoculation for the prevention of pleuro-pneumonia, the precautions to be exercised, the mode of performing the operation, with the favourable and unfavourable results. My statistics show the numbers done, the conditions under which they were done, so far as being infected or otherwise is concerned, and the loss attendant thereon ; but as the main facts, which really point to the value of the operation may not be just at once grasped, I will summarise my subject and my experience in the following conclusions :—

1. Inoculation is based upon the theory of pleuro-pneumonia being an eruptive fever.
2. Inoculation is the application to a healthy animal of the virus of pleuro-pneumonia.
3. Inoculation does not produce pleuro-pneumonia.
4. An inoculated animal does not infect another animal.
5. An inoculated animal cannot contract pleuro-pneumonia.
6. The time occupied by the operation is from four to eight weeks.
7. Inoculation in the case of milk cows does not materially interfere with their milking.
8. Inoculated animals thrive better after the operation, and are stronger and freer from other aliments than those not inoculated.
9. The loss arising from the operation need not exceed 2 per cent.
10. From the fact that an inoculated animal is exempt from the disease, and that the average time required to develop and mature an inoculation is from fourteen to twenty-one days. That period may be accepted as the time required to arrest an outbreak.

In drawing this paper to a close I would thank the Highland and Agricultural Society of Scotland for this opportunity they have afforded me of laying my experience, in a plain manner, before the great mass of stock owners which the society represents. I would ask them to bear in mind that I have penned only plain practical facts, not theories, and that these facts can be verified by close upon a hundred cattle owners in the area of my practice alone, who have had abundant reason to be thankful for the good the successful employment of inoculation has conferred upon them. For any crudity the paper may contain, I have to offer this apology, it has been put together in the spare minutes only of a busy life, and by one with no pretensions to being a literate. I hope I have shown sufficiently clearly, that in the event of another visitation, the country need no longer depend solely upon the working of the Contagious Diseases (Animals) Act, for that in inoculation for prevention of pleuro-pneumonia we have a measure which does its work with a minimum of loss and inconvenience to the owner, and with a certainty of so much gain to the public, that it ought to be bracketed in the Act (with the slaughtering of the affected) as compulsory.

## THE HISTORY, NATURE, SYMPTOMS, AND TREATMENT OF SHEEP-POX.

By Hugh Kidd, V.S., Hungerford, Berks.

*[Premium—Seven Sovereigns.]*

Our domesticated animals as well as man have each their peculiar form of variola or smallpox. It varies in severity of attack in the different species, and like all other eruptive febrile diseases, it affects in each of the different species much more severely than it does others, varying according to the quantity of the poison and the condition of the animal. The type of smallpox under consideration, *Variola Ovina*, very much resembles that of the smallpox in man, but they are nevertheless two separate and perfectly distinct diseases, and cannot be communicated from the sheep to man, nor from man to the sheep, either by contagion, infection, or inoculation.

Whether the pestilential disease "murrain," spoken of in scriptural history, which destroyed all the Egyptian cattle in one night, on account of Pharaoh's disobedience, was a special scourge sent by Providence for a special purpose, or whether we are to consider that it was only the commencement of certain plagues that were to visit the flocks and herds of all nations, are problems not easily solved. We do not think, however, that the "murrain," though a virulent epizootic disease, partook of the nature of the disease under consideration; for although the horses, asses, camels, oxen, and sheep, were threatened with the severe visitation, only the cattle died. Might not the plague which immediately followed be fairly considered to possess the nature and virus of variola? "boils and blains," or "the botch," which was a loathsome and painful disorder, which affected both man and beast, and which even the magicians could not withstand.

Ancient writers on the diseases which infected the flocks and herds in their times furnish us with a very imperfect account of the various disorders, most probably from ignorance of the nature and causes; but they soon observed that they were "full of infection," and with remarkable skill and forethought, separated the diseased from the healthy.

In various parts of the Continent this disease has been well known from a very early time. The notions as to its nature, cause, and origin, were as varied and numerous as they were novel; but they were unanimous from observation that it was a highly contagious and most fatal disease, almost decimating the herds. About the beginning of the eighteenth century it was observed in a part previously unknown (Lower Hungary), and from the description given there can be no doubt of it having been smallpox, although it is described as "a new kind of disorder associated with white pustules filled with matter insufferably stinking." In France about the beginning of the eighteenth century, it had become so established as to be considered that every sheep must suffer and have an attack of the malady at some period of its life, if it reached an average maximum of existence.

England has been visited at various periods by this affection, but on each occasion it has been clearly traced to importation. In *Animal Plagues*, by Fleming, it is stated that it has been known in England from a very early time. We have also records of a dreadful outbreak in the thirteenth century, which lasted for thirty years, from which large numbers succumbed. Another outbreak is said to have occurred during the sixteenth century scarcely less severe. The first authentic recorded outbreak of *Variola Ovina* is stated to have been seen about the beginning of the seventeenth century. "The distemper spread indiscriminately amongst all kinds of animals, killing great numbers after a few days' illness. A critical discharge manifested itself on the *thighs*, *neck*, and *head*, resembling smallpox." Rammazini did not scruple to declare these pustules to be smallpox, for they differed not from it in form or colour, or in the manner in which they went off; when they had dried off after the suppuration they left a black scar like that which remains after the smallpox. This epidemic contagion continued attacking the sheep chiefly and so violently that the breed was almost destroyed. It has been constantly observed that of all animals sheep are the most subject to smallpox."—*Mills on Cattle.*

A most decided outbreak of smallpox in sheep occurred in England in 1847. Professor Williams, in his *Veterinary Medicine*, says:—"Sheep-pox was unknown in this country until 1847, when it broke out on a farm at Datchett, near Windsor, where it was introduced by fifty-six merino sheep, brought to this country in the ship "Trident," from Tonning, in Denmark.

Professor Simonds in his treatise on *Variola Ovina*, says:—"We have not succeeded in tracing the subsequent distribution of each separate lot of this cargo. . . . Within a day or two of the arrival of the 'Trident,' two vessels, the 'Mountaineer' and 'Princess Royal,' each having on board a number of merino sheep brought from Hamburg, in some of which the disease has shown itself." . . . Professor Gamgee, in his *Domestic Animals*, says:—"A very satisfactory explanation of the alarming introduction of smallpox in 1847 is to be found in the extraordinary sudden increase in the importation of sheep. In that year no fewer than 139,371 sheep were imported, whereas the total number for the five years previously was 111,222. . . . The foreign dealers were exerting themselves to increase the supply of sheep, and it is

c

not at all to be wondered at that smallpox spread westward.
It must not be forgotten that the countries with which we
immediately trade were as healthy as our own in the early days
of our importation, and it was only when they had to import for
our supplies that they suffered and injured us."

At this particular period the disease committed great ravages
in several counties in England, and continued at intervals to
attack fresh flocks for a period of seven years before it was
eradicated. This country then remained free from any further
outbreak until 1862, when it appeared in Wiltshire. This outbreak was believed by many to have originated spontaneously.
Professor J. Gamgee visited the parts at this time, making strict
and most searching inquiries, from which he concluded as
formerly, that it was due to contagion. He thus sums up the
result of his inspection :—" The outbreak occurred in one of the
choicest flocks in Wiltshire. It was exclusively home bred, and
consisted of 992 ewes, 9 rams, and 710 lambs. But the district
turns out to be one not unfrequently visited by contagious disorders, and my attention was specially directed to the peculiarities of that portion of the country, which renders it liable to
invasions of scab and the foot-and-mouth-disease, as well as the
sheep-pox . . . The lowland portion of the Allington Farm
is skirted by the canal; and it is said that the sheep were near
this canal when the disease first broke out. I find, however,
that the first case occurred amongst a portion of the flock that
had been daily to the down for a week. My authority is the
shepherd who drove them. I visited the downs repeatedly, rode
across them with gentlemen who knew the country well, spoke
to drovers, shepherds, and other persons, and the more I inquired, the more evidence did I obtain in confirmation of the
facts gleaned by me the first morning I commenced my investigation."

### Nature.

In studying the nature of sheep-pox we shall confine our
remarks on it as observed in the flocks and herds of this country,
because we are not sufficiently experienced in its particular
phases and variations in foreign countries. Indeed, the reports
from the various continental authorities are not agreed as to its
regular course. One asserts that it is epizootic—originates and
spreads rapidly by contagion or infection, while others maintain
that it is enzootic, originates spontaneously, and confined to
particular districts or localities. It is very difficult to draw
the line of demarcation between an epizootic and enzootic
disease. But it is sufficient for our present purpose if we
understand epizootic when applied to sheep-pox as existing
and spreading rapidly amongst the flocks over an extensive

tract of country, and extending to several counties; whilst enzootic relates to a circumscribed domain, and confined to a small district, and spreading slowly. We recognise *Variolæ Ovina* to be of the nature of a specific eruptive febrile disease. It may be enzootic by being confined to a district, or even one flock, while at the same time it may be epizootic by the diffusion of its virulent principle, it being propagated slowly or rapidly according to the inherent vitality of that virulent principle or agent. Science has not yet clearly discovered in what manner this particular virus is developed and propagated. We do know, however, that this specific virulous agent has the power, under certain circumstances, of multiplying itself and producing the same series of a characteristic morbid phenomenon, and capable of inducing a disease identical with that which has produced it in the same species. It is of a highly contagious constitution, and can be easily conveyed from one flock to another in various ways, and by the most simple media, such as dogs, &c. Shepherds readily convey it.

There are several separate and distinct stages of development. The latent or incubative is the first stage; it is the period of implanting the disease and its development, or that of its rise and spread. This stage varies according to age, local influences, feeding, condition of the blood, and the condition of the sheep. During this stage the specific virulous agent produces certain effects on the blood, various tissues begin to swell, and the state of primary fever sets in. The flowing of the saliva, also one of the effects, is at first abundant, but gradually and quickly subsides. The primary fever in a few days generally remits and gives place to eruption, which may either be distinct or confluent. When the eruption becomes confluent the fever does not subside, but fluctuates in degree, and becomes less regular. There is an aggravated form which sometimes appears instead of suppuration, in which we have ecchymosis, and, instead of vesicles, we have pustules and pedunculated spots. When the malady is once developed its advance to other stages cannot be averted by any remedial measures. It then advances from one stage to another in the regularly defined course of the various stages of development, and after it has passed through all the stages it may end in recovery or death. If it should pass through all its different morbid phases and convalescence follow, then, as a rule, there is permanent immunity from a second attack. The characteristic feature of this disease is, that it originates through a virulent agent or specific blood-poison, and never arises spontaneously. If we were to entertain the idea of spontaneous origin we then attempt to cover our failure in tracing the relation of cause and effect by an impossible theory that it could exist without a cause.

The spontaneous generation of this and other contagious diseases is a subject that is being investigated at the present time by eminent and scientific medical men, but as yet their conclusions are far from being unanimous; the majority, however, incline to the belief that spontaneous generation is impossible. Dr. Budd, in writing to the *Medical Times* in 1864, says:—" I have myself come to the conclusion that there is no proof whatever that they ever do so. That the evidence, in fact, on which the contrary conclusion is founded, is negative only; that evidence of precisely the same order, only to all appearance still more cogent, would prove animals and plants, even of large species, to originate spontaneously; that this evidence is therefore of no weight; and, lastly, that as in the case of plants and animals all the really important facts point the other way, and tend to prove that these poisons (to use a word that is probably provisional yet), like plants and animals, however they may have once originated, are only propagated now by the law of continuous succession."

The nature of the viruliferous agent has not yet been clearly demonstrated. There are records of some very interesting experiments and numerous investigations, but no definite decision has been arrived at as to what is really the character of the virus. Various theories have been propounded, such as bacteria, parasitism, and fermentation. Even with the aid of the microscope much remains to be done to bring practical facts and the various theoretical views into harmony, and never can veterinary science and medicine prevent and control the spread of contagious diseases till we can thoroughly grapple with, and understand the intimate nature of the contagious element. Dr. Beale, in his work on *Disease Germs; their Real Nature*, on this point says:—" The materies morbi of contagious diseases does not consist of lifeless organic matter or inorganic matter, nor of any form of gas or vapour generated in the decomposition of animal or vegetable substances, nor by any matter set free during the decomposition of fæcal or other excrementitious matter of animal origin. Nor is it any species of animal or vegetable organism or parasite; but the active contagious material consists of exceedingly minute particles of living germinal matter, which may be regarded as the direct descendants of the germinal or living matter of an organism which has been for some time living under unusual conditions. Contagious poisons affecting man and animals originated in their organisms. The living or germinal matter of some contagious diseases originating in the bodies of animals may grow and multiply in man and *vice versa*. . . . The smallest particle (less than the hundredth-thousand part of an inch in diameter) being introduced into the body, already in a fit state for its nutrition, may grow and multiply, giving rise, in due time, to the symptoms characteristic of the particular disease, and producing millions of particles like itself." Monsieur Chauveau, of Lyons Veterinary School, has made some very interesting experiments with the virus of several contagious diseases. He found in the virus of *Variola Ovina* a liquid and solid portion, the first being merely the medium, the second the active principle, the latter alone being endowed with virulent properties. He found that the character of the virulent matter of smallpox in the human subject was, in appearance, the same as that of variola in the sheep, but the difference in the degree of virulence was most marked, the difference being due to the number of virulent granules in a given quantity of matter. After inoculating a sheep with the virus of ovine smallpox, he remarked:—"At the commencement the irritation is distinctly limited to the skin itself, extension of the morbid process ultimately involving the subcutaneous connective tissue. If one of the variolous vesicles is excised at this initial period, when the skin is only red and slightly swollen, and the traces of the gelatinous substance which is beginning to appear on its under surface be removed, then squeezed into a little water on a glass and a healthy sheep inoculated with the matter, the animal will become affected as readily and effectively as if the matter had been extracted from a perfectly developed pustule."

However astonishing these experiments may appear to us, we cannot help accepting them, because they do not stand as having been observed by one only, for they are corroborated by Cohn, who also found, on examination of perfectly fresh smallpox lymph, the presence of bioplasts most carefully preserved. Karstein, also a German, corroborates this view, and believes that the bacteria are developed from altered cells, the mode of development of the cells depending upon the chemical nature of the cell-fluid, and the matter and force acting from without. The contagium of the virulous agent of *Variola Ovina*, when once it enters a flock, has no preference for one animal more than another, but towards the close the virus loses its potency and becomes, to a very great extent, weakened by transmission, and some of the flock offer mild and incomplete symptoms of the disease.

## Symptoms.

This disease is developed by various characteristic and distinct stages—incubative, febrile and papular, vesicular, pustular, and desquamative. During the incubative stage, the symptoms, which are of a local and general kind, are obscure, and we are unable to make a diagnosis for a time after exposure to the contagion. The period between the implanting of the disease and its development varies from five to twelve days; generally about the tenth day the disease begins to manifest itself by indications of a slight dulness, with diminution of appetite, accompanied by feverishness. The fever is generally most intense before the eruption appears, and the respirations are increased, with gradual elevation of temperature, which decreases when eruption sets in. In the febrile state the rythmic action of the heart is altered so that the heart is unable to drive the blood through the obstructed blood-vessels fast enough to carry off the animal heat which is being generated, and in consequence the temperature of the whole body therefore rises, and the action of the various organs that are adapted to act perfectly at a fixed temperature is deranged. The head is carried low, and the ears drooping. The conjunctival and schniderian membranes become highly injected, with a muco-purulent discharge from the nostrils. The breath and cutaneous exhalations have a characteristic fœtid smell. The skin is hot, with tenderness over the back and loins, and there is also a scantiness of urine, which has an offensive odour, with a dark brown coffee colour. As this disease progresses and passes through the different phases which we have been describing, the local symptoms begin to exhibit themselves by certain characteristic alterations and appearances on the parts of the body. Where the skin is finest and hairy, instead of woolly, as in the flanks, thighs, and belly, there appear little pimples resembling flea-bites, which increase in number and size, and having a purple colour. These pimples assume a vesicular form, and the vesicles contain a sero-purulent fluid, which is extremely virulent. These have an umbilicated aspect which is peculiar to the disease, and are sometimes distinct and sometimes confluent. If they are confluent, and the fever remain unabated, then we may almost be certain of an unfavourable termination. In due course the contents of the vesicles have become transformed into pus, which constitutes the pustular stage, when they are considered to have become mature. From three to five days from this time, if ulceration does not follow, the pustules dry up, leaving brown scabs, perfectly formed, which then drop off, if not injured by rubbing, and leave a little red depression in the skin.

There are two forms of this disease, regular and irregular. The symptoms enumerated in the preceding description may be designated under the regular form, but it is found that in a flock the methodic course is rarely followed or marked, nor is it to be wondered at when we consider that the constitutions, conditions of the blood, and the general health of the animals differ, while in some there is a peculiar idiosyncrasy to the contagion of variola. In the irregular or malignant form the eruption appears slowly and intermittent, and has a greyish red tint. The eyes are dull and have a muco-purulent discharge. The head, nostrils, and lips become thickened, and the schniderian membrane is thickened and ulcerated; there is great difficulty in breathing, with a fœtid froth discharged from the mouth. The vesicles, instead of gradating into pustules, subside, dry up, with a gangrenous appearance, wool drops off, and the animal becomes rapidly emaciated; this state is frequently accelerated by a fœtid diarrhœa, and the animal succumbs under this form of the disease.

The favourable or unfavourable termination of this malady is regulated according to the type it assumes, the intensity and duration of the fever, the extent of the local appearances, to the exposure the sheep are subjected to, and to the care and attention bestowed, not only on the diseased, but also on the healthy. A favourable termination generally follows a limited and distinct eruption, when the fever runs its course and subsides, if the weather be neither cold nor hot, the atmosphere clear and dry, the animal of a robust and healthy constitution, and if proper dieting and a rigid separation of healthy sheep from diseased be attended to. Opposite conditions to these just stated lead very often to an unfavourable termination, although that is most to be feared when the fever alternates in severity and is long in subsiding, and when the pustules are close together, confluent, or gangrenous. Should any animal survive this worst form it is left so sickly and debilitated that it is of little or no value.

### Treatment.

No general rule can be laid down for the curative treatment of this disease. It assumes so many different phases that if medical treatment is to be adopted, most benefit will follow the adaptation of remedial agents according to the particular course and symptons exhibited in each particular case. Keeping before our minds that it runs a fixed and determined course, our aim should be to let nature do her work, but assist her chiefly by keeping up the strength of the animal by good nourishment, such as oats, cake, bran, fresh turnips or carrots if in season; a plentiful supply of fresh air, shelter from either sun or rain, giving them comfortable housing, the temperature of the above regular, and by no means hot. In the febrile condition, if there be no diarrhœa, small quantities of nitrate of potass, chloride of sodium, and sulphate of iron three times a day in a little linseed tea or warm ale, will hasten the development of the eruption, and also prevent it from disappearing rapidly. Should the handling excite the animals—which would do harm—it would be more advantageous to substitute a little chlorate of potass in the water they drink, and pieces of rock salt placed at convenient spots for them to lick. If diarrhœa be present it is best treated by the chalk mixture; dysentery by opium and chalk. Care should be taken to sponge the lips, nostrils, and eyes with a weak solution of vinegar and water, after having removed the muco-purulent discharge. But whilst we have given a few excellent remedial medicinal agents they by no means cut short the disease. We incline more to the plain simple method of fresh air, good nourishment, punctual and careful attendance, and cleanliness. To apply curative treatment to the cutaneous eruption would not only be futile but positively injurious, except in those cases that had recovered from the very worst form, when a little oxide of zinc ointment and carbolic acid applied to the abrasions on the skin would soothe and heal.

### Preventive Treatment.

Prevention is a more important branch of veterinary science in regard to this malady than the curative, as very little reliance can be placed on the medical preservative treatment. Past experience of therapeutic measures in respect of contagious and zymotic diseases, such as the one under consideration, give us little encouragement to hope that medicines will be discovered to hinder the development of the disease, or assist in the removal of the abnormal and septic agent silently but seriously at work. If science, then, has not yet discovered remedial medicinal agents to combat and conquer the contagious element, all that can be done is to watch the progress of the disease, and to administer only such regulating medicines as will prevent and allay any aggravation. It is a fact, proved beyond a doubt, that *Variola Ovina* is introduced into this country by importation. The risk is greatly obviated by the system of inspection at the ports of debarkation; and with the powers given by Act of Parliament and Orders in Council to a port or government inspector, it should be next to impossible for *Variola Ovina* to get introduced into this country, so long as the law as it now stands is carried out both in spirit and letter. If only the same system of inspection were carried out at the ports of embarkation, the agriculturists of this country might then enjoy much greater liberty in the transit of stock, and with an absolute absence of risk of introducing amongst their stocks of cattle and sheep any of the exotic contagious diseases.

Prevention will in almost every instance of *Variola Ovina* be found most profitable and satisfactory. Assuming an invasion should take place, the first and most important act, which is now compulsory, should be to separate at once the diseased from the apparently healthy. The healthy should be frequently and carefully examined, each sheep being scrutinised separately, and the moment that one is suspected remove it to a place by itself, apart from either the healthy or diseased. Exclude all and sundry from going near the affected sheep on any pretext whatever, except the attendants and inspector, who ought to have their clothes regularly disinfected. Let one set of attendants be provided for the healthy, another for the diseased, and a third set for the dead, and on no condition should they be allowed to come in contact. Cleanliness should be rigidly attended to amongst both the healthy and diseased. Sheltered dry places, provided with good ventilation, good nourishing food given at regular intervals, with an abundant supply of pure water, a due observance of disinfecting the place the flock has been, and the careful interment of the dead, are the principal points to be attended to.

Ovination is extensively practised and greatly recommended on the Continent, but it has not been so effectual in this country in preventing its spread, nor so favourably received. Professor Simonds says:—" Our experiments are too limited to suggest correct conclusions, and they have shown a result so different that were we to found an opinion on the merits of ovination, on them alone, it would not be in favour of the practice." From observations made by Professor J. Gamgee in 1862, he condemns ovination entirely, " as undoubtedly it serves to increase the centres from which the contagium may extend in every direction." He gives a tabular statement as to the outbreak in Wiltshire in 1862, and adds :—" Had all the flock seized been inoculated, I am quite sure that the outbreak of smallpox would not have been brought to so quiet a termination." . . . " It is satisfactory to notice how very insignificant the losses were amongst the non-inoculated, as contrasted with the inoculated flock."

His investigations on the Continent are also unfavourable to inoculation. On his way from Hamburg to Rostock, he examined a flock of 400, and from his observations he remarks—" In August all the sheep were inoculated, and with apparent effect. I examined the seat of inoculation, the ears, in many, and the appearances indicated that the inoculations had taken effect. Many severe cases resulted from the inoculation, and some apparently natural cases occurred, and early in October a very severe outbreak was witnessed in which many of the sheep had a well-developed eruption, and others were seized chiefly in the head." On various parts on the Continent, inoculation used to be regularly practised with the idea of securing a flock from an outbreak of the malady. This mode has of late years been abandoned, because the flocks on which this preservative inoculation was performed were always centres from which the disease was carried to neighbouring flocks. The mode of performing inoculation is by first providing a sufficient quantity of variolous lymph, which is best obtained from pustules from a previous inoculation, and taken from young animals. The best lymph is a transparent fluid, with a slightly reddish tint. The best seasons for inoculating are spring and autumn, when it is neither too cold nor too hot. Having made due preparations, then, take a small lancet and make an incision between the epidermis and true skin on any convenient part of the body bared of wool, frequently in the ear or tail, then charge an ivory point, shaped like an arrow, with the lymph, and insert it in the incision made for a few minutes, using slight pressure in withdrawing the point, to ensure its being deprived of the variolous lymph.

It is of the utmost importance to be able to distinguish the symptoms of this malady from those of the other eruptive ovine diseases. Ovine scabies or sheep scab exhibit certain characteristic symptoms resembling smallpox. They are both eruptive diseases of the skin; but though the general features resemble each other, the two diseases are, nevertheless, quite distinct and different. The period of latency in smallpox varies from five to twelve days; in that of scab from ten to twenty-five days. There is neither loss of appetite, nor fever, nor dulness, nor increase of temperature in scab previous to the eruption. The earliest symptom is itchiness of the skin, the sheep frequently rubbing itself against posts, gates, fences, trees, &c., twisting the head, and nibbling amongst the wool. After the disease is fairly established, tufts of wool are pulled out by their teeth, thus causing the ragged appearance the wool then presents. When a considerable part of the body is affected, the animal becomes very uneasy, and frequently attempts to scratch the affected part with its hind foot. If we rub the skin with the hand, it seems to exhibit delight, stretching the head and neck, moving the lips and jaws, and attempting to scratch those who in some degree lessen the acuteness and continuance of the irritation.

The situation of sheep-pox differs from that of scab. In the former it has been shown that the favourite seats of eruption are those where the skin has a hairy instead of a woolly covering; but scab is developed on those parts of the body where the wool is thickest, as the neck, shoulders, and back, where the acari can be well sheltered. After the parasite has deposited itself, a little vesicle is soon developed, containing a reddish yellow serous fluid. When the contents of this vesicle are discharged, a crust or scab is formed of the same colour. On the border of this crust the parasites multiply with remarkable rapidity. The vesicles in scab become confluent; they form more rapidly, and burst without degenerating into pustules as in sheep-pox. The symptoms, which are of special importance, are mainly two in each disease, and these show the clear distinction between them. In sheep-pox we have a high state of fever, with a general constitutional disturbance. In sheep-scab we have no fever, and the health of the animal is not impaired, unless the disease be allowed to spread to such an extent that the poor animal has no rest night or day from the incessant irritation, which causes debility and emaciation, in some cases followed by death. A much larger number succumb from the application of strong mercurial dressings, than from the disease itself.

Sheep-pox and sheep-scab are both due to contagion. The former is due to a specific virus, which enters and acts on the blood as a poison; the latter to a parasite known as the dermatocoptes ovis, which soon goes to the bottom of the wool, and confines its operations to the skin. Sheep-pox will run its course unless interrupted by death. Sheep scab can have its progress cut short at almost any point of severity by adopting remedial measures for the certain destruction of the parasite. There are several other symptoms which distinguish smallpox from the other eruptive ovine diseases, but they are of minor importance. As smallpox is the most dangerous and fatal ovine disease, and as repeated observations and investigations have clearly proved its attacks in this country to be solely due to importation, the most effectual mode of dealing with it is to prevent its introduction by the use of the legal precautionary measures, which are sufficiently practicable and powerful to stamp it out, if it should unfortunately reach our shores.

## THE RESULTS OF DIFFERENT MODES OF FEEDING ON THE QUANTITY AND QUALITY OF BUTTER AND CHEESE.

By DAVID WATSON WEMYSS, Newton Bank, St. Andrews.

*[Premium—Ten Sovereigns.]*

MILK in its natural state or manufactured into butter and cheese must be regarded as an object of considerable importance in the domestic economy of every household. It is, in fact, one of those indispensable necessaries of life which we cannot do without in some shape or another. Hence it is evident that the treatment of the milk cow is a matter of no small importance.

The milk of the cow is composed of three distinct ingredients —the curd, the whey, and the butter. The two first form the largest portion, and the last the most valuable, which is the fat or oleaginous part of the milk. The comparative value of the milk of different cows, or of the same cows fed on different pastures, is estimated chiefly by the quantity of butter contained in it, and in this respect some breeds of cows are far superior to others.

The union of the component parts of milk is chiefly mechanical, as they separate by subsidence according to their specific gravities, the cream being the lightest, and the curd the heaviest. The curd, however, requires a slight chemical change for its separation from the whey, which, at the same time produces lactic acid. From the moment that milk is drawn from the cow it begins to be affected by the air and changes of temperature; and circumstances almost imperceptible will materially affect its quality; hence the importance of great care and cleanliness, especially in butter-making.

Before giving a statement of results of different modes of feeding on the quantity and quality of butter and cheese produced, I will describe several other circumstances which affect these, independently of the sort of food given to cows, which is also of material importance.

In the first place, it will rest with the farmer to make the selection of his breed most suitable for the nature of his soil and climate, also for the particular branch of dairying he intends to pursue. If his object is to sell milk or to rear calves, quantity must be the chief consideration, and quality if he means to produce butter and cheese.

It is often the case that cows of the same and of the best breeds will not always yield the same quantity of milk, and the milk of those that yield the most is not unfrequently deficient in quality. These points, however, which are of great importance to the dairy, may be easily determined by keeping the cows on the same food, measuring their milk, and then keeping and churning it several times separately. Thus, reckoning the cost of their keep, and the produce of the milk of each, and comparing the result, it would soon be ascertained which was the most profitable animal.

Although feeding on the same description of food, both quantity and quality of milk will vary; likewise under similar circumstances the housing, feeding, and general management, the yield of milk will be perpetually varying in the same animal. Also, one cow may be found at one time to yield milk rich in butter-giving constituents, while at another it will have the very opposite characteristics, or be most valuable for cheese making; and yet the system of feeding and management remains the same.

Still farther, there are other circumstances which exercise an important influence upon the productive capabilities of dairy-stock, even under the same system of feeding, both as regards quantity and quality of milk, such as the bad state of the atmosphere of the byre, and the irritating tendency of flies or insects in the field. Those who are in the habit of keeping their cows filthy and indifferently fed will soon find out that it is a most wasteful and extravagant plan. In all dairy establishments ventilation and cleanliness are indispensable ; and if butter is made, the dairy ought to be as near the cow-house as possible, as the milk suffers more or less considerably from being agitated, or too much cooled before it is set for the cream to rise.

Again, it is not the mere kind of food, but the condition in which it is given, that exercises an influence, as well as the soil on which the crops are grown, as it appears evident that the feeding qualities of grass or turnips grown on good land will be superior to those grown on inferior soil, each crop possessing its own distinctive feeding qualities, as well as its own cultural characteristics.

From observations taken by various persons, the amount of solid food consumed by cows is little or not at all affected by the fact that the animal is giving milk, but that the quantity of milk produced is in exact proportion to the quantity of liquid consumed or water drunk by them. A cow which, before calving, will be satisfied with from two to four gallons of water, when milking will require from six to ten. A change from succulent herbage to dry forage will immediately reduce the quantity of milk to three-fourths or even two-thirds. The necessity for a supply of water is different in different circumstances, such as, a lean animal will have a more violent desire to drink than a fat one, hence it would appear the milk-producing power of any substance depends, as might be expected, on the quantity of water it contains. If mere quantity depends on the liquid drunk by the animal, the amount of solid matter contained in the milk, that is, its real value, must necessarily depend on the quantity and quality of the solid matter consumed by the animals. In many systems of feeding the object aimed at is simply to aid the increase of the milk, without attending to the maintenance of the condition of the animal; but highly nutritious feeding will soon repay the expense, by greatly increased quantity and quality of milk, and also in the improved condition of the animal.

As I have previously stated, the mode in which food is given to cows exercises considerable influence upon its milk-producing value. Some advocate the use of raw, some the use of boiled food, and some of a mixture of various foods. Each system, no doubt, may have its own good qualities in the localities, and under circumstances for which it is intended.

Besides those that I have already described, there are other circumstances which have been found to influence materially the quantity of milk, such as the breed of the cow. The smaller breeds, such as the Ayrshire, will often give a larger quantity of milk than a cross-bred cow of larger size, although fed on the same description of food. I have had an Ayrshire cow giving twelve quarts of milk daily, and a cross-bred one of the same age, and the same time calved, giving only eight quarts, which made a difference of at least one shilling per day, which at the end of ten months would amount to the value of the cow herself.

As a general rule with all cows, the quantity of milk gradually decreases after the first two or three months after calving, but the quality increases.

I may mention another point which, if not attended to, will greatly influence the quality of milk, that is, the cows should be milked in the cool of the morning and evening, and they ought not to be much driven before milking ; also, it is better to bring them to the byre some time before the operation begins. Hurrying a cow when she is full, heats both her blood and her milk, raises its temperature, increases its odour, and modifies the butter and cheese made from it. Also, when cows are abused by an ill-tempered milker, it is most astonishing what an effect it has upon their milking and the quantity of cream as compared with the cream taken from the milk of cows always kindly and gently treated. All severity is sure to make a cow keep back all the milk she can. The more quiet and peaceable cows can be kept while being milked the more perfect will be the relaxation of their udders, and the longer will it last. If anything occurs to disturb, excite, or attract their attention, the relaxation will cease in a moment, and, if it occurs near the close of milking, some of the best milk will be held back till the next milking, when it will become the poor quality that is first drawn. A double loss ensues from such an occurrence, because, leaving milk in a cow's udder always tends to diminish secretion. Each milker should also have certain cows to milk. Changing milkers attracts the attention of the cow, and excites a little feeling of cautiousness, therefore she will not give down as freely as if always milked by the same person ; the same result will follow if not milked quickly. The quickest milker will always get the most and best milk.

I have now described what I consider the chief circumstances which influence the quantity of milk, independent of food. I shall now endeavour to describe those which influence its quality under the same circumstances.

Milk from cows inhaling bad odours has been found to be tainted and unfit to be made either into butter or cheese. For this reason, they ought not to be allowed to inhale offensive emanations, or to go near stagnant pools to quench their thirst.

In warm weather, it is very important that milk be cooled as early as possible after being taken from the cow, so as to prevent its becoming sour; more especially if it is to be used for making butter or cheese, as the butter would then become rancid, and the cheese would not keep. Although a cure for rancidity is to wash and beat the butter well in cold water, in which have been put a few drops of chloride of lime, and mixing it well, then washing it anew in fresh water after being left for a few hours. Butter never by any means acquires a bad taste during the operation of churning; the mischief is done in the gathering of the milk. Attention to feeding, to the keeping of the milk, the speedy churning of it after it is collected, the temperature when it is put into the churn, and the rate of agitation kept up during churning, all influence quality, both as regards the taste, and the colour of the butter. Cheese of a sour taste and of inferior quality, is generally the result of allowing milk to become sour before separating the curd from the whey, which ought to be done as quickly as possible, by means of an acid juice, which will readily curdle it.

There are several other circumstances, independent of food, which affect the quality of milk, such as the age of the cow. The milk of a cow in her third or fourth calf is generally richer in quality than a younger one, and will continue so for several years. In dry seasons, the quality is generally richer, although cool weather favours the production of cheese, hot weather increases the yield of butter.

The poorer the condition of the cow, good feeding being supplied, the richer, in general, is the milk. If a cow be milked only once a day, the milk will yield more butter than an equal quantity of that obtained by two milkings, and even less by three. I have also observed that the morning milk is of better quality than that of the evening.

The colour of the cow has also a considerable effect on the quality. For instance, white cows, whatever may be the breed, generally, as a rule, give milk of poor quality; for this reason, many who keep cows to make butter and cheese never keep a cow of this colour. Preference is always given to cows of a brown or brown and white, and black or black and white colour, as their milk is generally of richest quality.

A bad state of the atmosphere of the byre, and cows inhaling bad odours, all affect the quality of milk, which imparts the same to butter and cheese made from it.

These, I consider, are the principal circumstances which are liable to affect the quality of milk, and butter, and cheese made from it, independent of the food, and having explained those affecting the quantity under the same circumstances, I shall now give results of the influence of food over these.

The kind of food upon which cows are fed, has certainly more influence upon the quantity and quality of milk and butter than any other circumstance, the taste and colour being easily affected by it. For instance, when wild plants or weeds are eaten by cows, the taste and colour of them are perceptible both in the milk and butter, as well as the cheese made from the same.

The mode of feeding milk cows may be divided into two branches, namely, pasturing and house-feeding. In order to obtain a good supply of rich milk, when the pasturing system is being adopted, it is not only requisite that there is plenty of it, but also that it is of that quality which is relished by the cows. The best quality of butter and cheese is made from the milk of cows fed on old natural grasses, which also has a better flavour than from artificial grass. Certain wild plants which often grow in meadows or marshy soils, such as the yellow-buttercup or crow-foot in particular, when eaten by cows, gives a disagreeable taste and colour both to butter and cheese; for this reason, these weeds ought to be cut down and extracted where practicable.

I have had cows producing from five to six pounds of butter per week on young grass, but when put out to old natural pasture the quantity increased to seven or eight pounds from the same quantity of milk.

Italian rye-grass and clover are often highly esteemed for feeding dairy-cows; but many people, as well as myself, have found rye-grass alone to be a better butter-producing food than clover, which has also a sweeter flavour. For this reason, the second crop of clover ought seldom to be given to cows.

But when these are made into hay and well got, circumstances are altered, as they then form a nutritious and palatable food, and impart a sweet flavour both to butter and cheese, especially when given regularly to cows in winter, in addition to their ordinary food a few hours before being milked.

Tares given to cows once a day form a healthy and nutritious food, and no disagreeable flavour either to the butter or cheese was ever discerned by me when they were getting them, although some people think otherwise. As a rule, I give the cows as many as they can eat to their supper during the summer months while they are green and fresh, and the milk is generally richer in quality, and the butter finer flavoured than when the cows are fed on grass alone. Tares abound in vegetable curd, therefore they give a rich and productive milk to the cheese-maker. It is advisable and advantageous to sow a quantity of peas and beans along with the tares, which will considerably enhance their value, as the quantity of milk will be greatly increased, and the butter and cheese produced will be of the finest quality.

Carrots when given to cows not only render the milk richer

in quality, but they also communicate to the butter and cheese a fine colour, equal to that produced by the most luxuriant grasses, and the flavour is superior. The fact that carrots are the best root for cows when the cream is to be churned, ought to induce dairy farmers to bestow more attention on their cultivation.

Potatoes, on which cows will thrive well, when given with a plentiful supply of good oat-straw.or hay, will yield as large a quantity of good rich milk as the richest pastures; and the butter is generally of a rich colour, especially when they are given in a raw state. This root is rarely given to milk cows, as it has little influence in increasing the yield of milk; also, it has a tendency to make the butter difficult to extract.

Mangolds, in some localities are preferred to turnips for milk cows, the quantity and quality of milk is the same, although turnips are usually preferred on account of mangolds requiring good rich soil to grow them to perfection. The only good quality they seem to have is, when well stored they will keep fresh and good, when turnips have lost a portion of their nutritive qualities. At that time they will cause an increase both in the quantity as well as enrich the quality of milk, as they will then have lost many of their watery particles; also, the butter and cheese will not have the bad flavour which turnips frequently give.

Cabbages have always been esteemed as a valuable food for milk cows, yet they are seldom cultivated in Scotland for this purpose alone. They require to be given with a considerable portion of good hay; but like turnips, they are apt to impart an unpleasant flavour to butter and cheese, unless great care is taken to remove all the decayed leaves, but they assist the colour of the butter, and are a highly nutritious food.

The greater proportion of the winter food of cows in this country is made up of turnips, especially swedes. These, unfortunately, give a remarkable and by no means agreeable taste to milk, as well as butter and cheese. When farmers become more aware of the value of carrots and mangolds as feeding for their cows, by which the use of turnips would be greatly supplanted, and their exclusive use rendered unnecessary, this bad flavour so often prevalent in winter would be less frequent. It has been recommended as a preventive to give cows their turnips immediately after, instead of before being milked, which is the usual custom. If this plan was attended to, I have no doubt it would be the best and simplest means of preventing the turnips tainting the butter and cheese. But this turnip flavour may also be prevented by adding a little sour milk to the new milk, which would hasten the souring of the latter, and thus prevent the formation of this flavour, which is partly caused by allowing the milk to sour slowly. Another useful

D

preventive is to put a small piece of saltpetre into the milk-pail which will dissolve while milking, or a small quantity of it ground, put into the milk-basins, will serve the same purpose. There is no feeding for milk cows equal to turnips, especially the yellow varieties; they afford a rich taste and colour to the butter and cheese, and produce a larger quantity of milk than any other vegetable feeding.

Oil-cake and linseed cake are highly esteemed as food, or rather an addition to the ordinary food of dairy cows. By this addition considerable nutriment is thrown into the system, and the quantity and quality of milk are thereby greatly improved. A sufficient quantity requires to be given to have the desired effect. I have tried two and three pounds a day to each cow, along with their ordinary food, but this had little or no effect either on the quantity or quality of the milk; but by increasing the allowance to four pounds, a considerable difference was observed, and when getting turnips the milk had not so strong a flavour of them. By giving oil-cake, the secretion of milk is not only greatly favoured, but also the healthy development of the animal. It also produces butter and cheese of exquisite flavour, and has a great richness in butter-making principles.

Cotton-cake is also a good addition to the ordinary food when given in the same proportion as oil-cake, especially when quantity and not quality is desired. I have given it to a cow giving five quarts of milk, which then increased to eight quarts, but the quality was inferior; which was of no consequence, as it was quantity that I desired; the cost was also much less than either oil-cake or linseed-cake.

Rape-cake is well adapted to promote the production of milk, being rich in phosphates and also in oil; but I have observed that it did not add to the richness of the milk, but tended rather to bring the cows into higher condition. Three pounds were given per day during the winter months, and it had the effect of counteracting the unpleasant flavour of the turnips to a great degree; so much so, that although the tops were often given with the turnips, no unpleasant taste could be detected in the butter or cheese. Rape-cake also gives to butter a closeness of grain and a soft consistency even in frosty weather, which is a great recommendation.

Malt and barley are extensively used as food for cows, with a view both to increase the quantity and enrich the quality of the milk. When used separately, barley has been found to produce more milk than malt; but malt produced more butter, which circumstance tends to prove that the difference depends greatly upon the readiness with which food can be assimilated by the animals, and for this reason, when barley is used, it ought to be cooked and also bruised, which will greatly aid this assimilation. The feeding of cows kept near large towns is conducted more with a view to produce quantity than quality of milk, hence the succulency of the food is more looked to in such cases than its nutritive properties. For this reason malt, also the grains and refuse obtained from breweries, are much used by dairymen. When these are given along with turnips, the milk is better flavoured, than it is when cows are fed on turnips alone.

Beans and leguminous seeds are much better milk-producers than any of the cereals. Beans and peas cut green in autumn and given to cows once a day are considered the best and most profitable sort of food that can be given at that season, especially when quality of milk is the main object desired, as they tend to enrich it very much as well as to increase the quantity, and the butter and cheese produced is of the finest colour and flavour. Bean-meal given to cows produces a greater yield of butter than equal quantities of either oil-cake or rape-cake, or indeed any other sort of extra feeding. In fact, I would consider it the most profitable sort of additional food to give to cows, especially when prepared and supplied in the following way:—Boiled turnips and chaff combined, and the meal added afterwards, before being given, and supplied morning and evening with as much hay or straw as the cows can eat. I may mention, the yield of butter was never so great when the meal was added before as when after the turnips were boiled, which ought to be attended to.

Boiling or steaming dry food is recommended by many as the most economical method of feeding milk cows, but I must admit I am not in favour of such a practice, although I have often been compelled to adopt it for a short time for the sake of economy. Although it forms an agreeable mode of administration, still I consider that it is the means of withdrawing from the roots a good deal of their valuable qualities, and leaving only the watery and fibrous portions. But there is no doubt, when turnips or other roots are boiled, and mixed with chaff or cut hay and straw, with a certain quantity of either oil-cake or bean-meal added afterwards, a greater abundance of milk will be obtained than if the same had been given in a dry or raw state. In cold weather I have no doubt that this would be the most economical and most desirable method to feed milk cows. A portion of salt, mixed amongst boiled or steamed food, is of the utmost importance, and is very beneficial in several ways. It restores the tone of the stomach when impaired by the excess of other food, and corrects the crudity of moist vegetables or grasses in a green state. It helps digestion, keeps the body cool, and prevents many disorders arising therefrom. It renders inferior food palatable, so that the animals eat it with eagerness. When given to cows, perhaps at the rate of from two to four ounces daily, the quantity of milk is increased, and it also has a material effect in alleviating the disagreeable flavour acquired from turnips. During the winter months, cows are generally fed three times a day, and, as I have previously mentioned, turnips ought never to be given as the first diet in the morning or immediately before being milked, unless they are boiled or pulped.

It has been often remarked that plants given to cows in a green state impart a bright yellow tint to butter and cheese, but when given in a matured and dry state they have a different effect. Feeding on hay or straw, with or without bruised grain of any sort, produces butter and cheese invariably of a white colour, except from cows that have recently calved.

I have tried several methods of feeding cows, with a view to increase both the quantity and enrich the quality of milk, and the following I have found to be the best:—The cows are put to grass about the second week in May, taken home and milked three times a day. In the morning before milking they get four pounds of oil-cake or linseed-cake each for about two months, and in the evening cut grass or tares. The first week before commencing to give them cake, cows that were giving six quarts of milk per day increased to eight and even nine quarts after getting it. After the first two months when the pastures begin to fall off, the same allowance of cake is given at mid-day instead of in the morning, and grass or tares given morning and evening. This method I found to keep up the quantity of milk, but the quality was not so rich; the quantity of butter falling off about two pounds per week for each cow. This arrangement is carried on till October, when the cows are on the stubbles, then a few white turnips are given in the evening with plenty of hay or oat-straw at their command. In a few weeks they get an additional feed of turnips in the morning after being milked, and gradually retained in the house for the winter. No additional feeding is given so long as white turnips are in use. By this feeding the milk increased a little in quantity, but the quality was inferior on account of the soft nature of the turnips. In November or December yellow turnips are given morning and afternoon, four pounds of oil-cake or linseed-cake in the forenoon, and a small quantity of cooked food, with a little bean-meal added, the last thing at night. I have found this sort of feeding to increase both the quantity as well as enrich the quality of the milk, and the flavour of the butter and cheese was superior. The expense of the extra feeding, I consider, was repaid by the increase of milk and butter, as well as saving of turnips, also the better condition of the animals, and superior quality of the manure. About Candlemas Swedish turnips are given, and continued till the grass, the same allowance of cake and additional food being supplied. Sometimes a few raw potatoes have been given in the afternoon instead of turnips, which I have found to work very well, but no difference either in the quantity or quality of the milk could be detected. Cows relish this feeding very much, and it is also the means of saving the turnips, which there has been great need to do for some years past. As a rule, turnip tops ought never to be given to milk cows, as they impart a disagreeable flavour to butter and cheese.

It is always the case when milk has any disagreeable flavour, caused by feeding or otherwise, the same is also imparted to the butter and cheese made from it.

Butter made in winter is generally of a pale colour, but this may be corrected to a certain extent by putting a little red carrot juice, or what is preferable, a small quantity of annatto into the churn just before the butter is ready to come. When intended for sale, butter ought not be kept above a few days after it is made, as there is a chance of the quality being injured, however carefully it has been made.

The annual average produce of butter from a cow of good breed and well fed ought to be from 190 to 200 lbs., after allowing two months for being dry before calving. If it exceeds this quantity, the cow is a superior one, and if less she is scarcely worth keeping. The average quantity of milk required to produce 1 quart of cream is generally 13 quarts. The average quantity of butter from 1 quart of cream is about 15 ounces. But 12 quarts of milk to 1 lb. of butter may be considered an extra good return. One gallon of milk produces on an average 1 lb. of cheese. The expense of keeping a cow cannot be reckoned at less than £15 a year, and the dairy expenses £1 for each cow.

To conclude my remarks I will make a few general observations. Attention to the feeding of milk cows is a matter of the utmost importance, as the nature of the food influences to a great extent the quantity and quality of milk, as well as the colour and flavour of the butter and cheese, which are often important points, as the price obtained for them may be thereby influenced to the extent of from 20 to 50 per cent.

Winter feeding is generally found to give butter a deficient colour from that obtained when cows are fed upon natural grasses in summer; it is also a brighter shade of yellow from old pastures, than from sown grasses. Of the turnips, I consider the yellow varieties to be the best and most suitable, as, while they tend to induce an abundant flow of milk, a certain yellow tint is imparted to the butter and cheese. The natural differences in the quality of the milk affect also that of the cheese made from it; if milk be poor in butter, so must the cheese be. If the pasture be such as to give milk rich in cream, the cheese will partake of the same quality. If the herbage or other food affect the taste of the milk and cream, it will also affect the flavour of the butter and cheese.

I have now given a statement of the results of different sorts of feeding, on the quantity and quality of butter and cheese produced, also how these may be affected by other circumstances. I have also stated the quantity of milk, as well as butter and cheese, a good cow ought to produce annually, also the expense of her keep. These remarks, I may state, are the result of several years' experience, and are founded on facts.

I must say in conclusion, that if more attention was paid to the sort of food given to milk cows, especially those kept for dairy purposes, I am convinced that fewer diseases would be heard of in the large towns which evidently arise from the effects of unwholesome milk imparted from the food the cows are generally fed upon.

## THE *PINUS INSIGNIS*, AND ITS VALUE FOR PLANTING IN SCOTLAND.

### By ROBERT HUTCHISON of Carlowrie.

[*Premium—Five Sovereigns.*]

*Pinus insignis*, Douglas, the Remarkable Pine.

Synon.—*Pinus radiata* (Hartweg).
      „   *californica* (Loisel).
      „   *adunca* (Bosc.).
      „   *montereyensis* (Rauch).

*Leaves.*—In threes, of a rich deep grass-green colour, rather slender and tapering, twisted considerably, very densely set on branches, various in length, from 4 to 6 inches long, ribbed on the inner sides and sharp-pointed; sheaths, short, smooth, and about ¼ of an inch in length.

*Branches.*—Numerous, rather irregular, and thickly set with close slender branchlets near the extremities.

*Cones.*—Ovate-conical, pointed, chiefly developed on the exposed side, and chiefly so near the base on the outer side, 3¼ to 4 inches in length, and about 2¼ inches wide, chiefly in clusters of from three to five in number round the stem near the top of the tree, or round the principal branches near their tips, of a pale yellowish-brown colour, extremely hard, and with a smooth, glistering surface; they grow pointing downwards and inwards towards the branch, and remain for several years on the tree if undisturbed.

*Scales.*—Spirally disposed in five rows the one way and eight the other, thickest at the base, tapering into a four-sided blunt pyramid, with a sunken scar in the centre, terminated by a very short prickle, largest on the outer side, and chiefly towards the base, while those towards the points are very small and little elevated.

*Seed.*—Of medium size, almost black in colour, with an ample wing, fully an inch in length. Two years are required to ripen the seed.

*Habitat.*—California : on the higher parts of the Coast Mountains, but not more than from 200 to 300 feet above sea-level. In quantity at "Point Pinos," near Monterey, where many of the trees are one-sided, owing to the prevalence of strong north-westerly gales in that region for a considerable portion of the year.

THIS beautifully-foliaged pine is a native of California, where it is found in its usual habitat attaining to a height of from 80 to 100 feet, with a girth of from 8 to 12 feet in many instances, and feathered to the ground with gracefully drooping branches. It appears to be one and the same with *Pinus radiata*. Dr Coulter found it attaining a height of 100 feet when growing singly in its native home, with a peculiarly straight clean stem, feathered to the very ground with branches. Gordon states that it attains to a height of from 80 to 100 feet, and with a stem from 2 to 4 feet in diameter, while Dr Torry in his Report in the *United States Railroad Explorations Commission* (vol. iv. 1854) says that the ordinary height of the tree is only from 30 to 40 feet, which is probably under exceptional circumstances of site and soil, for it promises to attain in this country a considerably higher altitude and growth.

*Pinus insignis* was originally found by Dr Coulter in Upper California, near sea-level, and growing very luxuriantly down almost to the beach. It was also noticed about the same time (1832) by Hartweg, growing in splendid luxuriance on the descent towards the sea, on the mountains of San Antonio near Monterey, and also along the Coast Mountains of California, and to these districts its native habitat seems to be confined.

It was first introduced into Britain by Douglas and Coulter in 1833, both having sent seeds simultaneously. Their encomiums of the beauty and extreme gracefulness and luxuriance of the peculiar green foliage of the tree at once drew public attention to the new acquisition, and it was eagerly planted by pine-fanciers throughout the country in all sorts of soils and situations of altitude and exposure. The beauty of the tree was reputed to be its lovely green foliage of rare abundance, as well as its striking and imposing habit of retaining its foliage to the ground, and its rapid growth. How far these anticipations will be realised the future statistics of the progress of *P. insignis* in this country will show; but it is to be feared, from the experience already recorded of its growth, and from a general consensus of opinion amongst pine growers, that, like many others of the *Pinus* or *true pine* genus, this species will in many soils and situations prove unsuitable to our climate.

It is a fact worthy of notice—for we fail to observe it recorded elsewhere—that of the more recently introduced Coniferæ, the *Abies* and *Picea* families succeed much better than the *Pinus* or true pine family. We have only to refer to the *Abies douglasii, menziesii, albertiana,* and others, or to *Picea nordmanniana, nobilis, grandis,* and others of that family, to show their thorough hardihood, and the success attendant on their introduction, as prospectively valuable timber trees; while in the *Pinus* family, we almost look in vain for any successful introduction with a view to future profit of any species introduced from beyond the limits of Europe. *Pinus pindrow, ponderosa, sabiniana, jeffreyii,* and others, are all more or less to be looked upon merely as specimens for the lawn or policy, and not as timber trees, the exceptions in this respect being confined to those of European origin, such as the *Pinus laricio* or Corsican pine, *Pinus pallasiana, P. austriaca,* and *P. maritima, cembra,* and a few others. And we consider that, from the experience already gathered regarding *Pinus insignis,* it is no exception to this rule in regard to its order; and herein lies its weak point, which is to be regretted, as it is a decided bar to its further introduction with a view to profitable planting in Scotland. It must remain a mere ornament in the park or pleasure ground, for the reasons stated, and for others to be given. But while we thus assign to this, doubtless, beautiful pine, so isolated a position amongst our newer introductions, we must in fairness record some notable examples of what it will become in suitable sites and stations; for in many parts of England, and also in Ireland (to the mild moist climate of which it is *peculiarly well adapted*), as well as in favourably sheltered sites in Scotland, it is thriving very well, although it appears to be more fastidious as to soil, and exposure, and altitude, than many others of our "*newer Coniferæ,*" as they are now so generally termed. Hitherto these have generally proved quite satisfactory in any ordinary soil, and few have evinced any peculiarity in the way of a predilection for or aversion to any particular soil; but as they advance in height and growth, the suitability of their nature for given altitudes, soils, and exposures is more apparent; and we find many, as they advance in stature, quite altering their habit and growth, but whether this be from their having percolated into the subsoil, or become altered, by the site, and altitude, or exposure, in their general characteristics, it is perhaps still premature to decide from the examples already before us. Of one thing in regard to *P. insignis,* we may be well assured from the results of the growth of many specimens in this country —that it is frequently most wayward in its habit, declining to observe or adhere to any allotted place, and frequently in consequence assuming somewhat of an amount of irregularity in its general contour, quite irreconcilable with its earlier progress and development.

But while we have thus indicated from the results of observation in many districts, that the *P. insignis* evinces little special partiality for any particular soil, there can be no doubt that with regard to altitude of site it is much more markedly fastidious. Its most important qualification appears to be, from the experience of its growth in this country, that it seems to succeed much better in low altitudes near the sea—if not actually exposed to its salt-charged breezes—and in sandy soil in such situations, than at higher altitudes where the true pine (or *Pinus*) family generally prefers to luxuriate. In this respect it seems to be an outcast from its race, and to follow in this wayward fancy the nature of *Pinus maritima*, which in many respects, as regards habit of growth, it considerably resembles. Regarding its immunity from the effects of wind in this country, we have hardly data sufficient upon which to found a definite opinion; but that heavy blasts do not severely interfere with its progress and vitality, may be gathered from the fact that its first discoverers tell us that at Point Pinos, near Monterey, on the shores of California, and swept by continuous gales, it there becomes one-sided, from the prevalence of the northerly winds, which beat upon the trees during the greater part of the year. Indeed, we find it in this country, in such similarly situated positions, thriving better than in more sheltered sites at higher altitudes and with milder exposures, as, for example, in many parts of Ireland, into which country it has been more extensively introduced than into England or Scotland, owing doubtless to its greater suitability for the moist and genial Irish climate, and where it is to be found standing up well against the prevailing strong south-westerly winds, which, so frequently wafted by the wide Atlantic, sweep for days and weeks together over the Emerald Isle.

From these statements, and from experience of the progress of *Pinus insignis* in many other localities in this country, there can be no doubt that it is best suited to a light sandy loamy soil, upon a cool subsoil, in a reasonably near proximity to the sea, and in a moist atmosphere. For instance, in such a situation as the Isle of Wight, it is admirably suited for successful cultivation, and has, in fact, been grown there from its first introduction to this country. At Osborne House the late lamented Prince Consort introduced it with marked success. Planted there in 1847, when 4 feet high, it is now fully 80 feet in height, and girths 10 feet 6 inches at 3 feet from the ground. In 1849 this tree actually made 3 feet 9 inches of annual growth, while in 1850 it made no less than 5 feet 9 inches, and in 1851 6 feet 6 inches of annual growth! This rapidity of growth in a congenial soil and site is a remarkable characteristic of this pine; for whereas in ordinary cases we see it progressing fairly, and keeping pace with other species and varieties, if it actually gets the soil, and especially the site, peculiarly its own, the rapidity of its growth is truly astonishing. It is not true, as has been sometimes asserted, that the *Pinus insignis* is *unconditionally hardy* in the climate of Britain. We find that in numerous instances it has failed in many places to resist even moderately severe winters when young, although after it has become established in a site, and acquired some height above the dew-line, it will prove more hardy and robust. Still in many localities it has proved a failure under a sharp and continuous frost of ten degrees, such as we have experienced in many places during the last two winters.

During the severe winter of 1860-61 the losses sustained from the effects of the frost were so numerous that pine fanciers in many parts of Scotland were so discouraged that they did not again replace the blanks caused by the failures of *Pinus insignis*, and even at the present day numerous correspondents write bewailing their losses at that time of many most promising specimens of this pine, and which, until then, they had considered to be quite hardy. Thus at Glamis Castle (Forfarshire), even in sheltered situations, and in good, black loam soil, on a moist gravelly subsoil, it will not stand the winter's frost, and all that have been tried have now died out; yet in this locality *P. grandis, A. douglasii, menziesii,* and other Coniferæ succeed well. The altitude of this site is 200 feet above sea-level. At Murthly, Perthshire, which may be styled the home of the Coniferæ, for they luxuriate there as they do in their native habitats, and seldom result in failures, we find that the only specimens of *Pinus insignis* which Mr. Mackenzie, the able and experienced forester, has under his care, are yet small trees, but he finds they are doing no good. The soil is a sandy loam resting on a gravelly subsoil, with red sandstone rock at a depth of from four to five feet below the surface, with a northern exposure, and at an altitude of 200 feet above the sea. Most of the other newer Coniferæ thrive there in beautiful luxuriance. Coming still further south, and crossing both the Tay and Forth, we learn that at Hopetoun, Linlithgowshire, the best specimen of *Pinus insignis* was killed in the winter of 1860-61, and a surviving tree was cut down on 27th July of the present year, being in a very weakly and dilapidated condition, and very sickly, from the effects of the severe frost of last winter (1879-80). It grew in a good, rich, rather clayey soil, with retentive subsoil, and at about 250 feet altitude above sea-level, in a northern exposure. Mr. M'Laren, whose experience as forester at Hopetoun extends over a quarter of a century, and whose knowledge of all the newer Coniferæ is large, reports that he can "say nothing in favour of *P. insignis*, and indeed does not think it suited for our climate, but probably in some particular sites may be found thriving, and proving a beautiful variety as a specimen tree for the Aboretum, but quite beyond the possibility of ever being successfully cultivated in Scotland as a timber-producing tree for planting in quantity as a crop."

At Lambton Park, co. Durham, *P. insignis* has been repeatedly tried, and failed. It will not stand the frost in this situation, and the smoke-charged atmosphere of the district is very inimical to the life of Coniferæ. Last winter (1879-80), in this locality, the damage done by the severity of the winter was excessive. Hundreds of *Wellingtonia gigantea* were killed by the frost, and were cut down and sent to the colliery works and made into posts; the wood was very soft and porous. At Lambton Park alone 350 cart loads of evergreen bushes and trees killed by the winter's frost were carted away; and thousands of common English yews, up to 25 feet in height, were killed, and scarcely one left with a live terminal shoot, and even *Rhododendron ponticum* suffered severely. These facts are mentioned, not to suggest that the situation is severely exposed, liable to suffer from extremes of temperature such as were experienced last winter, but to show that where *P. insignis* has *repeatedly* failed, only in very extraordinary seasons (such as in 1879-80) have many hardy and long introduced and acclimatised evergreens also succumbed.

In the more southern counties of England the introduction of the *Pinus insignis* has been more successful. At Dropmore, Maidenhead, at an altitude of 200 feet above sea-level, in a soil of a red, hard, gravelly nature, and rather sterile, and in other sites of a peaty description and in poor sandy loam, it has done well. The soil was prepared, however, for the plants, which, as seedlings, were planted in 1839, and are now trees 11 feet in girth at 5 feet from the ground, and fully 70 feet in height. In this place plants from cuttings, planted also in 1839, and receiving in every respect the same treatment as the seedlings have done and growing under identical influences, are now only about 60 feet high and 10 feet in circumference at 5 feet from the ground. This is interesting to mention, as it clearly corroborates the opinion that seedlings rush away at first much better, and obtain a start and superiority of habit in developing their boles, which the artificially created tree from a cutting never equals. Again, at Possingworth, Hawkhurst, in Kent, about twelve miles from the south coast, at an altitude of 450 feet above sea-level, and much exposed to the gales from the south-west, the briny wind seems in no way to affect *P. insignis*, and it is there developing a rapidity of growth truly surprising, and is the only other pine, excepting *Picea pinsapo*, which can be pronounced really hardy. The following are dimensions of some of the principal specimens presently growing at Possingworth kindly taken in August of the present year by Mr. Huth:—

No. 1. Height, 49 feet; girth at 3 feet from ground, 5 feet 2 inches; and at 5 feet, 4 feet 11 inches; age, thirty years. This plant was transplanted, and brought by machines a considerable distance fifteen years ago, but does not seem to have suffered by the operation, being quite vigorous and well-furnished with branches.

No. 2. Height, 47 feet; girth at 3 feet, 5 feet 2 inches; and at 5 feet, 4 feet 7 inches; age, thirty years. Transplanted to its present site by Mr. Huth on 4th December 1865.

No. 3. Height, 37 feet; girth at 3 feet, 5 feet 3 inches; and at 5 feet, 4 feet 4 inches; age, twenty-nine years. Very heavily branched.

No. 4. Height, 40 feet; girth at 3 feet, 4 feet 10 inches; and at 5 feet, 4 feet; age, twenty-five years.

In 1870 Mr. Huth received from California some seeds of *Pinus insignis*, which have grown and thriven amazingly. The largest plant, put out on 31st October 1873, has now attained a height of 18 feet 10 inches, and girths at 3 feet from the ground 2 feet. At Buxted Park, Uckfield, Sussex, there is a fine specimen of *Pinus insignis*, over 40 feet in height, and 6 feet in circumference at 5 feet from the ground. It has been planted twenty-five years in its present site, in a rather poor soil of a clayey nature upon a subsoil of rock, and at an altitude of 170 feet above sea-level, and in a rather exposed situation. It was slightly injured by the frost of last winter (1879-80). At the Rocks, Uckfield (Sussex), there is a fine specimen of this pine, now 45 feet in height, and girthing at 5 feet above ground 3 feet 4 inches; growing in a peat soil, and upon a subsoil of sand. At Maresfield Park, also in the neighbourhood of Uckfield (Sussex), there is another fine example of *Pinus insignis*, which at present is 46 feet in height, and girths at 5 feet above ground 2 feet 10 inches; the soil there is a sandy loam upon a sand subsoil, and situation exposed. At Montpelier, Hawkhurst (Kent), there are, besides many other fine coniferous specimens, some fine examples of the *Pinus insignis*. The soil there is rather poor, marly in nature, and on a sandy-clay subsoil, but the sites of the trees have been *forced* with good loam, and mounds formed for them, into which they have been placed when young plants. These mounds, situated at an altitude of 500 feet above sea-level, and exposed to wind from every quarter, were planted in the spring of 1867, and the trees are now fully 20 feet in height. At first they seemed to suffer from the exposure, but have quite outgrown the habit; and, as a proof of their suitability to the site and altitude, it may be mentioned that even in the very trying winter of last year (1879-80) they were very slightly affected by the frost and cold. Their immunity from the severe season may perhaps be accounted for from their being placed on mounds, and being consequently free from any stagnant water in the soil while the subsoil was porous and well-drained. At Montpelier, Hawkhurst, several young *Pinus insignis* trees have been cut down, and the wood presented a remarkable rigidity and considerable hardness. As to its durability there has as yet been no experience of its use for a sufficiently long period to express any opinion. In some places in the southern districts of England, as Kent, Sussex, Hants, Devon, &c., there appears to be some confusion in regard to the *Pinus insignis*. It seems to have been given out to the planters in several localities in these counties as *P. radiata*, which it very closely resembles. *Pinus radiata* is decidedly more hardy than *Pinus insignis*, and perhaps some instances in which the *P. insignis* has been unexpectedly—owing to site, exposure, soil, &c.—reported to be perfectly hardy may be accounted for by the fact that the specimens quoted are not *Pinus insignis* at all, but *Pinus radiata*, its close congener! At Redleaf, Penshurst, near Tunbridge, where there were a number of fine specimens of *Pinus insignis* some years ago, only one good example now remains. The others either perished in the severe winter of 1860-61 or were very much injured. Two fine plants, successfully removed from a distance of ten miles some years ago, and which were developing into grand specimens, were killed in the severe winter of 1879 down to the ground. No more will be introduced there. The surviving tree is 66 feet in height, and at 3 feet from the ground the bole is 10 feet in circumference. The soil is a stiff yellow clay to a considerable depth, with ribs of sand and iron intersecting it, and the subsoil at 15 feet deep is a hard rock. This tree is very healthy, and cones profusely; it throws out very long side branches, which are apt to get broken in heavy snowstorms. The bark is wonderfully roughened, presenting the appearance of large plate-like scales, with wide fissures intervening. So rugged and open are these fissures that a full-sized hand may be inserted sideways into the clefts.

At Bicton, in Devonshire, where there are many fine specimens of Coniferæ of recent introduction, we find one of the largest, *Pinus insignis*, now 70 feet in height, girthing 13 feet 6 inches at 3 feet above the ground, with a spread of branches measuring 78 feet in diameter. The soil is a sandy loam, and subsoil red sandy rock. In this locality the *P. insignis* has not suffered in the least during the last two severe winters. The specimen of which we have been able to give the dimensions is about forty-five years of age; and in 1861 it measured fully 50 feet in height; so that, even after attaining to so considerable an altitude, it has grown, and is continuing to grow, at the rate of a foot per annum. Once fairly acclimatised in any locality under ordinarily favourable circumstances, the *Pinus insignis* appears to acquire greater hardiness with age.

Other fine specimens, growing as ornamental trees, in various parts of the more southern and central districts of England might be referred to, such as at Longleat (Wilts), at altitudes from 480 to 700 feet above sea-level; at Eastnor (Hereford), at 520 feet elevation; and at Watcombe (Devon), at 450 feet. And such examples show that the tree is not injuriously affected by the nature of the geological formation, for these places vary in that particular considerably; and as regards soil, it is by such evidence ascertained that a sandy light soil suits it better than a low lying damp heavy loam; but from the *insignis* being so sparsely grown, few materials are at hand to show the comparative rate of progress of the growth of trees of the same age, in various soils, in the same district. In the district of Cornwall, it succeeds splendidly, and better than either the Austrian or Pinaster pine which are very often, in that locality, associated with it as nurses. At Porthguedden, near Truro, in Cornwall, there is a fine specimen over 70 feet high, growing within 100 yards of the sea; and quite uninjured by the sea-breeze. In situations which suit it, the rapidity of its growth is marvellous, after being fairly started. Thus we find that at Osborne (Isle of Wight), in 1851, it actually made shoots of $6\frac{1}{2}$ feet in length; and at Nettlecombe (in Somersetshire), it made shoots 7 feet long during the growing season of 1861; and after the previously very severe winter; which had not affected it there. It was then 48 feet in height. Some observers have fancied that it makes young wood all the year round, but this is a mistake probably caused by the early period in spring at which it puts forth its young buds, which are in very favourable spots sometimes seen in the month of January, 8 inches in length at that precarious season! To this tendency is its failure to be ascribed in many places, and especially in low-lying and damp heavy soils, exposed to the south.

Turning now to Ireland, we find that the climate there is in some districts peculiarly favourable to the growth and development of *P. insignis*. Indeed, if this pine is to be grown for timber purposes at all in Britain, it is to the southern and south-western counties of Ireland that we must look for its most probable success, both physiologically and pecuniarily. Near Arctrum, Inniscarra, co. Cork, growing on the estate of Fota, and, in the vicinity of Queenstown, we find a handsome tree, 50 feet high, with a girth of 11 feet 8 inches at 3 feet from the ground, and under thirty years planted. It grows on a dry marly subsoil, with a western exposure, and not more than 20 feet above sea-level. In any instance where the timber has been sawn, in this district, it has a blotched appearance, with resin-like spots through the grain of the wood, and is found superior to Scots fir, spruce, or silver fir of the same age. It grows rapidly, and has a very majestic appearance, and is quite hardy in this district. From Limerick, Waterford, Queen's -County, and Tipperary, similar reports are received as well as from many other districts of Ireland. At Emo Park (Queen's County), at an altitude of 520 feet, it is thriving admirably, and escaped injury during the memorably severe winter, so frequently already referred to. The soil is light and sharp, on a limestone and gravel subsoil. At Ballinacourt, Tipperary County, at an altitude of 530 feet, well sheltered, in a rich loam, resting upon limestone rock, we find a magnificently furnished specimen, planted about thirty-two years ago, and now measuring 9 feet 2 inches in girth at 3 feet from the ground, and 48 feet high, with a diameter of spread of branches of 61 feet. From this tree a large number of thriving seedlings have been raised, which are now interspersed throughout the woods, some being at higher altitudes, and more exposed, but in every instance growing very freely, and well adapted to the locality. The only instances of failure here are in situations where the roots got into contact with stagnant water in the subsoil. At Coote Park (Gort), co. Galway, at an altitude of 30 feet above sea-level, and in a light limestone soil, with subsoil of limestone gravel, this pine thrives wonderfully, and is the most successful introduction that has been made into the district, and it has never failed, or suffered from frost. At Hamwood, Clonee, co. Meath, *P. insignis*, planted thirty years ago, is now 65 feet in height, girthing 9 feet at 3 feet from the ground. The soil is limestone, and close to the limestone rock which is within 3 feet of the surface, it is a stiff soil; altitude above sea-level 300 feet, and thirteen miles distant from the coast. The situation is exposed to strong south and south-easterly winds, but sheltered from the north by beech trees. At Langford Lodge, co. Antrim, on the shore of Lough Meagh, in a soil of a clayey loam and gravelly subsoil, *P. insignis* does well. One specimen there is now 40 feet in height, and girths 4 feet in circumference at 5 feet from the ground. It suits this locality well; and proves hardier than *P. excelsa*.

But even in the congenial climate of Ireland, it will be observed from what has been already stated that *P. insignis* will not succeed in very damp soil, or water-logged subsoil; and if further evidence upon this point were requisite, we may state that at Glaslough, co. Monaghan, at 154 feet altitude, and in a yellow strong loam, resting upon a heavy yellow clay, one specimen which had survived for twenty-seven years succumbed during the severe winter of 1867. Being cut up for planking and other purposes, the bole, which was 10 inches in diameter, was found to present a timber of coarse, knotty, loose appearance, and of little value at that age at all events, as a timber-tree. But another example from the extreme south of Ireland, where we have already recorded its general suitability, may be

given to show further proof of the occasional uncertainty of the
success of the *P. insignis*, under favourable auspices of climate,
altitude, &c.; at Curraghmore, Portlaw, co. Waterford, this
pine was planted some years ago in considerable numbers.
Having doubts about its thorough reliableness as to hardiness, a
piece of land was selected, which it was thought would suit
it admirably. The ground was thoroughly drained, as was
supposed, some years previously, and was well sheltered. The
situation, in fact, was all that the most painstaking and thoughtful planter would have desired. Sufficient shelter without too
much shade being provided, and with exposure sufficient for
Coniferæ to ripen their young shoots before winter. The soil
was a clayey loam, with porous subsoil, and the trees were from
ten to twelve years old, and from 10 to 23 feet in height, last
season, when the severity of the winter 1879–80, which was
unusually keen for the south of Ireland, came, and killed them
outright. Two trees, which had barely survived, endeavoured
this spring to put forth buds, but ineffectually, and they also
soon succumbed. In this instance, we probably learn the
risk of too carefully sheltering the doubtfully hardy species of
newer Coniferæ, for they being prone by nature to bud early in
spring, as is especially the case with *P. insignis*, the frost overhead of the spring months during night settling within the
sheltered area where they grow, and the bright sunshine by day,
during that season upon their tender young buds, soon effects
their destruction. Had these trees been more exposed to an
open sweep of the wind in that site, probably a different result
would have been experienced, always supposing the subsoil to
have been as well-drained as it appears to have been in this
case. The altitude of this site is 80 feet above sea-level.

From the foregoing remarks it will be seen that hitherto in
this country there have been few opportunities for estimating
the prospective value of *P. insignis* as a timber-producing tree
of intrinsic merit,—from any examples we have been able to
cite wherein it has been cut down and manufactured into
timber. Dow, however, states, on the authority of Coulter, that
in its native habitats it yields excellent timber, exceedingly
tough, and well suited for boat building; for which purpose
it is much used. In San Francisco, it is largely used for street
planking and paving, for, owing to its large amount of resin, the
wood, cut into blocks, stands better, and resists the tear and
wear of heavy traffic better than any other variety of timber.
Another authority, the late Mr Rogers of Penrose (M.P. for
Helstone), states that if the timber of *P. insignis* can be judged
of in this country, at so early an age, he has found it light and
tough, rather knotty, but the knots are easily worked and soft,
yet firm, having the softness of the lime-wood, rather than the

usual fibrous rend of fir-timber, and when young the wood is beautifully spotted with darkish eyes like the markings of bird's-eye maple.

*P. insignis* is very liable in this country to suffer from the ravages of the *Hylurgus piniperda*, or pine beetle; this little pest seeming to have a decided preference for it. It is not, however, liable to be readily attacked by rabbits.

It is to be feared that the only conclusion to be drawn from the preceding evidence of the true amount of hardiness hitherto evinced by this pine generally over the area of Britain is, that while in some particular localities, notably the south and south-western counties of England, and a wide area of Ireland, it may be grown profitably as a timber tree in quantity, its chief use and suitability in our climate generally will be to enhance, as specimen trees, the beauty of the scenery of the lawns and pleasure grounds,—for which its rich coloured foliage and finely feathered sweeping branches so admirably adapt it.

## THE EFFECTS OF THE SEVERE FROST OF THE WINTER 1879–80 UPON TREES AND SHRUBS.

By ROBERT HUTCHISON of Carlowrie.

*[Premium—Five Sovereigns.]*

IT seldom, if ever, has fallen to the lot of any meteorological student or close observer of nature to record in succession two winters of unwontedly severe character in the climate of the British Isles. Mercifully we are exempt from winters of undue severity except at long intervals; so long, indeed, as to make these exceptional seasons stand out in full prominence, and to render them, in the literal sense of the word, "memorable." During the past twenty years, however, whether from any climatic change of the seasons—whether from, as is sometimes alleged, the diversion of the course of the Gulf Stream—whether from the presence of sun-spots of unusual magnitude, or from any other of the many whimsical reasons too frequently assigned and rashly advanced for any unusual phenomena in the physical world—it has been the lot of the present generation, during the period mentioned, to experience four winters of unparalleled severity, and each marked by an extreme lowness of temperature quite abnormal to the British climate.

The winter of 1860–61, so frequently now quoted as "memorable" for its frost and snows and persistent severity, left its mark upon our woodlands and gardens, some of which are to the present time still unobliterated by the softer touch of more

E

genial seasons. That of winter 1874–75, though less severe, was intense enough to render it a season worthy of being chronicled and recorded amongst the annals of remarkable winters in most agricultural and horticultural periodicals; while the frost and cold of 1878–79 are quite recent in our memory, and from the effects of which, still quite visible, the woodlands and plantations throughout the country, and especially in the lower lying localities, were in no hardy condition of health or robust vigour to enable them to encounter with impunity the extreme bitterness and intense frost of another recurring winter, so unmistakeably to be recorded as "memorable" in severity in some districts, as that of the past winter of 1879–80. The effects produced in consequence thereof upon trees and shrubs in many localities have been very marked and injurious. Many of the results of the frost are still latent, and are only now developing themselves, while others have already been apparent during the spring and summer, and warrant the Society in calling for a record of the casualties which have been observed, and of the injuries inflicted generally on trees and shrubs throughout the country, so far as has been accurately ascertained and recorded.

We have already stated that to the debilitated condition of many trees and shrubs in various situations, resulting from the unwonted severity of the previous winter of 1878–79, from which they had not had time to recover, much of the damage done in 1879–80 must be ascribed. At all events the injuries inflicted last winter were considerably increased from that cause, coupled with the unfortunate circumstance that the summer of 1879 was so ungenial and sunless that the weakened and shattered dislocations of all vegetable organisms which had suffered from the severity of the previous winter had no opportunity of developing their recuperative powers or ripening their young shoots and growths sufficiently to undergo a second ordeal, such as that to which the weather of December 1879 subjected them. There is no doubt that we cannot by any process of acclimatisation render any plant of a different climatal condition of natural habitat "frost-proof" in this country: although, under otherwise favourable relations of circumstance, we sometimes find trees and shrubs in Britain withstanding lower air temperatures than they would usually be subjected to in their native countries; still, all vegetable organisms—more than animal—are peculiarly liable to suffer in more or less degree from relatively slight deviations of both heat and cold; and while heat above the ordinary degree of temperature natural to trees and shrubs when removed from their native habitats would eventually kill them, the results so produced are slow, indeed, and protracted, as compared with the corresponding effects of undue cold.

Frost, as seen from the effects of the several severe winters we have named, is very decided and marked in its immediate action; and the results to vegetation generally, and to recently introduced shrubs and trees from strange countries, arising from an unusually low and abnormal temperature occurring in the land of their translation, are, by all the experience of these several memorable winters, most destructive and severe. The modifying conditions are the nature of the soil, subsoil, situation, and altitude, governed by the quantity of moisture in the soil and atmosphere; and in no instance were the beneficial effects of these surroundings more apparent than during the past winter 1879–80, when we find that in every case, in low situations, in heavy soils, with damp subsoils, even where such conditions were accompanied with shelter and mild exposure, far more injury was sustained than by the same species of trees and shrubs with northerly exposures on lighter and dry soils and at higher altitudes. The shorter and smaller shoots made under the unfavourable auspices of the sunless summer of 1879 in such situations proved themselves more independent of the absence of the climatal conditions necessary for ripening the young wood, for which the ensuing autumn was so conspicuous.

The peculiarity, however, of the effects of the very low temperatures recorded in December 1879 was not that the winter's ravages were most apparent and severe upon the newer introduced species of trees and shrubs, but it has been observed that the injury done last winter has been quite unusual and hitherto unrecorded to anything like the same extent amongst the common hard-wood trees of large size and considerable age, hitherto considered quite impervious to any amount of frost, and some of them even known to be indigenous to our country. Thus we find, where the lowest readings of the thermometer have been accurately recorded, even the common oaks, of two or three hundred years' growth and in pristine vigour of constitution and habit, have had their young wood of four and five years' growth killed outright. Hollies of 60 feet in height perished entirely; and even the common elder, tree box, ivy, privet, lilac, hazel, spiræa, were most severely injured, and in some instances are now quite dead, having been unable to throw off the scathing effects of the frost from their young branches, so as to push forth buds afresh this season. Many other varieties of forest trees of large size, in various localities, notably the English elms, walnuts, beeches, and horse chestnuts, are showing very scant foliage this summer, and the many dead twigs of young wood all over the trees, and especially on those sides which had been exposed to the prevailing cold current of air during the winter, evince the weakness of nature's recuperative powers after so very severe a trial, and plainly indicate that it will require several genial seasons ere the effects of this memorable winter will be completely effaced, even from our hardiest common hard-wooded timber trees, while it is almost certain in some instances, from the injury sustained by them, that at their age and maturity the harm done cannot reasonably be expected to be ever completely overcome, however genial and auspicious may be the succession of seasons that ensue.   Like the blight which is caused by the ravages in one season of an insidious insect over a vast tract of pine-forest, and of which there are many melancholy examples on record, chiefly on the continent of Europe, so the destruction in many districts of Scotland among forest trees and other specimen trees and shrubs, caused by the winter of 1879–80 has left an indelible stamp to mar for ever what was hitherto a wealth of foliage of luxurious beauty and richness.

Some general narrative record, compiled from notes kindly supplied by observers in different districts, of the progress of this severe winter may be interesting.

The winter of 1879–80 may be said to have fairly set in about the middle of October 1879.   The previous summer (if such it can be called) and autumn were singularly sunless and unpropitious, and were marked generally by an unusual amount of wet, cold weather.   On the 15th October 5° of frost were recorded at various stations.   Continuously till the 28th of that month several degrees of frost were nightly registered, when the temperature rose above the freezing-point for a few days, falling again, however, on 1st November below 32° F., and varying daily. till the 14th November, on which night we find 10° of frost recorded.   A thaw then took place, which continued till the 22nd November, when the real intensity of the winter fairly set in, and proved the coldest season since 1860–61, varying from 5° to 10° of frost nightly till December, which was ushered in with very low temperatures, generally prevalent over a wide area, chiefly in the south, east, and south-easterly districts of Scotland.   Indeed, the characteristic peculiarity of the winter of 1879–80 is that its intense severity seems to have been confined to a belt stretching in a south-easterly direction in a mean line from about the north-western districts of Perthshire to the south-eastern borders of Roxburghshire, and embracing on either side within its area of destruction from undue severity amongst trees and shrubs, most places within the counties of Perth, Forfar, and Fife on the one side, and Stirling, Kinross, Clackmannan, Linlithgow, Midlothian, Peebles, Selkirk, Roxburgh, Haddington, and Berwickshire on the other, and in the three last-named counties there were recorded the lowest readings of the thermometer during the storm.   Some of them, indeed, are unparalleled even in the annals of the memorable winter of 1860–61.   By the kindness of Mr. Buchan, Secretary to the

Scottish Meteorological Society, we are able to give some of the more remarkable registers, as verified by him with his usual accuracy.

"The lowest temperature," he states, "occurred on December 4, 1879, and was at Springwood Park, near Kelso, where 16° below zero was marked; at Paxton House, Berwickshire, 12° below zero; and at Thirlstane Castle, 8° below zero; and at Milne-Graden, also in Berwickshire, 4° below zero were noted on the same night. Other very low temperatures are recorded on this same night in East Lothian, Berwickshire, and Roxburghshire, but these were *exposed temperatures,* and the indicating thermometers were mostly unverified. Thus the temperature 23° below zero recorded at Blackadder, Berwickshire, was with an imperfect thermometer fully exposed on a post over the snow. Similarly, at Allanbank, Berwickshire, we find 13° below zero; at Ninewells, 8° below zero. At an altitude, however, of 300 feet higher than at these localities, but in the same district, one of Kemp's registering thermometers (verified) recorded 5° above zero; but the severe frosty mists and winds nearer the Blackadder and Whitadder rivers invariably intensify the cold, and may so far account for the great difference in temperature in so short a distance geographically." At East Linton, Haddingtonshire, on the bank of the Tyne, the protected thermometer marked 1° below zero; the same instrument, on the same site, having recorded 4° below zero on the night of Christmas 1860. At Eyemouth, on the coast of Berwickshire, and quite within the mitigating influences of the sea—so well known as an ameliorating factor in every severe frost—the cold was more intense than anything known since 1860–61, having reached the unusually low reading of 3° above zero! From Dumfries, Aberfeldy, and the Clyde districts reports of the severity of the storm show it to have been there also particularly intense. From the geographical area of the extent of the storm, it will be noted that it chiefly embraced the basins of the Tay, Forth, Tweed, Tyne, Whitadder, &c., and tributaries and other smaller streams; and in every instance the most severe damage to trees and shrubs occurred in the low-lying localities within the influence of the mists and hoar-frosts which prevailed in the proximity of such situations. For example, at Craigiehall, near Edinburgh, and at Carlowrie, a short distance farther west, and both close to the River Almond, far greater injury has been sustained during last winter than in 1860–61, and at both sites (within 100 feet altitude) many coniferous and evergreen shrubs were killed to the ground in that remarkable year.

A very remarkable peculiarity of the manner in which trees and shrubs suffered from the effects of last winter's and the previous year's severe weather was noted at Carlowrie, where, in

heavy soil and upon a close, damp clay subsoil, at an altitude of
92 feet above sea-level, hollies, coniferæ, and hard-wooded
shrubs, including even the common double red-flowering thorn,
have succumbed to a melancholy extent.   Those most seriously
injured grew in two belts on either side of the main avenue
running due north and south, and fully exposed to the sun's rays
during day, and to the mists which rise from the valley of the
Almond at night, coating them over with hard frozen hoar-frost.
The Coniferæ, *Taxodium sempervirens, Picea albertiana, Welling-
tonea gigantea, Pinus excelsa, Pinus monticola, Picea balsamea
Cedrus deodara, Cedrus atlantica, Picea pinsapo, Juniperus re-
curva,* and *Araucaria imbricata* all suffered most severely in
every instance in the terminal shoots and tips of the side
branches, some being killed down to the ground entirely, while
hollies in every instance growing alongside and amongst the
Coniferæ, with their tops equally exposed, were killed in the
lower branches, and around the lower side branches, from the
stem outwards to the very tips, the foliage was killed off, while
in every case (and they were many) the tops of the hollies were
quite uninjured.   The snowfall overlying them could have
nothing to do with this anomaly from the shapes and habit and
situation of the plants ; but it would appear as if the top-shoots,
leaders, and strong side-shoots of the coniferous genus had their
wood in these points less well ripened, while the hard-wooded
genus, being better ripened at these identical points than in the
wood and branches near the roots, escaped, while these latter
parts in them suffered.   Each holly looked as if its lower half had
been burnt round by fire, while the Coniferæ presented exactly
the opposite appearance, as if a current of cold frozen air had
cut down their tops in some cases to a length of six feet.   Many
of them so affected have since entirely succumbed, although
hopes were in spring entertained that they might recover.   All
sides of trees and shrubs exposed to the north-west were most
severely browned and injured.   From that quarter the current
of cold air appears to have chiefly prevailed.

In the Royal Botanic Garden, Edinburgh (also a low elevation),
Sir Robert Christison remarked that in June 1880, as in some other
places, he had observed in the neighbourhood (in the Cramond
district) the terminal twigs of the common birch, on the north
and north-east sides of the trees, were killed from the effects of
last winter's frost—a circumstance not recorded in previous
storms.   When his attention was directed to them in June last,
many had fallen off, and the ground below the trees was strewn
with these relics of the severity of the frost of 1879–80.   In the
Royal Botanic Garden also some species or varieties of some
families have resisted the winter's effects better than others of
the same genus.   Thus the Hungary or Turkey oak is quite

untouched, and growing this year at its normal rate in the formation of wood, while the *Quercus pedunculata*, or common and indigenous oak-tree, has suffered in some places around Edinburgh severely in its young twigs of one or two years' growth. It is also a fact worthy of record that the Hungary oak in 1879 made more wood and increased more in girth—notwithstanding the unpropitious nature of the previous season for the ripening of young shoots of hard-wooded trees—than any other variety of oak. Many of the thorns did not flower this season nearly so profusely as usual, owing to the severity of last winter. At Craigiehall, however, while there was comparatively little bloom this year, one variety (a light-coloured double pink or almost white thorn) was quite laden with blossom, although in no perceptible way better accommodated as to site, soil, or shelter than its fellows of other varieties.

Of the newer Coniferæ, *Cupressus lawsoniana* appears to have stood better in every instance than any other, and may be said to be almost universally untouched by the frosts; and all the Japanese Coniferæ and evergreens of recent importation, excepting the privet, which at Newliston, in West Lothian, is killed to the ground, have enjoyed a remarkable immunity from the frost. This has been in previous severe winters occasionally noticed; but now that the various species are so generally distributed over the country, their remarkable hardihood and capacity for enduring very sudden and severe variations in the temperature has been more prominently brought to public notice, while the beauty and elegance of their varied foliage has made them general favourites, worthy of wider introduction in our parks and pleasure-grounds.

Besides the thorn, many others of our hardy early-flowering trees and shrubs have this season been conspicuous generally by the noteworthy absence of blossom in almost every situation and exposure. This has been especially noticed in lilacs, rhododendrons (including the hardy *Ponticum*), *Philadelphus*, *Deutzia*, *Weigelias*, *Ribes*, &c. Horse-chestnuts also have been without a single spike of flower excepting in rare instances, and then the flowers on this tree, as on most others which have made an effort to put forth blossoms this year, have been quite small and puny, and anything but luxuriant or healthy. The laburnum probably forms the only exception in most districts to this rule, as in many places it has flowered profusely after an interval of two seasons. Holly berries, usually in scarlet profusion at Christmas, were very scant and only green and half-grown at that date; and on many of the trees in sheltered situations, on which the crop of berries was at all abundant, they were only ripe in May of this year, and in several places the scarlet crop remains uneaten and has fallen to the ground, owing to the scarcity of the members of the feathered tribe, caused by the decimating effects upon them, also, by the severity of the winter's cold. Other sorts of fruiting trees appear to have suffered similarly, although of the deciduous order, and the injury they sustained was in the destruction of their young wood and terminal twigs of their branches. For example, in many localities the common walnut had two-thirds of the length of its previous year's shoots killed outright, while in a few instances, in heavy soil of a clayey nature and damp situation, the injury which this generally hardy tree suffered was much greater, whole limbs of six inches in diameter having died off this summer upon large specimens. Wall-trees in fruit-bearing orchards suffered more than standard trees in the open ground, and the injury sustained by peaches, plums, and all " *stone fruit*" trees upon walls, and by apple and pear trees also, was very general and severe, all the two years' growths of the imperfectly-ripened wood of these seasons being killed. Roses in every situation suffered very much, many of the grafted varieties being totally killed; but in this respect, as we shall by and by find when we refer to the continental winter, this country has not been singular, nor so severely dealt with perhaps, as our neighbours across the Channel. We have not been able to observe any cases of bark or tree splitting during the past winter, probably owing to its being the second very severe winter in succession, so that probably any organisms liable to suffer in that way had already suffered, and were too imperfectly closed again to show any fresh fissures; and, moreover, the deposit of young wood was in 1879 much under the normal average, so that less soft *cambium* was present to be affected by the intensity of frost, and to cause the splitting so frequently observed in most exogenous trees after unduly low temperature.

Another course of probable damage may be found to consist in the very sudden and extreme variations in temperature during this winter. It is not so much the number of degrees of continuous frost which a plant is called upon to resist that proves fatal to its vitality, as the sudden and rapid rise from an unduly low indication of cold, or *vice versa*. Trees and shrubs will stand a continuous run of a steadily persistent frost of many degrees much better than a short frost of no greater severity, followed by a sudden rise, with sunshine during day in the early springtime. Hence it is that probably less damage was done over the same area by the winter of 1860–61, when the frost was steadily continuous, with clear nights, and dull snow-laden cloudy skies by day, than by the winter of last year, when the frost, though quite as intense, was only so for a short period. For although it is quite admitted that the 4th December 1879 was everywhere the night of the greatest cold, yet the fluctuations were so great and so erratic, within the space of a few hours even during that severe week, that probably it is not altogether to that one night's frost that must be attributed all the mischief done to trees and shrubs, but partly also to the sharp alternations, both prior and subsequently, which accompanied it.

These violent fluctuations or vibrations in the temperature will be best illustrated by the figures returned by one of the correspondents at Clovenfords station, at the respective dates as given below :—

| | At | | Altitude. | | |
|---|---|---|---|---|---|
| On Monday, December 1, snow fell to a depth of 8¼ inches at night. | | | | | |
| Thermometer indicated at | daybreak, | . | 12° of frost. | | |
| ,, | ,, | darkening, | . | 20° | ,, |
| ,, | ,, | 10 P.M., . | . | 31° | ,, |
| Tuesday, 2nd December. | at 2 A.M., . | . | 32° | ,, | |
| ,, | ,, | daybreak, | . | 18° | ,, |
| ,, | ,, | darkening, | . | 4° | ,, } and 5 inches snow fell. |
| ,, | ,, | 10 P.M., . | . | 10° | ,, |
| Wednesday, 3rd December, | at 2 A.M., . | . | 22° | ,, | |
| ,, | ,, | daybreak, | . | 28° | ,, |
| ,, | ,, | 9 A.M., . | . | 32° | ,, |
| ,, | ,, | noon, . | . | 24° | ,, |
| ,, | ,, | darkening, | . | 40° | ,, |
| ,, | ,, | 7 P.M., . | . | 42° | ,, |
| ,, | ,, | 10 P.M., . | . | 44° | ,, |
| ,, | ,, | midnight, | . | 46° | |
| Thursday, 4th December, | at 3 A.M., . | . | 48° | | |
| ,, | ,, | 5 A.M., . | . | 50° | |
| ,, | ,, | daybreak, | . | 50° | |
| ,, | ,, | noon, . | . | 30° | |
| ,, | ,, | darkening, | . | 40° | |
| ,, | ,, | 7 P.M., . | . | 41° | |
| ,, | ,, | 10 P.M., . | . | 39° | |
| ,, | ,, | midnight, | . | 33° | |
| Friday, 5th December, | at 3 A.M., . | . | 21° | | |
| ,, | ,, | 4 A.M., . | . | 15° | ,, and snow. |
| ,, | ,, | 6 A.M., . | . | 18° | |
| ,, | ,, | daybreak, | . | 14° | |
| ,, | ,, | 10 A.M., . | . | 10° | |
| ,, | ,, | noon, . | . | 2° | |
| ,, | ,, | darkening, | . | 10° | |
| ,, | ,, | 6 P.M., . | . | 14° | |
| ,, | ,, | 9 P.M., . | . | 18° | |
| ,, | ,, | midnight, | . | 12° | |
| Saturday, 6th December, | at 3 A.M., . | . | 22° | | |
| ,, | ,, | 5 A.M., . | . | 30° | |
| ,, | ,, | daybreak, | . | 24° | |
| ,, | ,, | 9 A.M., . | . | 16° | |
| ,, | ,, | noon, . | . | 2° | |
| ,, | ,, | darkening, | . | 18° | |
| ,, | ,, | 7 P.M., . | . | 22° | |
| ,, | ,, | 9 P.M., . | . | 24° | |
| ,, | ,, | midnight, | . | 26° | |

From this we see that within twenty-four hours between 4th and 5th December, from daybreak to daybreak, no less a variation had occurred than 36° in the temperature, being from 18° below zero to 18° above zero. Again, between 7 P.M. on the evening of 4th December and 6 P.M. on 5th December there was a fluctuation of 27° of temperature, being from 9° below zero to 18° above zero. Other equally startling variations within a few brief hours may be noticed by reference to the figures given, and which may be taken as a fair specimen of similar severe dislocations in the usually steady and equable temperature of our ordinary winters, and the consequent effects upon all vegetable, and no less perhaps also on animal, life may easily be conceived.

The 4th December 1879 being thus undoubtedly the morning of lowest recorded temperature, we append for comparison the various indications of the thermometer on that memorable morning at some of the chief points within the area of the most severe damage done by the winter's intensity :—

| Locality. | County. | Altitude in feet. | Snow depth. | Thermometer. |
|---|---|---|---|---|
| | | | inches. | degrees. |
| Moncrieff House, | Perth, | ... | ... | +2 |
| Haddo House, | Aberdeen, | ... | 6 | +2 |
| Glamis Castle, | Forfar, | ... | 8 | +8 |
| Cortarchy Castle, | „ | .. | 8 | +12 |
| Hamilton Palace, | Lanarkshire, | ... | ... | −2 |
| Culzean Castle, | Ayrshire, | .. | ... | +10 |
| Calowrie, | Linlithgow, | 92 | 12 | −4 |
| Royal Botanic Garden. | Edinburgh, | .. | ... | +1 |
| Dalkeith Park, | „ | ... | ... | ... |
| King's Meadow, | Peebles, | ... | ... | −12 |
| Clovenfords, | Selkirkshire, | ... | ... | −9 |
| Yester House, | Haddington, | ... | 4 | +3 |
| Haddington, | „ | ... | ... | −4 |
| East Linton, | „ | ... | ... | −1 |
| Springwood Bank, | Roxburgh, | ... | ... | −16 |
| Ormiston House, | Kelso, | ... | ... | −18 |
| Allanbank, | Berwick, | .. | ... | −13 |
| Thirlstane Castle, | „ | ... | 10 | −8 |
| Paxton House, | „ | ... | ... | −12 |
| Milne-Graden, | „ | 100 | ... | −4 |
| Blackadder, | „ | ... | ... | −23 |
| Ninewells, | „ | ... | ... | −3 |
| Eyemouth, | „ | ... | ... | +3 |
| Drumlanrig, | Dumfries, | ... | ... | 0 |
| Dumfries, | „ | ... | ... | +8 |
| Arran, | Bute, | ... | ... | +31 |

It should be noted that while the greatest care has been taken to obtain only accurately verified registrations, some of those given of this remarkable night are furnished by careful observers, but from the readings of thermometers under different circumstances, some being in a "louvre" box, usually arranged for meteorological instruments, others being the lowest registers by thermometers in the open air, in exposed situations; so that while mathematical accuracy cannot be claimed for the figures given, the whole presents a very popularly correct idea of the intensity of the storm in the various localities indicated.

Having thus shown that the exceptionally cold night of 4th December 1879 culminated, as it may be said to have done, in destructive agency, by recording the lowest falls in the thermometer within the memory of "the oldest inhabitant," we must proceed to sketch the supervening and subsequent course of the winter and early spring temperatures and general weather over the country, for it has yet to be observed that to the condition of the atmosphere and temperature during the early months of the year, vegetation owes much of its future luxuriance or retardation during the future season; and it is also found that to the effects produced in that critical period of the year, after so intense a frost, much of the damage upon trees and shrubs observed at a later stage is to be fairly attributed. Many plants may have out-lived the severe chilling frost-bite of December, but which, debilitated thereby, are unable to resist frosty nights and damp foggy mists of evenings in the early spring months, accompanied as these invariably are in our climate by cold easterly winds extending even into May, and frequently accompanied by days of cloudless sunshine, a combination of circumstances, we feel quite assured, far more detrimental to the life of all trees and shrubs than the mere intensity of extreme frost alone.

Resuming then the general narrative of the course of this severe winter, we find that from the night of the 4th December so memorable, there was uninterrupted frost of various degrees till the 27th January 1880, the average being about 8° nightly. During this interval the night of the 13th–14th December had again been remarkable for a very severe fall in the thermometer over nearly all the various districts, resembling somewhat, although not with the same degree of intensity, the frost of the 4th December. Again several degrees below zero were at some stations recorded, the thermometer rising thereafter with the same severe and telling rapidity, farther confirming the damage done to many plants in the low-lying situations. We have records of as low as 4° below zero in some localities near streams, at this date in the south and east of Scotland, and again also low readings were recorded on the 26th December, some situations returning 12° of frost which on the previous night had only noted 35°, or 3° above freezing-point as the lowest register.

The weather during the early week of January 1880, although frosty, was comparatively mild for the season, yet there was no vegetation whatever, probably resulting from the unparalleled check the vegetable kingdom had sustained by the frost of the early part of December 1879. About the end of January the temperature rose, and between 27th January and 17th March little frost worth notice was recorded, excepting on one or two nights; from the 17th to 28th March there was more or less frost every night, and during the whole month of March almost daily there was bright sunshine, with chilly fogs and mists at night. In April there was sharp frost at several stations on several nights, and the treacherous sunshine continued. Many injured plants showed unmistakable symptoms of increased debility and decay, and when May was ushered in, on some nights there were from 3° to 4° of frost in several localities recorded during four successive nights, until the 8th and 9th of that month, when mild genial weather prevailed, but the steadily persistent easterly and north-easterly winds of March and April, which still prevailed, had greatly and obviously to the most untutored eye, increased the injury done by the winter to the trees and shrubs, which was now visibly apparent on the slowly advancing growths.

During June 1880, and in the early weeks thereof, more particularly in several places in the south and south-east districts of Scotland, the thermometer at night fell several degrees below the freezing-point, while the day temperatures continued high; for example, on 2nd, 3rd, 11th, 15th, and 18th of that month 68°, 70°, 64°, 73°, and 67°, were noted at the Royal Botanic Garden, Edinburgh,—and there are similarly high returns from other quarters. This, accompanied by bright sunshine and cold arid easterly winds, and with frequent cold mists and fogs at night, all told most severely upon the weakened survivors of the last winter, and sent many dying or pining specimens for ever beyond recovery. In situations where the supposed dead branches of laurels, hollies, lauristinus, Lombardy poplars (thirty feet high), and many evergreens had been cut out months before, it was now seen that such action had been rather premature, and that many branches left as then evincing life and promising buds, were now hopelessly killed, and that a second crusade was inevitable to remove the numerous dead branches and stumps which the generosity and hopes of the arborist had spared in spring, but for which the deceitful sunshine and chill winds of March and April and May had proved too severe in their debilitated and frost-bitten condition.

Such is a general cursory survey of the fluctuations in temperature and weather of this memorable winter, and the effects produced on trees and shrubs, but before closing this report we must give a few individual experiences of losses among various species of trees and shrubs from a few of the most reliable returns obtained from various localities and altitudes.

From Thirlstane Castle, near Lauder, Berwickshire, common and Portugal laurels are reported as killed to the ground, also roses of sorts in every position, clematis, green and variegated hollies, *Escallonia macrantha*, *Pernettya mucronata*, *Acer negundo variegata*, *Abies menziesii*, *A. polita*, *Libocedrus decurrens*, *Cedrus deodara*, *Cotoneaster simmondsii* and *microphylla*. The following have suffered severely, but are not killed outright:—Rhododendrons, *Wellingtonia gigantea*, tree box, yews, ivy, privet, lilac, *Spiræa*, *Viburnum*, *Berberis*, and hazel. Old timber trees are showing very scanty foliage this season. Young wood of all wall-fruit trees is quite destroyed. Standard apples and pears, in many cases, are dead.

From Yester, Haddingtonshire, Mr. Shearer reports that the winter has not proved so very disastrous amongst laurels and evergreens under his care as it has done at many neighbouring places at lower elevations. Old lauristinus plants of some considerable size, and *Aucuba japonica* are severely injured. Dwarf-roses are killed to the ground, and standards very much injured. He attributes his losses more to the cold and wet summer previous to the sharp winter, than to the amount of frost. This is further proved by the weakly condition this year of many of the common sorts of garden vegetables, such as asparagus, which is producing very weak and slender stems, and globe artichokes were nearly all killed, and it will require some hot and dry summers to bring vegetation back to its normal condition, in almost all varieties of cultivated plants, trees, and shrubs.

Mr. A. M'Intosh, the experienced and observant gardener at Paxton House, Berwickshire, reported in May last, that the effects of the previous winter upon all plant life was only then becoming day by day more visible. Portugal and common laurels, yews, lauristinus, *Aucuba japonica*, *Cedrus deodara*, *Andromeda procurva*, *Salisburia adiantifolia*, *Cryptomeria japonica*, *C. elegans*, *Cytisus*, *Jasminum*, *Clematis*, *Cotoneaster*, *Garrya eliptica*, are wholly killed. Many wall fruit trees have also perished. Rhododendrons very much damaged, and in some places killed entirely. Fruit standards severely injured, and roses killed.

In the Kelso districts where, it has been already stated, the injury was everywhere very severe, we learn from Mr. Boyd, Ormiston House, that more damage has been sustained there last winter than has been experienced within the memory of any one living. During the night of Wednesday and Thursday morning, 3rd and 4th December, 50° of frost, or 18° below zero, were registered. The thermometer was about two feet above open ground. During the previous winter, 1878–79, nearly all the large oaks at a lower altitude than fifty feet above the bed of the river Teviot had all the young wood of the previous season's growth killed, and owing to their weakened condition thereby induced, the winter of 1879–80 has proved so severe that many of them are now almost entirely dead, several actually so. These were trees from fifty to eighty and a hundred years old, and hitherto quite healthy. One or two, at the date of his report (June 3rd, 1880) were attempting to push out a few buds and twigs from the main trunk, but others appeared altogether dead or dying off. Spanish chestnuts, of similar age and size, are also severely injured, and present the same declining appearance. Walnut trees are likewise dead. Sycamore and large ash trees are also very severely injured. Common laburnums in the open ground are dead, and *Sambucus nigra* is killed to the snow-line or ground. *Araucaria imbricata, Cedrus deodara, Cupressus lawsoniana,* common and Irish yews, tree box, *Libocedrus decurrens,* and hybrid rhododendrons, and all varieties of ivy, are entirely killed. *Wellingtonia gigantea, Picea pinsapo, Aucuba japonica,* and tree peony, common and Portugal laurels, *Ribes, Berberis, Jasminum,* quince, *Wistaria,* and all the Virginian creepers, excepting *Veitchii,* are dead to the ground or snow-line. It is worthy of remark that this variety of *Vitis virginiana,* or *Ampelopsis,* viz., *Vitis veitchii* and *Ampelopsis tricuspidata,* has proved so hardy during last winter both here and in other places, as it is one of the recent introductions from Japan, and is a further testimony to the extreme hardihood of the natives of that country, and their suitability for more extended introduction in Great Britain.

At King's Meadows, near Peebles, and adjacent to the mists that rise from the Tweed, in low-lying situations, the thermometer was 12° below zero, and many shrubs of every variety, usually hardy in this and such like sites, are all but irretrievably lost. Tall Lombardy poplars close to the river side at Peebles, having suffered very much from the previous winter, 1878–79, have entirely succumbed to the severity of 1879–80.

At Dalkeith Palace Gardens (alt. 180 feet), Mr. Dunn informs us that many shrubs on the walls and in the open have been much injured. *Aucuba japonica* suffered very much where exposed to the sun by day, but on dry ground, with northerly and north-western aspect, they are comparatively uninjured. *Laurus nobilis* cut down to the ground. *Berberis beali* killed to ground. In low lying spots and damp soils common broom is killed. *Daphne ponticum* in damp places is also dead. *Erica mediterranca, Eucalyptus globulus,* 25 feet in height, planted out last year, *Euonymus, Elæagnus reflexa* are all killed. *Escallonia macrantha* is much injured. *Eurya latifolia variegata* is killed after having withstood with impunity the winter of 1878–79. Many plants of large dimensions of the common holly have lost all their foliage. Many limbs of the common Portugal laurel are dying off, Privet is much injured, and young shoots killed. *Quercus ilex* has lost its foliage. *Robinia pseud-acacia* has had all its young shoots killed outright. *Cedrus deodara* is looking very sickly and is shedding its leaves, while *Pinus pindrow* is entirely destitute of foliage; but other conifers in this district do not appear to have suffered so severely. Those from Japan have proved particularly hardy. Walnuts, and other hard wooded trees of various species of old growth, have lost a number of their younger twigs, and an unusual number of dead points all over the trees have become more apparent every day, since the foliation in spring of the various varieties.

In Drummond Castle gardens, common Portugal laurels are severely injured. Several standard specimens have lost all the previous year's growth, and singularly the *Avcuba japonica*, which formed a closely grown carpet underneath them is quite safe. This is the only recorded instance of this shrub having escaped untouched. In other places, even with the shelter of shrubs overhead, it has been killed outright.

In the mild and genial climate of the west, at Maybole, Ayrshire, Mr. Murray reports from Culzean Castle that the damage has been greater than that of any winter since 1860–61. Old and well-established fuschias and hydrangeas, which usually prove quite hardy in the open border, have been killed outright. *Euonymus, Tumarix, Phormium tenax,* cornelia, myrtles, *Lonicera aurea variegata* are very severely damaged. Lauristinus, sweet bay, *Veronica,* and *Camellia japonica,* were for a time looking very sickly and brown in a well-sheltered situation, but appear now to be recovering slowly, and may be considered safe. The lowest reading here was on 4th December, 22° of frost.

But we need not multiply evidences of the extreme ravages amongst all descriptions of trees and shrubs throughout the country. Similar reports to those already detailed have been furnished, all telling the same dismal tale of loss and disfigurment to favourite specimens, and closely tended recently introduced varieties, as well as to old and gnarled forest trees,—from Moncrieffe House, Perthshire; Hamilton Palace, Lanarkshire; Carlowrie, Linlithgowshire; Craigiehall, Midlothian; Drumlanrig, Dumfriesshire; Haddo House, Aberdeen; Glamis Castle and Cortachy Castle, Forfarshire, and from various other localities.

The only county from which the accounts of the winter's severity are more cheering is Bute, which appears to enjoy a specially salubrious and mild climate, differing considerably from the west of Scotland, in its suitability for the growth of trees and shrubs, which will not survive even in other parts of Scotland. From Arran the Rev. D. Landesborough reports that little injury was sustained there. Many of the Australian palms and New Zealand tree ferns and blue gums being uninjured. The situation is very well sheltered and very mild. The lowest registers of the thermometer were on December 1st and 3rd, 1879=31°; January 12th and 21st, 1880=31°; February 26th=36°, and March 27th=35°, being thus in the minimum temperature of winter from 12° to 14° above that of Glasgow. As an instance of the immunity enjoyed by this district, we may state that in March 1880, a fine plant of the old single red camellia was untouched, and was then in full flower with twenty-five beautiful blooms in perfect condition. A cork tree (*Quercus suber*) and a specimen of *Cunninghamia sinensis*, which have both grown at Brodick Castle for twenty years, are quite uninjured by the frost of the winter of 1879–80.

While we have thus endeavoured to sketch the effects of this severe winter upon trees and shrubs, and have shown that its ravages have not been so widespread over Scotland generally as those of the winter of 1860–61, although in those places to which last year's destruction has been more immediately confined, the results have been equally if not more disastrous in many particulars, it would not be proper to omit a passing notice of the severity of the season over a far wider area than that of Scotland only, for we find that in many parts of England and over the Continent of Europe, especially the eastern and south-eastern countries, much destruction to plant life was sustained from the unwontedly severe and protracted winter, similar in intensity and in its effects on trees and shrubs to what has been recorded in this report. The severity appears to have set in simultaneously at all points about the 2nd December, when from Hamburg it was reported: "Very severe frost—river full of heavy drift ice." From Antwerp, December 3rd: "Severe frost set in yesterday. Thermometer fell to 12° below freezing-point. Navigation to Brussels closed." Bremen, December 2nd: "Temperature to-day 7° Reaumur. River navigation closed." Hamburg, December 4th: "Temperature 17° below freezing-point. Wind cold, and off east. Fog." Haarlingen, December 3rd: "Severe snow squalls." Paris, December 4th: "Snow falling all over the country. No business was done to-day on the Boulevards in consequence of the heavy fall of snow. Railway traffic partially suspended, and telegraphic communication has been rendered defective from same cause." The damage done by the severe frosts of December 1879 and January 1880 to the trees, shrubs, and plants, in the parks and public gardens of the municipality of Paris, is estimated at something like £40,000. In the Champs Elysées alone more than 10,000 trees and shrubs have been more or less affected, about 3000 being entirely killed, while many thousand shrubs will have to be cut down to the roots. The Trocadero Garden, laid out during the exhibition year at great cost, has suffered still more severely, from the plants not being thoroughly established in their new site. In the Bois de Boulogne it will be necessary to replace 50,000 evergreens, 20,000 Coniferæ, and 30,000 deciduous trees, besides about 5000 other plants. The nurseries at Auteuil have sustained damage to the extent of £3500, and the estimate for making good the losses in other parks are:—Vincennes, £9500; Paris Gardens, £8500; Cemeteries, £1600. It was also remarked that many species which had appeared to have become acclimatised in France, have been, in many places, unable to resist the extreme temperature of the past winter, and many of the newer coniferous trees, and Cedars of Lebanon around Paris, including Araucarias, and Pinus of many varieties, have been killed. All over the country, and far to the south of France, the frost proved equally fatal. One firm of plant growers, who possess large nurseries near Orleans, are actually purchasing grafts and young plants in this country this summer to replace lost stock from the undue severity of the winter of 1879–80.

## THE TAY BRIDGE GALE OF 28th DECEMBER 1879, AND THE DESTRUCTION CAUSED THEREBY TO WOODS AND TREES.

By ROBERT HUTCHISON of Carlowrie.

*[Premium—The Minor Gold Medal.]*

No report upon the winter of 1879–80, and its disastrous effects upon trees and shrubs, would be complete did it leave unnoticed one feature of that memorable season, which of itself alone was calculated to rank the winter in question as one of the most noteworthy on record. While to the intensity of the cold, many thousands of plants and trees and shrubs succumbed, an amount of damage to old trees and woodlands throughout the country was done in one night by a violent gale of wind from the S.W., which is quite unparalleled in the annals of any previous storm, and the commercial loss to proprietors in blown timber, within the area of the gale, it is almost impossible to ascertain, so much of the wood has been so twisted and broken across at ten and twelve feet above ground in many cases, splintering and shaking the whole timber in the trees, as to render them absolutely unmarketable, and comparatively valueless.

This gale will long be remembered as the "Tay Bridge Gale,"

or "Storm," from its severity having occasioned the fall of that structure, carrying with it in its fall, and embedding in its ruins, an entire railway train, with its living freight of passengers, who were crossing its span at the awful moment when the crash took place. It was on the night of Sunday, 28th December 1879, and between six and seven P.M., when the gale was at its highest, that this sad catastrophe took place, and next morning, when the placid and calm waters of the Tay smiled as if no such dread secret were enclosed in their breast, many a broad plantation in Perthshire, Fife, Forfar, Aberdeen and Inverness, was lying confusedly hurled into one mass of debris of fallen timber, trees of giant growth toppled over against each other, others snapped across as if they were mere willow wands, and acres upon acres of thriving larch and Scots fir in the Athole plantations were swept over, and lay as flat as a floor. Individual standard trees, of several centuries' growth, did not escape, and probably the previous wet summer had left the ground so soft and moist, that many of the masses of woods which were levelled, owed their utter destruction, in no small measure, to this circumstance  The storm was confined to a broadish belt of country, whose mean line may be said to have extended from Iona to Inverness, and to that track, with wide parallels on either side, the damage to trees and woods is found to be chiefly confined. The extraordinary barometric fluctuations at all points, ascertained from observations made with sufficient frequency, were very remarkable, and characteristic of this storm, its rates of progress during the worst hours of its continuance, were in statute miles :*—

| | | | | |
|---|---|---|---|---|
| 4 to 5 P.M. | . | . | . | 30 miles. |
| 5 to 6 P.M | . | . | . | 45 „ |
| 6 to 7 P.M. | . | . | . | 53 „ |
| 7 to 8 P.M. | . | . | . | 70 „ |
| 8 to 9 P.M. | . | . | . | 70 „ |

This latter rate for the two last hours being three and a half times the average progressive rate of storms in this part of Europe. Mr. Buchan of the Meteorological Society finds that taking much shorter periods than sixty minutes, the traces show still greater velocities, and he estimates the hourly rates for the undermentioned intervals as follows :—

| | | | | | |
|---|---|---|---|---|---|
| From 6 25 to 6.30 P M. | . | . | . | 96 miles per hour. | |
| „ 6.55 to 7 P.M. | . | . | . | 72 „ | „ |
| „ 7.15 to 7.18 P.M. | . | . | . | 120 „ | „ |
| „ 7.30 to 7.35 P.M. | . | . | . | 84 „ | „ |
| „ 7.45 to 7.50 P.M. | . | . | . | 96 „ | „ |
| „ 8.43 to 8 46 P.M. | . | . | . | 110 „ | „ |

* * *Scottish Meteorological Society Journal,* vol v. p. 357.

It was observed that the strongest blasts recurred at intervals of about five minutes between each gust, and the recurrence of these intense gusts was marked by a strong swirling and lifting power, accompanied at the same time by a cracking, rumbling sound in the upper air, giving one the impression that it was descending towards the earth, a feature which, Mr. Buchan states, has been observed in former storms. It should be noted that the damage done to plantations was observed to take place at different heights from the ground, as evinced by the stems being twisted and broken across, as we have stated, frequently several feet above ground, and branches torn off and wrenched about at different points in the woods, which is accounted for by this swirling power referred to. Several steep barometric gradients* were ascertained to have characterised this storm, as is generally the case in very severe gales. Between Braemar and Logie-Coldstone very severe damage was sustained by the young and thriving plantations of about fifty years' growth, the principal destruction taking place about 9 P.M., when the firs were cracking and snapping, and being blown about and athwart each other in every direction, and it is ascertained that at that hour over that district, the gradient was as steep as one inch in 118 miles, which is pretty severe, and will tend to account for the confusion into which the victims of the gale in these woods were hurled.

In the grounds of Dunecht, Aberdeenshire, many hundreds of trees of about fifty years' growth were blown down between 9 and 10 P.M., many of them being severely twisted and destroyed. These were chiefly larch and Scots fir, and were very healthy and thriving. In the forests of the Perthshire Highlands, and generally in the central districts of Scotland north of the Forth, the loss sustained by woodlands has been very severe. In Glen Lyon, for instance, whole plantations of fine old Scots fir and larch have been levelled with the ground, not a tree left standing to mark the spot of what was last autumn a thriving and well-wooded district, in rich luxuriance of pine-clad verdure. Many of the trees were of very considerable age, and may be termed heavy timber. As illustrative of the extreme force of the hurricane, it was observed that where the trees had rooted themselves in the fissures of the rocky headlands and crags, the lower portions of their thick trunks were twisted round and shivered into the consistence of matchwood, and so forming a joint near the roots. At Rossie Priory, near Dundee, several thousands of trees have been overturned. The storm seems to have struck right on the broadside of a large plantation, and at once to have cleared for itself an entrance into the heart of the

* *Scottish Meteorological Society Journal*, p. 359, et infra.

wood, forcing a clear pathway through it for its triumphant career, uprooting some, and in its wild freaks snapping others across at various heights varying from six to forty feet above ground, in the most fantastic and indescribable manner. Many fallen specimens girthed from nine and ten feet to twelve and fifteen feet in circumference at three feet from the ground, and included all species of mixed hard wood and fir and larch. One beech tree, growing at a point within two miles of the ill-fated bridge, and fully fifteen feet in girth at four feet from the ground, was torn out of its site, and its heavy limbs, six in number, springing from a short bole of about fifteen feet, each girthing from eight to nine feet, were literally twisted round and round, their fibrous wood split up, and the limbs rendered more like huge ropes, spun by some giant power, than mere tree branches. The losses in Perthshire are wellnigh incalculable, and many reports, which we should have been able to embody in this paper from correspondents in various localities, have not been forthcoming, from the sheer inability of the foresters to estimate aright the extent of the damage sustained. The distance from facilities of transport in many instances is so great, that the enormous quantity of fallen timber, especially when twisted and wrenched across, is almost unmarketable, and not worth the heavy cost it would entail for removal for sale in such quantities. Mr Barbour of Bonskied reports that on his beautiful property on the Tummel he has lost over 4000 trees, many being fine old well-grown larch; while on the Athole estates of Dunkeld, Kinnaird, and Blair, Mr. M'Gregor, the intelligent forester at Ladywell, informs us that no fewer than 83,003 trees, and all of large size, have been blown down, and many thousands rendered useless for constructive purposes, being so shaken and twisted in their best "cuts" by this memorable storm. In Forfarshire, during January, and in other districts, the ordinary forest work had to be suspended to enable the workmen to clear away the debris and blown-down trees. In some localities in Scotland the work of destruction in young plantations was extremely severe, the ground being naturally damp, and with the previous wet summer's rains to increase the softness of the ground, the wind was enabled to get a better hold of the more sheltered trees, by having had easy work in forcing gaps here and there through the outskirts of the woods, thus, besides laying waste large tracts of plantation, reducing at the same time, amongst the survivors, the temperature of the whole interior of the woods. In exposed sites in the country the damage done has been unusually severe, large park trees have fallen in all directions, woods have been thrown over on their broadsides, and the tops of many healthy promising young trees of position have been snapt across. The large trees blown over in the

Kinnaird district of Forfarshire consist chiefly of *Picea pectinata* (silver fir), *Abies excelsa* (spruce), *Pinus sylvestris* (Scots fir), and others of the evergreen species, whose heavy foliage and large branches permitted the wind to take such a grasp of them that they were blown down with irresistible fury, killing and damaging in their fall many other healthy and valuable timber trees and specimen shrubs within their compass. At Dunipace House, Larbert, Stirlingshire, the largest beech tree in a row was overturned. It girthed at three feet from the ground fifteen feet, and other handsome old trees suffered severely in limb and displacement. At Lanrick, near Doune, 4561 trees were prostrated, many being fine healthy spruce, larch, and Scots fir. At Arden, Lochlomond, the gale was severely felt, and fully 1000 trees succumbed; and at Boquhan and Garden, Stirlingshire, the loss is irreparable, many fine old specimen trees and hard-wooded veteran landmarks in the properties having been completely wrecked. At Blair-Drummond, Perthshire, many fine specimen ornamental trees perished. Several of the largest silver firs, larches, and poplars fell, besides numerous Scots firs and beeches of large dimensions, although not the largest in the park. Mercifully these have been spared. The following note of the dimensions of some of the trees blown over may be given:—Silver firs, girthing at 3 feet from the ground, from 10 feet to 11 feet 6 inches and 12 feet 1 inch; Scots firs, 9 feet in girth; larch, from 9 feet 2 inches to 12 feet; beeches, from 11 feet 9 inches to 12 feet; and poplars, 12 feet 4 inches. At Keir, Stirlingshire, the well-known magnificent specimen *Araucaria imbricata*, the finest in Scotland, was overturned by the gale. It was 48 feet 9 inches in height, and girthed 7 feet 4 inches at the ground, and 5 feet 3 inches at 1 foot, and 4 feet 4 inches at 6 feet up. The loss of so truly fine a specimen as this is much to be regretted, but it is satisfactory to know that no effort has been spared to restore it by having it again set upright in welltrenched ground, and properly moored, so that we may hope that it may yet overcome the accident, and be spared to continue an ornament and prominent tree among the many fine Coniferæ which form the grand collection at Keir, and make the place so attractive. In the Strathspey and Morayshire districts considerable damage was sustained, although, considering the richlywooded nature of that locality, the injury was perhaps less than was to be anticipated. There the strongest force of the gale was felt about 9 P.M. Mr Thomson, wood manager at Grantown, reports that he lost about 2500 trees, and these he had at once disposed of to timber merchants, and at the prices current for standing trees; what remained unsold were used for estate purposes. Very few were broken or twisted, being chiefly thrown right over and uprooted; with few exceptions they were principally Scots fir, only about a dozen spruces and fifty larches having suffered, and not a single hard-wooded tree. The plantations which suffered most were fully exposed to the blast, and one in particular had been recently severely thinned purposely for the preservation of many naturally sown plants of larch and Scots fir with which it abounded. Had the gale blown from any other quarter, the destruction would probably have been far greater; for in this district trees are seldom uprooted by the westerly winds, which are the prevailing winds, and against which the trees seem by nature to fortify themselves. In the natural woods of Abernethy and Duthil, and others in Inverness-shire, only a tree here and there perished; the wind, although it blew in strong gusts, was fairly in one direction, so that very few blown trees crossed each other, but lay parallel, or the one on the top of the other. A considerable number of trees, from thirty to forty years of age, had their tops broken off, but these had all been injured by squirrels, the greatest tree enemy in that thickly wooded country. In some adjacent counties, where the same precaution of selling the fallen timber at once was not adopted, and where it was not offered for sale till February or March, the highest offer made for it did not come up to twopence per foot, and that for beautiful large and heavy trees.

From an estimate we have endeavoured to prepare from data roughly furnished by various correspondents, we are inclined to arrive at a definite conclusion as to the probable loss to Perthshire alone, and probably to Scotland also generally, from this gale. Approximating the total number of trees blown over in the entire county at 230,000 (one reliable practical opinion places it at 250,000), and assuming one-half of these to be larch of from thirty to sixty years' growth, we may estimate say 100,000 trees at 6s. each, or £30,000; and taking the remainder, or say 130,000 trees, chiefly spruce and Scots fir, of similar age and size, at 3s. 6d. per tree (surely a low estimate), we have further £22,750, or a total of £52,750 value of timber overturned by this storm in this county alone. If we further estimate the entire number of trees blown down in Scotland by this gale at 750,000—and we have reason to believe they exceed 1,000,000 of all sizes—and divide the quantity into probably 350,000 larch, and 300,000 spruce and Scots fir, at the previous valuations we arrive at a total loss of £157,500 value in growing wood to the shelter and amenity of the country, and in this estimate no account is taken of hard wood or park timber of old and heavy dimensions, the value of the loss of which in these respects is incalculable. Prior to the gale, the demand for home timber was very sluggish, owing to the unsettled state of the mining industries, and the large supplies of foreign timber now used for railway sleepers. Before the storm good measurable larch was sold at from 1s. 2d. and 1s. 3d. per cubic foot, but since the gale it will not fetch 1s. for the same quality; and as no large quantity can be disposed of readily, as larch will keep without deterioration, many proprietors are accordingly holding on their stocks. Spruce, which was before the gale sold at from 5d. to 6d. per cubic foot, cannot be sold now for more than from 3d. to 4d., and frequently for only 2d. per cubic foot, so much has the value of timber fallen, by the enormous quantity thrown upon the markets from the effect of this disastrous and ever memorable storm of 28th December 1879.

## INSECTS WHICH PREY UPON AGRICULTURAL PLANTS.

By PRIMROSE M'CONNELL, Agricultural and Veterinary College, Glasgow.

*[Premium—Fifteen Sovereigns.]*

INSECTS are one great source of loss and annoyance to farmers, and, as a general rule, there is no subject which is less studied and understood by them. In the following report it is proposed to describe the life-history of the most prominent of them, and also the means, if any, of coping with them.

It is advisable to take the various orders and describe those in each order which fall within our limits as the best method of classification, for the reason that the same insect, or an allied species, sometimes affects more than one kind of crop.

A typical insect passes through four stages in the course of its life. First, there is the egg—the majority of insects being oviparous; second, the caterpillar, larva, grub, maggot, or "worm," as they are variously called; next, the chrysalis or pupa; and last, the imago or perfect winged insect. Some, however, do not pass through any metamorphosis, while others again are only partially metamorphosed, and they have accordingly been divided into the three great sub-classes of *Ametabola*, *Hemimetabola*, and *Holomctabola*. The greatest damage, as a rule, is done by them in the caterpillar or grub stage, though there are many exceptions, as for instance, the "turnip fly," which works the greatest mischief as a perfect beetle.

Taking the sub-classes as they come, we find that there are none occurring under the *Ametabola*. The others are classified as follows:—

HEMIMETABOLA.

Order 1. HEMIPTERA.
    Sub-order, (a) HOMOPTERA.
        (b) HETEROPTERA.
Order 2. NEUROPTERA.

HOLOMETABOLA.

Order 3. DIPTERA.
  „   4. LEPIDOPTERA.
     5. HYMENOPTERA.
  „   6. COLEOPTERA.

## HEMIMETABOLA.

### HEMIPTERA.

The mouth is a beak-shaped sucking organ, suited for imbibing the juices of plants. The male has generally two pairs of wings, while the female is wingless. The larva differs from the imago chiefly in having no wings and in being smaller in size.

### Sub-order, HOMOPTERA.

*Aphis fabæ* (the Bean Aphis).—This insect is known in the country as the "collier fly" or "black dolphin." The females suddenly appear in large quantities on the leaf-stalks of the beans, and being viviparous multiply with extreme rapidity. They suck the sap and exhaust the plant, so that the crop is greatly injured or destroyed. The females are of a sooty black colour, have a pear-shaped body, and are about the eighth of an inch in length. The males are also black, but are much smaller, and have four membranous wings. The only way to deal with them is to cut off the infected tops, and crush them with the foot. As it is the wingless females which do the damage, they cannot easily regain the stalks; but perhaps the best way is to carry off the cut tops and destroy them. This operation need not be expensive or tedious, as many farmers do it to cause the plants to "pod" better, when otherwise healthy enough.

*Aphis pisi* (the Pea Aphis) is large and of a light green colour, being called the "green dolphin" in the country. There are both winged and wingless females—both viviparous. The male is winged, and black or brown, with long antennæ or "feelers." It infests many plants besides the pea, notably vetches, lentils, sainfoin, clover, &c. There are no means of saving the crop when it becomes attacked, as the winged females can remove from place to place, so that it must be cut and used immediately, giving it to cattle and pigs, or if the crop is too far gone, rolled down and ploughed in, and a catchcrop tried.

*Aphis cerealis*, *A. avenæ*, or *A. granaria* (as it is known by these three names).—This (the Corn Aphis) infests all the corn crops, and is plentiful in the month of July. The females crowd on the young ears, and by sucking the juices hinder the full development of the grain. They go through the same phases as other aphides, and are of a red, green, brown, or yellow colour, with a distinct lobe and a row of black dots on each side. The females are often apterous. The *Aphidius avenæ*, an ichneumon parasitic fly, with long filiform antennæ, keeps them in check. The females of this species bend their abdomens under their victim, insert their ovipositor into the belly of the aphis and lay one egg. This hatches into a grub, which lives on the substance of its "host," and eventually kills it.

*Aphis humuli* (the Hop Fly).—This is the great pest of the hop crop. It appears in the middle of May, when the bines are about four or five feet high, on the under side of the topmost leaves. The aphides are very susceptible of atmospheric changes, and do not appear some seasons at all. Syringing with an infusion of tobacco juice is the method usually employed to kill them, while the "lady-birds" destroy them in large quantities.

*Aphis brassicæ* (the Cabbage Aphis).—This is one variety of aphis which infests cabbages and turnips, doing much harm by inserting its suckers and drawing away the juices, and thus causing a diseased growth. It is dull green covered with a grey powder. The females are wingless. Syringing with soap-suds or tobacco juice would be the best method of dealing with them on a limited scale, as in a garden. Turnips affected with mildew are, in the early stages, more apt to succumb to them as they (the turnips) are not healthy enough to resist their attacks, so that keeping up a good strong growth is the best way of treating this pest.

*Aphis dianthi* (the Turnip Aphis).—This species is especially hurtful to turnips, swedes, and potatoes when growing, sometimes occurring in vast swarms so as to completely smother the plant. There are both winged and wingless females, the former of a black colour, and the latter greenish. Dressings of any kind of wash cannot be economically applied to a large field of turnips, but if these are supplied with sufficient food at their roots they will not suffer so much.

*Thrips cerealium* (the Corn Thrips).—This is a little black slender insect which does much damage to the corn crops. The imago is smooth and shining, and about one-sixteenth of an inch in length, the female only being winged, and the wings being ciliated with long hairs. They cause intolerable irritation when they alight on the hands and face by running and leaping with their bladder-shaped feet. Injury is done to the seed by their sucking the juice, and they attack various corn crops. The only preventive is to sow as early as possible, in order to have the plants vigorous before they appear.

*Euptcryx solani* (the Potato Frog-fly.)—It is of a lively green colour, but fades to yellow after death. The abdomen tapers to a point; the head is broad with lateral prominent brown eyes; the wings are twice as long as the abdomen, glossy, and the upper ones or "elytra" are rusty at the extremity. The length of the full-sized insect is about one-eighth of an inch. The mouth is modified into a "rostrum" or snout which folds under the head and thorax.

*...x picta* (the Painted Frog-fly).—This is like the last in ...pe but much larger, and having spotted buff-coloured elytra, and black abdomen; the length is about one-fourth of an inch. This and allied species, are the common leaping insects seen on plants, and are hence called "frog-flies." The larvæ of one kind (*Ptyelus spumarius*) cause the secretion on leaves which is called in the country "cuckoo spittle."

## Sub-order, HETEROPTERA.

*Lygus contaminatus* (the Green Potato Bug).—This is an insect of a vivid green colour, about one-third of an inch in length, with long yellowish antennæ and yellowish legs. The head and "neck" are thick and closely set on the thorax. It lives on the foliage of potatoes and other plants, and turns yellow when dead.

*Lygus bipunctatus.*—The Double-spotted Potato Bug is a stronger looking insect than the last, but resembles it in everything except colour, as it is of a rusty hue, and further distinguished by two spots on the thorax, though these require a lens to be seen distinctly.

*Lygus umbellatarum* (the Painted Potato Bug).—This is allied to the previously mentioned Lygi. It is more oval in shape, and has slenderer horns than any of the others; the "elytra" are of a pale green colour clouded with red, and tipped with brown; the wings are dusky but vary much, some examples being rosy; and the thorax is coarsely punctured. It is met with from May to September.

These three insects all live by sucking the juices of plants, chiefly potatoes, as they are provided with a folding rostrum. The damage they do, however, is inappreciable.

*Anthocoris nemorum.*—This insect has a general resemblance to the preceding, but is flatter. It is of a dark buff-colour marked with black, and has two circular black marks on the upper wings or elytra. The head and neck are much elongated, black and shining. It hides in cracks and chinks when disturbed, hybernates in winter and comes forth in spring again. *Triphleps minutus* is a smaller species, exactly similar in shape and colour, but not having the two spots on the upper wings. These two insects are very useful, as they live on aphides, sucking their juices with the bent rostra with which they are provided, and thus killing them.

## NEUROPTERA.

These have four membranous wings all nearly equal in size, with numerous delicate nervures; mouth masticatory. The only insect in this order coming within our limits is—

*Chrysopa perla* (the Golden Eye).—This is one which lives insects, as the larvæ feed on aphides, like the "lady-birds," in fact, are called by the French "lions des pucerons" or "plant lice lions." These vary much in colour, but are mostly whitish with orange spots, and have a row of hairy tubercles down each side. They cover themselves with the empty skins of their victims, or with lichens, so that they are not easily seen. The female deposits her eggs in groups of a dozen or so on plants, and these resemble vegetable growths, as each egg is fixed at the extremity of a sort of stalk. The chief distinguishing features of the imago are the brilliant golden coloured eyes, and the pale green colour of the whole body; the wings expand one and a half inches, are four in number, and membranous—this being the distinguishing feature of the *Neuroptera*. *Hemerobius obscurus* is the brown variety. They fly at night, and frequent hedgerows and plantations.

## HOLOMETABOLA.

### DIPTERA.

The two-winged insects or "flies" proper. The posterior wings are represented by two club-shaped processes called "halteres" or "balancers." Mouth suctorial. Larvæ generally destitute of feet, soft and fleshy.

*Tipula oleracea* (the Crane Fly).—This insect is familiar to every one as the "Daddy-long-legs" or "Jenny-spider," and is generally seen swarming on all hay and grass land during summer. It lays its eggs among grass or herbage, where they are more likely to be protected from the frost of winter, and when the spring comes they are hatched, and the larvæ—known as the "grub" or "leather-skins"—immediately set about eating through all the roots of plants near them. They do most damage to the oat crop, for the reason that oats generally follow pasture in the rotation, or are sown first on newly broken-up ground. Paring and burning the turf previously is a sure preventive, though an expensive one. The writer of this report has seen salt tried but with no appreciable effect, as it is obvious that what would kill the grub would also kill the plant. Rolling the land with a ribbed roller *across the furrows* would hinder their movements very much as they are destitute of feet. They come up to the surface at night to feed; but rolling the land at night is not calculated to do much good, as they are so tough in the skin that the pressure of a roller would not injure them unless they should happen to be squeezed against a stone or hard clod. Mr. Carruthers, naturalist to the Royal Agricultural

Society of England, recommends the ground to be dibbled full of holes into which the grubs would fall, thus giving an opportunity to destroy them; but it is not very easy to see how this plan could be economically carried out on say a field of twenty acres.  The grubs can easily be found at any time in the spring among the young braird at an inch or so below the surface. They are thick and short, about one inch long, and of an earthy colour.  In a quick growing and mild spring the damage they do is not so apparent, for the reason that if there is heat they quickly develop and attain the full-fledged state, and the crop is also better able to withstand their ravages.  They delight in moisture and can scarcely be drowned, and consequently we see them swarming among grass in meadows—both fly and grub, a sign that draining would act as a material check.  This insect will destroy the roots of almost any crop—grass, grain, or green crop.

*Cecidomyia tritici* (the British Wheat Midge).—A small yellow gnat about one-fourth of an inch in length.  It is provided with a very long slender retractile ovipositor, to enable it to lay its eggs at the foot of the glumes of the wheat flowers in contact with the germen.  These when hatched produce minute yellowish grubs, which feed on the pollen, and thus prevent the fertilisation and consequent swelling or "filling" of the grains. They frequent many plants besides wheat,—couch grass especially.  The antennæ of the imago under the microscope resemble hairy beads remotely strung.  The eyes are large, forming the bulk of the head, and visible to the naked eye on account of their black colour.  The eggs are laid in June in the ear whilst it is in flower, and the larvæ live there until fully grown, when they change to pupæ upon the sound grains and inner valvules, or enter the earth to undergo their transformations; some of the flies hatching out during the same summer, and others not until the following June.  The only remedy which can be applied is to clean the seed well, so as to get rid of the adhering chrysalides.  They fly in the evening between seven and nine o'clock, and are easily distinguished by their bright yellow colour.

*Cecidomyia riciæ* (the Vetch Midge).—This insect is allied to the preceding species.  It attacks the flowering heads of the vetch and other legumes.  The affected heads grow distorted, and on opening them out one finds little orange-coloured larvæ, which taper at the head and are blunt at the tail.  They live concealed in and amongst the calyces of the flowers, and entirely consume the incipient pods.

*Cecidomyia destructor* (the Hessian Fly).—This is a species of wheat midge very common in America, where it is exceedingly destructive to the wheat crops, some districts having to give up wheat-growing altogether for years on account of its ravages. It is called the "Hessian Fly," from the opinion among the Americans that it was introduced by the Hessian troops in their straw. The larvæ live in families in the sheath of the leaves just above the crown, are of a pale green colour, and one-sixth of an inch in length. The fly is not so large as a common gnat, is of a shining yellowish colour, and clothed with short black hairs. The female lays eight eggs only, in autumn, and the larvæ live head downwards in the sheath of the leaf during the winter, though the mischief done is only discoverable when the wheat is far advanced. They are materially kept in check by the *Ceraphron destructor*, a minute ichneumon fly which deposits its eggs in the larvæ.

*Psila rosæ* (the Carrot Fly).—The maggot of this fly is that which causes the well-known "rust" on carrots, tunnelling into the roots, and giving the part injured a rusty brown appearance. The fly is of a shining greenish-black colour; the wings lie horizontally on the back when at rest, and extend beyond the tail; the nervures are a bright ochreous colour. It is about one-fourth of an inch long, and the wings expand nearly half an inch; the abdomen is furnished with a retractile ovipositor. The maggots are clear, ochreous, and shining, with a black horny pointed head. They will be found sticking half out of the carrots when newly pulled, but quickly withdraw themselves on exposure to light. They leave the roots to become pupæ in the earth, in which they remain till the spring, though the summer ones emerge in three or four weeks. Liming the soil will help to keep away the flies and kill the maggots, as also a dressing of spirits of tar mixed with sand and sown on the drills, or watering with a mixture of one of carbolic acid to fifty of water. When the plants are affected it is best to pull them and use at once, being easily known from the withered appearance of the leaves.

*Anthomyia betæ* (the Mangold Wurzel Fly).—The maggot of this insect is well known as the one which mines out the cellular tissue of the leaf and produces the blistered appearance on it. It is of a greenish colour, one-fourth of an inch long, and pointed at the head; it turns to a pupa in the leaf resembling that of the turnip fly. The imago is about the same length, of an ashy-grey colour, with black bristly hairs, and striped longitudinally on the trunk. It is rarely that any great damage is done to the plant, though possibly the affected leaves may injure cattle. The only way to check them is by squeezing the maggot between the finger and thumb, the blistered spots on the leaves being easily seen; though it is of course out of the question to do this on a large acreage.

*Anthomyia brassicæ* (the Cabbage Fly).—The maggots of this

fly injure the cabbage and turnip crop by eating passages in the stem and roots, and thus inducing disease or decay. They are whitish, round, and apodal, with tapering head and blunt tail, and when full grown are about one-third of an inch long. They turn to pupæ in the earth, and issue as flies of an ashy-grey colour in about a fortnight or three weeks; the later ones, however, lie dormant till spring. The affected plants turn yellow and fade in the heat of the day. The application of lime has been found beneficial, and two crops of cabbages should not be taken in succession.

Another pest very similar to the above is the Root-eating Fly (*Anthomyia radicum*). The grubs of this variety are of a yellowish-ochre colour, but otherwise the economy of the two insects and the appearance of the flies are very much the same.

*Trichocera hiemalis* (the Winter Turnip Gnat).—The maggot of this insect is found in the diseased excrescences on turnips known as "Anbury." It is not the cause of this disease, however, but simply an accompaniment of its progress: "clubbing" in cabbages being a similar affection, and most likely due to the same cause. The larvæ are slender, shining, and pale yellow in colour, scarcely half an inch long, thick at the tail, where there are two brown spots, and pointed at the head. The imago much resembles a miniature crane-fly, and is of an ashy-grey colour, the wings, which are irridescent, being folded over one another in repose.

*Drosophila flava* and *Phytomyza nigricornis* are the "Turnip Leaf Miners." The maggots of these insects eat out the 'parenchyma" or cellular tissue of the leaf—the former (yellow variety) on the upper side, and the latter (slate coloured) on the under —causing it to have a blistered appearance. The flies are about one-eighth of an inch in length; they do no material damage.

*Tephritis onopordinis* (the Parsnip and Celery Leaf-Miner).— This is a very lively little fly, which delights in sunshine, and is very abundant from May to July. The wings, which expand nearly half an inch, are carried erect when walking, and are irridescent but spotted with brown. The body is of a shining tawny colour, with a few black spots over the head. The female has a broader abdomen than the male, and is provided with a long retractile ovipositor. She deposits her eggs singly under the cuticle, and the little green maggot eats out the parenchyma, causing the blisters. It grows to one-third of an inch in length, and either turns to a pupa in the leaf or falls to the ground and does so in the soil. An ichneumon fly, the *Alysia apii*, keeps it in check. This is of a pitchy black shining colour, one-eighth of an inch in length, and the expanse of the wings one-third of an inch.

*Chlorops tæniopus* (the Ribbon-footed Corn Fly.—An insect

of a pale yellow colour, about one-third of an inch in length. There are three broad black stripes down the back. The egg is deposited at an early stage—May or June—on wheat, and the young maggots, which are of a dark orange colour, and about one-fourth of an inch in length, eat into the stalks and ears, and thus cause the plant to become stunted and barren. They change to pupæ in the same place, and become hatched in September. They also infest rye and barley, sometimes seeming to prefer these.

*Syrphus balteatus.*—One of the useful flies, the larva living on aphides. It is longish and slender, with two little horns in front, and resembles a small bee in general appearance, but the abdomen has yellow-edged segments. It is about half an inch in length. There are two other allied species, viz.:—*Syrphus pyrastri* and *Syrphus ribesii*. These are larger, and bear a still greater resemblance to bees or wasps. The maggots are mostly green, thick at the tail and small at the head; the pupæ are horny and pear-shaped, and attached to walls or plants by the tail.

## LEPIDOPTERA.

This order comprises the butterflies and moths. The mouth is suctorial, the spiral trunk or "antlia" being easily seen as a curled-up process below the "face;" the caterpillar, however, is provided with masticatory "jaws." The wings are four in number, covered with modified hairs or scales. Antennæ conspicuous. The butterflies are diurnal in their habits, the moths mostly crepuscular or nocturnal.

*Pieris brassicæ* (the White Cabbage Butterfly).—This is the well-known white and yellow butterfly, the caterpillar of which is common on cabbages in gardens. The two antennæ are black, the upper wings are tipped with black, the body also is covered with black down, and a long proboscis is curled up below the head. The female deposits her eggs on various Crucifers—cabbages, turnips, mustard, rape, &c.—in little yellow clusters on the under side of the leaf, where they hatch into "kailworms," striped with yellow, black, and green. When full grown they change into chrysalides, and these may be found attached to walls or under ledges, where they remain dormant till the spring.

There are two other allied species which resemble this one very much in appearance, but are smaller—*Pieris rapæ*, the "Small White" or "Turnip Butterfly;" and *Pieris napi*, the "Rape Seed" or "Green-veined White Butterfly." Both of these lay their eggs singly on the under sides of leaves, and the caterpillars are greenish, the former with yellow stripes, and the

latter with a row of yellow "spiracles" down the sides. The
best way of dealing with them is by hand-picking, or, if the
affected plants are small, by driving troops of ducks up and down
the drills. In Russia hemp and cabbages are planted in alternate rows, as the former is said to be obnoxious to these insects.
The small yellow cocoons sometimes seen attached to the caterpillar about to become a chrysalis should not be destroyed, as
they contain an ichneumon fly (*Microgaster glomeratus*), the larva
of which lives in and destroys the caterpillars.

*Triphæna pronuba* (the Great Yellow Underwing Moth).—
This conspicuous insect is often seen in meadows during summer
in turning hay. The body and wings are a dull brown or ochreous
colour, and the under wings of a bright orange colour. The larva
is one of the "surface grubs"—the large dirty green species
which is often turned up in green-crop land. This feeds on roots
of various plants, especially turnips and other Crucifers, coming
up to the surface at night. In the larva-stage it exists through
the winter, becomes a large 'reddish chrysalis in April, and
emerges as a moth early in summer. Little damage is done
by it.

*Mamestra brassicæ* (the Cabbage Moth).—This is another of
the "surface grubs," and is allied to the last. It is abundant in
May and June, laying its eggs on the leaves of cabbages, and
the caterpillars which emerge are of a green colour, and feed at
night, lying concealed in the soil during the day. They can
accommodate themselves to almost any plant. The horns of the
imago are like fine threads; the wings are deflexed when resting,
and are of a rich brown colour, the inferior ones a dirty brown.

*Agrotis exclamationis* (the Heart and Dart Moth).—So called
from the markings on its wings. It is of a clay colour, and
three-fourths of an inch long. The larva is also a surface grub,
and is of a dull lilac colour, living on the roots of various plants.

*Agrotis segetum* (the Common Dart Moth).—Resembles the
last very much, but is of a reddish-brown colour, though the
upper wings vary greatly, and are often of a clay colour; the
feelers are "pectinated" or combed. The grubs are of a pale
livid colour, with dark lines down the back, and they feed on
nearly every kind of root. They are hatched in autumn, and
live through the winter.

*Plusia gamma* (the Y-Moth). — This moth, which flies
about by day regardless of the weather, lays its eggs on the
under side of turnip leaves and on other plants. These eggs
when magnified resemble the shell of an echinus, or sea-urchin.
The caterpillar is greenish, with six white lines down the back.
It spins a woolly white cocoon between the folds of a leaf, in
which it changes to a pitchy-coloured chrysalis, having a pro-
tuberance on the base of the abdomen, caused by the long

proboscis being bent back. The moths are abundant from July to October; these have a long spiral tongue, and horns like fine bristles, the head and thorax purplish. The wings, which are a little deflexed when closed, expand half an inch, and are of a brownish colour. In the centre of each is a pale golden mark, like the Greek letter *gamma*, or English Y, hence the name. A rainy season seems to be congenial to them. The only practicable method of dealing with them is to put ducks or poultry on to the affected crop.

*Depressaria applanella* (the Common Flat-body Moth).—This insect is often mistaken for the common clothes' moth when it enters houses, as there is a great resemblance between them; but this species has a flattened abdomen, from which it takes its name. The females live through the winter, and lay their eggs in the umbels of the carrot and parsnip, which they affect. The caterpillars spin webs amongst the flowers and capsules, greatly injuring the seed. They are of a grass green colour, and undergo their transformations rolled up in the leaf. The moth is of a dull reddish ochre colour, and shines like satin.

*Acherontia atropos* (the Death's Head Moth).—This noble-looking and handsome moth is as large as a bat, with the well-known mark of a skull distinctly imprinted on the back of its thorax. It can utter a cry like the faint squeak of a mouse. The larva is as thick and long as the middle finger of a man's hand, and of a yellowish or greenish tint, with seven oblique bands on each side, of a bluish colour. It lives on potato leaves, coming out at night to feed on them, and it, as well as the moth, has the power of uttering a faint squeak in captivity, being the only British species which can do so. It has the audacity to enter bees' hives in search of honey, and for this reason is sometimes called the "Bee Tiger Moth," its horny velvet-covered case protecting it from their stings.

*Plutella xylostella* (the Turnip Diamond-Back Moth).—A small grey moth, very abundant in turnip fields. The caterpillar is spindle-shaped, half an inch long, of a delicate green colour, and lives on the leaves of the turnips. When at rest the wings of the moth are reflexed at the posterior part, and the feelers are projected forward in a straight line. The inferior wings have a very long fringe, and are lance-shaped; the upper ones when closed have white diamond-shaped markings across the upper parts, and there are two little upcurved horny processes projecting from its "mouth."

*Tinea granella* (the little Wolf Grain-Moth).—Resembles the last very much, but is darker in colour. Its little white grubs infest grain in granaries, and cause the seeds to adhere together by their excrement and webs. They form cocoons in chinks in the floor or walls, which look like grains of corn dusted over, in

G

which they form chrysalides when the winter is over, and emerge fully fledged in March or April.

*Hypena rostralis* (the Hop-vine Snout Moth).—The upper wings of this insect are of a brownish tint, variegated with dark lines across the middle, and it is provided with a large upcurved beak or rostrum. The caterpillar, which lives on the hop leaves, is green, with a fine white stripe down each side, and it forms a chrysalis in a web spun over an incurved leaf. There are two broods in the year, April and July. Syringing the bines is the only remedy that can be applied.

*Hepialus humuli* (the Otter Moth).—The larva of this insect will feed on carrots and other root crops, though hop roots are its natural food. It is yellowish white in colour, with a few scattered hairs, and grows until it is from one to two inches in length. The wings of the imago, deflexed when closed, are satiny-white on the outside, and dusky brown on the inside, and while flitting about in the twilight they appear and disappear suddenly, and thus have got the name of "ghost-moths." The female, which is much the larger, lays her eggs in June, and the young caterpillars immediately bury themselves and commence their depredations.

*Bombyx trifolii* (the Clover Egger Moth).—The large ochreous-coloured caterpillar of this moth lives on clover leaves, often attaining the length of three inches; it spins a cocoon, and eventually comes out a large moth. The horns are inserted towards the back of the head, and form nearly a straight bristle. The wings, which expand two inches and a half, are deflected when closed, and form a ridge down the back.

*Leucania obsoleta* (the Oat Wainscot-Moth).—The caterpillar of this moth attacks oats by notching the edges of the leaves. They are of a flesh colour, about one and a half inch long, and feed only at night; if touched, they curl up and fall down. After hybernating in the stubble, they descend into the soil in spring to become chrysalides, emerging as moths in June. They are particularly plentiful in fenny districts among the reeds. The wings are of a satiny texture, freckled with black, and expand one and a half inch; the under wings are white, a little freckled, and ochreous at the margin.

*Euclidia glyphica* (the Burnet Moth).—The stems and leaves of clover fall a prey to this insect. The larvæ are of a buff colour, striped, with the head and belly brown, and get the name of "semi-loopers" from their peculiar action in walking. They conceal themselves among the lower leaves of clover, and undergo their transformations in an elongated white cocoon, the chrysalis being brown, powdered with blue. The head and thorax of the imago are of an orange brown colour, the body black. The upper wings are rosy brown, with a dark patch at the base, and have an expanse of one inch; the under wings are of an orange colour, with the base and fringe black. These moths fly about in the sunshine like the smaller butterflies or "skippers," and are most prevalent in chalk districts.

*Euclidia mi* (the Shipton Moth).—This insect is allied to, and very much resembles the last, and it also flies in the day time. The caterpillars, which are of a whitish lilac colour inclining to ochre, infest clover, lucerne, yellow medick and grass crops, and arrive at maturity in the end of August. The moths are found in June. The upper wings have a broad blackish band margined with ochre across them, and expand rather more than one inch: the under wings are black, with a large bright ochreous spot near the base.

*Endopisa pisana* (the Pea Moth).—This moth is the cause of "maggoty" pease, as the "larvæ" devour the young seeds in the pod or after they are stored. They are about three-eighths of an inch in length, of a yellow colour, covered with bristles and spotted black. They bury themselves in July and August, and change to pupæ in fine webs. The moth itself is about the same size and has the same appearance as the common house moth.

*Orgyia pudibunda* (the Pale Tussac-Moth).—This insect infests the hop-bines in the south, its caterpillars being known as "hop-dogs." These have the appearance as if a fungoid growth were proceeding from each of the segments of the body, and they are provided with a long hairy rose-coloured tail. The trunk is of a greenish colour with black stripes dividing its segments. They spin a whitish yellow web in which to become a pupa, and the moth which emerges is of large size, greenish-white colour (the upper wings freckled and having four irregular transverse darker lines) and it is provided with hairy antennae and legs.

### HYMENOPTERA.

The "four-winged flies."—The mouth is provided with biting jaws or mandibles. The female has the extremity of the abdomen provided with a sting or ovipositor as in bees.

*Athalia spinarum* (the Turnip Saw-Fly).—The larvæ of this insect are the black caterpillars or "negroes" which feed on turnip leaves, often sweeping away an entire crop in the south, leaving nothing but the bare stalks. The flies make their appearance in July, August, and September. After impregnation the female fixes herself on the edge of a leaf, and using the saw-like processes at the extremity of the abdomen proceeds to make a slit in which she deposits one egg—proceeding thus till all are laid. The caterpillars are nearly all black, but change to a slaty colour on casting their skins the third time.   They have the power of emitting a thread from their mouth when alarmed, by which they descend to the earth, and reascend when the danger is over.   Little cocoons are formed in the earth by them in which they pass the pupa stage, and in three weeks a bright orange-coloured fly escapes; the females much larger than the males.   They feign death when touched, are lively during sunshine, but dull during cloudy weather.   Powdered lime or soot scattered over the leaves when wet will check their ravages, but the most reliable method is to drive a regiment of young ducks up and down the drills.   They will snap up the caterpillars, but must be kept moving or they will attack the leaves, so much nitrogenised matter requiring to be "toned" with vegetable food. Probably the ducks will require training to eat them at first; and this may be done by mixing some of the caterpillars with grain.

*Cephus pygmæus* (the Corn Saw-Fly).—This insect is of a shining black colour, with large head and prominent eyes.   The abdomen is long and slender, with yellow margins to the segments; the legs are bright yellow, and the insect is about one-third of an inch in length.   The larva is apodous—that is, destitute of feet—and of a yellowish white colour.   The female pierces the stalk of corn—mostly rye—below the first knot and lays an egg; the young grub, when hatched, eats the interior of the stalk and cuts through the knots; the affected plants speedily assume a ripened appearance, but if examined will be found worthless.   It descends into the stump when fully grown, and becomes a pupa from which issues a fly in May.

*Ichneumonidæ.*—The Ichneumon Flies are amongst the most serviceable of the enemies of insects: nearly every one has a parasite peculiar to itself and belonging to this family.   Some are very minute and others fully half-an-inch in length, and they are usually distinguished by their long slender and reddish abdomen.   They generally lay their eggs in the caterpillar by inserting their ovipositors into it while feeding, and the young when hatched feed on the fatty substance of their "host," avoiding by instinct the vital parts.   In due time the larva assumes the pupa condition, but instead of a perfect insect coming therefrom, the minute parasitic ichneumons issue from the dead chrysalis of their victim.   A familiar example is that of the cabbage butterfly caterpillar, which is often seen when about to become a chrysalis surrounded by a number of minute silky cocoons which contain the ichneumons (*Microgaster glomeratus*) that had lived in it.   Care should therefore always be taken not to destroy these useful little parasites.

## COLEOPTERA.

This order includes all the insects known as "beetles." The upper wings are modified into two horny cases known as "elytra," which serve as a protection to the flying wings beneath. The mouth is masticatory.

*Phyllotreta undulata* (the "Turnip Fly").—This destructive little pest is properly a beetle, and about one-eighth of an inch in length, of a black colour, but distinguished by a yellow stripe down each wing case. It is of an active habit, leaping away whenever an attempt is made to catch it, but duller in cloudy weather, when it draws itself together and falls down if touched. Its appearance is made in the month of May as soon as the young turnips are beginning to peep above the surface. The little soft "cotyledons" or seed leaves are what it attacks, and the insects being innumerable, acres are cleared in a very short time, necessitating the resowing of the crop. They have a powerful scent, and fly against the wind, so that they can readily shift their quarters from one turnip field to another. The eggs are laid on the under side of the rough leaf, and, when hatched, the young grubs bore their way into the leaf, and live on the soft cellular matter or "parenchyma," like the "turnip-leaf miners," and in so doing make long tunnels in the leaf which look like blisters; as this happens on the rough leaf, however, no appreciable damage is done. When the grub is fully grown it makes its way to the earth, and burying itself just beneath the surface, becomes a chrysalis, and after the expiry of a fortnight emerges a beetle ready to renew operations. It lives in a torpid state under bark of trees and in chinks all winter, and only wakes up when the sun becomes warm. Knowing that it is not until the season is well advanced that the beetles appear, and that it is the smooth cotyledon-leaf which they prefer, we have a clue to the means of coping with them. Early sowing and forcing the young plants on into the rough leaf stage are the best means of doing so. There is no reason why turnips should not be sown in the end of April, except the difficulty of getting the land ready in time, as it is only with the softer varieties that there is any danger of running to seed, such as the Tankard, White Globe, and Greystone—the Yellow Bullock and Swedes stand well. Again, it is a good plan to force on the young plants at first; and this may be done by using a small quantity of nitrate of soda along with the other manures, say ¼ cwt. per acre, or by watering with the liquid manure drill; or, again, by steeping the seeds in manure-water if there is a likelihood of there being sufficient moisture in the soil to carry them on afterwards. Mr. Fisher Hobbs' remedy was to broadcast a mixture composed of 1 bushel of fresh lime, 6 lbs. of sulphur, and

10 lbs. of soot on every two acres, applied in the morning when the dew was on the leaf. There is another beetle allied to the above (*Plectroscelis dentipes*, the "Brassy" or "Tooth-legged Turnip Beetle") which differs principally from the former in not having the yellow stripes on its wing cases, otherwise it resembles and generally accompanies it. All cruciferous plants are subject to the attacks of the turnip-fly, such as wild mustard, cabbage, cole-wort, watercress, cauliflower, radish, &c., and these serve to support it when there are no turnips, so that, therefore, all weeds belonging to this order especially should be kept down. It has even been noticed on the mangold wurzel crop, but it is only to the turnip braird it does material damage.

*Psylliodes exoleta* or *affinis* (the Leaping Potato Flea).—This insect is allied to and resembles the preceding. The thorax is of a deep ochreous, and the elytra of a pale ochreous colour, with eight faintly punctured striæ on each. The leaves of the potato and bittersweet are riddled by it, but no serious damage is done.

*Elateridæ* (Wireworms).—There are many species of these insects which infest crops in Great Britain, but for our purpose they may be looked on as one. The larvæ are small elongated "worms" of a pale ochreous colour, and with a shining skin. They are about an inch in length when full grown, and furnished with six small legs only on the first three segments of the body, and a "proleg" or false leg on the terminal one. They eat through the roots of plants just below the surface, and as they exist in the larval state for four or five years, the damage done by them is enormous. There is scarcely a crop they will not attack, as they can live on corn, turnips, mangold-wurzel, potatoes, grass, and garden flowers. After pairing, the female beetles descend into the earth and lay their eggs on the roots of plants—mostly grass —their ravages being worst in dry seasons. When full grown the grub descends a considerable depth, forms a cell of the surrounding soil,—not lined with anything,—and becomes a chrysalis from which the beetle emerges in a fortnight or three weeks. These beetles are well known as the "skipjacks" or "clickbeetles," from the power they have of springing from their backs on to their feet by using a peculiar apparatus on the under side of the thorax, making at the same time a clicking noise. The different species vary in size, but average about half-an-inch in length, with elytra mostly brownish and thorax dark. They run with the head down and feign death when touched, folding down their jointed antennæ. There are several plans recommended to check their ravages. It is in the first crop after lea they do most damage, so that paring and burning will destroy them—if the soil is suitable for this operation—as well as all other noxious grubs and eggs. Soot and lime applied to the land will have a good effect. Rolling the land with a ribbed roller across the furrows, or drilling the seed, will hinder their movements very much as their legs are few and weak, and if they come to the surface are pounced on by the small birds continually on the watch. The mole feeds largely on these "worms." There is a curious parasite belonging to the class *Arachnida* which infests the Elaters, and known as the *Uropoda umbilica*. It is a species of minute tick, oval shaped, and of a rusty brown shining colour, and about one-sixteenth of an inch in length. From one side of the back arises a white transparent peduncle as long as the animal itself. The other end is attached to an elytron of the elater, and is probably used to suck up nourishment from it, and by means of which the parasite keeps fixed on the back of its victim.

*Pterostichus madidus.*—This is the moderately-sized shining black beetle often seen running about when the surface of the ground is disturbed. The thighs are reddish, and it is wingless, as the elytra are soldered together, and these are seen to be delicately striated under the microscope. It is provided with powerful masticatory organs to suit it for a predaceous life, as wire-worms form a principal part of its food, it being one of the useful insects. It prowls about at night, and delights in moisture, retiring into cracks during a drought.

*Coccinellidæ* (the Lady-birds).—These well-known little dumpy beetles are the friend of the farmer, as the larvæ live totally on the aphides or plant-lice. There are two varieties which are more particularly noticeable—the seven-spotted (*Coccinella septempunctata*) and the two-spotted (*Coccinella bipunctata*). The beetles hybernate, passing the winter in chinks, under bark of trees, &c., and leave their hiding places in spring. They lay their eggs in clusters of fifty or so on the under side of the leaf, from which issue the leaden-coloured, orange-spotted larvæ, ready to pounce on all aphides they come across.

*Tenebrio molitor* (the Meal-worm Beetle).—The larva of this insect is about one inch long when fully grown, has six pectoral legs, and a smooth ochreous coloured skin, with rusty bands. It generates in meal, bran, and flour bins. The beetles are of a pitchy or chestnut colour, resembling elaters in general appearance. Cleanliness is the best preventive.

*Staphylinidæ.*—The Rove-beetles are some of the serviceable varieties, as they live mostly on other insects or on decomposing matter. One large black species—the Fœtid Rove-beetle (*Ocypus olens*)—is known in the country as the "Devil's Coach Horse," and is capable of emitting a disagreeable liquid from its mouth when irritated. The *Staphylinidæ* in general have powerful, prominent jaws; the elytra short and quadrate, not covering the abdomen; the wings not sufficient for flight; the abdomen longer than the rest of the body (covered with grey and irridescent down in one variety), and pointed. They are often seen during harvest and the raising of root crops.

*Melolontha vulgaris* (the Common Cockchafer).—This insect is very injurious to the young plants of wheat, rye, mangold-wurzel, &c., living on their roots while in the larval state. The grubs are thick and fleshy, white or yellowish in colour, with strong jaws, and three pairs of legs. They feed on roots for three years, and at the end of this time, when full grown, descend into the earth to a depth of two or three feet and change to pupæ. During the next winter they develop into perfect chafers and emerge in the summer, thus taking four years to go through all their stages. The beetle is about one inch in length, face and wing cases of a rusty brown, with lighter ferruginous spots across them, and the extremity of the abdomen (which is exposed) is of a black colour, and pointed downwards.

*Crioceris melanopa* (the Oat Crioceris).—The slug-like larva of this beetle attacks the leaves of oats just as they are coming into ear, and eats the epidermis in longitudinal lines. The beetle is of a black or dark green shining colour. The thorax is reddish-orange, often with two dusky spots on the disc : antennæ twice as long as the thorax, the latter being rather small comparatively ; eyes black and prominent. They are plentiful from the middle of April to the end of September.

*Cassida nebulosa* (the Clouded Shield Beetle).—The larvæ are oval-shaped, of a pretty green colour, and live on the under side of the leaves of mangold. The head of the beetle is concealed under a large, broad, shield-like thorax ; the whole of the body is tawny coloured, and about one-fourth of an inch in length.

*Silpha opaca* (the Beet Carrion Beetle).—The usual food of this insect is dead animals, but the larvæ feed on mangold leaves, and may be found in May or June on beetroot. They resemble the wood-lice ("slaters") very much when full grown, and change to pupæ in the earth. The beetle which emerges is of a dark brown or blackish colour, with a broad thorax and large triangular "scutellum." There are three large striæ down each elytron, with a bump between the second and third beyond the middle. Neither salt nor lime affects them, and they appear to be bred in the field, as the beetles appear on the flowering stalks after July.

*Bruchus pisi.*—The Pea "Bug" deposits its eggs during the night in the newly-formed pea pods—one opposite each pea—and the little, soft, whitish apodal maggot penetrates into the pea, in which it lives during the summer and through the winter, and comes out in spring, leaving only the empty shell. It does not touch the germ, so that the pea will still germinate, though it will only yield a sickly plant. The beetle is of a black colour, densely covered with short, brightish brown hairs, more grey and silky beneath. There are ten fine striæ on each side, two black or brown spots on the exposed part of the abdomen, and it is about one-fourth of an inch long. It is a native of warmer climates, but has become acclimatised.

*Bruchus granarius* (the Bean Weevil).—This is an insect very similar to the preceding, and is, in fact, the native variety. It is black and punctured with two whitish spots on the disc of the thorax. The wing cases are sprinkled with whitish spots of hairs, and the anterior pair of legs are ferruginous. It is abundant on furze when in bloom, and both peas and beans are subject to its attack, late-sown plants suffering most. Immersion of the affected grains in hot water for one minute will kill the contained insect, and not injure the seed. Kiln-drying at 133° Fahr. will destroy them, but also kills the germ, though the feeding properties are not injured.

*Doryphora decemlineata* (the Colorado Potato Beetle).— Although this is not one of our native insects, yet, as it has been so prominent of late years, it may be as well to devote a few words to it. It is a native of the Rocky Mountains, and was first noticed in 1824. At that time it lived on wild potatoes, and it is only of recent years that it has taken to the cultivated variety and begun to creep eastwards, appearing on the Atlantic seaboard in 1870. The beetles hybernate at a depth of two or three feet in the soil, and emerge when the potatoes are sprouting. The insect goes through its transformations in one month. The larvæ are about one half inch long, thick and fat, and of a reddish colour. The only way to deal with them is to water the plants with water containing "Paris green" (arsenite of copper), or to dust over the plants a mixture of one of the same to nineteen of damaged flour. The chemical kills the grubs it comes into contact with, while it does not injure the plants. It has got no footing in this country as yet, though it is an open question whether it could exist here or not, seeing that it can stand a great amount of cold and moisture. The beetles themselves are about three-eighths of an inch long, with five yellow stripes down each elytron, from which they get the name of "ten-lined," and generally resemble large turnip "flies," to which they are allied.

*Calandra granaria* (the Granary Weevil).—This insect infests the grain stored in granaries; the female buries herself in the corn heap, and boring a hole obliquely into the seed with her beak, or "rostrum," deposits one egg and seals it up with a kind of gluten the colour of the grain. When the egg is hatched the maggot proceeds to eat out the entire contents and changes to a pupa in the hollow shell, whence it emerges in eight or ten days a perfect insect, eating its way out of the husk. The affected grains cannot be distinguished by their appearance, but if put into water will float. The beetles vary in colour from black to chestnut: the head is provided with a long snout—the distinguishing feature of all the weevils—at the end of which is the masticatory mouth, and at its base the eyes: the geniculated, clubbed feelers are placed about its middle. The thorax, which is delicately "punctured," is as large as the abdominal part. The whole insect is about one-fourth of an inch in length, and the flying wings are not developed in this country. They are never found in the fields, and do not like the light, being always buried to a depth of several inches in the corn heap. The best way of killing them is either by exposing them to cold by opening the granary windows on a frosty night, or else a sudden raising of the temperature to about 75° Fahr. The place should be kept clean, the walls smooth and whitewashed, and no crevices left which will harbour them; fumigation is of little use as they are always buried in the heap. Frequent turning of the grain will retard their operations.

*Apion apricans* (the Purple Clover Weevil).—This is a shining bluish-black, pear-shaped insect; about one-eighth of an inch in length, the thorax and snout being much elongated. It is in greatest abundance when the purple clover is in flower, at which period the female deposits her eggs. If the withered heads be examined a little white maggot with brown head will be found eating the base of the calyx and the germ of the future seed; it changes to a pupa in the same situation. The weevils shun the light, and are not easily found. It is only to the seed they do damage, so that an affected crop should be cut early and not seeded. They are provided with wings for flight, and are very active in running about, and like most weevils feign death when touched.

*Apion flavipes* (the Yellow-Legged Dutch-Clover Weevil) is very similar to the last, but more slender in form; its economy, however, is exactly the same—the maggot feeding at the base of the calyx of the floret, and the affected heads assuming a prematurely ripened appearance. It differs from the common clover weevil mostly in the legs, which are bright yellow. It is kept in check by the *Eubazus macrocephalus*, a minute fly provided with a long ovipositor which enables it to reach to the bottom of the florets, and deposit an egg in the maggot feeding there; which maggot in due time assumes the chrysalis state and then dies.

*Apion pomonæ* (the Vetch or Tare Weevil) is larger than the Clover Weevil, and the female deposits her eggs in both the cultivated and wild variety, the larvæ—which are at first of a dirty ochreous tint—eating out the interior of the seeds in the pod. They change to pupæ in the hollowed out shells, and emerge in autumn, when they may be found on heaths, firs, and oaks: they appear as early as May on the white thorn. The females are black but covered with a greyish down; the males are of a dark bluish tint. The wing cases have punctured furrows down them, the spaces between being flat; the first joint of the horns reddish at the base. The peak is stout, thick, and curved downwards; large prominent eyes. They fly well, even when the sun is not shining.

*Sitona lineata* (the Striped Pea Weevil).—This Weevil commits great ravages among peas, both field and garden, eating the leaves and tender tops of the plants. When feeding it stands on the edges and these soon appear notched like a saw. It delights in bright sunshine, and is very difficult to catch, dropping off to the ground whenever any one makes his appearance. It appears in April, and is supposed to hybernate. It is not known where the female lays her eggs or where the larvæ feed, though it is supposed that the galls on the roots of beans and clover contain them, and that the eggs must be laid in summer or autumn. The beetles are found on broom or furze in early spring, and attack peas, beans, lucerne, clover, &c., till autumn. A dusting of soot, ashes, or lime, when the plants are wet, would render them unpalatable, but would not otherwise affect the insects. The beetle is of an ochreous grey colour, having in some lights a coppery tint, and provided with a blunt notched snout. There are three ochreous lines of scales down the thorax, and ten punctured striæ down the elytra, of a light and dark clay colour alternately. The legs are reddish, and two ample wings are folded beneath the elytra, though they seldom fly: length one-fourth of an inch.

*Sitona crinita* (the Spotted Pea Weevil).—This insect is very similar both in economy and appearance to the last. It is shining black, but covered with short greyish hairs, and with four dark stripes on the thorax: the elytra are rough with short bristles behind, and the interstices of the striæ are irregularly spotted with black: the legs are ferruginous. It is a little smaller in size than the preceding one, and it attacks the same plants.

*Ceutorhynchus sulcicollis* (the Turnip Gall Weevil).—If the little knobs which are sometimes seen growing on the sides of turnips be opened, they will be found to contain the grub of this weevil. The female punctures the rind of the young growing turnip and deposits an egg, which hatches into a whitish or flesh-coloured maggot. The gall grows over the wounded part from the irritation, caused probably by an injected fluid. This maggot becomes a pupa in the earth, and eventually a small weevil of a shining black colour, and about one eighth of an inch long. It is very similar to the next insect,—the turnip seed weevil,—but is smaller and black, the latter being grey, and all

the thighs have a small tooth beneath.    Partridges are very fond
of the maggots, picking them out of the galls.

*Ceutorhynchus assimilis* (the Turnip Seed Weevil).—It
deposits its eggs in the pods of the seeding turnips and other
cruciferous plants, the maggots devouring the germs, and thus
doing much damage when the crop is grown for seed.    The
beetle itself is black, but clothed with very fine hairs, which
give it a greyish appearance, and it is about three sixteenths of
an inch long, including the beak, which is slender and arched.
It may be seen running about on turnip leaves, and when
touched falls down until the danger is over.

*Ceutorhynchus contractus* (the Charlock Seed Weevil).—This
insect is nearly allied to the preceding, being similar in form
but much smaller in size.    It is believed to form small galls in
the larva state on the roots of charlock, but the beetles attack
turnips as well, eating the seed before brairding, and the coty-
ledon leaves after.    Much of the damage done to the turnip
crop during the past season was by this insect, and not by the
ordinary "turnip-fly" at all.

The following are several other pests of farm crops, which,
though not insects, may be conveniently described along with
them:—

*Julus Londinensis* (the London Snake Millipede).—So called
from having been first found in the neighbourhood of the
metropolis.    It is usually about one inch long, of a slate or
leaden colour; the legs are of a dirty white colour, 160 in number, in pairs on each side, each segment having two pairs.    It
grows for two years before the organs of generation are developed,
and changes its skin five times.    It is at first only provided with
six legs, and an offensive liquid is secreted from its body.    It
lives on the roots of grain and green crops.    Another variety is
the *Julus pulchellus* or "Beautiful Snake Millipede."    This is
about half an inch in length, of a pale ochreous colour, and with
a double row of bright crimson spots down each side.    It turns
purple when dead.

An ally of the above is the Flattened Millipede (*Polydesmus
complanatus*)—one of the "Meg-many-feet" of the country.
This variety is of an orange or pale lilac colour, the segments
not being so numerous, but more distinct than the last.    The
respiration is by "tracheæ" or breathing-tubes, like that of
insects.    There is no distinct line of demarcation between the
thorax and abdomen; one pair of feelers; mouth masticatory.

*Limax agrestis* (the Milky Slug).—This animal needs no
description, as it is too well known.    It is always of a whitish
or ashy colour.    The true snails are provided with a shell, but
in this and the black slug, the only approach to it is in the

"shield," or rough leathery patch on the anterior part of the back. The eyes are fixed at the extremity of the retractile horns, and may be seen by the naked eye as little black specks. The aperture on the right side forms the "breathing sac,"—taking the place of the lungs of higher animals—and generative opening. Snails and slugs are hermaphrodite, each individual thus laying eggs. These eggs are found under stones, and at the roots of grass, as clusters of little white pellucid bodies like sago in appearance.

*Limax ater* is the large black species. There are scarcely any more destructive pests than these two creatures, and no kind of crop comes amiss to them. Troops of ducks are a capital cure if driven over the affected crop in the evening or after rain, and a dressing of lime or soot put on when the leaves are wet, renders them unpalatable, if not deadly to them.

*Vibrio tritici.* This creature, which belongs to the Infusoria, is the cause of the disease known as "purples," or "earcockle" in wheat. The affected grain assumes a purplish-black colour, and becomes rounded in appearance; if one be taken and opened, the inside will be found to contain a cotton-like substance, into which the original starch, &c., has been changed. In this bed will be found a number of microscopic eel-like animalcules, which readily separate in warm water. When an infected grain is sown, the vibrios make their way from it to the sound stalks, which they gradually ascend until they reach the ovules, where they make their nidus, deposit their eggs, and die. As the diseased grains are light, winnowing will separate them.

There are, of course, many more insects which infest farm crops at home and abroad, but the above-described kinds comprise the most conspicuous and troublesome of them that are found in this country.

In conclusion, a few general remarks may be offered on the manner of coping with these tiny enemies. Mostly all insects delight in moisture, so that draining is prejudicial to them, while beneficial to the soil and crop. When land is broken up for the first time the practice of paring off and burning the turf and rubbish is sometimes carried out, thereby killing the "grubs" and wireworms hiding therein, and the good crops often seen after this operation are partly due to their freedom from insect injuries. Many of the weeds belong to the same natural orders as our crops, and are thus suitable for food to insects when there is nothing else, so that these should be kept down. Early ploughing and autumn cultivation for the purpose of exposing the soil to the action of the frost is a good plan, as many are thus killed. All our feathered songsters are insectivorous, and should therefore be encouraged. When a crop is growing, dressings of lime, soot, or salt, if they do not hinder their operations, at least act as a manure to the plant. Handpicking of the larger caterpillars is rarely to be thought of except in a garden, but a regiment of young ducks is an infallible remedy. And finally, if a farm is in good "heart," the crops on it will be the better able to withstand their depredations.

## THE COMPOSITION OF CROPS IN AVERAGE PRODUCE PER ACRE.

### By WILLIAM HAY, Tillydesk, Aberdeenshire.

*[Premium, the Medium Gold Medal].*

THE elementary substances of which plants are composed are very commonly spoken of as divided into two more or less distinct portions,—organic and inorganic,—or what is, perhaps, more definite, into combustible and incombustible, this latter portion being also called the *Ash*. This ash forms only a very small proportion of the weight, and still less of the bulk of all vegetable substances. Yet it is with this ash, with its amount and the elements of which it is composed, that the cultivators of the soil have mainly to concern themselves. In addition, there is, however, just one other elementary substance of importance as a constituent of all our cultivated crops, namely, Nitrogen ; and this element again forms only a very small proportion of the organic matter of plants. The value of all manures and of all fertilising substances whatever, consists simply in the amount of this ash, or of one or more of its elements, and of this nitrogen which they supply in available form.

Of this so-called inorganic matter or ash, vegetable substances, generally speaking, contain only from about 1 to 4, or at most 6 or 7 per cent. of their whole mass. The rest, that is the great bulk and weight—94 per cent. and upwards—of all vegetable, and, for that matter, of all animal substances also, consists of organic or combustible matter ; and this organic matter again consists almost entirely of carbon and the elements of water. The carbon is mainly obtained from the atmosphere, and the water, from the generally abundant supply in the soil. It thus appears that the farmer has not to concern himself at all about providing, in the shape of manure or otherwise, the materials which go to make up the greater part of the bulk of his crops. The organic matter, we have just said, consists mainly, but it does not consist entirely, of carbon and water. It contains in small amount relatively, but nevertheless as an indispensable part of its organised structure, the other element to which reference has been made, namely, nitrogen—an element which, in its combined forms of ammonia and nitric acid, is of vast importance to the farmer. Of this elementary substance plants generally contain only from 0·2 to 2 per cent., or at most 4 per cent. It is only in some leguminous plants, beans, and pease that it reaches 3 or 4 per cent. The whole care of the farmer, then, in all the manures which he applies, and in nearly all his operations on the soil, is to provide his crops with sufficient supplies of this relatively small amount of nitrogen in proper condition, and of the above-named almost equally small amount, relatively, of mineral matter, or ash as the chemist calls it. He may apply to his land twenty tons of farmyard manure, or five or six hundredweights of extraneous and more concentrated fertilising matter per acre ; the whole value in either case consists in, and depends upon, the relatively small amount of combined nitrogen and of mineral matter which the manure contains : and if chemistry has taught us anything, it has taught us, and proved beyond all question, that there is a close connection between the composition of manures, of whatever kind, and of the plants which they serve to nourish.

It is manifestly of the utmost importance that we should know and keep distinctly before us how much of this one organic substance (nitrogen), and how much of this mineral matter our several crops require,—how much of them and how much of each of them go to form, not 100 parts of this or that vegetable product, but the whole crop of grain and straw, turnips, or potatoes, that is usually produced upon, and removed from, an acre of land. With tolerably satisfactory information to guide us on this head (if it were properly understood and applied), the indefatigable labours of chemists in this country and on the Continent have now supplied us. But the form in which it is commonly supplied has rendered it less available and less useful to practical farmers than it might have been, and has even led to a good deal of misunderstanding or misapprehension, not among farmers only, but even, in not a few cases, among writers of papers and books on agricultural subjects.

The mineral matter to which we have referred consists of nine elementary substances. Four others are occasionally found in certain plants, but, being of no importance to the farmer, they need not be named. Of these nine, only four or five are of much importance as constituents of plants or manures, namely, phosphoric acid, potash, lime, magnesia, and sulphur, or sulphuric acid. One of these again stands out from the rest as of paramount value and importance, namely, phosphorus or phosphoric acid. (We shall not render what we have to say less acceptable to the common reader by using the new chemical nomenclature, *phosphoric anhydride*, &c.) Phosphoric acid, and Nitrogen (in available form) are indeed the two grand requisites in the

business of the farmer.    Give him these in sufficient abundance
and at a sufficiently cheap rate, and the rest would be easily
found.   Nearly one-half (45 per cent.) of the ash of wheat,
and one-tenth of the ash of turnips, consist of phosphoric acid.
Potash, which may be placed next in importance, forms nearly
one-third of the ash of wheat, and one-third or upwards of the
ash of turnips.    Lime, which indeed is in many respects exceptional in its importance, would rank next; but, on account of its
abundance in nature, its pecuniary value is less than that of
magnesia and sulphuric acid.    This last appears largely,—to the
extent of one-tenth or more in the ash of turnips, and to considerable amount in that of potatoes.

Now, if the reader were hastily to suppose or infer from what
has just been said with respect to the relative composition of
the ash of wheat, and of the ash of turnips, that a "crop" of
wheat requires more phosphoric acid than a "crop" of turnips,
and that each requires from the soil about the same amount
of potash, he would make an enormous mistake.   Yet this
absurd mistake is often made, and made too sometimes by those
from whom more accuracy of thought might be expected.    The
truth is that a crop of turnips requires from an acre of land
nearly twice as much phosphoric acid, and five times as much
potash as a crop of wheat.

When the chemist proceeds to find by analysis the composition of a plant or vegetable substance, one part of the process
consists in burning a given weight of it; and, having done so,
he finds that the ash (not to speak of the water or the combustible matter, amounts to only 1, 2, or 3 per cent. as the case
may be, of the whole weight; or, if the substance contains much
water, as in the case of turnips, the ash may be rather less
than 1 per cent., say 0·6 to 0·8 per cent.   But whatever the
relative weight of the ash may be, he takes say 100 parts—call
them grains, grammes, or ounces—of it, and ascertains how
much, how many parts in 100, of each of the nine elementary
substances above referred to, the ash contains.   He states the
results in percentages in the form of a column of figures—
integers and decimals, the sum of which is of course 100 or
nearly so.   Now, by looking at this column of figures without
considering the relation which the whole ash bore to the whole
weight or 100 parts of the normal substance analysed; and
without considering, it may be, the relative value and importance
of the several elementary substances named in it, many farmers,
and not a few others, are liable to be greatly misled, and to form,
and carry away, ideas as to the composition of crops which are
quite erroneous.   They are liable to be still further misled, and to
form opinions still more erroneous if, without such consideration,
they proceed to compare the ash of one plant or crop with that

of another plant or crop of a different order in the vegetable kingdom. As evidence of the prevalence of this misapprehension and misapplication of scientific truth, it may be worth while to refer briefly to the last example of it that happened to come under our notice. In a very useful book on "Manures" by an American gentleman, Mr. J. Harris, which has gone through two or more editions, the author takes up the consideration of the manures suitable for wheat and for turnips, and says that, judging from analyses, we would think that the manure for an acre of wheat would require to contain more phosphoric acid than the manure for an acre of turnips, and then goes to tell his readers (quite truly) that we know from experience that the reverse is the case,—that phosphoric acid is the great and special manure for turnips and nitrogen for wheat. He even goes the length of showing by calculation, that judging from the ash-analysis of the crops, a "special manure" for wheat should contain 42½ lbs. per cent. of phosphoric acid, and a manure for turnips only 18⅓ lbs. of the same. It is to be regretted that the teaching of science should be thus misunderstood and misapplied; and it is hoped that some service may be done by an attempt to correct misapprehension on a point of so much importance. After a rather fruitless attempt to account for the supposed anomaly, the writer referred to takes refuge in a quotation from Dr. Voelcker to the effect that " the ash-analyses of plants do not afford a satisfactory guide to the practical farmer in selecting the kind of manure which is best suited to his crop,"—a remark which is true only with certain qualifications and under certain circumstances as to soil, &c. We have thus not only a palpable mistake, but an attempt to generalise upon it. And yet the author shows otherwise a very fair acquaintance with practical farming and with the chemistry of agriculture, both of which, he takes occasion to tell us, he studied under Dr. Lawes at Rothamsted.

The mistake lies, as already indicated, in comparing 100 parts, or say pounds, of the ash of one crop with 100 lbs. of the ash of a different crop without considering the *amount* of ash which the respective crops yield, and, of how much valuable, or comparatively less valuable substances that ash may consist. It is quite true that, in 100 lbs. of the ash of wheat, we find 42 to 49 lbs., or 45 lbs. on an average, of phosphoric acid, and that, in 100 lbs. of the ash of turnip bulbs, we find only about 10 lbs. of the same valuable ingredient; but, nevertheless, as we have already said, an average crop of turnips draws from an acre of land twice as much phosphoric acid as a good average crop of wheat requires from the same. If we take a crop of wheat at 4 quarters, and a crop of turnips at 20 tons per acre, we have 2016 lbs. of grain and 4480 lbs. of turnip bulbs. But then more than nine-tenths of this latter consist of water, whereas the grain consists of what may be called dry matter. If we bring them to a level in this respect, we have 2016 lbs. of the one, and 4032 lbs. (or as it happens, just double the weight) of the other. But this immense quantity of water in the turnip crops does not exist there as pure water (although the chemist can draw it off as such in his hot-water bath); it is in intimate combination with a large amount of organic matter, and holds in solution, so to speak, a large amount of mineral salts. If we reduce the dry matter in both cases to "ash," we get ten times as much from the turnips as we get from the grain: or, in point of fact (taking the average of ash), we get 34 lbs. in the one case, and 350 lbs. in the other. But, reverting to the phosphoric acid per cent. in each,—one-tenth of 350 is just something more than twice as much as one-half of 34. The round numbers here used come pretty near the averages—which we must take in all such cases;—but the ash of wheat does not contain quite 50 per cent., but only 45 per cent. of phosphoric acid, whereas the ash of turnips contains pretty exactly 10 per cent. of that substance. In this case the difference in the amount of ash yielded by the two crops is very great; but even when there is no such difference in the gross amount of ash which the crops yield, and when we compare one cereal crop with another, we find that the relative percentage of a substance in the ash does not indicate the relative amount of that substance which the crop draws from an acre of land. But, before making such comparison, it seems necessary for the sake of clearness, and by way of illustration of what has just been said, and of what we propose to add,—to note down in the usual form the composition of the ash of three of our most common crops as follows:—

COMPOSITION OF ONE HUNDRED PARTS OF ASH.

|  | Wheat. | Oats. | Turnips. |
|---|---|---|---|
| Phosphoric Acid, | 45·00 | 25·14 | 9·85 |
| Potash, | 31·37 | 15·13 | 40·10 |
| Lime, | 3·61 | 3·59 | 9·93 |
| Magnesia, | 12·36 | 6·32 | 2·61 |
| Sulphuric Acid, | 0·34 | 1·75 | 12·12 |
| Soda, | 2·72 | 1·33 | 4·96 |
| Chloride of Sodium, | ... | 0·44 | 7·13 |
| Oxide of Iron, | 0·81 | 0·84 | 0·46 |
| Silica, | 3·66 | 45·03 | 1·81 |
| Carbonic Acid, | ... | ... | 10·96 |
|  | 99·87 | 99·37 | 99·93 |
| Loss (Carb. Acid, and Sulphur?), | ·13 | ·43 | ·07 |
|  | 100·00 | 100·00 | 100·00 |

It may be added parenthetically, that these figures represent very fairly the *average* composition of the ash of wheat and oats as grown in this country. It is more difficult to give an average of the ash of turnip bulbs, as the proportions of the constituents vary within certain limits according to the crop, its state of maturity, soil, manure, &c. The potash is sometimes less and sometimes greater than that above given; but when that is so, there is generally a corresponding increase or decrease of the soda or chloride of sodium. There is more uniformity when analyses are made both of the bulb and top of the individual plant, the composition of the one appearing to be, in some measure, the complement of the other.

But to return: the comparison above instituted between wheat and turnips with respect to phosphoric acid, might be carried out in the same way with respect to amount of potash which these crops respectively require. Suffice it to say that, though the percentages of potash are respectively 31 and 40 of the ash, yet an average crop of, say 20 tons of turnip bulbs requires from the soil 150 lbs. of potash, while 4 quarters of wheat, grain and straw, require only 35 lbs. In fact turnips require more potash than any crop that we cultivate—exceeding even potatoes in that respect, and exceeding beans and pease nearly as much as they exceed wheat. And yet we find the French agricultural chemist, M. Ville, led away apparently in the same manner as the American writer referred to, classing potatoes, pease, and beans as " potash plants " while he does not include turnips in the same category (*Artifical Manures*, pp. 225 and 402). The case of potash—or of any other mineral—is not like that of nitrogen, supplies of which, in combined form, may be carried to the plant in rain or dew; the needful potash must exist in the soil or in the manure; and happily, it generally exists in considerable abundance in the former. We have been here considering two plants of different orders—as widely different as can well be in their characters and habits of growth. But if we now look at the above statements of the analyses of two cereal plants, wheat and oats, we shall find that the same considerations and similar allowances are necessary before we take the analysis of 100 parts of ash as indicating in any definite degree either the amount or the relative proportions of mineral substances which the respective crops draw from a given extent of land. The weight of a good average crop—say 6 quarters of oats—is 1920 lbs. as compared with 2016 lbs. of wheat. The difference, therefore, is not very great. Neither have we any extra quantity of water to be allowed for on either side. But if, on glancing at the above columns of figures, a person were to conclude that a crop of wheat requires from an acre of land twice as much potash, and nearly twice as much phosphoric acid as a crop of oats, he would make a very great mistake. He has only, however, to give due consideration to the amount of the last item (silica) in the respective columns, in order to see that such a conclusion would be erroneous. Of 100 parts of the ash of oats, more than two-fifths, or only something less than one-half, consists of silica, against only about $3\frac{1}{2}$ per cent. of the same in the ash of wheat; that is the ash of oats has an excess of silica to the amount 41 per cent., or more than two-fifths of the whole. But it may be said, if 41 parts in 100 of the ash of oats consist of this comparatively valueless matter, silica, the remaining valuable constituents, phosphoric acid, potash, and magnesia, must needs be less in oats than in wheat, which is not contaminated (so to speak) with such an excessive amount of that substance. But, neither is that so, because we find that this excess of silica in the ash of oats is only a sort of incidental make-weight which necessarily results from the silicious shell or husk which adheres to the oat grain in its ordinary state, and, consequently, in the state in which it is taken for analysis. If we reduce 2016 lbs. of wheat, and also 1920 lbs. of oats to ashes, we get on an average 34·3 lbs. of ash from the former, and 57·6 lbs. from the latter; that is, the oats give more ash by two-fifths than the wheat. But these two-fifths are just the silica resulting from the oat shells. If we deduct two-fifths from 57·6, we have 34·5, or as nearly as may be the same amount of ash as the wheat affords. In point of fact, we find that average crops of wheat and oats, afford very nearly the same amount and relative proportions of their more valuable constituents— phosphoric acid, potash magnesia, and sulphuric acid. Taken weight for weight the wheat generally yields a little more of the three first-named ingredients than oats. Nor do average crops of these two cereals differ materially in the amount of nitrogen which they require. It will be observed that in the crops per acre that we have assumed, namely 4 quarters of wheat and 6 quarters of oats, the difference in the weight of grain produced is only 96 lbs.

From what has been said, it seems abundantly manifest, first, that not only farmers but others are liable to be misled by these statements of the results of analyses of different crops given in percentages of the ash; and second, that it might therefore be of some service not only in dispelling the misapprehension referred to, but by affording both interesting and practically useful information to farmers and students of agriculture generally, if tabular statements were drawn up of the composition of our most common crops in average produce per acre,—that is, if it were clearly set forth how many pounds' weight of each of the more important constituents of plants these several crops draw from an acre of land. This is really the direct information which the farmer requires. An attempt to do this is made in the subjoined tables. We have included in them only those elementary constituents of plants which are commonly added, or may require to be added, to the soil as manures, or fertilisers, as they are sometimes called. For the sake of brevity, and on other considerations, *lime* is not included. Of the importance of lime, not only as a constituent of the ash of plants, but as having special functions in the soil, there can be no doubt. But in this country, at least, we do not usually apply a modicum of it *per se* in ordinary manuring. We endeavour to ensure a fair amount of it in the soil at all times by giving a considerable *dose* of it when necessary, amounting, in Scotland, to from two to three tons of dry caustic lime per acre. It has been long recognised as a rule over the greater part, if not the whole, of Scotland, that the first thing to be done on newly reclaimed land, is to give it a *liming*—greater or less in amount, according as the soil is heavy or light. The cost of lime is also much less than that of the other principal constituents of plants; abundant supplies of it can be obtained with comparative ease at about £1 per ton, whereas potash costs at least twelve times, and phosphoric acid twenty times as much.

But it is at least of as much importance that we should know and have distinctly before us the amount of combined Nitrogen which the produce of an acre of our ordinary crops requires, as that we should know the amount of mineral matter required by the same. We have therefore added a column containing the *average* amount, in pounds, of nitrogen which the several crops in their normal condition require.

It is needless to say that no precise or absolute accuracy in figures is possible in this matter. An approximation, more or less close, to fair averages is all that is aimed at. A large number of carefully executed analyses of some crops is now available for comparison. In the cases of some other crops, the *data* at our disposal are less ample or less satisfactory. In some cases, results which are manifestly exceptional have to be left out of consideration. Our plodding and persevering brethren in Germany have of late years done a good deal towards the building up of the structure of which their distinguished countryman, Liebig, may, in some respects, be said to have laid the foundation forty years ago. Our authorities in ash analysis are mainly Professor Emil Wolff of Wurtemberg, Way and Ogston, Lawes and Gilbert, Dr. Voelcker, and the late Dr. Anderson, together with a few others who have devoted special attention to particular plants or to particular points either in this department or in organic analysis. The authorities for nitrogen or "albuminoids" are partly the same, but with a

somewhat wider reference to others.    In the case of potatoes
the discrepancies between the older and later analysts are considerable, arising probably from want of sufficient precaution in
the process of ignition by which the ash is obtained for analysis.    In so far as sulphur or sulphuric acid is concerned, it is
doubtful whether the average results yet arrived at are quite
satisfactory.    In the cases of beans and pease the averages
given rest on narrower bases than those stated in the other
cases.    Moreover, the crops per acre of these leguminous plants
vary so widely according to the character of the season and
other circumstances that it is almost impossible to say what are
average crops even on soils suitable for their cultivation.    The
weights of produce per acre in all cases are meant to represent
good average crops; but not necessarily the average of the
actual produce of the country generally.    For several reasons,
which need not be stated, it has been deemed advisable to take
such crops as would be produced on fairly good soil in a good
state of cultivation.    From the weight of crops here given, the
composition of crops of somewhat greater or somewhat less
weight per acre, can easily be calculated by "simple proportion"; but it must not be assumed that the composition of a
good crop will, relatively to gross weight, represent quite accurately the composition of an inferior crop of the same plant.
The average produce of straw in the cereal crops can be estimated with some approximation to accuracy; but it is obviously
more difficult (even with some amount of data at command) to
fix on the average relative weight of tops and bulbs in the case
of turnips, while in the potato crop the weight of haulms
depends on the stage of maturity (not to speak of disease) at
which the crop may have arrived when dug up.    In this crop,
however, the weight and composition of the tops are only of
subordinate importance.    The relative proportions that we have
taken for grain and straw bulbs and tops, &c., are as follows:—
Wheat, grain to straw as 1 : 1·6; barley, do. as 1 : 1·4; oats, do.
as 1 : 1·3; turnip bulbs to tops as 1 : 0·27—that is, the tops are
taken at between one-third and one-fourth of the bulbs.    That
may be deemed a moderate average for tops, and implies that
the crop has arrived at a fair condition as to maturity.    Potato-
tops uncertain, but taken at one-sixth of the weight of the
tubers.    Beans and pease;—very little satisfactory evidence to be
had; but, following the estimates of Stephens (*Book of the Farm*)
and others, one ton of straw per acre is assumed in both cases.
We give, however, the constituents of grain, roots, &c., separately
from those of straw and tops: for many purposes the amount of
nitrogen and mineral matter drawn from the land by the former
only may be deemed of importance, inasmuch as the greater
part of the materials which go to the formation of the latter

(including, in the case of straw, a large amount of silica, with potash and lime), is, directly or indirectly, returned to the soil whence it was taken. That, however, is true with respect to nearly the whole of the turnip crop, and also with respect to the hay crop if wholly consumed on the farm on which it is produced. Along with the amount of the principal constituents of our common crops, it is interesting to consider and to compare the amount of the same substances found in, say ten, fifteen, or twenty tons of farm-yard manure. In order to facilitate such comparison, we have appended the amount, in pounds, of nitrogen and principal ash constituents in ten tons of average fairly well rotted dung. If the decimal points be removed one place to the left, the numbers will, of course, represent the composition of one ton; and from these the amount in the several substances in any number of tons can readily be obtained. Dr. Voelcker's admirable series of analyses forms our chief authority here; but as the manure with which he dealt was made up partly of the excrements of pigs, along with that of cattle and horses, it seems probable that it was rather richer in nitrogen and phosporic acid than the common average. In deference to other authorities, it has been deemed advisable slightly to modify the results obtained at Cirencester. The figures give as fair an average as can be obtained of dung that has been moderately well preserved for five or six autumn and winter months. It is needless to say that much will depend upon the nature of the food which the animals producing the dung consume. If any amount of cake and corn has been used, the farmyard manure will be richer in nitrogen and phosphoric acid than that here represented, to the extent of at least 2 or 3 lbs. per ton of the former, and 1 to 1½ or 2 lbs. per ton of the latter. The potash, &c., will not be materially increased. The average of lime (not stated in the table) is about 23 to 26 lbs. per ton. On the calcareous soil at Cirencester, Dr. Voelcker found the lime to be considerably above what seems to be the average. In well-rotten dung, nearly one-half of the phosphoric acid, one-half of the ammonia, of the magnesia, and of the sulphuric acid, and nearly the whole of the potash, are in a soluble condition.

It is worthy of notice how nearly the crops that we have assumed approach each other in the weight of the total air-dry produce per acre. In so far as the cereal, the pulse, and the hay crops are concerned, that can be seen in the following table—the produce both of grain and straw being assumed to be in what is called an air-dried condition. It may be worth while, and not without some interest, to bring all the crops to a level in respect of water, by giving the amount of the completely dry matter of the grain and straw, roots and tops, of each crop per acre; and,

COMPOSITION OF CROPS: PRINCIPAL CONSTITUENTS IN PRODUCE PER ACRE.

| Crops per Acre. | Weight of Crop. | Nitrogen. | Phosphoric Acid. | Potash. | Magnesia. | Sulphuric Acid. |
|---|---|---|---|---|---|---|
| | lbs. | lbs. | lbs. | lbs | lbs. | lbs. |
| Wheat, 4 quarters. | | | | | | |
| Grain, | 2016 | 44 0 | 15 8 | 11·3 | 4·4 | 1·0 |
| Straw, | 3225 | 16·8 | 6·7 | 23·5 | 3·2 | 3·4 |
| Whole Crop, | 5241 | 60·8 | 22·5 | 34·8 | 7·6 | 4·4 |
| Barley, 5 quarters. | | | | | | |
| Grain, | 2120 | 36·0 | 14·8 | 10·0 | 4 2 | 0 4 |
| Straw, | 2968 | 19·0 | 5·0 | 21·0 | 3·2 | 3 3 |
| Whole Crop, | 5088 | 55·0 | 19·8 | 31·0 | 7·4 | 3·7 |
| Oats, 6 quarters. | | | | | | |
| Grain, | 1920 | 38·0 | 15·0 | 9·0 | 3·6 | 1·1 |
| Straw, | 2496 | 14·0 | 6·0 | 25·0 | 4·5 | 4·7 |
| Whole Crop, | 4416 | 52·0 | 21·0 | 34·0 | 8 1 | 5·8 |
| Turnips, 20 tons. | | | | | | |
| Bulbs, | 44800 | 80·6 | 36·3 | 148·0 | 13·4 | 36·0 |
| Tops, | 12096 | 36·3 | 11·0 | 33·8 | 6·0 | 17·0 |
| Whole Crop, | 56896 | 116·9 | 47·3 | 181·8 | 19·4 | 53·0 |
| Potatoes, 8 tons. | | | | | | |
| Tubers, | 17920 | 61·0 | 32·2 | 107·5 | 8 2 | 12·5 |
| Tops, | 2986 | 16·4 | 4·1 | 13·1 | 8·3 | 3·0 |
| Whole Crop, | 20906 | 77·4 | 36·3 | 120·6 | 16 5 | 15·5 |
| Hay, mixed, 1½ ton. | | | | | | |
| Rye, ½ ton, Clover = 2 tons, | 4480 | 77·0 | 29·0 | 84·9 | 15·2 | 17·8 |
| Beans, 30 bushels. | 1982 | 80·8 | 14·8 | 19·5 | 2·0 | 2·1 |
| Straw, | 2240 | 36·5 | 9 2 | 26·5 | 8·3 | 6·2 |
| Whole Crop, | 4222 | 117 3 | 24·0 | 46·0 | 10·3 | 8·3 |
| Pease, 26 bushels. | 1664 | 59·6 | 13·5 | 15·6 | 2·5 | 2·2 |
| Straw, | 2240 | 23·2 | 6·7 | 25 4 | 10·0 | 8·4 |
| Whole Crop, | 3904 | 82·8 | 20·2 | 41·0 | 12·5 | 10·6 |
| Well-rotten Farmyard Manure, 10 tons. | 22400 | 121·0 | 70·0 | 119·0 | 33 6 | 31·4 |

in order further to facilitate comparison, the figures representing the total ash constituents of each crop may be brought together, as here subjoined. By "dry matter" is, of course, meant the whole mass of organic and inorganic substances which remains after deduction of the water that can be separated at 212° Fahr. With respect to the amount of water in the cereal and pulse crops, we have relied chiefly on the authority of Messrs. Way and Ogston, and with respect to turnips, partly on the same authority, together with that of Lawes and Gilbert. It seems probable that the results obtained by these gentlemen represent more closely the crops of this country than those of the continental analysts. These latter seem to give the water in grain and straw about 1 or 2 per cent. higher than we have taken it. The percentage of water in turnips varies—as is well-known—considerably, namely from 88 to 92, or even occasionally to 93. We have taken 91 per cent. as a fair average. We append a line giving the dry matter, &c., of ten tons of well-rotten farmyard manure.

DRY MATTER (AT 212°) IN WHOLE CROPS, TOPS, AND STRAW, WITH ASH, &c., PER ACRE.

| Crops per Acre. | Dry Matter. | Nitrogen. | Phosphoric Acid. | Potash. | Magnesia. | Sulphuric Acid. |
|---|---|---|---|---|---|---|
|  | lbs. | lbs. | lbs. | lbs. | lbs. | lbs |
| Wheat, 4 quarters, | 4612 | 60·8 | 22·5 | 34·8 | 7·6 | 4·4 |
| Barley, 5 „ | 4126 | 55·0 | 19·8 | 31·0 | 7·4 | 3·7 |
| Oats, 6 „ | 3886 | 52·0 | 21·0 | 34·0 | 8·1 | 5·8 |
| Turnips, 20 tons, | 5604 | 116·9 | 47·3 | 181·8 | 19·4 | 53·0 |
| Potatoes, 8 „ | 5376 | 77·4 | 36·3 | 120·6 | 16·5 | 15·5 |
| Hay, 2 „ | 3360 | 77·0 | 29·0 | 84·9 | 15·2 | 17·3 |
| Beans, 30 bushels, | 3654 | 117·3 | 24·0 | 46·0 | 10·3 | 8·3 |
| Peas, 26 „ | 3385 | 82·8 | 20·2 | 41·0 | 12·5 | 10·6 |
| Rotten Farmyard Manure, 10 tons, | 5600 | 121·0 | 70·0 | 119·0 | 33·6 | 31·4 |

Here we observe a general accordance in the cereal crops with respect both to the nitrogen and the valuable ash constituents. But in the root crops, while there is a considerable increase (about 1000 lbs.) of dry matter, there is a great increase of nitrogen, phosphoric acid, and magnesia, with an enormously increased amount of potash, and, in the case of turnips, a still more remarkable demand for sulphuric acid. We at once see the reason why we cannot obtain what we regard as a normal produce of these root crops without the direct and immediate application of manure. On glancing at the amount of fertilising matter afforded by ten tons of well-rotten dung, we find that the quantities of the several ingredients correspond in a certain degree with the requirements of the root crops, phosphoric acid and magnesia being, however, considerably in excess. Now, we find that in well-rotten dung nearly one-half of the nitrogen— something less than one-half of the phosphoric acid, the sul- phuric acid, and the magnesia, and nearly all the potash—are in a soluble condition—that is, ready for the immediate use on the crop to which the dung is applied. Twenty tons of dung per acre would then supply the immediate wants of the root crop, and leave, roughly speaking, something more than one-half of its fertilising matter for the subsequent crops of the rotation.

But, without noticing any of the numerous other points which these figures suggest, we conclude with a few remarks on the main question that arises, namely, Does the composition of a particular crop indicate the special manure which that crop requires? Not necessarily in so far as *nitrogen* is concerned. But then there are means by which a certain amount of that element of manure (in its combined form) can be carried to plants *ab extra*, so to speak, that is, beyond what may exist in the soil or in the manure supplied to it. Of these means it seems evident that some species of plants have much greater powers of availing themselves than others. Such power of gathering compounds of nitrogen seem to belong to plants having a large extent of leaf surface, such as turnips and clover, and having consequently large powers of transpiration—that is, of passing a great amount of water through their substance in a given time. A sunflower having thirty-nine square feet of leaf surface has been found to exhale twenty ounces of water in a day. Every one must have observed the immense power which the turnip plant has in this respect. The cereal plants have comparatively a limited extent of foliage. A turnip plant will probably, in a given time, pass ten times as much water through its tissues as several plants of wheat. The water, having performed its office of carrying food into the plant, is given off. Every gallon of water so passing through the tissues will carry some amount of combined nitrogen. That nitrogen may in part have existed in, and come from, the soil or manure; but may also have come partly from the atmosphere in the shape of ammonia or nitrites, either brought down by rain, or absorbed from the moist air in its con- tinual passage through the heated particles of the loose, porous soil around the plant. Its growth is greatly promoted by having the soil around it in that open and porous condition. Its large powers of exhalation must be kept in action; it is impatient of excessive or long-continued heat without moisture and free currents of air. Its active foliage has also the power of absorbing moisture when the air supplies it in excess, as it does in summer nights, in the shape of dew. That dew is richer in the compounds of nitrogen referred to than ordinary rain. The turnip is, moreover, the plant of a comparatively cold and moist climate. It cannot stand a southern sun; its rapid growth during a brief summer must ever render it the sheet-anchor of the northern farmer. Such are its powers of rapid development that, within a space of four months, a crop of turnips will gather up from an acre of land and (with the aid of carbon from the atmosphere) form into a mass of vegetable cells and tissue fit for animal nourishment, twice as much nitrogen, and—leaving the silica of straw out of consideration—more than twice as much valuable mineral matter as a crop of any of our cereal plants can collect and assimilate from the same extent of land. And this brings us back to our subject from the digression into which we have been slipping.

Potatoes, hay, and pease approach the turnip crop, and the uncertain and variable bean crop occasionally equals it in respect of nitrogen; but none of these, not even the potato crop, approaches it in the amount of mineral matter gathered up from an acre of land. Something of the same considerations which we have here indicated with the respect to the turnip crop could be shown to apply *quoad* the means of obtaining nitrogen, to the clover and pulse crops. But let what has been said suffice here to indicate the importance of a point which deserves more investigation than it has yet received. Certain it is that, though the turnip crop requires a great amount of nitrogen, it can in a large measure dispense with that element in the manure applied to the soil.

But, with respect to the purely mineral constituents of plants, it is manifest that the case is different. No such considerations can apply to any of them,—except, indeed, sulphur can be held to be, in some slight degree, an exception. They must necessarily exist in the soil; or, if they do not exist there in sufficient abundance, or in an available form, they must needs be supplied in the manure. And, consequently, the composition of the ash of a plant does afford an indication of the sort of manure that the plant requires, but with this important qualification, that the soil comes in as a factor to be considered in the case. If a plant or crop requires a large amount of potash, as turnips, and in a somewhat less degree, potatoes, require, then that potash must exist in the soil, or be supplied in the manure. Not to speak of the imperfect indications which analyses of soils supply, we know from experience that many soils do contain some of the elements of plants in such abundance that any additional supply seems to have no sensible effect. Potash is one of these elements : phosphoric acid is not, except in very rare cases indeed, such as on the "Greensand Formation," or near its borders. Potash may be deficient in soils formed almost entirely from, say quartzose rock or from chalk ; but it can never be so, to any great extent at least, where any of the numerous minerals classed under the general name of felspar exist, as they do very generally in this country. If a plant like the turnip, whose period of growth is brief, and range of roots limited, requires ten times as much sulphur and twice as much phosphorus from an acre of land as a crop of wheat, it must needs obtain such comparatively large supplies of these elements of manure in available form, within range of its roots, or, if not,—its large powers of transpiration continuing in operation —the water which passes through its cellular tissues will gradually become too poorly supplied with its essential elements of food, and, even under circumstances otherwise favourable, it will be more or less stunted in its growth, or at least, it will not yield that abnormal weight of produce which it is the object of the agriculturist to obtain. Under favourable conditions of climate and cultivation, it has great powers of speedily gathering up all its necessary mineral food that exists in a soluble condition near the surface of the soil; but such mineral food, especially phosphorus, potash, and sulphur, must exist there in considerable amount; it has neither the power nor time to go to any depth in search of them. An acre of land may yield to the limited amount of water passing slowly through the wheat plants growing upon it, 23 lbs. of phosphoric acid; but the plants of a turnip crop on an equal surface, after having exhausted that quantity, demand as much more, or 47 lbs. in all, of the same prime requisite in the formation of every vegetable substance which serves for animal nourishment,—but a requisite which, though thus in general demand, no other crop demands in equal quantity, and no soil affords except in very limited amount.

## THE BREEDING AND REARING OF HORSES FOR THE FARM, ROAD, OR FIELD.

By JOHN W. J. PATERSON, Terrona, Langholm.

[*Premium—Ten Sovereigns.*]

CLYDESDALE horses, the best type of which are perfect models of strength with shapes eminently calculated for endurance and activity, undoubtedly are, as generally admitted, the best breed for farm work ; how to breed and rear them, is therefore an im-

portant question, and one which our national society does well
to encourage. Having selected the breed best adapted for our purpose, it is imperative that the breeder should begin laying a sure
foundation, by securing the very best material possible. This
will be most speedily accomplished by obtaining a fresh young
mare, not less than three years old, bay or brown for choice,
with as little white as possible, as although white markings are
considered as denoting pure breeding, still a whole colour will
ever be the favourite with most purchasers; many will and do
object to white, while few, if any, will find fault with the want
of it. Perfection of shape must be aimed at. The head, well set
on to the neck, should be broad in the jaw with wide open
nostril. Eyes not too close set but rather wide, the pupil of
which should be large and prominent bespeaking courage,
docility, and intelligence. Ears nicely set on, should be proportionate to the size of the animal, moving or still, as the
motion of the eye directs, with a strong muscular neck coming
well out from the shoulders, which should not be too upright,
otherwise the long sweeping action, so great a disideratum in
any horse, will be in a manner lost. Well sprung deep ribs are
most essential; the back ribs especially must not be too short.
Broad massive quarters lying well up to them, giving additional
strength and taking away from the length of the back. Thighs
with well-developed muscle showing down to the hock, which
should be broad, wide, clean, and not too straight-up, otherwise,
the probability will be unsoundness in the shape of bog spavin,
thorough pin, &c.; neither too much bent, which detracts much
from the appearance if not from the value of a farm horse.
The forearms, like the thighs, should show great muscular
development down to the knee, which should be broad and flat,
the shank bone from knee to pastern being short, with the
tendons coming well out from the back, giving the broad flat
leg so much desired for wear and tear. Care, however, should
be taken, that the shank bone comes properly away from the
knee joint, otherwise, the weakly and unsightly back knees, or
what is termed calf shins, will be the consequence. Upright
short pastern joints should be rigidly guarded against, yet not too
long, which would introduce an element of weakness. Good
round healthy feet, with open heels, must be insisted upon.
The back part of the leg, from the knee downwards, should be
clothed with long fine silky hair. A mare with these attributes,
standing square upon her legs, must have true action, and if
about 16–1 or 16–2 in height, *if* mated with a sire inheriting
these characteristics, must produce an animal profitable and
creditable to the breeder. It is the utmost folly using an
inferior stallion merely because he calls weekly at the homestead. The very best sire should be sought out, and no reason-

able expense spared in doing so, keeping ever present the golden
rule in breeding, that "like produces like," and never forgetting
that a good animal is quite as easy and cheaply reared as a
bad one, the former giving a halsome return for care and
expenditure, the other bringing nothing but vexation, trouble,
and loss. Having thus found the mare and put her to a sire
worthy of her, she will be quite competent to undertake the
ordinary work of the farm for even months after being stinted.
It will then be prudent to keep her as much as possible out of
the shafts, still using her in the chains, up to within a month of
foaling (which we find on consulting a long record carefully
kept, of the time the different mares have carried their foals,
averages ten calendar months and twenty nine days, or as near
as possible, eleven calendar months); the mare should then be
eased in her work, but still daily sharing it up to the very day
of her giving birth, of which due notice will be given by the
adhesive matter that will form about the teats. She is thus
kept in a healthy thriving state, and under these conditions we
have through a very lengthy experience scarcely ever had a
mishap in any shape or form.

Now having obtained a foal promising to inherit all the good
properties of sire and dam, it is important that the breeder
should "act well his part" in rearing the youngster. It is
pleasing and instructive to watch its growth and development
under his fostering care, which, while yet deriving its sustenance
from the dam, will not be very onerous: in thus speaking we
do not allude to the rearing of animals, pampered from the day
of their birth for show purposes, a large percentage of which
are utterly ruined by this unnatural forcing.—how many of such
come to maturity sound in wind and limb, let the exhibitions at
any of our national shows disclose, not to speak of those
irretrievably ruined while undergoing the necessary preparation
for such a purpose. We advisedly say necessary, for no one
can successfully compete against young animals thus prematurely
developed, with those naturally and more profitably reared. Let
the young growing colt or filly, be well, be generously fed, kept
growing, not stinted in any way, until attaining the age of
three; the constitution will then stand any amount of judicious
feeding, fitting it to compete, and successfully against the mush-
room production of modern times; if the foal is to be reared,
brought to maturity, in a healthy growing state (the dam giving
birth if possible in good season, say beginning of May), the
mother should be kept comfortably in her loose box, for about
nine days, getting plenty of bran mashes, and boiled oats, with
good sweet hay, which will induce the flow of milk; after this
period the mare with her foal should be turned out daily for
an hour or two, when the weather is favourable into a well

sheltered pasture field, thus gradually preparing them to remain on the pastures through the night, whenever the weather will admit. Once out let them remain through the season, giving them the run of the best grazing, well-watered and sheltered, that the farm can afford. As a rule, little or no more trouble is requisite till weaning time. It will be in the recollection of many seeing the foal as a common occurrence following its dam in the cart, doing her regular work; happily this practice, which cannot be too highly condemned, has become nearly a thing of the past; still many yet work the mare a few hours, the foal being shut up in the house, which is only admissible on the most urgent occasions. It need scarcely be pointed out how detrimental to the foal such practices must prove. The mare is most certain to get heated, either through her exertions or excitement, for want of her offspring, most probably both; the foal when getting to its dam, drinks greedily of the heated milk, which invariably excites the bowels in a greater or less degree, and checks its onward progress; the foal should be weaned at the end of six months, the dam shut up in a loose box for a few days on dry food, when the milk will quickly disperse if she be occasionally milked, the foal being allowed to roam through the day with a companion, such also being desirable through the night, giving them a comfortable roomy loose box, supplying the racks with some well got hay, the mangers with a handful of oats, which they will soon begin to munch and learn to eat greedily. Without loss of time the youngster should now have the halter put upon him; it is an excellent practice to have a little collar put on, with just enough leather shank to catch securely with the hand; when a few days old, it can then be led about in the box, or by the side of its dam, whenever she has occasion to go out; this they never forget, and it saves immense trouble and risk when they come to be tied up. With well bred blood horses especially this practice should prevail, they being more determined and active when they come to be handled. When they can be safely left tied for the night, they should have the privilege of a stall to themselves, thus securing to each the due share of food provided. Exercise is most essential for the growing animal, therefore, no matter what the weather may be, let them go out every day—of course only for a short time should the weather be excessively stormy, but if at all moderate from an hour or two after sunrise till sunset; three pounds of good oats given morning and evening, to which may be added a good sized carrot cut into small pieces, until they acquire a taste for them, after which the carrots (or swede turnips where carrots are not to be had) may be given whole, when they will break and relish them immensely. This, with a service for supper of about the third of a pail of turnips, light oats, or chaff, boiled or steamed together, and well mixed with bran and good oat straw for fodder, will keep the youngsters in a growing state until the month of May, or till such time as a good bite of grass is obtainable, when they can be turned out to graze for the season, and will readily lay on flesh if fair pasturage be given. This treatment continued year by year adding a pound or two more of oats, &c., when taken in for the winter, as their size and strength increases, will bring animals to an age fit for use in a healthy sound condition, and they will be found doing useful work years after their pampered brethren have been consigned to the knacker, or if prolonged days be granted them, to some unfortunate and miserable occupation. As with Clydesdales so with horses for road or field, which for the last sixty years on this farm, have been most successfully and extensively reared as described; in fact running out with and faring exactly as their less aristocratic brethren,—in proof of which we can point to showyard honours bestowed upon them at the Highland, Royal, and other showyards throughout the country, whether for Clydesdales, the thorough-bred, or half-bred hunter.

The breeding of horses for road or field and as remounts for our cavalry was considered so important as to engross the attention of a Select Committee of the House of Lords in February 1873; but the only result arising therefrom was the abolition of taxes on horses by Sir Stafford Northcote. The Highland and other societies have been, however, doing good work in offering large prizes (£100) for thorough-bred stallions, suitable for getting hunters, which are the stepping-stones, the starting-point of all improvement in this direction; and however much we may regret that their efforts have hitherto been so slightly appreciated, it is the only practicable means of encouragement, which, let us hope, will some day bear fruit. Scotland, as a rule, is not adapted for a hunting country, consequently few packs of hounds are kept, and therefore no great demand for hunters. On the other hand, Clydesdale horses have been bringing extraordinary high prices, which induced nearly all breeders to go in for them, and this to such an extent that the country is now flooded with young colts and fillies of this breed, which, except the very best class, can scarcely be turned into money profitably, and while they have become plentiful, road and field horses have become more scarce year by year. Here, then, is a field from which farmers need fear no competition. Foreign horses we have in abundance, and always will have, but they are only useful for the most ordinary purposes, and never will command a high figure, while the home-breeds, if well bred, will always maintain their prestige as the best horses in the world, sought after where attainable at any cost. His Grace the Duke of Buccleuch, who gives in the county of

Roxburgh £50 yearly in prizes for hunting stock to tenant farmers within the limits of his hunt, at a public dinner in connection with the Show, stated that, "He not only wished them to breed hunters, but liked to see them in the hunting field riding their young horses." This is the true ring of a patriotic heart, a noble, generous nature whose motto is "live and let live." No one knows better than His Grace that a farmer, with pluck and determination to take and keep his position at the tail of the hounds with his promising youngster, is the man that will bring most energy to bear on the conduct and management of his farm; and we hold that a farmer is as much in his place in the hunting field—preparing, and educating a young horse, which will probably enable him to draw a cheque from his landlord or others to the amount, it may be, of his half year's rent —as he would be at home engaged in the most drudging occupation upon the farm. No one would deem it right or proper for any farmer dependant on his farm for means of support to appear day after day at the covert side, but only that he should embrace the opportunity when the hounds come near his homestead.

How, then, shall we breed this hunter? By a careful selection of the dam, which should not have less blood in her veins than half, or three parts. If bone and substance can be obtained, the more blood the better. We have ourselves bred thorough-bred horses (in the stud-book) as hunters which were very rarely beaten in the Highland, Royal, or other show-yards, and afterwards made their mark in the hunting field, but as a rule it is not prudent for farmers to meddle with them. We shall therefore confine our attention to the half-bred: all horses coming under this denomination which are not pure. What we want to achieve is a horse able to carry from 14 to 16 stones with hounds, which will always command a high figure. If unfitted by accident or otherwise for a hunter, he is always valuable for the plough or cart, to drag the family to church or market, or to sell for town work at a fair price. In breeding for road or field our aim ought ever to be the shape and make of a hunter. We recollect many years ago selling a young blood-horse at York fair to Mr Wimbush, one of the greatest of London job-masters, for his son to ride. On asking if he ever bought hunters, he replied, "Very many, but not to make hunters of; my best and most stylish harness horses are all bred and fitted for being made into hunters." And true it is, a hunter, by training and education, develops into the stylish, high-stepping phaeton or carriage horse, while the purely harness horse, i.e., with upright shoulders —not out of place in a harness horse—can never be made a hunter. Taking, then, the most perfect shape of a hunter for our ideal, the perfection of which is so briefly summed up by a master's hand, the ever to be lamented sporting novelist and thorough gentleman, Major Whyte Melville, in these lines—

I

"A head like a snake, and a skin like a mouse;
 An eye like a woman, bright, gentle, and brown;
 With loins and a back that would carry a house,
 And quarters to lift him smack over a town."

We must use our best endeavours to possess such an one for the matron of our stud. The great property of a hunter is to be light in hand, therefore her head must be small and her neck muscular, yet thin and light at the throat, and not too loaded on the crest; jaws and nostrils wide, an eye full and bright, with good long sloping shoulders; deep through the heart, and round in her ribs, her back ones especially being long, going well home into her flanks; her quarters should be long and broad yet blood-like, lying well into her back, which, with oblique shoulders, gives the short strong back and loins, with wide hips and great length below; strong muscular arms and thighs, broad knees and hocks, the tendons standing well out from the cannon or shank bone, giving the legs that clean, hardy appearance so well described by horsemen as "legs of iron;" short from the knees and hocks to the pastern joints, especially should legs come well out and strong from knee and hock, which should be bent well under her, but not too much so, otherwise curbs will be the consequence. The pastern should possess considerable obliqueness, yet not be too long, with good broad open feet, guarding against very wide flat-soled ones; thus showing blood and quality from head to heel. If bending her knee and going square all round, such a one will prove a mine of wealth if put to a really good thorough-bred horse with like qualifications, and her produce must be most valuable for either road or field. We ourselves can recount very successful results from mares thus formed; one mare producing eight foals without missing a single year. When sold the stock realised £1000, nearly all unbroke, at ages from two to four, and at a time when horses were not half so valuable as they now are. At Christmas 1879 we sold into Yorkshire a horse unbroke, rising four, at a long figure. He was broken by his new owner, exhibited at the Yorkshire Show in the class for four-year-old hunters qualified to carry 15 stones, where he beat all the crack prize horses in England, and had five hundred guineas offered for him.

The most successful breeders of hackneys have pursued the same principle, as indicated in the breeding of hunters, in seeking the service of the thoroughbred sire or dam to impart quality and action—the *sine qua non* in a park hack. The late Mr Milward, whose annual sale of hackneys became quite a red letter day at Tattersall's, commenced breeding them by selecting strong ponies with good shoulders, and putting them to a thoroughbred horse—his best and highest priced horses having a double cross of blood in them. In September 1880 we witnessed the dispersal by public auction of the largest (100) and best stud of hackneys in the kingdom—that of Mr Wilson of High Park, Kendal, whose success in the National and other great shows throughout the country proved that no one could equal him for this description of horses. He reversed the system adopted by Mr Milward only in this, in choosing to have the dam thoroughbred, or very nearly so, in place of the sire, crossing these mares by the very best Norfolk trotting stallions he could procure. The produce were certainly all that could be desired in a hackney; yet with this perfection of quality and action, with manners perfected by a thorough master of the art, the highest prices realised for made ones were 200 and 180 guineas. None of those unbroken reached three figures. Two young hunters (bred as we have described as our own practice), a three-year-old gelding and filly, both unbroken, brought at the sale 185 and 125 guineas respectively. These horses Mr Wilson purchased from a farmer in the neighbourhood (Mr Dixon, Dalton Old Hall), and were only delivered to him the evening previous to sale.

This conclusively proves what class of horses for "road or field" are most profitable to the breeder.

Perhaps the situation and character of the farm is more important to the successful breeding of horses than the nature of the soil. Very hilly land is most unsuitable, as it sprains the hocks and tendons in every way; still, moderately steep, undulating ground is of advantage, as the gallops up and down hill tend to develop the muscles, and make the horses active on their legs, which is of great advantage to all breeds, but more particularly to the young hunter. Fertile, rich, loamy soils, containing everything in its constituent parts most calculated to create bone and muscle in a growing animal, generally command too high rents to admit of horses being profitably reared thereon, as the violent exercise they so generally take (and which is so conducive to their health and well-being in every way) destroys as much grass as they eat. Wet cold-bottomed undrained clay lands may be deemed the worst; the damp uncomfortable lair producing colds, degenerating into inflammation in the chest, gummy legs, and all other ills propagated by impaired constitutions. Fortunately for the horse-loving inhabitants of these realms nearly all soils are, however, more or less suitable for the breeding and rearing of this noble animal, if only rich enough to maintain them in a growing condition. A well drained sheltered sheep farm, where they can pick up a diversity of food, with a good mixture of lea, or light friable soil, and boggy, i.e., clay, or a few inches of moss with clay underneath, especially where there is underlying limestone rock, may perhaps be deemed the best.

Mr Jardine of Arkleton, upon his estate of Thorlieshope, a fine sheep farm lying at the head of the Liddel Water, not far from Riccarton Station on the North British Railway, has been most successful in rearing Clydesdales, which have often distinguished themselves in local show-yards, and gained higher honours after passing out of his hands. It is well mixed grassy land, with patches of heath and moor, limestone rock abounding nearly throughout the farm; and although lying, as indicated, in a high altitude, Mr Jardine scarcely ever houses his young horses until rising three, or when they are taken up to begin a useful life, merely throwing them a little hay when the weather proves very severe, or when the snow lies deep on the ground. They will thus lose much of their summer's gain. This must be inevitable to a certain degree, but Mr Jardine observes, " they more than regain it in early spring," getting much sooner into condition than those wintered under cover. At all events it has the great advantage of economy, and makes rearing horses pay, which is more than can be said of most industries upon the farm at the present time. Holding that all soils are, or can be made, by drainage and liberal dressings of lime and bones, suitable for the breeding and rearing of horses, we may now consider the diseases arising from pasturing on the various soils.

Horses depastured on enclosed lands must of necessity have a limited area to travel over. Where the soil is of a hard gravelly nature, the perpetual jar on the unyielding turf is almost certain to cause ringbone, if not a deeper seated injury in the coffinbone, commonly termed navicular disease; but with the exception of this, and wet undrained clays, we are not prepared to acknowledge that any particular soil superinduces disease. The great panacea for all ills is liberal, generous feeding, as we have experienced that horses, when kept in a healthy state, rarely take and readily throw off disease, such as strangles, to which all are subject, although most frequently in such a mild form that it passes away without being noticed. We have found horses are, as a rule, the healthiest of all live stock upon the farm, very rarely having lost a horse, and then only when disease has been imported by a new purchase brought on to the farm, and that most frequently caught in transit, through the slovenly manner in which horse boxes are kept and cleaned by railway companies. Disease in many shapes and forms may and does spring up in breeding establishments, the recurring frequency of which the owner may attribute to something wrong in the soil, in the water, in anything or everything they eat or drink. To such we would say—look well to the matrons of your stud that there be no hereditary disease or malformation inherited from them; be most careful in the selection of your sires, sparing no expense to secure the service of the most sound and perfect animal in make and shape that can be obtained. Give your personal supervision to their produce in the care and treatment they demand at your hands, and you will be amply repaid for all your trouble and expense, in the handsome sums drawn into the pocket from the sale of trusty, sound animals; or, if ambitious of honours in the show-yard, you will have the material ready at hand; besides the pleasure and honour, it may be, of having bred, reared, and sold to your landlord his favourite hunter, which ever carries him so well to the front; the petted park hack, or hunter, his lady loves so well; the pair of horses they drive together; or the sprightly, sturdy Clydesdales which, when at work in the field, attract the attention and admiration of every passer by, and the pride and delight of the cheery ploughman who so carefully tends them.

## THE MOST ECONOMICAL METHOD OF THRESHING GRAIN COMBINED WITH EFFICIENCY.

By WILLIAM SLOAN HAMILTON, Springside, Kilmarnock.

*[Premium—The Minor Gold Medal.]*

BEFORE entering upon the subject proper it might be profitable to consider shortly the different modes by which the object of separating the grain from the straw has been accomplished. From very early times, the Israelites appear to have had a machine of simple structure, consisting of a square of wood with wheels or rollers within it. This was drawn by oxen, and during their march over the produce, neatly placed in rows, the grain was pressed out by the wheels. It looks as if the Jews of later date had not been altogether satisfied with the rude instrument of their fathers, for we find them generally preferring to "tread out the corn" by means of oxen alone. The "flail" is still fresh in the memory of some, who were accustomed to this method in their youthful days. That the duty was performed in no half-hearted spirit may be taken for granted from the vivid, and characteristic manner in which some of its devotees portray their recollections of threshing days (or rather mornings) when no other means existed for providing the day's supplies for the cattle, &c., but this obsolete weapon. Certainly the feats performed in a morning before breakfast appear a little incredible to the uninitiated, but in any circumstances, it must have been a laborious undertaking. The advent of the old threshing mill must have been hailed with delight, and a completely new state of things would begin, when threshing and winnowing were incorporated into one operation.

A decided change has, however, taken place during the last twenty years, through the introduction of the portable engine and mill, which in course has been superseded by the traction engine and improved mill. The use of the latter has become so general and is so advantageous that in many cases good horse-power, and even fixed steam threshing machines have been altogether discarded and the entire crop on the respective farms threshed by the travelling mills, the only exceptions being in cases where water is the motive power, which nominally costs nothing, and has the extra advantage of being instantly available. With these circumstances in view it may very naturally be inferred that the abolition of fixed mills is a mere question of time; many other reasons might be adduced to strengthen this conviction.

Machinery of all kinds is a very expensive commodity, and its deterioration is quite as rapid from disuse, as from careful employment, and, consequently, with proper attention paid to it; again, there are so many improvements introduced from time to time, that the best constructed fixed mills become very soon antiquated, or ruinous expenditure is entailed in keeping them abreast of the times. It is a noticeable feature in some comparatively new horse-power mills, that although the draught is apparently light, still the horses by being put a little past their usual pace, it may be, in attaining the required speed, appear jaded after a long day's work, the effects of which is plainly visible for a number of days, and the opportunity may be taken of expressing the opinion that this exercise is better suited for horses trained in a circus, than for their less agile compeers accustomed to perform their duties in a straight line. Further, a great deal of space is occupied in this manner which might be made available for storage or other purposes by their removal. It may be here argued, that being entirely dependent on the travelling mills might occasionally cause inconvenience, but that can be guarded against by judicious arrangements. So long as grain is grown to the same extent in Ayrshire as it has been, the probability of them gaining ground is the more apparent,— they, as it were, condense more work in one day,—consequently allow more attention to be given in the direction of improving the farm. A far higher standard of efficiency is likely to be attained by men devoting their whole time and attention to the theoretical and practical working of machinery than could be hoped for from the spasmodic and haphazard efforts of the ordinary farm-servant, however intelligent.

The most casual observer will notice that these men, in regular charge, are stimulated by a desire to have their respective implements always in a presentable form for public inspection, and the carrying out of this principle ensures that the premonitory symptoms of dissolution will be discovered and failings rectified before the whole culminates in a breakdown. The proprietors of these travelling mills may safely calculate that, as long as they are enabled to maintain the high-class of machinery that is engaged in this work in Ayrshire at present, combined with the services of two efficient employees for the sum of £2 per diem, their efforts will meet with appreciation. On their behalf it might here be represented that as their working expenses must be very heavy, viz., tolls, wages, oil, waste, belting, packing, rivets, and occasionally a considerable outlay may be necessitated to meet the requirements of the law, &c., that the transaction ought essentially to be a cash one. However, a change from one custom to another may require a few minor alterations, before its benefits can be fully taken advantage of; for instance, how often do we see valuable time lost in unsuccessful attempts to drive ponderous engines into soft fields, or other totally unsuitable situations, with the ostensible purpose of gaining proximity to stacks erected there. Such a high pressure of steam is sometimes required to extricate them, that that point is passed where safety ends, and consequently danger begins, before attention is directed to the matter. Expensive machinery is thereby subjected to an enormous strain, and future discoveries will clearly demonstrate the folly of these proceedings. Again, if the mill be set to work on some advantageous spot, and " carting in " have to be resorted to, this is still unsatisfactory, as many horses become restive and impatient, the liability of risk from accident is increased greatly.

Extra workmen are required (which means increased cost), a further handling of the sheaves is necessitated, and a proportionate loss in grain thereby sustained. To avoid this, and get a proper starting-point for operations, it is imperative that the stackyard be properly macadamised with stones, ashes, gravel, or other hard substance, and so made impervious to the pressure caused by the evolutions of the traction engine; the benefits accruing from this arrangement at various seasons are so numerous as to amply repay the outlay.

Great care must be taken to obtain a passage for surface water, so that it may be prevented from saturating the stack bottoms; then assuming that these conditions have been satisfied, and that the entire wheat crop on the farm is to be stacked with a view to economical threshing, erect six pegs in a straight line, sixteen feet apart, and parallel to them other six pegs at the same distance apart so as to leave twenty-seven feet of clear space in the centre; these pegs must be put to the square, for the least angle will place the forker at a decided disadvantage, describe a circle thirteen feet diameter round each peg, and fill in with sufficient straw only. Raise each stack to the height of fourteen feet at the eaves with a little swell and a corresponding top; when the two rows are completed in this manner they will represent three days' work for a mill. If space be limited four stacks can be erected thereon, and the same end attained. When the mill has been introduced between the stacks, and spread out, it will be found that one man will be in a position to fork two of them on each side taken in succession, and, in average seasons, these ought to yield from twenty-five to twenty-eight bolls each, according to the description of wheat they contain, or, in all from 100 to 112 bolls for the day's work. As strict economy is to be observed, the arrival of the mill ought to be anticipated by the preparation of the required number of oat straw straps for tying the straw; these must be each five feet long, and thirty-six bundles of them, with fifty in each, will meet the requirements of one day. One hundred and twelve sacks (all whole) will also be necessary to hold the grain.

Under these conditions the fewest number of attendants that can be proceeded with is thirteen (exclusive of engineers), viz., seven men, four women, and two boys; as a given quantity of work requires to be accomplished in an allotted period, it is essential that they be all competent and experienced hands. If the straw be put up outside, this duty is the most important one in connection with the operations, consequently it demands the attention of the most experienced workmen. Much straw is rendered almost valueless owing to careless and inexperienced builders, who appear to think they discharge this duty satisfactorily by putting as few sheaves in the heart as is consistent with their not being buried altogether, the result being that every drop of rain that falls upon its surface percolates to the inside as it could not possibly do otherwise. Before the straw can be neatly bunched, care must be taken by the feeder, as the mill will eject it very much in the same state as it has been inserted, and it is impossible to make a square bunch from material fed upon an angle. One man will fork the sheaves on to the feeding platform, two women will loose them, three men with the assistance of a boy to hold the straps (already made) will bunch, tie, and dress the sheaves handsomely, one woman will convey them to the forker, who in turn will pass them to the builder, one woman to remove the chaff to its destination, one man with the aid of a sack barrow will bag, weigh, tie, and deposit the wheat in any suitable house forty yards distant from the mill, and one boy to attend the engine with water.

It will be ascertained, under these circumstances, that, with a little experience, the work can be executed with exceeding neatness, and no one will be harassed. The straw may be erected upon the space where it stood formerly, whenever one stalk has been cleared away, and should be built in short sections; it will thus not only be more easily taken down, but will have the advantage should the work be overtaken by rain, of presenting less of an unfinished surface than would be the case in a long section similarly exposed. As drenching showers will occur suddenly in the winter season, a waterproof cover ought to be in reserve to meet this emergency; when it has been thrown over the grain stack the work can be suspended or abandoned with safety.

Bad effects accrue from threshing wheat during rain or even a drizzle. Unless the weather is very promising, the thatch ought to be removed from only one stack at a time, being likewise carefully bunched to prevent confusion and facilitate its future replacement. Before proceeding to state the cost of the day's work, it may be explained that nothing is allowed for time occupied in making the straps, as opportunities will occur when the men and horses cannot be judiciously employed outside, and in any case it need not be a prolonged affair, because one man and stout boy, setting to the work with a little animation, will throw off thirty-five bundles with fifty in each in ten hours, but if, on the contrary, it be gone about as a pastime merely, no approximate indication can be given of the result.

| | £ | s | d |
|---|---|---|---|
| Hire of mill, . . . . | £2 | 0 | 0 |
| Seven men at 3s. each, . . | 1 | 1 | 0 |
| Four women at 2s. „ . . | 0 | 8 | 0 |
| Two boys at 1s. „ . . | 0 | 2 | 0 |
| Coals, 4s., . . . . | 0 | 4 | 0 |
| Total, | £3 | 15 | 0 per diem. |

Now, as most farms can command three men and one boy, the actual extra cost need not far exceed £3, 3s. per day, which, for the work accomplished, and considering the manner in which it has been executed, will compare favourably with any other method. It ought to be part of the person's duty in charge of the water to drench the ashes as soon as they are drawn from the furnace, otherwise the master may find a quantity of burning cinders deposited in alarming proximity to a stack, though he is still assured by the engineer that no danger can possibly accrue from that source.

Upon farms where a large quantity of chaff is required for dairy purposes, and, in a season like the present one (1879), when an unusually small percentage of chaff is removed from the straw in the process of threshing, the presence of the engine can be further utilised by placing a straw cutter on a portable frame three feet high, immediately behind the engine, and attaching a pulley twenty inches diameter on the reverse end of crank shaft from fly-wheel, the extra power required from the engine to drive the cutter not being perceptible, with the addition of three extra hands the work can be carried on simultaneously, and the "shorts," which are always more or less mixed with chaff, can be passed through the cutter as they are ejected from the mill with satisfactory results. If the chaff bing requires further augmentation this can be achieved by putting a quantity of hay through the cutter, and the mixture will be a most nutritious one; where this suggestion is carried into effect it is imperative that the cutter be a large-sized and first-class one, as steam is a searching power, and will very soon detect any weakness in it. For oat threshing a different arrangement of the stacks is necessary. In most situations it will be found a very difficult matter to attain that point of dryness at which oats will keep satisfactory in stacks of the dimensions given for wheat, and as a precautionary measure, ten feet is recommended as the width of base, and twelve feet as the height to the eaves; other conditions the same as for wheat. Only six stacks of this size can be overtaken in a day, the mill being in the centre, one extra forker is required to place the sheaves of outside stacks on the centre one, where the principal forker stands, as he could not be expected to do more. It is not to be inferred that the amount of work here indicated is the maximum that can be performed, on the contrary, it can be increased from twenty to thirty per cent. if desired, but experience proves the wisdom of the motto, "a fair day's work for a fair day's pay," and the average stated will be ultimately found to yield the most satisfactory results.

As oat straw is almost exclusively used for fodder on the farm, the custom is to put it up loose in ricks like hay. From the tangled way in which it is ejected from the mill, it is not possible to bunch it neatly like wheat straw, consequently one of the men can be dispensed with to assist the forker, thus making the outlay correspond with wheat threshing. It is the duty of every one employing these mills to detain them as short as is consistent with the work required to be performed, allowing for the state of the weather, by being in a position to set them agoing immediately after their arrival. Many a favourable day is allowed to pass unimproved from one or all of the following reasons:—the necessary fuel has not been provided, sacks to hold the grain have not been procured, a sufficient number of hands cannot be rallied, or some such kindred obstacles, all of which clearly betrays a want of forethought on the farmer's part, and the squel to it in all probability is that the following day will be unsuitable for the purpose (as regards weather).

The irregularities consequent upon such delays tend to unpunctuality, are a direct loss to all concerned, and therefore ought surely to be avoided. When the work to be executed is approaching completion, every facility ought to be afforded to the engineers to collect, hap, and otherwise prepare for removal;

it often occurs that the most onerous part of their duties just commences after their day's threshing is over, and a little assistance in this direction will certainly put them in a good mood to undertake the difficulties. As a matter of course after two or even one day's threshing, a considerable amount of confusion and displacement exists in the stackyard, and the following morning is the best opportunity to set things in order. The wheat straw stack must be supplied with a good rigging, the thatch (carefully removed on the previous day) will come in very opportune for this purpose, and must be securely tied down. If properly built, and this precaution taken, the straw will stand for months without receiving injury; a crown will suffice for the oat ricks, and the one from which the daily requirements are being withdrawn can be protected with the waterproof stack cover already referred to. All wet or loose straw ought to be removed to the dungstead, and any weak or damaged grain ought to be swept up, otherwise it will germinate and render the site sloppy and unsuitable for future operations.

Anent the disposal of the grain; if it be intended for sale, in nine cases out of ten, it will be found that the best method is to accept market price and get rid of it. Grain does not improve sitting in sacks, and few steadings possess storage accommodation, with sufficient ventilation for keeping large quantities of produce.

On farms of average size, where the entire crop will occupy say six days of a mill to thresh, it is most advantageous to take two days at a time (one at wheat and one at oats), in this way no long shift is incurred the first day, consequently steadier performance is ensured, and future needs will be provided for a considerable time, whilst tolls (and the attending tear and wear) are saved to the proprietor. It has been ascertained, although it seems incredible, that wheat straw tied up from these mills (with twisted straps) into bunches, can be packed into a railway truck so that a greater quantity or weight is held than could possibly be the case were the straw put up in bales, and further possesses such superior qualities for thatching purposes as to be entirely beyond comparision with straw threshed by ordinary mills. It is a wise policy to retain as much straw as will thatch the succeeding crop; it is sooner available for that purpose, and prevents a serious inroad being made upon the new crop at a time when the grain is apt to be unmarketable in its natural condition.

This paper is not intended by the writer as a means of trumpeting forth any superior knowledge; on the contrary, it is meant to stimulate to a more general adoption of the travelling mill, by pointing out the most economical way in which it is available, at a time when the most rigid economy requires to be exercised in all agricultural affairs.

## THE TREATMENT OF BORDER LEICESTER EWES AND LAMBS.

By A. Septimus Alexander, 4 Belhaven Terrace, Glasgow.

*[Premium—The Medium Gold Medal.]*

The Border Leicester breed of sheep has been found suitable for those districts where the pasture is fertile, and where the sheep can be tended with much care and without much exposure. Being a breed which has a weak constitution, and a much greater tendency to inflammatory diseases than many other kinds, it cannot bear hard living, travelling far, or exposure to cold and damp. The good quality of the breed is, however, the facility with which it will cross with other varieties, and to this we owe some of our most useful crosses. One of these, the half-bred sheep, is derived from the union of a Leicester tup with a Cheviot ewe. This cross is much more hardy than the Leicester, has a better skin, smaller and sweeter mutton, and is adaptable to higher ground, and requires less attention in sheltering. When a half-bred ewe produces a lamb to a Leicester tup, the progeny is termed "three-quarters" or "three-parts" bred, and of this variety there are many flocks upon the Borders. The lambs of this cross are easily fattened, but are largely used as store sheep, the wether hoggs being sold for winter folding upon turnips.

Having described the three breeds of sheep with which we intend to deal in this report, we shall now proceed to explain their management as it is carried out upon some of the most noted farms in Northumberland.

In order that we may treat in the most thorough manner our subject, it will be advisable to commence with the management of the ewes immediately after the season's lambs have been weaned; and if we follow their treatment up to the corresponding period of the succeeding year, we shall have a fair idea of the course generally pursued. After the lambs have been separated from their mothers at weaning time, the latter are placed upon good fair pasture, where they will live well without obtaining much good grass, and after a week or so those which are to be removed from the breeding flock are drafted. This is usually accomplished when the ewes have ceased to bleat for their lambs, or about a week after weaning. At this period all those ewes which have had three "crops" of lambs are taken out of the breeding flock to allow the gimmers to come in and fill up their places. According to the system of ear-marking (which will be explained further on), these old ewes are at once detected by having a "forebit" in the far ear.

Not only must the old ewes be removed, but any sheep among the young ones which has suffered from disease, as garget or

udder clap, which has ruptured or "broken down," or has a bad
mouth, should be drafted and sent to a field where it will fatten
for the butcher. In addition to these causes for drafting, any of
the following defects render a ewe unfit for the purpose of
breeding:—Faults of fleece, form or character, bareness of the
hair on the crown of the head, or what is generally called
"blueness" of the head, deficiency in eyesight, and casting lamb,
which latter may be expected to occur again.

It is not probable that every ewe flock will present so many
causes for drafting; nor is it possible, seeing that a certain
number of breeding ewes must be retained, for the farmer to
remove every sheep which does not attain to his standard of
perfection. This being the case, the number of gimmers suitable
for breeding purposes should be ascertained, and the old ewes
drafted accordingly. To give an example of this:—In a breeding
stock of sixteen score of half-bred ewes there should be left,
after drafting, ten score of young first and second crop ewes,
which, with six score of gimmers drawn in April, will maintain
the sixteen score which it is usual for the farm to keep up.
This flock is now placed upon ordinary pasture until drawn to
the tup in October.

To return to the treatment of those ewes which have been
drafted after weaning. Any of the old or "three-crop" ewes
which have bad mouths, &c., are placed upon good pasture,
where they should receive additional feeding to bring them on
quickly for the butcher. Those three-crop ewes which, on the
other hand, have good mouths and udders are placed upon good
pasture until September, when it is customary in Northumberland to send them to draft markets in Yorkshire, or to draft ewe
sales held at Kelso, Coldstream, and other places, where they
realise from 50s. to 60s., according to condition or name. At
the Yorkshire markets they are purchased by holders of luxuriant
grass pasture, who take another crop of lambs, and then feed
mothers and young for the fat market. Under this treatment
the ewes will increase in size by almost a quarter of their
previous bulk, even the wool becoming much longer than it was
while on the poorer pasture of their native county.

The farmer having now decided upon those ewes and gimmers
which he intends to breed from, must endeavour to provide
them with good and sufficient food for the purpose of securing a
good crop of lambs. Two or three weeks before the 10th of
October, which is a common time for sending the tup among
Leicester ewes, they should be placed on good pasture, which
many farmers consider to be all that is necessary. To produce
a large crop of lambs, with plenty of "double couples," as they
are called, each ewe should receive daily of bran and oats half
a pound, or one load of turnips daily to every sixty ewes may

be given with advantage. Some give cotton-cake to bring the ewes in season.

It is usual for one Leicester tup to serve fifty ewes, or even sixty if he be a shearling, but if aged, forty will be sufficient. A half-bred tup serves seventy ewes, and he is usually sent among them at the 24th of October, or thereabout.

The period of gestation of the ewe being 151 days, the Leicester ewes should lamb about the 10th of March following, and the half-bred ewes about the 24th of March. No difference is made between three-parts bred ewes and half-bred ewes as regards the time of tupping. Although the period of gestation of the ewe is generally said to be at least 151 days, we have found by experience that many lambs are dropped in 147 days, and many ewes, more especially gimmers, pass their time before lambing.

The choice of suitable rams is a very important matter to the sheep farmer, as upon his selection depends the improvement of his flock. Since ram sales have become common, however, he has every opportunity for selection, and by constantly changing he is enabled to counteract the bad effects of "in and in" breeding. On going to a ram sale the farmer should bear in mind the defects of his flock, and by purchasing those tups which are of a good strain, and strong in those points in which his sheep are weak, he will at length arrive at a greater degree of perfection.

To buy a sheep just because it is cheap, without any regard to its conformation and adaptability to the improvement of the flock it is to serve, is a great mistake, and should always be guarded against. If the fleeces are usually too light, by crossing with rams which possess a heavier fleece, a vast improvement may be effected. In a word, all defects may be materially lessened by judicious selection of tups.

In all cases, however, it is well to beware of buying those sheep which are strangers to the purchaser—that is, such as have not gained a name for themselves, and which are not known to be free of any predisposition to troublesome hereditary diseases. There are some farmers who, seeing the benefit to be derived from the introduction of pure blood, do not hesitate to purchase a ram from the noted flocks of Mertoun, Millendean, or Mersington, even although the price rise to £50, knowing well that if the shape of the tup is suitable his offspring will repay the outlay when they in time come to the hammer.

If no care is bestowed either in selecting or culling the flock unquestionably both disease and defect will ensue; and if a connection be permitted between two animals, each predisposed to the same bad quality, the predisposition to such defect will exist in their offspring in a two-fold degree. If, on the other hand, proper care is observed—if those animals only are allowed to breed that possess good forms and healthy constitutions—then undoubtedly the stock will be preserved pure, disease will be warded off, and proper form and qualifications will be established.

Many farmers in selecting a tup confine themselves to one as distant as possible from their own sheep. Neglecting the due consideration of many important points, they imagine that by avoiding the practice of "in and in" breeding, they guard against almost all the diseases which sheep are heir to. In this they err, for it is the abuse and not the use that is to be reprobated, and in many cases it is the surest method of arriving at the greatest degree of perfection. Hence it is a practice which most of the eminent improvers of sheep, as Mr. Bakewell and the Messrs. Culley, have pursued with the greatest success.

Should a farmer find that a tup just suits his requirements and yet is a relation of his own sheep, he should not hesitate to employ it if previously his flock have not suffered from the effects of breeding from animals closely connected. Let us suppose that a farmer has 18 score of Leicester ewes and 16 score of half-bred or three-parts bred ewes. For the "bred" ewes he will require 7 tups, and for the half-bred 5.

The shepherd's aim should now be to match his sheep as well as possible, that is, he should draw his ewes into lots to suit the style and shape of the tups. For instance, if one ram has a good neck and rough fleece, all those ewes which have inferior necks and fleeces should be placed in his lot, so that their offspring will be better than the ewe, if not so good as the tup. This should be carried out with all the ewes, care being taken to match properly the faces as well as the fleece and frame.

The ears and necks are, in Leicester sheep, often deficient, the former being badly placed, and the necks having a tendency to be "scraggy;" where this is the case the ewes should be placed with that ram which excels in those special features. It is, however, unnecessary to say more upon this subject, for almost the whole art of sheep-breeding lies in the selection of a breeding stock, and farmers, and those shepherds who are worthy of the name, are, as a rule, good judges of the sheep most suitable to match.

This careful matching is followed out with half-bred, three-parts bred, and Leicester ewes alike, the only difference being in the number placed with each ram. When all the lots have been drawn each is taken to a different pasture, where the ewes are turned loose with the selected tup, his breast having been previously "keiled" red by the shepherd. This is done to enable the herd to know which ewes will first lamb, and for this purpose he marks every ewe which has taken the ram during the first week with a red spot on the shoulder. During the second

week he places the mark on the rib, but at the third week no
mark is imprinted, then at the fourth week, and afterwards, the
breast of the tup is keiled, or rather blackened, with a mixture
of soot and oil, so that those ewes which will be late lambers
are readily recognised.   As some of the ewes served in the first
or second week will again come in season and be served by the
blackened tup, the attendant will have little difficulty in knowing them seeing that they bear the black mark as well as those
ewes served during the fourth week.   The black stain imprinted
at this period remains on the fleece until lambing time; this
being the case no error can occur.   For sure work the tup should
be fresh keiled once or twice a day, and if this be done the
shepherd will be able to keep the statistics of his flock with
perfect accuracy.

That the offspring of the different sires employed may be
compared after lambing, it is advisable to mark the separate
lots of ewes either with different paint, or upon other parts of
the body from those with the other tups.   Again, we can follow
up our knowledge of the parents when selecting lambs for tups
or ewe-hoggs for the breeding stock.   If, unknown to us, one of
the rams has had a predisposition to inherent disease, it will
show itself in his offspring, and thus we are warned, not only to
get rid of him, but against using his lambs for breeding purposes.
Should the offspring of another ram, on the other hand, turn out
as desired, we not only prize him, but are careful to retain his
good qualities in the flock by using his lambs as ewes, and by
raising his progeny for selling-tups we not only benefit ourselves
but our neighbours also.

After four weeks or thereabout have elapsed, the tups should
be removed from the ewes and placed upon good pasture, as they
will have lost condition during the tupping season.   At this
time the gimmers and thin ewes are put on behind the feeding
hoggs to eat off the turnip "shells" which they leave behind.
At night they are turned on to a lea-field intended for oats,
where, by their droppings, they help to manure it.   This method
of treatment is continued until January, at which time the
hoggs are fed with cut turnips.   Shells are those parts of the
turnips left below ground when the sheep have eaten the upper
half.   The shells are picked out of the ground by the shepherd
with an implement made for the purpose.

While the gimmers and thin ewes are on "shells," the
remainder of the ewes receive turnip-shaws upon lea until
December, and after that date turnips.   In January the worst of
the gimmers and thin ewes are placed with the ewe hoggs on the
"break," that is, they are netted on turnips.   The other gimmers
are kept separate and fed with turnips on lea, in fact preference should be given to gimmers, as regards feeding, all through.

The ewes and gimmers, after January, should be provided with turnips or swedes sufficient to serve them until four o'clock every afternoon; should snow come on while the sheep are getting turnips, hay should be provided for all, as it enables them to digest their more succulent food, which, without this addition, would be liable to produce illness. Fourteen pounds of old-land hay per diem to every score of sheep in winter, but as spring advances they will gradually eat less.

At this period of the year the shepherd must be careful not to give his charge any salt, either to lick, or used with hay which has been salted, as it is a well-established fact that salt is apt to produce abortion. If turnips are given in unlimited quantities to ewes in lamb, they are likewise liable to produce abortion, particularly if the season is mild, and vegetation rank and forward. To counteract the effects of the superfluous moisture in the turnips hay is given. A week or ten days before the first of the ewes are expected to lamb, all are brought into a lea-field near the steading. Here Aberdeen yellow turnips are given, and to each ewe by degrees, of oats and bran mixed, half a pound, or of cotton cake the same quantity, the latter feeding-stuff being rightly considered best for milk, and may generally be bought cheaper than oats.

By thus keeping the ewes constantly in good condition without having them at any time too fat, there should be no danger of incurring inflammatory disease. It is quite true that the digestive organs do not easily, and all at once, accommodate themselves to a change from low to high diet. But the great point is to guard against having the ewes in too low or too high a condition, so that when they begin to receive oats or cake there may be no sudden change, but only a gradual bringing forward at the right time. The majority of shepherds prefer their charge to be in good condition, rather than thin, at lambing time. Indeed, they would sooner run the risk of having them really fat than have the trouble of tending thin, poor-conditioned ewes, which neither thrive themselves, nor are able to bring forward their lambs early by supplying them with a sufficient quantity of milk.

One of the chief points for consideration in sheep-breeding is that of producing healthy, strong-constitutioned, easily fattened lambs, and it is well known that unless a lamb thrive from birth it will never make a really good sheep. However much a plethoric condition may conduce to disease in wethers or store sheep of all kinds, yet the reverse is the case with the pregnant ewe. The flock that has been badly kept, the animals being poor and thin at time of parturition, is that in which the greatest losses, both of ewes and lambs, will take place.

K

## SHELTER.

Having now brought our ewe flock up to lambing time, we must say a little in regard to the shelter which they require at that season. Most farmers give this point too little consideration, although there is no economy so thriftless in the whole range of agriculture as that which denies proper shelter to the ewes at this period. In the first place, ewes should lie on a good pasture during the day, the late-lambers on a lea field, and the early-lambers on the lambing field which should be in close proximity to the lambing fold. Every evening those ewes which are in the lambing field should be brought into the fold for the night, while the rest are allowed to remain out all night. Lambing ewes are all the better for exercise if properly given, but to drive them long distances by means of dogs, without any due consideration of their state, is a serious mistake. The proper plan to adopt is this—When the gate of the pasture is opened, let the shepherd not roughly hound on his dog, but let the ewes quietly wend their way out of the field, allowing them to regulate their own pace on the way home. It frequently happens that a ewe is seized with the pains of labour on the road, or just before she leaves the field. In this case it would not only be inadvisable but cruel and dangerous to drive her hard. There is certainly no occasion for hurry upon the shepherd's part, and the ewes, if left to their own inclination, will naturally prefer to walk slowly.

But to return to the question of shelter. The thriftless economy that would deny to the ewes shelter from the pitiless blast, or expose them during the lambing season to the unprotected rigours of winter, has been proved, both by practice and theory, to be as unprofitable as it is cruel. There being much room for improvement in respect to shelter, it is a matter worthy of much consideration. If the lambing season should be early or the weather severe, the benefit of shelter will be doubly apparent. It is a pleasing circumstance to find that the profit to the breeder and humanity to the sheep are so closely allied. We shall now proceed to describe some of the more common methods of sheltering ewes at night.

A lambing-fold for sixteen score of half-bred ewes is constructed as follows:—A small field of half an acre is chosen behind the homestead. At the north side there is a high stone wall, and on the east a thorn hedge, which effectually breaks the force of east winds. Along the north wall are erected a row of twenty houses, "parricks" or pens, the roofing of which is made by fixing timber from the top of the wall to the posts which form the doors and fronts of the pens. One door serves for two pens, there being in the interior a middle division, which does not quite come to the same line as the walls in front. The door is closed by means of a small hurdle or "flake," which moves between the partition and the inside of the walls.

The roof is thickly thatched with rye or wheat straw tied in bundles, and on the outside or front, bunches of straw resembling sheaves are set on end, so that their tops meet the thatch, and when fixed in this position by means of "tarry" string or old sheep netting, a most effectual covering is made, the straw materially adding to the warmth during the cold nights so commonly prevalent in March. This row of pens forms the north side of a rectilineal figure. On the east is the hedge, and to form the other two sides west and south a fence of larch posts, with three spruce rails, is erected of the same height as a common fence. To make this enclosure as comfortable as possible, bunches of straw are fixed all along the inside of the fence and hedge, and when fixed in position form as it were a solid wall of straw, which is quite impervious to the strongest wind. The enclosure, which is called the court, is provided with two gates—one for driving the ewes in at the evening, at the west end, and one at the east end, where ewes and lambs are turned into a "seed" field after a day or two. There is also a little gate formed of two bundles of straw, at which the shepherd enters at night. Some say that it is necessary to provide sheep with hay for night use while in the lambing pens. This is entirely a mistake, as it is not only a waste of food, but may even tend to endanger the lives of some of the ewes. Anyone who has had experience will have noticed that just before ewes are taken out of their day-pasture to be put up for the night, they suddenly become hurried and endeavour to eat as much as they can possibly manage. In some way or other they know when the time for removing them is approaching, and it is astonishing to notice what an immense quantity of turnips or other food they will put out of sight in so short a time.

From this cause, when ewes enter the lambing court at night, they are well-filled with food, and are kept busy all night in rumination, which is at that time their natural employment. Seeing that this is the case, it would only be waste of hay to supply the sheep with what they do not require. Taking into consideration all the advantages which efficient shelter has over poor accommodation for ewes, specially of the Leicester breed, and of the annual trouble and expense which is incurred in repairing, thatching, and enclosing the pens and lambing-courts in common use, we have come to the conclusion that every landlord should erect suitable and permanent lambing sheds of wood.

We should propose to construct them entirely of larch timber, the roof also of timber, to be covered with felt and tarred; gates or doors made to each pen, and provided with hinges, instead of the old-fashioned and awkward hurdles. That more inside room should be given, that the lamber may have more freedom when employed inside the pen in hand-suckling the lambs.

Where the shepherd's house is not in close proximity to the lambing shed, a small house should be erected where he may rest, and in which a fire should be placed, not only for his own comfort, but that by having the necessary warmth close at hand, he may be able to save the life of a lamb which otherwise in all probability would have died. In this house too, he could keep any instruments considered necessary, as well as such requisites as carbolic oil, lard, olive oil, and any of the more common remedies which a herd is often called upon to administer.

The walls of the lambing-court should be built of stone, about 5 feet high, so that every protection may be given to the ewes when cold winds prevail; suitable gates should be constructed for ingress and egress, and a stack of straw for littering would not be out of place. A small turnip-house as well as a box for cake and corn, should also be provided under the same roof as the lambing-pens.

As an illustration of perfect accommodation for ewes, we shall describe the pens to be seen on the farm of Crookhouse, Lanton, Northumberland. All the pens are erected under one roof of larch timber and slate, and enclosed in front and behind by substantial walls of stone. The partitions between the pens themselves are constructed of larch hurdles fixed at each end to larch uprights, which support at the same time the roof. Each set of pens is divided by a passage communicating with the outside court, where the unlambed ewes lie at night. On entering a passage we have three pens on each side, provided with gates, hung on hinges, and fastening by means of an eye and drawbolt. A few pens are made six feet square, so that, should the shepherd have ewes with trins, he may have ample accommodation for them, should he not require the third lamb for another ewe. There are fifty-four pens, and the reason for such a large number is that, should severe weather—as a snow-storm—come on during the season, the ewes may be penned instead of lying out.

By having a number of doors into the lambing shed instead of a few, the lamber is enabled to house the ewe at the point nearest the place where she lambed. This is often a great saving of time and trouble, as, should a gimmer lamb, she will not readily follow her lambs to a distant pen, and when the attendant is in a hurry to attend to other sheep he is glad to be able to put the ewe or gimmer in, without having far to drive her. To make it all the easier for him, the pens are constructed round three sides of the square court, so that at whatever part of the court a ewe lambs he has shelter at hand. A covered court, enclosed with hurdles, is also in connection with these lambing pens, into which on stormy nights ewes and gimmers having single lambs are placed. There is also a storehouse for food under the same roof.

A lambing shed like the above would cost too much for the farmer to erect, but landlords should provide one on every farm where a ewe stock is permanently kept.

The field into which the ewes go by day should be provided with an hospital. It is constructed in the following manner :—A small square at one side or corner of the field is enclosed by means of a wooden fence, a space being left for a gate. Each side of the square is then made windtight by means of the bundles of straw already described. Inside the enclosure are constructed six or more small pens which are not provided with roofs as in the case of lambing pens. These small pens are made in the same way as the outside walls, and covered with straw in a like manner, so that a ewe when placed in one of them is entirely protected from all cold winds. In one corner of each pen a small box should be fixed to contain corn, roots, &c., which it is usually necessary to supply to weak ewes. The part of the hospital not occupied by pens is well littered with straw, and on a cold day when a ewe is about to lamb, she should be turned into this outer court that she may have protection from the severity of the weather.

These field-hospitals are not seen on every farm where ewes are kept, but we are certain that they will repay the farmer for the trouble and expense in erecting them. They do not cost much to put up, as the spade-hind or ditcher will erect a suitable barrack in a forenoon, with posts and rails which have been used before for fencing, the straw having previously been drawn and bunched in frosty weather, when such employment was required to occupy the hands. Instead of this bunched straw, many farmers are in the habit of using straw ropes, wrapping them round and round the rails of hurdles. They form an efficient shelter, but give unnecessary trouble and expense in their construction.

### AT LAMBING.

March having now arrived, with all its wind and severe weather, and its too frequently recurring storms of sleet and snow, the shepherd begins to feel anxious about his charge, while the owner looks forward to a good crop of lambs, and to more genial weather, that he may begin the busy work of getting in the seed.

At this time, when all is bustle and hurry on the farm, the shepherd, like the rest, is thrown all at once into his busiest season. But the task which is to occupy him is a much more difficult and responsible one than that which falls to the lot of any other hired servant on the place. Not only has he to perform his usual routine of daily labour, but while sleep is refreshing the tired ploughman, the shepherd can only snatch a very few hours of repose, which is frequently anything but rest. At all hours and in every kind of weather he must be ready to perform duties which are often the reverse of pleasant, and while doing so he knows that on his shoulders rests the whole charge of the flock, and that to his care and skill the farmer trusts for immunity from loss by death, and for a good return of lambs. Taking these facts into consideration, the farmer should see that everything possible be done to lessen the trouble and anxiety which in most cases rests heavily on the shepherd at this season.

As there are always numerous cases in which it is required, milk should be supplied to the shepherd for his weak lambs, or if he has a cow of his own he may supply it himself as needed, putting down the amount daily used, that he may be allowed for it by the farmer after the lambing is over.

During last lambing season the following amount of milk was used for the lambs of 16 score of half-bred ewes :—163 pints (imperial), costing, at 1½d. per pint, £1, 0s. 4½d., which was paid to the shepherd, as he supplied the milk from his own cow. In the very severe lambing season of 1879, for the same flock of ewes, 316 pints were used by the lambs, costing £1, 19s. 6d.

The milk used in another flock of 18 score of Leicester ewes averages yearly about 200 pints. A large quantity of milk has usually to be supplied to the twin lambs of gimmers, for their mothers have frequently a very small supply, quite inadequate to the purpose of bringing up a good pair of lambs.

At this period of the year, just when the lambing season has begun, the sheep marked to lamb the first and second week should be separated from the rest and turned into the lambing field, while the remainder of the ewes are left upon the lea or rough pasture. About 5 o'clock, P.M. during the beginning of the season, the herd should remove the ewes from the lambing field and take them into the court of the lambing shed, the other portion of the flock being left out all night upon the lea field. After bringing the ewes quietly into the lambing court at night they may be left, unless any ewe has commenced to lamb. In this case it will be necessary for the herd to remain at least close at hand, in order that, should his assistance be required, it may be promptly rendered. If no ewe is lambing, however, he may leave the flock, and after the first night or so they will make themselves comfortable, and proceed to ruminate quietly.

## RUPTURE.

When the ewes are brought into the lambing field in March, and are receiving turnips, the shepherd frequently notices that a ewe is giving way at the side (usually the left), or straight down. This occurs when the ewe is close at the lambing, and is caused by the lambs growing so large and heavy that they cause a hernia of the intestines. If not attended to the belly of the ewe almost touches the ground, and when it goes thus far nothing will ever bring it back to its normal position.

When the shepherd notices the first tendency to this mishap, he should provide himself with a deal plank six inches broad, and the length of the ewe from the top of the shoulder to the tail head. He must now take a corn sack, cut it open, and nail one side of it along the plank with tacks, then placing the board on the ewe's back at that side which is farthest from the rupture —the right side—he must place the sack under the ewe's belly and draw it up so that it sustains or supports the broken-down side. When he has drawn up the sack as tightly as necessary he must tack it on to the plank, and cut off that portion of the sack which is left over. The best time to place this support on the ewe is in the morning before she has had time to fill herself, and if it is done in time the rupture will never go any further.

Of all the plans which have been tried this is decidedly the best and most successful. After the ewe has lambed the support may be removed, in order that the lambs may obtain milk.

When ewes are so near lambing-time the shepherd must be very careful how he allows his dog to go amongst the sheep, and should see that the fences are good, for were his ewes from any cause to break pasture and jump the dyke, abortion would be very apt to follow. At this time, and more especially upon sunny days, the shepherd is caused considerable trouble from ewes lying "awkward," that is, they roll over on to their backs and are then very often quite unable to rise. Where there are deep furrows in the field this accident is most dangerous, as should a ewe roll over in one of them, she cannot by any chance get up again. Many ewes are not badly affected by lying for a length of time upon their backs, but others which have any affection of the lungs go almost at once, and before the shepherd has time to rescue them from their perilous position. Some dogs have the natural instinct to lift a ewe when lying awkward, but they are few, and the great majority of sheep dogs are quite unable to render any assistance.

Some few sheep in a flock seem to have a special tendency to take this position, causing the shepherd much trouble, as he has frequently to lift them twice or thrice a day. In this case it is a good plan to tie a whin or thorn bush upon the back of the ewe, which will, after the first attempt, prevent her from rolling over.

On passing through his flock the lamber will now probably notice that one of the shoulder-keiled ewes has drawn away from the others, which are busily engaged with the turnips provided for them. On approaching this ewe he will notice that she carries her tail a little higher than usual, that the parts below are unnaturally red, that she frequently bleats, and walks round and round snuffing the ground, and pawing as if she were trying to prepare a bed to lie down upon. She will now lie down, but almost immediately rise up again, showing renewed indications of pain and uneasiness. These are symptoms of lambing which continue until the bag of water has been discharged from the vagina. After this has happened, the pain evidently becomes more acute, and the ewe lies down and endeavours to expel the lamb by rapid spasms of contraction. The shepherd must not, on seeing these severe symptoms, interfere prematurely as too many do. He should watch the ewe closely, however, and so long as she gets up when he comes near her, he may be sure that nothing is amiss.

These symptoms may continue for two or three hours before he feels that it is absolutely necessary to render assistance. Should he notice, however, that anything is wrong as to the position of the lamb, making him fear that it may be sacrificed, he should at once proceed to catch her, and make an examination as to the state of affairs. (The proper method of handling a ewe when making an examination cannot be satisfactorily explained in writing, but should be learned by practice.) He will perhaps find that the presentation is perfectly natural, that is, the head coming with a foot on each side of it, but from want of room the ewe is unable to expel the lamb. He must now proceed to disengage the lamb, drawing the legs outwards and slightly downwards, first the one and then the other. This is generally accomplished easily, but considerable difficulty is frequently caused by the head. When this is the case force should not be used, but all possible tenderness should be employed in facilitating its passage. Pressure should be applied to the back of the lamb's head in a downward direction, and this is best done by passing the forefinger of the right hand up the rectum until the back of the head is felt. Holding the legs in the left hand, the attendant must now gently pull them, while at the same time pressure is applied by the finger to urge forward the head, in this way it is usually easy to extract the lamb.

In giving assistance to a ewe, it is always advisable to wait until she presses before endeavouring to help her by means of pulling, this method being more according to nature than the application of force when the struggles of the ewe have ceased. We have been told by an American farmer that in cases of this sort, where there is little room and a large lamb, by rubbing the sides of the vulva with belladonna, the parts become relaxed, and deliverance is much facilitated. Not having tried this method in practice, we cannot vouch for its efficacy. When the lamb is extracted, it should at once be placed before the ewe that she may lick it. If this be not done, and especially if she is a gimmer or young ewe, she may get up and run off without looking at her lamb at all. If the ewe does not begin to lick the lamb at once, a leg may be drawn through her mouth, and this will usually make her recognise her lamb.

Before allowing the ewe to rise, the shepherd should ascertain whether another lamb is present by carefully manipulating the belly with his fingers, and if there is not another, he should take the opportunity of ridding the udder of any wool which would hinder the lamb from sucking. If the weather is fine, there is no necessity to take the mother and lamb into a shelter; but should the weather be inclement, they should be at once driven quietly to the hospital, which has been described in treating of shelter. If the lamb or lambs be weakly, the shepherd should turn the ewe and suckle them, and after they have had one good drink, with sufficient shelter and warmth no danger need be feared. It is easy to know a weak from a strong lamb when born. A pink nose and white skin usually accompany a weak, and a black nose and yellow skin at birth a hardy, constitution. When the ewe and her offspring are placed in the hospital, a few turnips should be given her in a box in one corner of her pen, while those ewes which lamb on the pasture and have hardy lambs should receive nothing more than the ordinary keep.

Many ewes require no assistance whatever in lambing, and we have frequently seen twins dropped which were upon their feet and sucking in no more than ten minutes from birth. Where sixteen or eighteen score of ewes are kept, two lambers must be or are usually employed. If there is only one herd kept on the farm, an assistant should be hired to help him during the lambing season; for not only has he to attend to his ewes, but has the feeding of hoggs to attend to also, and at this time of year, when they are on turnips and getting cake and corn, he has a considerable amount of work on hand. He has not only to supply them with their cake and corn, but new portions or "breaks" of turnips have to be netted off, and hay must be "bottled" or bunched for them and carried out.

The shepherd, we consider, is the best judge of a suitable assistant for the lambing season; he is usually hired by the

week until he is no longer required, his wages being from 18s.
to £1, 1s. per week, with board and lodging in the farmer's
house, or sometimes it is more convenient for him to sleep at
the shepherd's.

During the first few days of the season few ewes lamb, and at
night there is little to be done in the way of watching. Where
two lambers are employed, it is usual to divide the night, one
watching until twelve and then going to bed, when the other
herd takes his place until morning. At this part of the season,
it will only be necessary for the shepherd to go through the
ewes every hour, although after the first week his duties will
come much more quickly upon him. When sitting up at night
a good fire should be kept burning, and we have found by
experience that a little hot coffee is not out of place.

When the shepherd goes out a lantern is indispensable, and the
glasses should be well protected with wire netting, as they
frequently receive a kick from a ewe's foot, which is apt to
break the glass and extinguish the light when it is most required.
In approaching the lambing court at night one should be
careful to hold the light steadily, as any sudden movement is
apt to cause the ewes to jump all over each other with fright,
which is very bad for them. With a little care at first they will
become quite accustomed to the presence of the lamber. It is,
indeed, wonderful, to see how quiet the ewes will lie after a few
nights, allowing the lamber to step over their backs as he goes
his rounds. The half-bred ewes are not usually so quiet as the
Leicester and three-parts bred ewes.

On entering the lambing court the attendant should quietly
raise his lantern and look round, when he will soon notice
whether anything is going on. Frequently the first signs he
gets are the cries of the ewe, which at this time have a different
tone, easily distinguished after a little practice. In fact, after a
few nights, on approaching the lambing court in the quiet dark-
ness, by listening to the cries of the ewes, it is often possible to
tell not only whether any ewe is lambing, but also what stage
she is in. Let us take a quiet walk through the lambing court.
Carefully threading our way amongst the ewes, which lie quietly
ruminating as they stare up fearlessly at the lamber and his
light, we come upon a ewe standing up. Her appearance at
once tells us that she has just begun to feel the first pains of
labour, and when this is the case we pass on knowing that at
present she requires no assistance. But now we come upon a
ewe stretched out in one of the corners, lying upon her side
without the least struggle, only her hard breathing and panting
sides showing that she is alive, and the tongue protruding from
the mouth, telling us that she is almost exhausted. As this ewe
is approached she will not endeavour to rise, but will lie quietly

while the lamber at once proceeds to make an examination. The cause for the exhaustion is soon apparent, for he finds that the lamb's head is present without any show of the legs. The lamber must now turn up his sleeves, well oil his hand and arm, and proceed to work. Taking hold of the lamb's head he must carefully pass it back into the womb and feel for the fore legs, which, when found, he draws out one after the other, taking care to place the head in a proper position. If the ewe is found in time, this operation may be accomplished quite successfully, and the lamb delivered alive; but if the ewe has long lain in this state, and the lamb has breathed the air before being replaced in the womb, there is great danger of suffocation.

When the first lamb has been delivered, the lamber should again insert his hand and ascertain whether another lamb is still to come, for if so it should be taken away at once. When this is accomplished, and the ewe able to rise, the shepherd must carry the lambs to one of the empty parricks, when the ewe will usually follow. After he has placed the trio inside, he may himself enter, take hold of the ewe, cast her, pull off the wool from her udder, and hand-suckle the lambs. This is a rather difficult task for a beginner, but after a little practice he will become an adept at it, and by doing this (which many lambers are too lazy to perform) many lambs are saved which would have died before morning, not having enough strength to feed themselves.

When the lambs have had a good fill, they will usually lie down and go to sleep, and on waking are quite capable of sucking their dams. When a ewe has been so exhausted as the one described, it will be necessary for the lamber to provide her with a warm drink of oatmeal gruel. He need not go specially to his house for it at the time, but may bring it out with him upon his next visit to the ewes. If he then finds that some single lambs have been dropped,—seeing that they are strong and on their legs,—he need not put them into a pen, for it is usual to take them into the grass field in which the lambing court stands; or some leave them in the court all night. The former is, however, the preferable course to pursue, for the lambs are very apt to lose their mothers, or to be taken up by another ewe to which they do not belong. It is a well known fact that a ewe about to lamb will often look upon a lamb as her own when in reality it is that of another ewe, and her own not yet born. Mistakes have happened in this way; we have known a lamber who placed a ewe which had adopted two lambs belonging to another in a pen, thinking that they were her own. In the morning the other lamber found her with four lambs, two of which had been born during the night. This mistake caused considerable difficulty, as it was not easy to determine which lambs belonged to the ewe which was found in the lambing court. Such a mistake as this could only arise from carelessness, as, had the first lamber turned the ewe when he placed her in the pen at night, either to pull the wool from the udder or suckle the lambs, he would have found out his mistake at once.

It must not be supposed that it is always a simple matter to entice a ewe into one of the parricks; on the contrary, it is often a most difficult task. After a ewe has lambed, she will frequently rise up and go straight off without once looking at her lambs, and, do what he will, the lamber cannot get her to follow the lambs into a pen. In this case he must have recourse to his lambing-crook, which should be always at hand for such emergencies. Grasping this instrument firmly with both hands, he must carefully approach the ewe from behind, and, taking a good aim, suddenly hook up the "near" hind leg of the ewe, the hock of which will be held by the crook. On feeling that the crook holds the lamber must run forward, slipping the handle of the crook through his hand, and catch the ewe by the leg; then, dropping the crook, he guides her with his other hand to the parrick, into which he has previously placed the lambs. He must now suckle the lambs, for probably the ewe will have nothing to do with them; but after the milk gets through their bodies she will generally recognise them as her own. Should the ewe not take to her lambs even after they have been suckled, she must be kept in the pen until she does so. To accomplish this the lamber must halter her to the side of the parrick exactly in the same manner as he would do a horse, and with a halter of light rope constructed upon the same principles. Some tie up one of the ewe's legs either to her own body or to the side of the pen, but the halter system is much better although it is not nearly so common. As long as the ewe is confined to her parrick, she must be regularly supplied with roots and corn or her milk will fail. If these points are attended to, she will take to her lambs in a day or two, and may then be turned on to a "seed" field. During one season with a flock of ewes it is surprising to find what a variety of difficult cases occur to try the skill and patience of the lamber; not only are there bad presentations, but deformities are only too often common.

Some of the presentations which frequently cause difficulty in lambing may be described:—Having shown how a case where the head alone is forward may be rectified, we shall describe the opposite, which also is often encountered. The forelegs are found thrust out to the shoulders, and the head is bent back and retained in the vagina. From the throes of the ewe it is often impossible to replace them so as to get up the head of the lamb. When this is the case the lamber should cut a ring round the lamb's legs above the knee, and the skin being thus severed the legs may be pulled away from the shoulder joint. When this is accomplished there will be room for the introduction of the hand, and then laying hold of the head he can deliver the ewe. After severe cases of this description it is necessary to pour a little digestive ointment into the cavity of the vagina to counteract any tendency to gangrene or inflammation. For this purpose Haig's Universal Remedy may be used with success; but what is even better is the following recipe:—Of Crace Calvert's carbolic acid (No. 5) 1 pint to 7 pints of Gallipoli olive oil to be used for bad cases, and for less severe 1 pint of acid to 15 pints of oil. If the ewe is much exhausted, half a pint of oatmeal gruel with a gill of good beer, warmed, and 2 to 4 drachms or so of laudanum should be administered and repeated every three or four hours until the animal begins to improve. Nitric ether might be given with advantage after the severe symptoms begin to abate; but such remedies are not usually found upon farms, and shepherds are forced to do without them. If; however, it is at hand, it may be given in doses of from 2 to 4 drachms. Shepherds usually give 2 ounces of Epsom salts along with laudanum, and this forms a good medicine when the ewe is not much distressed.

Another case, although not so common, sometimes occurs, and causes a good deal of trouble. This is the presentation of the hinderquarters first. To effect deliverance the lamber must endeavour to get hold of both hind legs at once, and, by drawing them gently but firmly, he may often remove the lamb easily in this position.

There are many more cases which demand a great deal of care and patience upon the operator's part, but it is needless to enter into details as to their treatment, for his own discretion and experience will generally enable him to save the ewe, although it may often be necessary to sacrifice the life of the lamb. Many other things, however, have to be attended to by the lamber at this time, some of which cause him more trouble than all the bad cases put together. These are ewes giving little or no milk, mothers refusing to recognise their offspring, trins, orphans, and single lambs with ewes which have abundance of milk to bring up twins.

Let us first refer to his troubles over ewes, and more frequently gimmers, which have twin lambs and little milk. This very often happens. Gimmers which have been well kept up to lambing time, after they have produced their lambs, frequently refuse to eat cake or corn, and thus the milk which is necessary for the maintenance of their offspring is not forthcoming. When this happens the ewe should be supplied with cotton cake, which, if eaten, will usually tend to materially increase the flow of milk. As the lambs have not sufficient milk to keep them alive, the shepherd must of necessity supply the deficiency. Many say that large numbers of lambs are killed yearly by receiving too much cow's milk, but our opinion is that many more are killed by getting too little; and were they to get none at all the shepherd would have often but a poor account to render to his master. In one flock of half-bred ewes, during the severe lambing season of 1879, a shepherd of our own acquaintance found it necessary to supply twenty pints of milk to the lambs in one day; and he assures us that none died from getting too much, but that one or two may have died from receiving too little. The milk supplied to lambs should be sweetened with sugar and well warmed, care being taken not to scald it, and given to the lambs from a tin flask by means of a quill. Some people feed lambs from a bottle fitted with an india-rubber teat. This may do very well for a few pet lambs, but when there is a large number to feed, the attendant will find that he requires something by which he can get his work sooner accomplished. For this purpose a quill is very suitable, for by means of it the lamb can suck at will, while at the same time the milk in reality is being poured down its throat.

It is said that many lambs are saved, when likely to perish, by being laid before a fire. This is indeed the case; but there is a more preferable course to pursue—which is to wrap the lamb in a plaid, piece of blanket, or even a sack, and then place it in a warm place, not in front of the fire. It is quite true that lambs do become lively when revived before a fire, but take them out and place them with their mothers, and then observe the difference. It will be seen that the lamb which was revived by means of a warm plaid will gradually get over its weakness, while the other, which was brought to life before the fire, will in all probability sink. The body seems to be rendered unfit to withstand the weather, when brought up at the fire, but with the other system these results do not ensue.

We have heard that on hill farms whisky is given to revive lambs; but not having seen it in practice, we cannot testify in its favour. In this case, too, there will, we should imagine, be some outcry about the shepherds drinking what is supplied for his lambs.

Of those deformities which are most common the following may be cited:—Lambs are very frequently born with "wry-necks," that is, with the head either to one side, or almost on a level with the feet. When this is the case, they are not only difficult to lamb, but afterwards are not worth bringing up, as they are often quite unable to suckle. These lambs are sometimes brought up as pets, but it is not remunerative, as they neither thrive or sell well, so that it is best not to give them a chance of living. A very troublesome deformity, which happily is not common on all arms, causes many deaths amongst ewes, as it is almost impossible to lamb them without rupturing the womb. This deformity consists in the fore legs having no proper knee-joints. The legs are curved towards the belly of the lamb, and are incapable of being bent. As these lambs generally come hindquarters first, it will be easily understood how dangerous these jointless legs must be to the ewe. What makes matters worse is that it is quite impossible to tell that anything is wrong, and the lamber proceeds to extract the lamb in the way usually practised with a breech presentation.

Such deformities as these are said to be the result of "in-and-in" breeding, and as they generally occur on low, damp farms, where inflammatory disease is common, it is more than probable that such is the true explanation. Along with such cases as this, lambs with cleft palate are frequently found; others with imperforate anus, and frequently hermaphrodite lambs. Occasionally there are instances of monstrosities, and these must be dealt with as the shepherd thinks fit, for no definite rule can be laid down for their treatment.

Very frequently a ewe goes about as if going to lamb, but does not exert herself, and the attendant notices that her look is both dull and exhausted. In this case an examination should at once be made. On inserting the hand, the lamber will find that the lambs have a soft, cold feel, and, if experienced, from the touch he will know that they are dead. He must now proceed to extract them, often piece-meal, and this is by no means a pleasant task, as the fœtus is in a state of putrification. In operations of this kind the assistant should use carbolic oil to rub his hands with, and the ewe should receive a cleansing drench composed of warm beer, 1 gill; nitre, 2 to 4 drachms; gentian (powdered), 2 drachms; and ginger, ½ or 1 drachm.

When a ewe has only one lamb, and sufficient milk to bring up a pair, and at the same time a gimmer has twins and only milk for one lamb, the usual plan is to give the ewe her own and one of the gimmer's twins, and to leave the gimmer to bring up one of her own lambs. Now, in a case of this sort, if the lambs are all born about the same time, the shepherd should rub all the three lambs together, so that they may have the same smell, and then place the gimmer's twins with the ewe and the ewe's single lamb with the gimmer. In this way a much better reconciliation is brought about, and the twins always thrive better, as they are more equally matched in every respect. It may be necessary to confine the ewe and even halter her, for she is always more crafty than the gimmer. Usually, however, there is little trouble in a case like the above. Again, if a ewe has twin lambs and one dies (if she is able to bring up two lambs), the shepherd should take a lamb from a gimmer which has two, or from a ewe which has twins; and, after skinning the dead lamb, let him cut holes in the skin for each leg of the lamb to pass through. Then. after placing this skin on the lamb he desires to mother, let him put each of its legs through a hole, and after doing so he will not require to sew or tie it on, as some do. Before the skin is put on it is best to rub over uncovered parts, such as the face, legs, and tail, so that the smell of the lamb may be uniform. After this is done the lamb may be placed with the ewe. If she does not take to it at once she should be haltered, as has been before described, and after her milk has passed through the lamb's body she will adopt it. To illustrate what may be accomplished by the halter system, the following will fully suffice :—

A shepherd sold a single lamb off a ewe (fat) at eight weeks old. As the ewe had abundance of milk, he was determined, if possible, to make her adopt two pet lambs, which were about seven weeks old, and very large and fat. Taking the ewe into a lambing-pen he haltered her in a corner, allowing only six inches of rope, then fixing a hurdle so that she could only move a little to each side, he placed the lambs beside her, and enclosed them all in the small pen. In this position the ewe could not stir, and the lambs were unable to escape; and at length, when they had sucked and she could not get away from them, the ewe gave in and took the lambs, which were sent out to pasture along with her. This saved the shepherd the time and trouble of hand-feeding the lambs. When twins are not equal in strength the strongest lamb takes too large a share of the mother's milk, and in this case the strong lamb should be muzzled. To accomplish the desired end properly it is necessary to construct a nose-bag of linen or unbleached cotton, provided with tapes to secure it to the lamb's head. Holes must also be cut, that the lamb may breathe and yet be unable to suck. This is the best plan which can be adopted to secure enough milk to the weaklier lamb. The nose-bag is removed often enough during the day to allow the lamb sufficient milk for its maintenance. Some endeavour to give the weak lamb an equal chance with the strong one by separating it from its mother part of the day. This is neither a safe or effectual plan ; for the lamb, having to be confined when it should be at liberty, and not getting the attention of its mother, as it otherwise would do if muzzled and allowed to accompany her, is very apt to become estranged. The muzzle system is all that can be desired, and is worthy of a trial. Do what he will, the shepherd must frequently have a few pet lambs to bring up, but more often there are too few lambs to place with ewes which are well able to bring up twins.

When ewes die, it is scarcely possible to avoid having pets, as of course it is very improbable that ewes will lamb single lambs just in time to receive those which have become orphans. These pets must be brought up on cow's milk, which, although not so good for them as that of their mothers, will keep them alive, and they very soon begin to thrive upon it. The method of feeding them has been described, and after a short time they will learn to drink out of a milk-pail. In bad weather it is advisable to place the lambs under cover between meal-times, but in good weather they may be put into a grass paddock during the day, and under shelter at night until the nights become warm.

The most usual cause for the occurrence of pet lambs is, that ewes frequently bear trins. On the farm of Holburn Grange near Belford the enterprising tenant was so much burdened last season, by the large number of trins, that he found it necessary to take one of every three for pets. The unusual loss of ewes by udder-clap also caused many orphans to be thrown upon his hands. As his return of lambs is rather singular, we may quote his figures. From a flock of twelve score and thirteen three-part bred ewes he weaned twenty-two score and nine lambs. Another gentleman took one score of draft ewes to Yorkshire last year and weaned thirty-nine lambs, one ewe having trins, two single lambs, and the remainder twins.

### INVERSION OF THE UTERUS.

After a severe case of lambing, when great straining continues, inversion of the uterus frequently takes place. It is caused by a violent spasmodic action of the womb, which turns inside out and protrudes. As this is one of the mishaps to which ewes are very susceptible at lambing time, the lamber experiences considerable difficulty in properly treating the affected sheep; and however simple the treatment may seem on paper, yet in practice this complaint is by no means easy to cure. Whenever it is noticed the shepherd must without delay proceed to replace the inverted uterus. This operation should be performed thus. The ewe should be placed on her back, her hindquarters raised, and the hands having first been lubricated with oil or lard, the womb should be gently restored to its natural position. This is, however, difficult to manage, as the ewe will press so hard that until she becomes exhausted, no success will be attained. By patience and perseverance however, the desired result is usually effected, and then the aim of the attendant must be to retain the uterus in its proper situation. There are many methods which may be tried with some degree of success, such as pinning the bearing with a stick, piece of leather, or metallic wire, &c. All these modes are useful, but they cause suppuration and renewed pressing on the part of the ewe. By forming a sort of net over the part with string, and fixing it to the wool of the ewe, this mishap is prevented from

L

recurring; without a drawing or demonstration it is, however, impossible to explain the operation.

### AFTER LAMBING.

When ewes and twins are turned on to "seeds" just after lambing, the shepherd will find it of great help to mark the lambs. While they are young and weak, and their mothers go about feeding, they invariably get huddled up, and it is now the shepherd's duty to "mother" them. Without the aid of marks this is a difficult matter. Many shepherds are able to tell which lambs belong to any particular ewe, but the difficulty is to match the twins, and therefore to save time, the lambs are marked with a bit of keil or hæmatite iron ore. Each pair of twins should be keiled with a distinctive mark, so that, however widely separated in the field, they may be brought together and placed with their mother. If marks are not resorted to, a great deal of time is wasted in properly pairing and mothering the lambs, but by the above system nothing can be more easy. When the ewe hoggs come off the turnip break about the 20th of April, it will be necessary to select or draw seven score for the Leicester flock, and six score for the half-bred flock. Where eighteen score of Leicester ewes are kept, there will be usually twelve score of ewe hoggs, out of these the shepherd must proceed to draw all the small indifferent sheep, and all those which have bad fleeces, weak constitutions (shown by pink noses and white feet) blue faces, bad ears and necks or woolly heads and legs. The five score of hoggs which remain are placed on good permanent pasture to fatten for market, or are sent amongst the wether hoggs where they will have better keep. The ewe hoggs selected for breeding purposes are placed upon good pasture where they will be kept in good condition until clipping time, after which they are called gimmers and are then well kept until placed with the ram in October.

On farms where tups are bred, where there are say eighteen score of ewes kept, if the farmer wishes to feed fifty tups he must draw eighty lambs at castrating time. These, until weaned, should have good pasture, and then cake and beans gradually given until April the year following. They are then brought forward on two pounds of cake and beans until clipping time, at which time those which do not come up to the standard of perfection should be sold fat. From this time to September, they must be gradually forced on, and in the beginning of August cabbages or tares should be given to finish them for the ram sales. We need not here enter into the much vexed question of trimming and clipping tups.

In going over the lambs to choose those suitable for tups, the shepherd must attend to a few points concerning which the farmer in many cases gives him his judgment at this time. In the first place, the lambs chosen must be of large and strong frame, care being taken to select only those animals which have black noses and feet, good necks and fleeces, white faces and well set on ears; and all those which have woolly heads and legs must be rejected. The symmetry of each sheep should be looked at as a whole; the back as nearly as possible in one line from rump to poll, the breast broad and full, shoulders broad and well rounded, no rising at the withers, barrel deep and round, and the wool white and fine. Although these points are not fully seen in the lamb, yet there are always indications of what will turn out as such when it has reached maturity; and from experience a good breeder knows well which lambs are most promising. The reason for selecting such a large number of lambs as eighty when only fifty are to be sold is, that, during the feeding and keeping of the tups for so long a time, many do not turn out all that was expected of them, and thus are unsuited for the ram sale. If there were no sheep to come and go upon, the breeder would not be able to sell the wished for complement. Many things, which were or could not be seen when they were lambs, will afterwards show themselves in the sheep, for they are always more tender than the ewe and wether hoggs. Thus some will fall victims to sturdy and other diseases, and frequently some showing symptoms of lung disease must be sold fat.

## CASTRATION.

About ten or fifteen days after birth, it is usual to castrate all the male lambs which are not to be kept for rams; and at this time the opportunity is taken to dock the tails of both ewe and wether lambs. The earlier this operation is performed, the less likely is it to be followed by injurious effects. A favourable day should be selected, dry, but neither cold nor hot. If the flock is large, it is better to operate upon the lambs at different periods—so that they can be operated on at pretty nearly the same age—than to wait and perform on the whole at the same time. There are different methods of operating, but the following, which we have usually seen and practised, is as expeditious, convenient, painless and satisfactory as any. The lambs to be operated upon are driven carefully along with their mothers into a pen constructed in a corner of the field, either of lamb netting or hurdles. If the flock is large, a portion only should be put into the pen, say two score, which when finished should be turned out and another supply put in. To perform the operation properly, three persons are required, one to catch, another to hold, and the shepherd himself to castrate the lamb. The operation itself is carried out thus :—The catcher having handed a lamb to the holder, the latter proceeds to turn the lamb and then seizing a hind and a foreleg together in each hand, he hoists the lamb upon his shoulder, and, by stretching the legs away from each side of the body, places the scrotum in a suitable position for being operated on. The operator having provided himself with a clean sharp knife, after feeling whether the testicles are present, with the finger and thumb of his left hand draws the lower part of the scrotum and cuts off a portion of the skin with his knife. He then grasps the upper part of the scrotum forcing the testicles forward, then, blowing back the wool, he seizes them with his teeth and draws them out. After the scrotum has been adjusted the assistant is directed to lower the lamb. Turning it, he grasps the tail close to the root, and the operator, catching it by the other end, cuts off such a portion as is customary in the district or according to the breed of the sheep. Ewe lambs have their tails cut in the same manner as the wether lambs, and some farmers even cut the tails of those lambs which they intend to keep for rams. This we consider is a mistake, as, were they to leave the tail until the lamb has grown, the back bone would be materially strengthened, and the testicles always come down better. It is a good plan to lower a lamb after castration by the tail, as by this means the parts are adjusted. Sometimes the tail bleeds considerably, and in this case a small piece of thin string should be tied round it, and left on for twelve hours, after which it must be removed to prevent mortification. The mode of operation which has just been described may to many appear rather barbarous, but practice has shown that it is both a safe and speedy method, and is the one which most shepherds prefer. Out of forty score of Cheviot lambs operated upon in this manner at Ingram near Glanton only *one* died, and this probably was not the result of the operation, but of some other cause. Every year previously, the lambs of this ewe flock had been castrated by means of the hot iron, at the sacrifice of much time and expense as a professional man had to be hired to perform the operation. It was determined however to abandon this plan and resort to the more expeditious method, and the result was that the lambs were castrated in about half the time, and with more satisfactory results. On going over the lambs at this time the shepherd usually finds a few lambs which have no testicles present in the scrotum, or in some cases only one. These lambs must all receive a special mark, as they are very troublesome, and must be fed off as soon as possible They are usually called " chasers." It sometimes happens that after a time the testicles do come down, and the shepherd should therefore examine them once or twice, so that, should this occur he may make an operation.

Many have cried out against the custom of docking sheep as a cruel and unnecessary operation, but we must plead in its favour, not only because it gives a compact appearance to the sheep, but because of its cleanliness. If diarrhœa should attack the lamb, as it is likely to do in some degree, the long tails harbour filth, and sometimes cause sores, on which the fly will deposit its eggs. Thus, were the tails left long the shepherd could hardly perform all the extra work which they would cause, for " cowing " or cleaning away the clotted wool on even short-tailed sheep takes a considerable amount of time. The tails of half-bred sheep are left longer than those of the Leicester breed, while those of the Cheviot lambs are left much longer than either, and the tails of the Dorset and Somerset sheep are allowed to grow to their natural length.

Another common method of castrating is as follows :—The lamb being held as in the previous description, the shepherd with his left hand causes the testicles to make the point of the scrotum smooth; then cutting through the integument of the scrotum with a sharp penknife, first to one testicle and then the other, he protrudes both testicles forward with both hands, and seizes first one testicle with his teeth, drawing out the spermatic cord until it breaks, and then treating the other in a similar manner. It is advocated for this latter method that the two simple incisions heal by the first intention, whereas the wound caused by cutting off the point of the scrotum takes a longer time to heal. This may be true, but frequently, when the wound heals by first intention, it would have been better open; for should suppuration set in, and no outlet for the pus be present, serious inflammation is certain to ensue. This cannot happen when the other method is followed, as all discharges are readily got rid of.

### EAR-MARKING.

At castrating time it is usual to perform another operation, *i.e.*, ear-marking. Although this practice has been much deprecated, we hope to be able to show that it is necessary, and not so cruel as many suppose. In a flock of sixteen score of half-bred ewes, the annual average produce of lambs will be about twenty-three score, and seeing that all these must be marked, what are we to employ as a mark which will not become effaced in a year? Now the practice is as follows :—At castrating time the shepherd, having provided himself with a pair of nippers (very similar to those used by ticket collectors), snips a small piece out of the far ear of each ewe lamb. This mark, being placed at the tip of the ear, is called a " forebit," and will remain in the ear for three years, until these sheep, having had three crops of lambs, are drafted out.

If this year the ewe lambs were marked with a "forebit" in the *far* ear, next year's lambs must be marked with a "forebit" in the *near* ear, while on the year after they might go without any ear-mark at all.

By this method the shepherd can at a glance tell whether a sheep is a gimmer, a "one-crop" ewe, a "two-crop," or a "three-crop," which latter must be drafted. Wether lambs which have only to be fed off require no ear-marks. If they are buisted when lambs that is all they require. In regard to the supposed cruelty of ear-marking, a few words may not be out of place. If the operation is done quickly, and with a proper instrument, very little pain can be caused to the sheep. When, however, a punch and mallet are used, as we have seen done, a great deal of pain must and does ensue, and those who practise this system deserve to be reprimanded for what is in reality unnecessary cruelty. Were they to provide themselves with proper instruments, we consider that the operation would cause very little pain, as the piece is small, quickly removed, and very little bleeding, if any, follows. Nevertheless, although the operation may be simple and almost painless, we have no doubt that hill farmers who have a large flock of both ewe and wether lambs to mark would be glad of any other system which would entail less work and give no pain.

### MANAGEMENT OF LAMBS UP TO WEANING.

The after-management of lambs is usually simple, and where there is a good shepherd the farmer will have little trouble. The first thing to be considered is, that as it is necessary to keep the lambs always advancing, what feeding will be needed for them? Now, as gimmers have not so much milk for their lambs as ewes, when they have twins they must be placed on the best pasture, and if possible on "seeds." Ewes which have twins are put on second-class pasture, while those ewes or gimmers which have single lambs are placed upon less rich grass than the ewes with twins. It is always desirable to give gimmers and their lambs the preference in the selection of grass. This feeding goes on to the end of June, but before we follow the lambs through the summer months it will be advisable to say something in regard to the clipping season.

Before clipping is begun it is necessary to have the sheep well washed, and then to leave them a sufficient time to allow the yoke to come up into the fleece, not only that it may weigh heavier when clipped, but that it may be more valuable to the manufacturer. About the 21st of May it is customary to wash Leicester sheep, and the *modus operandi* need hardly be described. Suffice it to say, that every sheep is hand-washed, and not swum through a pool, as is the case with Cheviot sheep. By the hand-washing method every sheep passes through five hands in the water, the last being the shepherd, whose place it is to see that the work is properly executed. After washing it is usual to allow eight or ten days to elapse before clipping is begun. The best time to begin is the 1st of June, although many farmers commence about the 24th of May.

Whichever date is chosen, the Leicester sheep are clipped first, and, if properly done, each man should shear from twenty to thirty a day, adopting the method called "Culleying," after the great improver of the Border Leicester sheep. This system requires a good deal of skill, and is gained by constant practice, until some shepherds can make almost perfect work. As the shears are used by both hands alternately under this mode, the fleece is always shorn quite regularly; whereas, when all the fleece is clipped with the right hand alone, one side must necessarily be rougher than the other, as it is clipped with the lie of the wool.

After the Leicester sheep are finished, it is usual to begin the half-bred, which, although not generally clipped so particularly, are treated in the same manner as the Leicesters. The average weights of fleeces on many farms runs about the following:— *Leicesters.*—Tup hoggs, 9½ lb.; ewe and wedder hoggs, 8 lb.; and ewe fleeces, 7 lb. *Half-bred.*—Hoggs, 7 lb.; ewes, 6 lb.

To return to the management of the lambs, they are kept upon the pasture until the end of June, at which time those which are not thriving well, and all the ewes which are to be drafted, should be drawn out and placed on permanent pasture, so that they may continue to advance in condition, and the lambs kept as equal as possible.

## WEANING.

July having arrived, lambs have to be weaned, and from the end of June until this is accomplished they must be kept on those pastures which will maintain them best. Leicester lambs are weaned about the 10th of July, and half-breds about the 20th of the month. Before beginning to wean lambs it is the usual practice of extensive sheep-breeders to secure grass pasture on a neighbouring farm or moor for a month, as all the lambs cannot be weaned at home. At weaning, wether lambs must be sent to the best pasture obtainable, and the ewe-lambs to a moor where they will live well for a month. If it is found, after sending lambs on to these pastures, that they do not thrive well, they should be brought home before the month is out and ewes sent in their place. When brought home at the end of the month, or before that time, the lambs are placed in the same fields out of which they were weaned (none on to second year's grass), these having been left empty or "hained" for them while away at the moor. From this change into rich pasture, after the poorer grass of the moor, lambs are very liable to become affected with "yellows" or gall-lamb as it is called by some. The liver is evidently disturbed in its functions; disordered bile is poured into the duodenum, and frequently is regurgitated into the abomasum or fourth stomach. From the absorption of bile into the system the skin assumes a yellowish tint, and the fat after death is also found to be coloured. This disease runs a rapid course, seldom lasting more than three days, and frequently carrying off the lamb in fourteen or fifteen hours. Although it does not always terminate in death, it never fails to leave traces of its presence upon the body of the lamb. A part which seems to be peculiarly affected is the head and ears. These at first swell immensely, the ears in time hang down, and in bad cases part of them crumble or drop off, so that ever afterwards the lamb appears as though it had been lacerated by a dog. Immediate change of pasture, and to a permanent grass field if possible; the loss of a small quantity of blood in the commencement of the attack, and purgatives, afford a chance, and but a chance, of a cure.

### MANAGEMENT OF EWES AND LAMBS AFTER WEANING.

After the lambs are taken from their mothers it is usual to milk the ewes once or twice in order to prevent any danger from overloaded udders. This practice is, however, rapidly dying out amongst sheep-breeders, although much may be said both for and against the custom. Certainly when ewes are in high condition they must be the better of milking, but when comparatively thin it will be an unnecessary trouble. It has been found by experience that from penning and milking ewes lose about one shilling per head. If it is intended that they should not be milked, the ewes should be at once placed on dry, bare pasture, where, in a short time, the milk will become gradually absorbed. Usually, even where it is not the general practice to milk ewes, there are a few particular cases in which it is considered necessary to draw off the superfluous milk, and in regard to this the shepherd must be left to his own judgment. Signs of distress are usually betokened by extreme distension and redness of the udder, and stiffness, more or less, of both hind legs. Where such symptoms as these are observed it will certainly be better for the shepherd to relieve the ewe by milking. On a farm where milking was common, and where it has now been given up, we have been told by the shepherd that since then more "spindled" teats have occurred in the udders of his ewes. The same injury, on the other hand, is frequently caused, when the ewes are milked, by the impatience of the women engaged, for by nipping the udder too severely with the hand, inflammation often ensues, and "deaf paps" are the result. When ewes are to be milked they should be brought into a pen at the steading at eight o'clock at night, and next morning at two the shepherd should call the women to milk, the special pens having been previously erected. The reason for beginning so early is, that in the morning it is much cooler, and thus better for both sheep and people. Each man holds ewes for two women in a narrow pen. The ewes are usually milked twice, the milk being preserved for the master; if milked a third time the milk is allowed to the shepherd for his own use. The women are generally paid 1s. 6d. for four hours, that is, from two to six, also food before and after milking, the shepherd feeding and paying the women the last day. Ewes' milk is mixed with cows' milk and manufactured into cheese, which, although strongly tasting, is much relished by some.

## "SWINGBACK."

A peculiar disease which frequently affects lambs is that called in the country "Swingback." From the name one is led to infer the nature of the disease, which is a weakness of the spine, causing the lamb, when walking, to bend its back from side to side, and if it be a bad case the lamb is almost unable to walk at all. This affection of the spine remains with the sheep during life, but is not hereditary. Although the cause of this disease has not as yet been explained, shepherds have noticed that when the ewes have had corn for a time after lambing no swingback lambs are seen in the flock. A lamb, when affected with this disease, should be fattened off at once, as, although safe to breed from, it is neither profitable nor is it handy to deal with at lambing time or after, as it will not be so well able to feed and keep up with its companions.

Examination of a swingback lamb after death shows that part of the back, just over the kidneys, has become black from a resolution of blood to that part. Weak-backed lambs occur in flocks which have been subjected to hardships. Owing to the long severe winter of 1880–81 the proportion of such lambs was unusually large last season. Ewes on poor, mossy land, or fed on second-rate roots without sufficient dry fodder, furnish a considerable number of such cases. Land newly limed, and throwing up a large amount of soft herbage, is stated in some localities to predispose to these attacks of weak back and trembling. Inadequate supplies of nutritive food appears to starve especially the nervous textures, and produces the symptoms complained of. It appears sometimes at birth, the little creatures trembling and occasionally having spasms. Frequently it is postponed until the lamb's strength is tried by weaning, and especially if, at this critical period, they are placed upon rough, hard pasture, are overcrowded, or follow closely other sheep which have stained the grass and rendered it unpalatable. Occurring in wet seasons, and on wet pasture, it is sometimes traced to ergoted grasses, and perhaps to mouldy fodder, the former of which has the peculiar property of contracting capillary blood-vessels and thus causing wasting, and even mortification, of the parts to which they are distributed. Sometimes the complaint appears like an enzootic, attacking considerable numbers of sheep in the same district. It is nearly allied to the nervous disorder known as "louping-ill." Concentrated nutritive food, occasional salines, and salts of alum, constitute the approved treatment. Prevention is effected by careful management of the ewe flock, alike during gestation and lactation, and by furnishing at all times, both to ewes and lambs, good food and water.

Having brought our ewe flock up to that point at which we began to describe their treatment, it is only necessary to say a few words in conclusion.

However simple treatment of ewes may appear on paper, more will be learned by one season's practice than by volumes of writing, and we strongly advise every intending breeder to combine science with practice. The experience has no doubt to be gained at the expense of a great deal of work which is by no means pleasant, but, when once gone through, the knowledge gained will more than repay the learner.

The best mode of gaining proficiency in the thorough knowledge of ewes and their treatment is for the young farmer to board with some shepherd who has a large flock of sheep to tend. Let him not fear to face the rough mode of living, the cold stormy nights, and the unpleasant tasks which he will be called upon to perform, for, by taking part in every detail, he will in a short time be master of the routine usually followed, and in after life will prove that "it is less painful to learn in youth than to be ignorant in age."

## EXPERIMENT ON THE CULTIVATION OF CABBAGE.

By PETER KILPATRICK, Darley Manor, Bishop's Waltham, Hants.

[*Premium—Ten Sovereigns.*]

*Situation of the Field.*—The field selected for this experiment is situated in the parish of Darley, Derbyshire. It contains over six acres, the soil is of medium tenacity, lying on a sandstone formation, moderately dry naturally, and rendered so by drains where necessary. The exposure is south-westerly, situated about two hundred and fifty feet above the level of the sea.

*Previous Cropping.*—The field experimented upon was only under the charge of the reporter for part of the time occupied by the two previous crops, so he can only vouch for details after that date; what was before that is taken from books to which he has access, and which he believes to be correct.

The crop immediately preceding the one reported on was oats, which was a fair one. The one before that was mangolds, grown with twelve cartloads of farmyard manure, no artificial manure being applied. This crop had just been sown when the reporter entered on the charge of the farm. During the very dry months of June and July the mangolds made very little progress, so little that the reporter had serious thoughts of ploughing them down, but before doing so he thought of giving them another chance, and had them deeply pared by a common plough from which the mould board had been removed. The improvement was immediate, and caused, in the reporter's opinion, by the paring having broken the crust which prevented the roots getting below the sun-burned surface soil. This crust had been allowed to, form by the land having been subjected to many shallow ploughings and no deep ones.

*Preparation of the Field.*—Encouraged by the success of deep paring already described, the reporter had the field ploughed with three horses abreast, during November and December following to the depth of between nine and ten inches, this he found to be very difficult work, but the extra labour was amply repaid by the fine, clean, free, porous seed-bed that was procured the following spring, the grubber having only to be passed through it twice to render the soil all that could be desired for the experiment.

*Manuring and Seeding.*—The field being thus prepared, the reporter selected four acres in the middle of the field for the experiment, of as equal quality as could be procured; two acres he determined to plant with cabbages, one acre with Fosterton hybrid turnips, and another acre with Skirving's swedes. The field was then drilled with the double mould-board plough in the ordinary way, the drills being 28 inches wide, thirteen cartloads of farmyard manure were applied per acre, and 2 cwts. dissolved bones, 1 cwt. nitrate of soda, and 1 cwt. guano were then sown broadcast, and the whole covered by the double mould board plough; thus far the treatment was the same for all the crops. The turnips and swedes were sown on 26th May (immediately after the manure was covered) in clumps 11 inches apart, quantity of seed nearly 2½ lbs. per acre.

*Mode of Planting.*—The cabbages were planted on 28th May,

at the distance of 36 inches between the plants, and 28 inches between the rows. Before planting, the plants were trimmed, and all stringy roots cut off; the roots were then dipped into puddle about the consistency of cream, composed of liquid manure and soil. Thus prepared, the following is the mode of planting adopted by the reporter, viz.:—The outside drill was measured and marked every three feet as a guide to the planter, who followed with a spade, making a hole (in a slanting position) at every mark, down to the manure, when a boy was ready to put in a plant, the planter then withdrew his spade and the soil fell around the roots, the planter then firmed the roots by treading on the soil while he made the hole for the next plant, and so continued until the row was finished. The next row was then begun, taking care that the plant was placed so that it should be between the two first plants of the row already planted. By this method the plants do not interfere with those in the adjoining rows, and a greater amount of food can be grown on a given space. When once a proper start has been made, the planter has no difficulty in placing them properly, having only to glance across the rows planted, to see where to put the plant, the lines "reading" several ways.

*After Treatment.*—The swedes and turnips were singled out between the 9th and 11th July to the distance of 11 inches apart. All the lots were horse-hoed twice during the summer, and hand-hoed once; the cabbages were earthed up to steady the plants. The earth was not "met" at the top of the drills, but was left about a span wide, to allow the moisture to reach the roots, which it would do better than if the drills were drawn to a top. The swedes and turnips were not earthed up.

*Mode of lifting the Crops*, with weight of each lot. All the lots were very equal, the reporter selected average rows, the cabbages were cut off the roots with a sharp spade just below the leaves; the turnips were pulled, the roots cut off, the top separated from the bulb, and all weighed separately. It is but fair to state that neither the swedes nor the cabbages were at maturity; the Fostertons were so; the two former lots being in all the vigour of growth at the time of weighing, 23d October. The portion of each kind weighed amounted to the twenty-eighth part of an acre. The following is the result:—

|  | Swedes | | Fostertons | | Cabbages | |
|---|---|---|---|---|---|---|
|  | Pt. wghd. | Per acre. | Pt. wghd. | Per acre. | Pt. wghd. | Per acre. |
|  | T. C. Qr. | T. C. Qr | T. C. Qr. | T. C. Qr. | T. C. Qr. | T. C. Qr. |
| Top, . | 0 4 2 | 6 6 0 | 0 3 2 | 4 18 0 | 1 5 2 | 30 14 0 |
| Bulb, . | 0 10 2 | 14 14 0 | 0 11 1 | 15 15 0 | ..... | ..... |
| Total per acre, . | | 21 0 0 | ...... | 20 13 0 | ...... | 30 14 0 |

*Estimated Value of each Lot.*—According to Sinclair's analysis, Drumhead cabbages contain 430 grains of nutritive matter and 280 grains of fibre per pound, and the average amount of nutritive matter in cabbages, as compared with common turnips, is 215 of the former to 160 of the latter, and inferior to swedes in the proportion of 215 of the former to 220 of the latter. Taking these as the standard, the following is the amount of nutritive matter per acre of the three lots experimented on, viz. :—

|  | Weight per acre as per former table. | | | Nutritive amount of each per acre, as per Sinclair's standard. | | | | |
|---|---|---|---|---|---|---|---|---|
|  | tons | cwts. | qrs. | tons | cwts. | qrs. | lbs. | oz. |
| Swedes, . . . | 21 | 0 | 0 | 0 | 18 | 1 | 0 | 5 |
| Fostertons, . . | 21 | 13 | 0 | 0 | 16 | 0 | 8 | 1 |
| Cabbage, . . | 30 | 14 | 0 | 1 | 2 | 3 | 18 | 0 |

By this it will be seen that an acre of cabbages is capable of producing a much greater amount of nutritive matter than either turnips or swedes, and this trial must not be taken as the full amount cabbages are able to produce, as they were planted later in the season in order to test them thoroughly against turnips, and to keep up a succession of green food for the cows. I have another two acres in an adjoining field, planted 36 inches between the plants, and 30 inches between the rows, that the reporter is now using, which is proved by weighing to produce at the rate of 37 tons 1 cwt. per acre; this lot was planted on 29th April. The relative value of each lot will be better seen by the following table, where I suppose the "consuming" value of Fostertons to be rather under 10 shillings per ton, or at the rate of £10 per acre, thus :—

Fostertons, . . . . £10  0  0  per acre.
Swedes, . . . . 11  7  1¼  „
Cabbages, . . . . 14  5  1¼  „

But in order to arrive at the true value we must deduct from each kind any seed or extra labour the one has more than the other, thus :—

|  | Plants. | | | Planting. | | | Seed. | | | Singling. | | | Total per acre. | | |
|---|---|---|---|---|---|---|---|---|---|---|---|---|---|---|---|
|  | £ | s. | d. | £ | s. | d. | £ | s. | d. | £ | s. | d. | £ | s. | d. |
| Swedes, . | ....... | | | ....... | | | 0 | 2 | 6 | 0 | 5 | 0 | 0 | 7 | 6 |
| Fostertons, . | ....... | | | ....... | | | 0 | 2 | 6 | 0 | 5 | 0 | 0 | 7 | 6 |
| Cabbages, . | 1 | 10 | 0 | 0 | 5 | 0 | ...... | | | ...... | | | 1 | 15 | 0 |

Deducting these sums from the former relative value we arrive at the true value of each lot per acre, thus :—

|  | Swedes. | | | Fostertons. | | | Cabbages. | | |
|---|---|---|---|---|---|---|---|---|---|
|  | £ | s | d. | £ | s. | d. | £ | s | d. |
| Deduct extras, . | 11 | 7 | 1¼ | 10 | 0 | 0 | 14 | 5 | 1¼ |
|  | 0 | 7 | 6 | 0 | 7 | 6 | 1 | 15 | 0 |
|  | 10 | 19 | 7¼ | 9 | 12 | 6 | 12 | 10 | 1¼ |

Showing by this experiment that cabbages are of more value than either Fostertons or swedes by £1, 10s. 6d. of the latter, and by £2, 8s. 7¼d. of the former, and my experience fully bears out this, as I have always observed that the cows increase in milk when put on cabbages.

*Method of storing Cabbages.*—It is always an important matter to have food stored for a storm during winter. The reporter has found a very cheap and simple method of storing cabbages by cutting them off root as already described, then turn them upside down to allow the water to run out of them, and by merely piling them up like a potato pit they will keep during any storm; care must be taken not to make the heap wider than 3½ or 4 feet at bottom, and about four feet high. It is also better to cut them when free from frost, as the outer leaves are very brittle when frozen, and considerable loss may be the result.

*Another mode of Planting* which the reporter has done, is to spread the manure on the surface of the field before the last ploughing, when it is ploughed in the ordinary way, and the plants are then put in with a spade between every third furrow, or at such width as may be desired. The reporter prefers the drilling, as practised in the preceding experiment, unless the bringing the land into fertility be the chief object, and where there is an unlimited supply of manure, which has seldom been the case in the reporter's experience.

*Another mode of Planting* which the reporter has seen, but not practised, is to put the plants and manure into every third furrow as the last ploughing proceeds. This method is chiefly done where manure is scarce, and where the present crop is the chief object, as the manure can be put near the roots, and where they will not have far to "seek" their food.

## TEA AND SILK FARMING IN NEW ZEALAND.

By WILLIAM COCHRAN, Overdale, Dunblane, Perthshire.

*[Premium—Fifteen Sovereigns.]*

EARLY in 1864 the writer visited China, with the intention of remaining in that country a few years. His main object was the practical study of tea management and sericiculture in the natural home of these interesting avocations, with the view of subsequently conveying the experience thus acquired to India, or to some other suitable dependency or colony of Great Britain, where it might afterwards be found that tea and silk farming could be profitably conducted, and where there were facilities for the creation of a large industrial establishment. At this period, and for fully twelve years previously, tea cultivation had taken root in India, chiefly on account of the transfer, in 1839 and 1840, of the bulk of the gardens, experimentally planted by Government, to the Assam Company; but the progress of the undertaking as a whole had scarcely answered the predictions of its earlier successes, as, up to 1864, the total export of Indian grown tea was only 3,285,000 lbs. per annum, as compared with the imports of China and Japan tea to this country that year amounting to 120,284,000 lbs. It was not that Indian tea enterprise lacked encouragement, because not only had the Government taken it up with all commendable energy from the first, and afterwards distributed thousands of tea-plants and hundreds of tons of seed gratis to all who chose to apply, but rather that the entire industry was new, and very few persons in India then, and for some years afterwards, thoroughly knew its details. The tyro, aspiring to reach the summit of any vocation, has from the remotest times been required to sit for a specified apprenticeship at the feet of some properly accredited Gamaliel until he had acquired at least the rudiments of the calling he proposed to follow. In proportion, also, to the abstruseness of the theorems, and the delicacy and difficulty of the manipulations he might have to learn—aided of course by his natural ability and industry—would be the demand for mental and physical application ere he could claim to be regarded as a master. This self-evident truth seems to have been almost forgotten or ignored during the earlier years of tea preparation in India. It is simply astonishing now to take a retrospect of these former days, and learn that intending planters, after perhaps a cursory acquaintance with a few tea samples in the London market, never thought of practically learning their business by flocking to the tea districts of China—the only existing school at that time, and probably the most efficient even yet—for a thorough tea education. Travellers through China, such as Lettsom, Kæmpfer, Huc, Ball, Jacobson, Rhind, Williams, Fortune, and others, had doubtless already published their impressions regarding the tea industry there and in Java, and one or two of these gentlemen did good service in connection with the infant enterprise in various parts of Hindustan, but with those exceptions, and probably a few of their readers, the prevailing degree of knowledge on the subject, extant at the time referred to, was of the most meagre description. Indeed, so far from many of the early tea planters of India being practical men, they were mostly retired officers and soldiers, civilians who had failed at other occupations, and chubby youngsters, sons of shareholders in tea gardens or owners of land, fresh from school or college, who, amidst the predominating ignorance of the period, were reckoned as likely to produce good tea, as if they had been trained for long years to the calling. Thus in 1864 the Indian tea enterprise was suffering from inadequate information and defective management, as well as from financial and other causes. There appeared to be an opening for some one with practical experience to improve matters, so the writer, having already acquired all the information possible in this country, determined to spend some years in China in an endeavour to accomplish the rest.

It would be out of place in an essay of this kind to chronicle the various odd incidents and adventures which occurred during the three years which were spent in various parts of the Chinese empire. Yet one little scene may be noted as illustrative of the intense desire for information about European habits and inventions which characterises the well-educated among the commercial classes of China, and to show some of the difficulties which beset the searcher after truth even in the houses of the wealthy.

The writer having been strongly recommended to visit, and if possible spend some time at, a particular tea farm in Hounan, on account of the admirable system upon which it was conducted, and the fine quality of the produce, went. It involved a journey of nearly one thousand miles by steamer, junk, and coolie carriage, and occupied some time. When nearly at his destination he sent forward his native letters of introduction, and nothing could have been kinder than his reception. He was cordially invited to spend weeks, months, all his spare time in fact, at several different hongs; but as this was impossible, he took up his quarters with the farmer to whom he had been specially recommended, who declined, indeed, to part with his guest during the period of his stay, and who also lodged and fed his five coolies. After each day's visits had been paid to the adjoining farms and manipulating houses, and the necessary notes and sketches completed, every evening brought saturnalia which generally extended into the following morning. After the recurrence of a number of these mild little scenes of dissipation, the writer began to fear that his small store of information and anecdote must fail under the constant battery of questions from an audience which was in great part renewed on each occasion. Curiously enough, no matter what topic might have been started, the conversation quickly drifted to machinery, which remorselessly swallowed up all others. Steam engines, marine and locomotive, pumping, boring, and hammering implements supplied an inexhaustible fund for discussion; all of which the unfortunate stranger was forced to describe and illustrate to the best of his limited ability, by the aid of his pencil and a few daubs of colour. On one occasion, the dawn of a lovely morning broke over the still unsatisfied Celestials, but without showing the slightest symptoms of weariness in them, or creating a pause in the hurricane of queries. What was to be done? Change the subject as he might, and yawn as he pleased, the writer was immediately brought back by his enthusiastic friends to pinions, cranks, pistons, wheels, boilers, and explosions; all of which he had to sketch over and over again, every scrap of paper so decorated being carefully pocketed and carried off. At length a bright idea occurred to his fatigued and whirling brain. Among the few instruments and articles of luggage the writer had with him was an atmospheric coffee-making apparatus. Obtaining a supply of hot water, sugar, milk, and cups, he put a spoonful of water into the bulb, set the fountain to work, lighted the spirit-lamp, and told his amiable tormentors to watch. Upon the fountain the eyes of the Chinamen were speedily rivetted as it presently began to boil, their wonder and excitement augmenting as the ebullition became furious without, to their apprehension, any apparent reason. It was a strange, weird scene, rendered all the more impressive by the attitudes of the eager beings as they contemplated the lambent flame caressing the apparently empty globe. From the dark brown, richly carved and varnished timbers of the roof many lanterns depended, some of which had gone out; the first faint blush of morning tinged the latticed tracery at the end of the hall, showing a huge grotesque idol in a niche before which the remains of four once tall candles guttered; the muffled hum from a thousand tea manipulators floated in from the adjoining factory; whilst in the immediate foreground stood the tired out demonstrator still holding his students with as potent a spell as the scarcest ancient manuscript, or the most unique fossil could have exercised over a meeting of savants in Europe. If the almond-shaped eyes of the Chinamen opened widely when the coffee began to boil without any immediate cause, they seemed as if about to start from their sockets when,

M

equally without interference, the ebullition ceased. But when the lamp was extinguished and the rich brown fluid rushed through the syphon into the bulb, their delight seemed boundless, and their expressions of amazement were not repressed until each member of the seance had quaffed his share of the fragrant beverage. The little device succeeded; a climax had evidently been reached; no more questions were asked; hands were shaken, and the bewildered yet transported audience slowly dispersed.

On the return of the writer to London in 1867, the commercial firmament offered little to the view except the gloom which accompanies widely-spread forebodings of approaching financial disaster. Strikes among all classes of workmen prevailed; horrible discoveries of deliberate and ruthless murders, planned and executed among the saw-grinders of Sheffield, thrilled the public with loathing; crimes scarcely less hideous came to light from among the bricklayers of Manchester; Fenian and democratic offences against person and property were almost of daily occurrence, the grim catalogue of human debasement being appropriately concluded in December by the dastardly Clerkenwell outrage.

Amidst the tea companies of India, and the coffee companies of Ceylon there had ceased to be rejoicing over abundant crops and bulky dividends; indeed a species of hopeless anesthesia had apparently settled over all enterprise, which rendered the period peculiarly unpropitious for the introduction of any new project. Even before leaving China symptoms of this state of commercial stagnation had reached the writer, and he had lost much faith in India as the probable scene of his future labours, and subsequent correspondence, conversation, and reading rather inclined him to look favourably on Ceylon, failing which, New Zealand.

In the course of 1867 he had interviews or correspondence with the principal persons in London connected with coffee planting in Ceylon, and strongly urged their making a trial of tea. Sericiculture he did not advocate, as he was early informed that the prejudices of the natives who were under the influence of the Buddhist superstition, could not be overcome, and that it was useless to attempt silk-rearing there.* Unfortunately the gentlemen consulted did not acquiesce in the proposals made then, although afterwards, in 1872, the tea industry began slowly to take root in Ceylon, and has since become one of some importance. Thrown back, therefore, upon his last, and probably strongest citadel, the writer immediately set about the institution of exhaustive inquiries respecting the suitability of New Zealand for tea and silk farming, the substance of which, as well as his Chinese experience, will be found embodied in the following pages.

* Since then this prejudice seems in the way of being conquered, as attempts are now being made to domesticate sericiculture in Ceylon.

## New Zealand, China, India, and Ceylon.

New Zealand is situated in the Southern Hemisphere, and consists of the North, South, and Stewart's Islands, with several small dependencies; the group lying between 34° and 48° S. lat., and 166° and 179° E. long.; measuring about one thousand one hundred miles in total length, with a varying breadth of from forty-six to two hundred and fifty miles, yet with no portion of its territory more than seventy-five miles from the sea. In extent the entire colony covers an area of about sixty-four million acres, so that it is somewhat smaller than Great Britain and Ireland. The islands were discovered in 1642 by Tasman, a Dutch navigator, who, after naming the cluster, merely sailed round without landing, and took no steps to gain possession for his government. From this date until 1769 there exists no reliable record of any stranger having visited these shores; but on the 8th October of the latter year the illustrious Captain Cook landed in Poverty Bay, on the east side of the North Island. Other voyagers in rapid sequence succeeded Captain Cook, who commenced, and for some years maintained, a tolerably friendly, although somewhat irregular, intercourse with the natives. Whaling and other ships got into the habit of calling, and sometimes a few of the Maories would return temporarily with their crews to Sydney and other Australian ports, in order to gratify their curiosity regarding the exciting accounts they had heard of the magnificence and power of the Pakehas, as they called our countrymen. This custom, both innocent and laudable in itself, led, unfortunately, in 1809, to a deplorable tragedy, which may be regarded as the beginning of that protracted period of mutual bloodshed and reprisals which endured, with only limited periods of tranquillity, for nearly sixty years. The trading ship "Boyd," from Sydney, with seventy persons on board, including four New Zealanders and the son of a chief, returning to their own country, anchored off Wangaroa to allow the Maories to land, and with the object of enabling the crew to cut some spars. The young chief landed alone, and succeeded in arousing the revengeful passions of his tribe, who were in the vicinity, by describing a flogging he had received on board for declining, on account of his rank, to assist in working the ship during the voyage. Returning to the vessel in a short time with some of his friends, they, with smiles and apparent amity, invited the Captain and part of the crew to land and point out what trees would suit. No sooner had they entered the forest, than the whole of the Europeans were, at a preconcerted signal, massacred. After dark the young savage and his people boarded and plundered the ship, slaughtering all they found except a woman, two children, and a cabin boy who had previously shown him some kindness. This outrage was quickly followed by other atrocities on both sides; mutual carnage becoming the order of the day, thus strengthening and prolonging the dismal vendetta.

It was not until 1814 that a rift in the gloom appeared, in the arrival of the first missionaries, who were presently succeeded by further reinforcements, when the process of civilisation slowly commenced. About this period the horrible traffic in preserved New Zealander's heads began. The natives had long been accustomed to decapitate their captured enemies, pickling and keeping their heads as trophies of their prowess, as the North American Indians did scalps. This habit had been noted with an eye to profit by some degraded European trader who, as a speculation, exported a few of the tatooed, dried, and ghastly objects; and these loathsome relics were eagerly purchased by curiosity-mongers in Australia and elsewhere. In a very short time the experiment expanded into a recognised occupation, and as prices advanced with the increasing demand and the diminishing supply taken in war, so did the original trade in the heads of the slain quickly merge into fearful bargains with assassins for the heads of persons who were still alive. There can be no possible doubt that this odious traffic, conducted as it was, according to the author of *Old New Zealand* (pp. 54–59), by the skippers of many of the colonial trading schooners, and the scum of the European settlers, retarded for years the progress of civilisation; paralysed the best efforts of the missionaries, as the Anglo-Indian opium traffic is now doing in China, and kept ever inflamed the moral sores originally produced by mutual treachery and violence. Fortunately, about 1830 the grim barter in human heads ceased; but it affords an eloquent satire upon the vaunted success usually claimed for the colonising ability of the Anglo-Saxon race, that up to the year 1839 only about two thousand emigrants had settled in the country. But the eradication of one evil seemed only to pave the way for another. Public attention had now been specially drawn to New Zealand, and during this year the first of the great quarrels connected with repudiations of bargains by the natives and encroachments by the settlers commenced. A tract of country as large as Ireland had been secured from the chiefs by a Colonel Wakefield for £1500 worth of jew's harps, tomahawks, muskets, gunpowder, and other articles; or at the rate of about sixpence per 1000 acres. Difficulties both with the Maories and with the British Government ensued, the former asserting that their chieftains had no right or authority to sell the land, and the latter deciding that "no subject could be permitted to enter into contracts with the natives in which they might be ignorant and unintentional authors of injuries to themselves." In consequence of this and similar disputes, an important change was determined on, which took the form of a public ceremony, by which, on the 16th November 1840, New Zealand was formally annexed to the British Crown, Captain Hobson being appointed its first governor. The immediate result of this wise step was that a tide of immigration set towards its shores, and for the first few years thereafter a degree of comparative calm prevailed. Thousands of colonists poured into the country from all Europe, and it seemed as if at last the good time, for which the well-wishers of the colony had so long been waiting, had arrived. Soon, however, the old jealousies and mutual recriminations reappeared; the natives sometimes taking the initiative by abjuring and disowning their own negotiations, as well as the bargains made for them by their chiefs; and the colonists adhering with the might of possesson to the acres upon which they had settled, and not hesitating occasionally to make the most unblushing encroachments on the reserved territories when favourable opportunities occurred. Thus, separate and independent colonial communities grew inwards from the sea-ports at which they originally landed, and these in time became the nucleus of the populations which now occupy the nine provinces into which New Zealand is at present divided. Thus, also, the aborigines were elbowed further and further out of the way, for it had long been evident that Christianity and cannibalism could not co-exist on the same territory; the colonists refused longer to tolerate the objectionable habits of the natives, and the natives on their part declined to be civilised. These and other points of difference, viewed in connection with the continually recurring land disputes and encroachments, explain the bitterness of the feeling which festered and matured on both sides, and led to the scenes of slaughter which raged with greater or less obstinacy during the succeeding thirty years.

Such, then, were the barriers which prevented the development sooner of some of the hidden resources of New Zealand. With a degenerate and dwindling native population, and intermittent war occurring up to 1870, and even later, it is scarcely surprising that, even among the more ambitious and scientifically inclined European settlers, only the ordinary grades of agriculture and manufacture had, until recent years, been attempted, and that the highly developed and refined industries of tea production and sericiculture are still reserved for the future.

Arrived at this point, the reader may legitimately ask, " What reason is there to believe that the cultivation and preparation of tea and silk are at all suited to the climate of New Zealand?" And this query having been satisfactorily answered, " What are the prospects of pecuniary success?" As the simplest and most effective way to a reply, it will be desirable to inspect some of the principal features offered by the practice of tea and silk farming in those countries where the industries in question have been long and successfully conducted. Of such, the tea and silk districts of China are evidently, on account of the antiquity and prosperity of the pursuits in that empire, entitled to our earliest and most careful examination.

From Chinese and other experience in various parts of Asia has arisen the Oriental apophthegm that "wherever the mulberry grows in profusion, there Nature indicates a suitable spot for tea." Without asking the reader to place any more reliance upon this dictum than would be bestowed upon the numerous wise proverbs connected with the weather and agriculture so popular and frequently quoted among ourselves, it may nevertheless serve for a convenient text, with this important qualification, that the tea-shrub, in one or other of its varieties, will thrive in localities too cold as well as too hot for the mulberry. In China the districts more especially devoted to tea-culture are comprehended between 23° and 25° N. lat., and 115° and 122° E. long., comprising portions of the provinces of Carton, Che-Kiang, Fokien, Hounan, Hupeh, Kiang-Si, and Kiang-Su; whilst those in which sericiculture has attained its greatest development are Che-Kiang, How-Quang, Kiang-Si, and Szechuen, all traversed by the thirtieth parallel of latitude. Both tea and silk of exquisite quality are produced together and separately in other parts of China outside the figures just given; but it is in the districts named that chasericulture has, in one or other of its branches, become most firmly rooted, and has exhibited the most satisfactory results.

A short paragraph may here be interpolated in explanation of the meaning of the word *chasericulture*, now employed for almost the first time to indicate the combined industries of tea and silk farming. Although the Chinese, strictly speaking, understand by the word *cha* only the watery infusion made from tea-leaves for use as a beverage, yet in the course of their commercial relations with Europeans it has also come to represent the dry prepared leaves themselves as they are exported. Hence the term *chase* they at an early period applied, during the East India Company's reign, to their tea inspectors and valuers at Canton, a word which is apparently an abridgement of *chatsze*, which specifies the broken refuse, fannings, and dust from the manufacture of tea for foreign markets, formerly used by the Chinese manipulators in place of soap for cleansing their hands. The next two syllables, *seri*, are derived from the Latin name for silk, *sericum*, which, as well as *serica* and *sereinda*, the Romans applied to China, believing that the people referred to in earlier times as the *Seres*, who were credited with the original discovery, production, and trade in silk, resided in that country. It is now thought that the *Seres* are more likely to have been the Persians, and this conjecture is not weakened by the circumstance that the Chinese Emperor Kaung-Shee, in his treatise on natural history, repudiates the appropriation of the honour by his countrymen, although he and others claim for the Empress Siling-Shi, wife of Hoang-Ti, who lived about 2700 years before the Christian era, the reputation of having originated silk manufacture. The latter part of the new word under review needs no explanation; and as space will be saved and exactitude imparted to the writer's meaning whenever reference is made in this essay to the combined industries of tea planting, growing, and manipulation; mulberry planting, cultivation, silkworm hatching, rearing, and silk production as far as the cocoon, the term *chasericulture* will be used.

It is perhaps a little unfortunate that no official records of thermal variations in China are available, so that it is impossible to collect a series of averages for any lengthened period, and such figures as are met with only refer to epochs of two or three years, and are only locally applicable. By personal observation, however, and comparison with the notes of previous and later residents, we offer the following table as a fairly accurate register of the monthly temperature at Shanghai:—

|  | Mean Max. | Mean Min. | Highest. | Lowest. |
|---|---|---|---|---|
|  | Deg. Fahr. | Deg. Fahr. | Deg. Fahr. | Deg. Fahr. |
| January, . . | 33 | 24 | 45 | 22 |
| February, . . | 33 | 26 | 46 | 24 |
| March, . . | 43 | 31 | 65 | 30 |
| April, . . | 54 | 42 | 63 | 41 |
| May, . . | 70 | 58 | 88 | 50 |
| June, . . | 80 | 69 | 97 | 65 |
| July, . . | 92 | 74 | 113 | 60 |
| August, . . | 91 | 75 | 99 | 66 |
| September, . | 80 | 66 | 96 | 65 |
| October, . . | 75 | 54 | 89 | 31 |
| November, . | 63 | 31 | 70 | 30 |
| December, . | 38 | 30 | 47 | 24 |
|  | 752 | 580 | 918 | 508 |
| Averages, . . | 62·66 | 48·33 | 76·50 | 42·33 |

This port, however, being only twelve miles from the sea, greater variations of temperature than those appearing in this diagram may be expected to occur in the more inland districts of the Upper Yangtsse, and on or near the shores of the Taho, Poyang, and Tungting Lakes. Accordingly a margin of temperature must be allowed, and some travellers consider that about 5° of Fahrenheit, judiciously added or deducted, ought to exhibit a fairly useful approximation to the actual average temperature of the Moyune country in the district of Kiang-Nan, a region in which most of the finest green teas of commerce are produced, and from whence our most copious supplies of the best China raw silk are derived. From another source (Archdeacon Gray's recent work on China, vol. ii. p. 358) we learn that the mean annual temperature of Canton, which is just within the tropics, is that which generally exists over the thirtieth parallel in that country; and, referring to the usual encyclopædias, we find the figures to be 70·50° of Fahrenheit.

A glance at the table, opposite the month of March, will show that, while the highest temperature indicated is 65°, or allow 70° for the Moyune district, the lowest reading is below the freezing-point, or say 35° for the same locality. It is during this comparatively cool season, and under the influence of gentle but frequent rains that the tea harvest usually commences. Beginning about the middle of the month, with a variation of a few days, or even weeks in widely separated spots, it may continue in its greatest briskness until the end of June, when the thermometer probably indicates the maximum temperature at 102° and the minimum 70° Fahr.

Among the earliest, if not the very first, of the spring shrubs to burst into foliage is the mulberry, but its available leaf harvest is not commonly much protracted beyond six weeks. During this period in the Canton district seven broods or hatchings, technically called "educations," of silkworms are fed and their silk obtained; so that, as a rule, the silk harvest is begun and ended ere the serious business of the tea season has far advanced, and the bulk of both these products is secured and their manipulation well forwarded within, or a very little beyond, the currency of the milder months of the year. It is the experience, indeed, of many intelligent natives consulted by the writer that the climate of the Chinese tea and silk districts is comparatively temperate during the spring and early summer; that the country is noted for its salubrity; and he can say, from personal observation, that the happy, thriving, well-dressed, and healthy appearance of the peasantry and all others with whom he came in contact during those seasons in the provinces of Hounan, Hupeh, and elsewhere, amply confirmed the native statements. Under these circumstances it may safely be regarded as true that a suitable and profitable tea climate need not necessarily be one involving extremes of heat and dampness, accompanied with fever and possibly premature death to the European planter, and that the dismal remarks of some authorities on tea planting in India, however applicable they may be to Assam, would be altogether misleading if used in reference to China, Ceylon, and New Zealand.

In the Island of Ceylon we have additional evidence that the tea industry may be, and is, satisfactorily conducted at a height above the sea which altogether precludes the presence of a very high temperature. On the estate of Abbotsford, at a height of from 4500 to 6000 feet, tea, closely resembling that produced at Dajeeling and Kangra in India, has been grown. At 6300 feet the hybrid Assam plant flourishes; even at 7000 feet some of the Ceylon planters are not disappointed with their experiments; and at the altitude of about 4600 feet ten years' observations by a Mr. Heelis show the mean temperature there to be 66·50° of Fahr. In short, it has been said on good authority that in Ceylon "tea will grow wherever coffee grows, and that it thrives at points too high, at levels too low, and in climates too moist for coffee." Such statistics, however, could prove of comparatively little value without some practical details of competitive results; but these we are fortunate in being able to furnish. At the recent International Exhibition at Melbourne the tea-planters of Ceylon took a distinguished place by carrying off eleven first-class awards out of a total of forty-nine bestowed; or altogether they secured thirty-six honours for the seventy-eight samples of tea they exhibited out of a total of 276 certificates of merit earned by the 506 samples submitted by the various tea-producing countries of the world.

That the indigenous tea of India, as grown in the gardens of Assam, Cachar, the Terai below Darjeeling, and the Western Dooars, is produced in a hotter, damper, and less healthy climate than that of the districts already referred to cannot be disputed. The outcome under such conditions of forced vegetation is shown in very frequent flushes of leaves and great strength in the finished tea; but the penalty exacted by Nature seems to consist in the sacrifice of that delicate and much-valued flavour so characteristic of the mountain-grown article yielded at Darjeeling and elsewhere, and of the fragrance and exquisite aroma which distinguishes the best teas of China. Ascend the Himalayas, however, it may be only a few hundred feet, or it may be several thousand feet, when the traveller will reach gardens producing tea similar in most respects to that grown in Ceylon, and not unlike some of the products of China, except that it lacks the charming perfume.

The elevation of the Indian tea-gardens varies considerably. At Nainee-Tal, where a landslip and appalling loss of life occurred a few years ago, tea-bushes grow to an enormous size at 6700 feet above the sea-level. The Darjeeling gardens are perched at a height of 5000 feet; in Kangra Valley tea is grown, mulberries are cultivated, and silkworms are successfully reared at 4000 feet; the Dehra Dhoon plantations are at the height of 1900 to 2000 feet; Assam is only a few hundred feet above the sea; and the Chittagong gardens but thirty feet.

As might be expected, the rainfall and temperature are quite as inconstant, varying in the one instance from 42 inches per annum in Kangra Valley to 252 inches in parts of Darjeeling; and in the other from 53° of mean temperature in the latter to 76° in Durrang, Assam. But as the tea-plant grows and flourishes under each and all of these diverse circumstances, there can be no doubt that every zone of cultivation possesses its own peculiar advantages, allied, perhaps, to certain drawbacks, a correct estimate of which will in time indicate to the planter at every altitude what particular sort of shrub he ought to cultivate and which to avoid.

Although the comparatively temperate climate of China during the spring and early summer is admirably suited to its own indigenous tea, it is not adapted, especially in the more northern districts, for the native Assam plant, the leaves of which cannot endure much cold, and are apt to shrivel up and wither away on exposure to even a very moderate degree of frost. On the other hand, the China bush grows well in India, and readily forms hybrids with the indigenous growths; still, the result of over thirty years' experience by the planters there does not seem in favour of hybridising. Deterioration, probably by reason of the intense heat, appears sooner or later to overtake the Chinese variety. We understand, indeed, that all hybrids have already been uprooted from some of the Indian gardens, and that a feeling is spreading among the garden managers to limit their future cultivation as much as possible to the native shrub, which certainly grows faster and yields more abundantly than the China kind or its hybrids do in the peninsula.

With these remarks as to the conditions of temperature and rainfall under which tea and mulberry bushes are successfully grown elsewhere, we come to some particulars of the climate of parts of New Zealand, and to the apparent advantages which invite the establishment of chasericulture there. If any reader of these pages chooses to institute inquiries, he will find that the climate in the interior of Otago, in the Dunstan and Queenstown districts, is like that of Greece, and has been pronounced by respectable Chinese resident on the spot, as well as by observant travellers, closely to resemble that of the tea and silk districts of China. He will learn that the thermometer indicates from 90° to 100° Fahr. nearly every summer; that as high as 110° have been noted at Alexandra, on the Molyneux River, and several other spots in both islands; and that the mulberry, ailanthus, and a few other silk-worm-feeding shrubs grow luxuriantly, particularly in the province of Auckland. It will also be ascertained that throughout this charming province snow is seldom seen, except upon the mountain tops; that even slight frosts are necessarily a rarity in a land where the forests are evergreen, and semi-tropical fruits grow profusely in the open air; that moderate and vivifying showers, to the extent of forty-seven inches, fall during one hundred to one hundred and eighty-six days of the year; that the mean of the coldest month is 51°, and that of the warmest 68° Fahr.; that the grape, vine, and olive are frequently found intermingled with the ordinary fences; and the hot, blighting winds and dust-storms of Australia and parts of Asia, so inimical to tea and mulberry culture and so fatal to the silkworm, are unknown. Probably no better certificate of excellence could be quoted in favour of this enticing province than the following diagram compiled from Dr. Hector's handbook prepared for visitors at the Sydney International Exhibition of 1879 :—

*Seasons and Climate of Auckland, New Zealand.*

| Seasons. | In Great Britain. | In New Zealand. | Difference of Mean Extremes in Daily Temperature. | Rainfall Inches. | Mean Temperature. Fahr. | Per Cent. of Rain per Season. |
|---|---|---|---|---|---|---|
| Spring, .. | February. | September. | 15·84 | 4·331 | 57·56 | 25 |
| | March. | October. | 16·56 | 3·520 | | |
| | April. | November. | 18·00 | 3·752 | | |
| | May. | December. | 18·90 | 3·409 | | |
| Summer, . | June. | January. | 19·80 | 2·071 | 66·92 | 19 |
| | July. | February. | 20·88 | 3·272 | | |
| | August. | March. | 19·80 | 3·150 | | |
| Autumn, . | September. | April. | 19·08 | 3·402 | 61·62 | 24 |
| | October. | May. | 16·92 | 4·771 | | |
| | November. | June. | 15·30 | 5·721 | | |
| Winter, .. | December. | July. | 15·48 | 5·279 | 52·34 | 32 |
| | January. | August. | 16·74 | 4·331 | | |
| Results, . . . | | | 17·77 | 47·009 | 59·49 | 100 |

Equally attractive are the sanitary temptations which Auckland offers to the weakly and toilworn, as well as to the robust and vigorous searchers after a pleasant home. The "Official Handbook" (1875), at page 244, informs us that "the percentage of deaths to births the previous year was only 17·75, a very much lower average than prevails in England and other European countries. . . . Serious epidemics of any kind have happily been unknown; cases of measles and scarlatina are also of rare occurrence. . . . The climate of Auckland is specially beneficial to asthmatic patients, and the northern portions of the province, particularly the Bay of Islands, are recommended by medical men for persons suffering from diseases of the lungs. The warm lakes and sulphur springs in the Rotorua district have become famous for the cure of rheumatism and kindred diseases."

Such are some of the many advantages and allurements which

beckon the enthusiastic chasericulturist and others to this seductive land.

For convenience of comparison we shall now epitomise the foregoing climatic statistics thus :—

1. We learn that a fairly accurate register of temperature kept at Shanghai, in China, for a few years showed the highest reading of a Fahrenheit's thermometer to have been 113° in the month of July, and the lowest indication 22° during January; that the mean of the highest readings was 76·50°, and the lowest 42·33°; that a margin of about 5° should be allowed as the approximate correction for the Chinese tea and silk districts; and that the rainfall there is gentle but frequent, with a salubrious climate.

2. We find that the mean annual temperature at Canton is 70·50°; that this is the prevailing heat generally along the thirtieth parallel; and that, according to Dr. Gray, the average annual rainfall is from 68 to 72 inches.

3. That the spring temperature of the Moyune district may range from about 35° to 70°, with frequent rains, and that it is during the comparatively cool months that the tea and silk harvests are obtained.

4. We glean that in Ceylon tea is successfully produced at heights of 4600 feet to 7000 feet above the sea-level in a mean temperature at 4600 feet of 66·50° Fahr., where there is neither the great heat nor copious moisture of Assam; and that at the recent Melbourne Exhibition the tea planters of that island earned a distinguished place for their produce, and a fair percentage of first-class awards for its excellence.

5. That in India tea is produced in gardens situated from 30 feet to 6700 feet above the sea-level under mean temperatures ranging from 53° to 76° Fahr., and with an annual rainfall varying between 42 and 252 inches.

6. That portions of New Zealand possess a climate resembling that of Greece and the tea and silk districts of China, notably the province of Auckland, the average of whose coldest months is 34°, and whose hottest 90·40° Fahr., with a well-distributed rainfall of 45·50 to 47 inches, spread over from one hundred to one hundred and eighty days of the year.

Apparently, therefore, as far as general climate, temperature, and rainfall are concerned, a fair theoretical case seems to have been stated in favour of the establishment of chasericulture in parts of New Zealand, especially in the province of Auckland; a district which promises to be equally suited to produce the hardy and flavoury teas of China, and the less robust, although more astringent, growths of Assam. And as the mulberry, ailanthus, and other shrubs and trees which afford food for different races of silkworms are known to grow there luxuriantly, we have evidently lighted upon a most desirable silk country also.

## SERICICULTURE.

Having thus endeavoured to show the suitability of the Auckland climate for the prosecution of chasericulture, the position assumed cannot be weakened, but may be materially fortified, if any moderately recent example of a successful essay at tea or silk production in New Zealand can be quoted. As yet, unfortunately, tea cultivation, we believe, has not been tried beyond the precincts of the Government Botanic Gardens or in private policies; but as mulberry bushes are numerous in various parts of the islands, are readily propagated from cuttings, and as the eastern aphorism already cited that "wherever the mulberry grows in profusion there Nature indicates a suitable spot for tea" is not undeserving attention, any illustration given of success in sericiculture there may reasonably be held to apply to tea production also. Before offering an example of this kind, however, it will be desirable in a few paragraphs to trace some of the circumstances which originally led those interested in silk to extend their hopes to new countries, instead of continuing to centre them as formerly upon the European districts, which had partially supplied their markets with this beautiful and valuable material for nearly a thousand years, or upon the Far East, where it had been an article of commerce from the remotest antiquity.

By whom and where silkworms were first reared for their produce is unknown, although sericiculture has been traced through native writers as having been practised in China 2700 years prior to the Christian era; and it is fairly well established that not until thirty-three centuries afterwards was the silkworm introduced into Europe. During the period of six hundred years which followed, sericiculture was almost wholly limited to the Ægean Islands, Corinth, Athens, and Thebes, when the Venetians appropriated the industry, and grew very rich on its gains. In 1130 Roger II., King of Sicily, envied the lucrative traffic, and immediately proceeded to kidnap numbers of the silk weavers of Palestine whom he transferred to his own territory. Having established his victims in Palermo and over Calabria, the present vast silk trade of Italy was founded. To the Moors Spain owes her success in sericiculture, as, on the capture of Grenada by Ferdinand in the fifteenth century, the industry was found in a flourishing state there, and in Cordova and Murcia. In France, although the habits of the silkworm had been studied by some of the nobles at Dauphiny in the year 1480, it was not until 1521 that Henri Quatre gave a decided impetus to sericiculture, by encouraging the visits and settlement of Milanese artisans at Nismes, where they taught the French the manage-

ment of the white mulberry (*Morus alba*), how to treat silkworms (*Bombyx mori*), and to obtain their silk.  France profited
greatly by those instructions, and it is interesting, as illustrative
of the intense vitality of this shrub, to note that the first white
mulberry introduced by these Italian foresters on that occasion
is said still to survive, surrounded by its numberless offshoots.
From 1521 to 1853 the progress of sericiculture over Asia and
Europe, except during time of war, seems to have gone on almost
unchecked, but at the latter date it received a blow from which
it has not yet recovered.  In that year the mysterious combination of maladies, usually spoken of in a general way as the
"silkworm blight," appeared in such strength as utterly to defy
all human skill.  For some years before it had been slowly gaining
ground, but not to such an extent in any one district as to cause
serious alarm until 1853.  Among these diseases probably the most
dreaded was that known in France by the term *muscardine*, and
in Italy by the name *calcinetto* ; the latter appellation suggested
by the appearance of the skin of the afflicted worm, which
assumes a chalky aspect ; and the former on account of a fancied
resemblance to a kind of sugar-plum made and sold in Provence.
Examined microscopically, the diseased grub is seen to be full of
the sprouting spors of a minute fungus (*Botrytis bassiana*), which
eventually pierce the skin, and produce the mealy, chalky, or
leprous aspect which lend the distinguishing names to the distemper.  The poor little creature, thus impaled on hundreds of
tiny stakes, could scarcely be expected to survive ; accordingly,
it usually perishes ere it has had time to commence its cocoon,
and the fungus, gathering additional sustenance from the worm's
decay, ripens its noxious spores, which, wind-borne, extend the
contagion far and near.  For the other minor distempers which
attack the worm, palliatives, if not absolute means of cure, have
been discovered, but for this deadly fungus-fiend—none.  The
result has been that the scourge maintains its hold in most of
the countries where the industry has been long pursued, and a
deterioration of the silkworm has followed, and is still unchecked.
Under these untoward circumstances it was suggested that the
Australian climate in some districts might prove uncontaminated
with the deadly cryptogam ; and as the mulberry was known to
grow luxuriantly about Sydney and elsewhere, that the rearing
of healthy grubs might succeed there.  The experiment was tried
with complete success ; strong and healthy worms were hatched,
and their eggs, when offered in the Italian market, sold at from
twenty to thirty francs per ounce, at a time when the finest
Japanese *grain* (considered till then the freest from disease) only
brought from fifteen to twenty-five francs per ounce.

If the climate of Great Britain, or any portion of it, had been
found suitable for sericiculture so as to yield a fair profit, we may

be satisfied that the industry would long ago have taken rank among our most cherished employments. True, the cultivation of the mulberry, and the rearing of silkworms here and there in the British Islands, have not been without a certain amount of encouragement, as at Poole, in Dorsetshire, in 1788; by Captain Mason at Aldershot some years ago, and at present at his residence, Manor House, Yateley, Farnborough; and in the suburbs of London and elsewhere frequently; but the success hitherto met with has been that of persevering and enthusiastic amateurs, to whom an immediate financial triumph has not been the chief object.

Among those who have already striven to introduce or promote the culture of the mulberry and preparation of silk in our colonies may be mentioned Mr. Powal, at Cape of Good Hope; Mr. Charles Brady, of New South Wales; Mr. Coote, of Queensland; Mr. Davenport, of Adelaide; Mr. Barlee, of Western Australia; and Mrs. Bladen Neill, of the Murray River, Australia, to the last of whom belongs the honour of creating the "Victoria Ladies' Sericicultural Company, Limited," New South Wales, with offices in Melbourne and London. This company—managed and worked entirely by ladies with a board of advice consisting of eight gentlemen—was projected for the purpose of mulberry culture, silk farming, &c., and was intended to spread its operations all over the Australian colonies, including New Zealand and probably Fiji. One of the first spots chosen by the company for a mulberry plantation proving unsuitable, the shrubs were afterwards transferred to their present site on the Murray River, the Government of Victoria very considerately awarding the ladies a sum of £700 as compensation for their lost time. Here the association, with a band of women and girls, assisted by a few Chinamen, prosecuted the work on land, and in a climate pronounced by Mr. William Brocklehurst, M.P. for Macclesfield, "so superior that it must be pre-eminently suited for the production of the finest silk in the world." This most interesting association has, of course, met with disappointments and successes, some of which we would like to chronicle, but must through the exigencies of space refrain. A few statistics, however, will serve as an illustration of what remarkable pecuniary results may be anticipated from sericiculture in a suitable climate, when prosecuted with the intelligence and energy which has already characterised the ladies of Victoria. The particulars of the following diagram were furnished by Miss Mary Hiles,* the company's manager in London, and is intended to show from previous experience the cost of establishing a small mulberry plantation in the Murray district, a year's

* Since this paragraph was penned the writer learns that the London agency has been abandoned.

maintenance, working expenses connected with the first crop of cocoons, and the financial result.

### Preliminary Outlay.

| | | | | |
|---|---|---|---|---|
| Cost of fifty acres, at £2 per acre, . . . | £100 | 0 | 0 | |
| Clearing and trench ploughing, at £7, 5s., . | 362 | 10 | 0 | |
| Cost of 20,000 mulberry bushes, at 5s., . . | 5000 | 0 | 0 | |
| Magnaneries, stores, and incidentals, . . | 700 | 0 | 0 | |
| | | | | £6162 10 0 |

### Estimate of Annual Maintenance.

| | | | | |
|---|---|---|---|---|
| Cost of ordinary labour, at £5 per acre, . . | £250 | 0 | 0 | |
| Incidental expenses, . . . . . . | 100 | 0 | 0 | |
| Interest on £6162, 10s., at 8 per cent. per annum, . . . . . . . . | 493 | 0 | 0 | |
| | | | | £843 0 0 |

### Estimate of Working Expenses.

A series of "educations," or hatchings, in connection with the food afforded from fifty acres of five-year-old mulberries would require six ounces of silkworm's eggs per acre, or 300 ounces requiring the services of—

| | | | | |
|---|---|---|---|---|
| Sixteen women and girls at £3, . . | £48 | 0 | 0 | |
| Eight Chinamen at £1, 16s. 8d., . . | 14 | 13 | 4 | |
| Four boys at 14s., . . . . . | 2 | 16 | 0 | |
| Cost of labour for each education, . . . | £65 | 9 | 4 | |

But as the climate of Australia allows seven hatchings to occur, therefore multiply by seven, . . . . . . . . . . . 458 5 4

Add annual cost of maintenance, . . . . . . 843 0 0

The cost of obtaining a season's silk from 300 ounces of eggs hatched and fed upon the produce of fifty acres of five-year-old mulberries . . . . . . . £1301 5 4

### Estimate of the Pecuniary Return.

| | | | | | |
|---|---|---|---|---|---|
| Say 30, 0000 lbs cocoons, yielding 3000 lbs. of raw silk at £2, . . . . . . | | | £6000 | 0 | 0 |
| Less cost of reeling, at 3s. 6d., . | £525 | 0 | 0 | | |
| And cost of obtaining as above, | 1301 | 5 | 4 | | |
| | | | 1826 | 5 | 4 |
| Thus yielding an apparent profit of . . . . . | | | £4173 | 14 | 8 |

It is only fair to add, however, that the accuracy of this example of successful silk rearing has been questioned as either exaggerated in regard to the income, or modified in respect of the outlay. That samples of Australian grown silk have been valued in the London market at 40s. per pound admits of no doubt, and it may equally be allowed that perhaps some items of expenditure may have been overlooked in the foregoing estimate; nevertheless, the large profit it exhibits of £83, 9s. 5¼d.

per acre, or a dividend of nearly 68 per cent. upon the outlay, is surely a result which, after making every reasonable deduction and allowance, no other among our ordinary agricultural products can show. It may well be taken into account, also, that the example given refers to a new mulberry plantation, which in the course of other five years would have doubled its yield, and correspondingly increased even the large return quoted.

Whilst the advocates for sericiculture in Australia, and elsewhere, were thus busily engaged, the subject had found exponents in New Zealand also, particularly in the person of Mr. T. C. Batchelor of Nelson, who, in 1870, endeavoured to arouse the Government and wake up the colonists to see the magnificent commercial prospect opening up before their eyes. The efforts of this gentleman culminated in the presentation of a series of printed papers on sericiculture to both houses of the Colonial Assembly the same year; but, unfortunately, the proposal thereafter gradually slid into oblivion. At a later date, however, it was again revived, partly through the display at the Sydney exhibition of 1879, of some beautiful specimens of cocoons and raw silk, reared in Auckland and Canterbury, and partly, no doubt, by reason of the untiring advocacy of the industry on the part of a few believers in this capability of the colony. For seven years prior to 1870 Mr. Batchelor had been cultivating the Tuscan mulberry, and producing silk to a limited extent; and in one of the printed papers referred to, he stated, for the information of the Government, that four year's experience had convinced him that an annual yield of value to the extent of £100 per acre would fall greatly short of the result he expected a few years later, when his trees had grown older. However, beyond calling attention to the suitability of part of New Zealand for sericiculture; eliciting some interesting information through official sources, and obtaining an offer of a Government bonus for the encouragement of the industry, no further issue of Mr. Batchelor's strenuous advocacy at that time appeared. But his agitation was not fruitless, as the subject of sericiculture was one of those taken up by the Colonial Industries Commission, which began taking evidence afterward, and finishing their labours in 1880. Symptoms of local interest in the matter had likewise appeared in the greater frequency with which recent travellers reported having noted patches of mulberry cultivation in widely separated districts, and that some of the colonists, as well as a few of the Maoris, were turning their attention to, and doing a little in, silk production. In the Commissioner's Report just referred to, at page 39 of the Appendix, notice is taken of a letter forwarded by the writer of this essay to a gentleman in Auckland, on the subject of sericiculture there, as follows:—
" Mr. Richard Dignan to Mr. Commissioner A. J. Burns, Auck-

land, 15th May 1880.—Sir, I have the honour to inform you that I have received a letter from a gentleman in Scotland, who has an idea that New Zealand is a suitable place for carrying on the silk industry. The writer states that competent authorities are of opinion that, unless some effectual remedy is discovered soon, the silkworms of Europe and part of Asia run a risk of early extinction. It will be to new countries, therefore, like Australia and New Zealand that the silk-brokers, merchants, and spinners of the future will have to look for supplies. The letter also contains a query—namely, 'Will the Government give any encouragement to persons willing to embark in this industry; and, if so, in what direction would such encouragement tend?' From the above you will understand that this colony is attracting the attention of silk-growers; and one reason at least is advanced why the question should receive some consideration. In and around the city of Auckland there are many mulberry trees, and if it were thought advisable, from these trees could be made the nucleus of a grove sufficient to try experiments in silk raising. The white mulberry grows readily from cuttings, and thrives well in this district. I have raised several hundred plants myself during the last few years. In 1870 the Government published valuable detailed information, collected by a Royal Commission specially appointed to inquire into the subject. Thus it will only be necessary to make a practical use of the important data already on hand. To bring the matter formally before the Commission, I would ask, on behalf of this part of the colony, which seems so well suited to the silk industry, if it is the intention of the Commission now sitting to recommend that encouragement be given to persons willing to take up this important industry? Would the Government be willing to revive the bonuses offered on similar conditions to those in force a few years back?—Signed, Richard Dignan."

In the body of the Report the Commissioners state that "there is little doubt that mulberry cultivation for silkworms could be pursued with advantage in some parts of New Zealand;" and they again direct public attention to the papers which they had already published on this industry, which in their "opinion could be pursued profitably even by cottagers, and without any costly appliances." For the encouragement of the silk-industry, the Commission also recommend that the bonus should be revived which was offered in 1871, namely, "A bonus of 50 per cent. on the value realised is offered for the production of the first one thousand pounds worth of the cocoons of the silkworm, or eggs of the silkworm, produced in the colony, to be paid on quantities of not less value than fifty, or more than one hundred pounds produced by any one person." The tea industry is not alluded to in connection with this bonus, although at page 42 of the Appendix to the Report, Mr. Thomas Kirk, in his evidence given before the Commissioners at Wellington, on the 8th June 1880, said, " There can be no question that the Assam variety of tea can be grown very well in the North Island, but the cost of labour would prevent its being cultivated at a profit." Doubtless, however, that important article would also be willingly acknowledged as forming one of the products for which the Commission recommend the Government, to " guarantee interest up to five per cent. on the outlay for a period of four, five, or six years, according to the nature of the undertaking."

To epitomise the present aspect of sericiculture in New Zealand, therefore, we would say that more than ten years ago it was proved to be, on an experimental scale, a success ; a government bonus was offered in 1871 for its encouragement, but was unfortunately allowed to lapse, the revival of this bonus has lately been recommended by the Colonial Industries Commission ; meanwhile the industry is being prosecuted to a small extent, both by colonists and Maories ; the mulberry is reported to be growing luxuriantly in different parts of the islands, so that the colonial nurserymen are able to supply the *Morus alba* in thousands (see *The Press*, Christchurch, 6th June 1881) ; and we learn from the official catalogue of the Sydney International Exhibition of 1879, that a gentleman in Auckland showed a case of crude silk, the produce of 1000 silk-worms reared by himself, and fed principally on mulberry, and occasionally on lettuce and fig leaves, and another in Christchurch, exhibited silk from worms fed in Canterbury.

After these statements and quotations the reader will not likely experience much difficulty in agreeing that parts of New Zealand, particularly Auckland, are evidently well adapted for silk farming, and by analogy for tea culture also. Further on we shall endeavour to explain why, in order to make these industries a mutual success, they must be linked together and conducted under the same head management, by the same general staff of servants, and on the same farm.

### COST OF PRODUCING TEA AND SILK.

Before entering upon the reasons for our belief, that in order to attain the best pecuniary result tea-farming and silk-culture in New Zealand must be combined and worked together, it will be judicious to examine such particulars of the cost of production in other countries as are available. Foremost in the expense connected with the prosecution of these industries in every country has been the item of wages, and, in a secondary degree, the cost of land, &c. In China the lands are all freehold, that is, are held by families direct from the Sovereign on payment of a fixed annual tax, and are usually sub-let to farmers and others at full rates. Wages are, according to our ideas, small. "Tea-gatherers," says Williams in his *Middle Kingdom* (vol. ii. p. 136), "are paid according to the quantity of leaves they bring in, at the rate of about four or five cash per catty, and expert pluckers can accomplish from thirty to forty catties per day, or from 40 to 53 lbs. of leaves, for which they receive from 6d. to 9d. But it is only very expert and well-trained hands that can make so much. Labourers in the tea districts receive from 2d. to 3d. per day and their food, which is always furnished by the farmer, and may cost about 3d. or 4d. more, making the whole day's outlay for labour amount to 6d. or 7d. The food is of the simplest kind,—rice, vegetables, and a small portion of pork or dried fish."

Coolies who carry heavy burdens, and who may be called upon to travel for days or weeks together, such as the porters who convey packages of tea from the interior to the canals or creeks which lead to the various shipping ports, are remunerated more liberally. According to a calculation made on the basis of some of Mr. Fortune's statistics given in his *Tea Districts of China*, these men receive at the rate of about 10d. per day. Another class of Chinese coolies, possessing some topographical knowledge, whose duties consist in carrying European and other foreign travellers about, are more highly paid still. Mr. Thornville Thomas Cooper, who for five years had wandered all over China, in his evidence before an East Indian finance committee of the House of Commons on the 23d May 1871, stated in reply to questions, Nos. 5468 to 5474 (page 253): "I had eight coolies to carry my chair at 250 cash each per day; 1000 cash are equal to one tael, and I have got the tael down at the value of 6s. 8d. They carried me on an average of 20 miles a day." In this example it will be observed that the wages paid were exactly double those previously alluded to, or 1s. 8d. a day; but it must be recollected that these men were probably paid at an extra rate on account of being with Mr. Cooper away from their homes for months, perhaps years, at a stretch, and that foreign employers of Chinese labour within the country are almost invariably charged more for similar service than natives would be. Probably, then, a fair overhead estimate of the average wages paid throughout the interior of China, and presumably in the tea and silk districts, would be from 8d. to 10d. per day. This estimate is also based on the circumstance that much of the manipulation, and all the lighter operations connected with both industries, are usually performed by women and children, whose remuneration is known to be very moderate.

In India the wages paid in the various tea districts vary even

more considerably than they do in China, as in certain localities
no aborignal population exists, or, if there be a sprinkling of
native peasantry, it is so scanty that supplies of labour must be
imported; a matter of increasing difficulty in proportion as the
neighbourhood bears an indifferent or bad sanitary reputation.
In 1869 the first conference on Indian matters was held by the
Society of Arts, London, at which some information was imparted on this subject by Mr. Fielder, hon. sec. of the Indian Tea
Planter's Association, and some of the gentlemen who took part
in the discussion. Mr. Fielder said that "The average rate of
wages per month in Assam (one of the districts requiring imported labour) was from two rupees, eight annas (5s.), to three
rupees (6s.) previous to 1857. In 1859 wages rose to four
rupees per month, and since then to seven and even nine rupees
per month through competition." This quotation, allowing 2s.
per rupee (a fuller rate of exchange than has been experienced
for some years, but sufficiently accurate for illustration), represents about 7d. a day. Mr. Horn afterwards stated that "He
had seen a deal of tea planting in Kumâon, but there was no
importation of coolies necessary, the labourers there being, generally speaking, natives of that part of the country, although in
some places it was very difficult to get them. The rate of wages
averaged from three to six rupees a month, or from 6s. to 12s."
By this gentleman's account, wages were evidently less in his
part of India than where Mr. Fielder's experience lay, being only
from 2d. to 4¾d. a day. In Darjeeling, at the end of 1879, we
learn from other sources that the average rate of wages was
about 10d. a day; and it should be borne in mind that whatever
the rate, the sirdar, or native overlooker, invariably levies a proportion, which in some districts reaches the monstrous figure of
25 per cent., or two annas per rupee. This, however, is partially
made up by the coolies receiving pay for Sundays, although no
work is done on that day—a charge on the planter of 14 per
cent., at which all of them grumble. The systems of paying by
results and by contract are also in vogue, as they secure the
utmost vigilence of the labourers, who generally make more
money thus than by fixed wages; and as by these methods the
coolies, having a personal stake, never overlook even the minor
flushes of leaves. By the former plan the coolie may earn 1s. a
day, and by the latter from 10d. to 1s. 2d. per day, or even more.
An epitome of these labour statistics will therefore stand thus:—

1. The daily wages paid in the tea and silk districts of China
may be stated as ranging between 8d. to 10c., average 9d.

2. In Assam, daily wages, exclusive of the cost of importing
labour, may be estimated at about 7d.

3. The natives of Kumâon receive about 4¾d. per day; no
imported labour required.

4. In Darjeeling at the end of 1879 the daily rate of pay was about 10d.

5. Paying by results and contract may yield a daily wage of from 10d. to 1s. 2d., average 1s.

Average of the examples quoted slightly over 8¼d.

The next inquiry necessary is that of the cost per lb. of producing tea. Mr. Rhind, in his *Commercial Products of the Vegetable Kingdom*, at page 393, say—"In order to afford some idea of the labour of tea manufacture, the following statement has been given:—To manufacture 80 lbs. of black tea per day 25 gatherers and 10 driers and sorters are required. To produce 92 lbs. of green tea 30 gatherers and 16 driers and sorters." With this information as a text, by a simple calculation it will be found that in the Chinese districts the cost of making black tea should be a shade above 3¾d. per lb., and of turning out finished green tea 4½d. per lb. precisely. These figures correspond fairly well with separate and independent statements made to the writer by Chinese and others, at different times, and at places in the empire widely asunder, which were that the cost is usually about 4d. per lb. for black tea, and 5d. per lb. for green. But there is another important allied item of cost, the outlay for conveyance to a shipping port. According to one of Mr. Fortune's calculations, which we consider reliable, the average distance that tea is transported in China is about 620 miles, at an expenditure of 1359 tael cents per picul (133⅓ lbs.), or, say, 1¼d. per lb. Thus the bare cost of China tea laid down in Shanghai or other shipping port, exclusive of the middleman's profit, barrier exactions, commissions, and export duty, may average 5¼d. per lb. for black, and 6¼d. per lb. for green tea.

In marked contrast to these comparatively moderate figures were those given at the discussion on Mr. Fielder's paper, already alluded to, by a Mr. Bainbridge, who said—"Coming now to Upper Assam, the result of my experience is, that taking the whole of the charges in the province connected with the manufacture of tea, they could not be put, in a large concern, at under 1s. 3⅜d. per lb. . . . Taking the case of Lower Assam, where local labour was obtained without importing it, the expenses were 1s. per lb." Major-General Clarke, another speaker on the same occasion, said—"Mr. Bainbridge had told them that the cost of producing tea would be 1s. 3d. per lb. He did not presume to contradict that. . . . Mr. Fortune estimated in 1851 that tea could be grown for from 4d. to 6d., and in Kangra, Dr. Jenkinson made the same estimate as to the cost of production. He did not know whether it could be grown for so small a sum, but the opinion at which he had arrived, from the best information he could obtain, was that it could be produced very well for 9d. per lb." The question of the moment,

however, is, not what should be the cost of producing tea in
India, but what does it actually cost? This query is answered
by a reference to the published accounts of the great Assam
Company (rightly regarded as the largest producer of tea for a
single firm in the world), where in 1879 the cost of the crop,
including every charge, is set down as 1s. 4d. per lb. From
these quotations it will be evident that the real outlay incurred
in preparing tea for the market in India greatly exceeds the
cost in China. This is owing partly to the expensive European
staffs maintained in the former country, partly on account of so
much imported labour being required, partly by reason of tea
production in India being comparatively a modern industry, and,
therefore, for some years at first but little understood, and partly,
no doubt, to the crushing incubus of interest payable on early
expenditure for land, plant, and unprofitable experiments.

We have referred already to the estimate of cost of Kangra
tea in 1851 and 1853, by Fortune and Jenkinson, as from 4d. to
6d. per lb., in more modern times, and as applicable to a different
part of India, we find the opinions of these gentlemen corroborated by Lieutenant-Colonel Money, whose work on tea
cultivation in that country has not yet been superseded. Exception has, it is true, been taken to some of this officer's statements
by critics in India, Ceylon, and elsewhere, but on the subject of
tea cost we are not aware that his figures have been challenged.
Having been himself a practical tea planter for many years, and
amassed great experience, we think this gentleman's observations,
particularly in regard to the cost of producing tea, are entitled
to every respect. At pages 157 to 159 of his manual (1878 ed.)
a table is given, exhibiting in detail the various items of outlay,
including the manufacture of Indian tea, sorting, packing, transport to Calcutta, with broker's or agent's charges there, the
whole amounting to 16 rupees 9 annas per maund of 80 lbs.,
which, if our sum of reduction be correct, shows a cost of 4¾d.
per lb., or one halfpenny per lb. less than that given as the
probable cost of producing black tea at a shipping port in China.
It may be said, of course, that if Colonel Money sometimes
acted as his own broker in Calcutta, he would save a very important item of outlay; and so he would if many of the agents
there have been in the habit of charging 12 per cent. on the
gross proceeds of all teas passing through their hands, according
to statements in the *Ceylon Observer* of 19th March and 10th
April 1880.

Coming now to the experiences of some of the other tea planting firms in India, we find the following list of gardens at present
in operation given in the *Indian Tea Gazette* of May 1879, which
will be found useful as furnishing some interesting details connected with the industry, as well as illustrative of the variations

which occur in the cost of production. Omitting one of the gardens given, on account of a manifest error which appears, we note the others thus:—

| Name of Garden | Outlay per Acre. | Yield of Tea per Acre | Cost of Tea produced. | Price Tea realised. | Per cent of Dividend. |
|---|---|---|---|---|---|
| | Rupees | Lbs | | | |
| Hoolmanie, . . | 358 | 315 | 14½d. | 21d. | 20 |
| Longshire, . . | 900 | 320 | 12¾ | 18 | 10½ |
| Socin, . . . | 650 | 276 | 12¼ | 18 | 10 |
| Phœnix, . . | 567 | 320 | 11½ | 20 | 9½ |
| Indian Terai, . | 500 | 314 | 15¼ | 21 | 8 |
| Punkabaree, . | 1245 | 243 | 16 | 22 | 7 |
| Tumanca, . . | 450 | 240 | 12¼ | 15 | 7 |
| Kangra Valley, . | [illegible] | [illegible] | 14 | 21 | 6 |
| Central Cachar, . | 846 | [illegible] | [illegible] | 18 | 5 |
| Singell, . . | [illegible] | 276 | 11 | 15 | 4½ |
| Dehing, . . | [illegible] | [illegible] | 10 | 15 | 4 |
| Divide by 11, | 7906 | 3085 | 156¾ | 205 | 91½ |
| Averages, | 718·72 | 280·45 | 14¼d. | 18½d. | 8·31 |

From this diagram we learn that the average cost of bringing these eleven tea gardens into bearing was about £71, 17s. 6d. per acre; that the average yield of marketable tea per acre was 280½ lbs.; that the average cost per lb. was 1s. 2¼d.; that the average price realised was 1s. 6½d., or an apparent profit of 4¼d. per lb.: and that the average dividend paid to shareholders was about 8¼ per cent.

Collecting the foregoing cost statistics into a focus they will thus appear, epitomised:—

*Cost of producing Tea.*

| | | |
|---|---|---|
| In China, according to Ball & Fortune, corroborated by the writer's interviews with natives, . . . . . | 5¼d. | per lb. |
| In Upper Assam, according to Mr. [illegible], . . . | 1 3[illegible] | " |
| In Lower Assam, do. do. . . . | 1 - | " |
| In Kangra Valley, do. Dr. Jenkinson, 4d. to 6d., say, | 5d. | " |
| Do. do. Major-General Clark, . . | 9d. | " |
| In Assam, do. The Assam Company, 1879, . | 1 4 | " |
| In the Himalayas and Chittagong, according to Lieut.-Col. Money, 1878, . . . . . . . . | 4¼d. | " |
| According to eleven tea companies, quoted from the *Indian Tea Gazette* of May 1879, . . . . . . | 1 2¼ | " |
| Divide by the above eight separate authorities, . . . | 8) 6 9⅝ | |
| Showing the average cost of producing tea in China and India taken together, according to the examples quoted, to be, . . . . . . . . . . | 10⅛d. per lb. | |

As the admission of Ceylon into the distinguished fraternity of tea-producing countries has been too recent to admit of the reliable collection of accurate and extended statistical experience connected with the cost of production, we have not included any. But it may be said generally that, judging from the reports and notices which have appeared from time to time in the local newspapers during the past three or four years, the planters there regard the sum of 10d. per lb. as representing their outlay on tea delivered free on board ship at Colombo.

It has been stated that the cost of labour in China applies in a general sense equally to tea and silk farming, nevertheless it may be remarked that the true average cost of the latter material among the peasantry of Asia, if it could be accurately ascertained, would doubtless prove in most cases to be very small indeed. If we except the comparatively few very extensive silk farmers there who do business on a really large scale, it will be found that an important percentage of the raw silk produced annually is the contribution from innumerable peasant homes. Whilst this circumstance complicates the attempt to get at the exact cost to the peasant silk-producer, it allows a considerable margin for possible error, as, keeping in view that skilled labour and expensive machinery are to him alike unattainable, and that the entire annual period of the harvest is short, it seems consistent with reason that his whole outlay must be insignificant in comparison with the average price his produce fetches in the markets of London, Lyons, or Florence. In Eugene Schuyler's *Turkestan* (p. 197) we are informed that a Turkestan peasant's family of four persons raise on an average each season about 108 lbs. weight of green cocoons. For this result one ounce of silkworms' eggs are required, which have previously been obtained from 1½ lbs. of cocoons, and the leaves from twenty mulberry trees costing 38s. Up to this point, without allowing anything for the peasant's labour and the use of such rude plant as may be within his reach to employ, his outlay amounts to 18 roubles or 45s. 7d., the rouble being valued at $30\frac{4}{7}$ pence sterling. An average price of 9 roubles per pud (36 lbs.) would be 27 roubles or 68s. 5d., yielding him a profit of 9 roubles, or 22s. 10d., after paying for his mulberry leaves. But in cases where the family possess a few mulberry bushes of their own the profit is increased by the cost of the leaves thus saved. In this example the peasant's profit seems to be a shade over 2½d. per lb. realised from the sale of his produce in its crude form, a profit which is greatly increased if he has the means of unwinding his cocoons. The next inquiry naturally follows :—What proportion of raw silk can he obtain from a given weight of green cocoons if he is in a position to unwind them? The answer appears at page 199, where it is stated that "In Tashkent it takes from 8 to 9 lbs. of good dried cocoons to produce 1 lb. weight of reeled silk; while in Samarkand, where the workmen are more skilful, 1 lb. of silk

can be obtained from 16 lbs. of fresh, or 5 lbs. of dried cocoons.
Russian silkwinders with their machinery have got 1 lb. of silk
from 14½ lbs. of fresh, or 3·9 lbs. of dried cocoons.   In Europe
12 lbs. of fresh, or 4 lbs. of dried cocoons will yield 1 lb. of silk.
Apparently, then, such cocoons part with about two-thirds of
their original weight when desiccated, so that the 108 lbs. reared
by the family just mentioned would shrink in drying to 36 lbs.,
and out of this quantity probably about 9 lbs. would be the
ordinary marketable silk of commerce, worth in London from
20s. to 25s., or even more, per lb., and costing about 5s. 0¾d.
per lb. to produce, or 4d. per lb. less if the peasant happens to
own a mulberry garden.   Keeping out of view the intermediate ·
gains on this transaction, which cannot fall short of from 10s.
to 13s. per lb., the peasant proprietor and producer gets 6½d.
per lb. of profit out of his little venture spread over a period of
only a few weeks.   This, it need scarcely be said, is a sum which,
if the outcome of tea, would gladden the heart of many an Indian
planter, and it would seem a return to the happy olden days to
not a few of our merchant princes, the complexions of whose tea
speculations in China of late years may not have been altogether
rosy.

Having thus seen what the uneducated peasant of Turkestan
can achieve, the reader will have no difficulty in crediting the
general results of the "Victorian Ladies' Sericicultural Company" in Australia, alluded to in a former part of this essay.
The founder and mainspring of this spirited association was
Mrs. Bladen Neill of the Murray River mulberry plantations
After commencing her own nurseries and experiencing the
annoyances caused by the various forms of silkworm disease as
perpetuated by dependence upon Asiatic and European grain,
she visited the principal silk districts of France and Italy in
search of healthy eggs.   Exercising the utmost patience, sur-
mounting many obstacles, and cheerfully submitting to considerable expense, Mrs. Neill at length procured a supply of
robust eggs in Switzerland from renovated breeds reared on the
confines of perpetual snow, and wholly free from disease.   These
were conveyed to the Antipodes packed in ice, and from this
importation the Australian magnaneries of the period were
stocked, with the happy and encouraging result that amongst
the first samples of silk produced some were valued in London
at 40s. per lb.   This energetic lady, along with some others,
afterwards founded, and we believe still conducts, the company
in question, whose cost of production, at an early period, by a
simple calculation from the data on page 192, will be found to
be about 8s. 8d. per lb.

It would be easy to multiply illustrations of the cost of producing silk in Italy and France which would undoubtedly show

a less figure than those already quoted, but as the conditions of wages, mechanical adjuncts, and general experience would prove wholly different in Europe to those we might expect to find, for a few years at least, in a new country like New Zealand, the search after examples need not be carried any further. It only remains, therefore, to condense the information given, thus :—

*Cost of producing Silk.*

To the peasant proprietor in Turkestan, about . . . 4/8¼ per lb.
To the Turkestan peasant,             „    . 5/0¼ „
To the Victorian Ladies' Sericicultural Company, about . 8/8 „

Divide by the examples given, . . . . . 3) 18/5½

Showing the average cost, according to the above, to be . 6/1¾ per lb.

## WHY TEA AND SILK FARMING SHOULD BE CONDUCTED TOGETHER.

Bearing in view the cardinal points of previous sections, the reader will now be prepared to learn our reasons for the belief that tea farming and sericiculture, to be remunerative in New Zealand, must be conducted together for probably the first ten years after their inauguration there.

It has been stated that there are seven separate hatchings of silkworms per annum in the Canton district in China, and that the season or harvest is usually over in about six weeks. In California, we understand, it is more prolonged; in Australia in favourable spots it may endure for even a greater period; and in parts of New Zealand, owing to a magnificent climate, absence of frost, and freedom from dust storms, there is every reason to expect the utmost extension in point of time of which serici-culture is naturally capable. Some expansion of the harvest may also be artificially effected by the judicious selection and introduction of other silk-producing worms besides the mulberry-feeding *Bombyx mori*—such as the *Attacus ricini*, which eats the leaves of the *Ricinus communis*, or castor-oil plant; the *Attacus atlas*, whose food is found on the *Terminalia*, and *Zizyphus jujuba* (a worm which yields the celebrated, almost imperishable, grey Tussah silk of China and India); the *Antheræa roylei*, which subsists upon the leaves of the *Quercus incana*, or common hill oak; the *Bombyx cynthia*, whose natural food is the *Ailanthus glandulosa*; the *Antheræa yama-mai*, another oak-leaf-feeding species from Japan, whose eggs are so full of vitality that in France they have been hatched at a temperature very little above the freezing point, and others which might be named—but after every known or theoretical variety or modification of serici-culture shall have been attempted, the bulk of every year must remain unimproved through the forced suspension of the industry from lack of material. Under such circumstances it will be evident that no farmer, engaged in the production of silk alone, could afford to keep a staff of skilled labourers about him unemployed during probably nine out of every twelve months. They must either be profitably engaged at some kindred industry; allowed to revel in unproductive idleness during two-thirds of the year, and so become a burden to their master and a nuisance to the district; or be discharged until the following silk season came round.

In old countries with settled and considerable populations a similar objection could not be urged, as employers of labour there, in almost every sphere of human industry, can nearly always arrange to procure a supply of hands in proportion to the orders they have undertaken to fulfil. But at the Antipodes, where a skilled staff must be collected from distant countries, and carefully organised at the expenditure of both tact, time, and money, the discharge of assistants so assembled, except for gross offences, would be, to speak in the mildest way, injudicious. This, then, is the great difficulty to be confronted and overcome by every one proposing to commence silk culture in New Zealand. Continuously and remuneratively to occupy the time of such a staff is the head and front of the problem to be solved, as it would indeed be the weak point of this enterprise were it limited to sericiculture alone. It may be said again, it has often already been alleged by superficial and ignorant persons, that silk culture is so trifling, so simple, so artless, so homely an employment that it requires no expensive plant or costly labour, but might be managed in an adjoining outhouse by the female members of every colonial family, that it might be made a cottage industry, that it might be conducted by any nurseryman, and that it might be tagged on to any ordinary farm. Half a century ago the same style of remark was made with equal reason regarding the spinning of yarn and the weaving of cloth, and yet it soon became evident that private fingers, however nimble and willing, were no match against public organisation, capital, and machinery: so it must be with sericiculture. Rearing silkworms will very likely soon be practised in an amateur way by our fair sisters in the backyards of their enviable New Zealand homes—and the sooner the better; every cottage may by and by have its mulberry patch, each nurseryman there may soon find it eminently profitable to strike mulberry cuttings by tens of thousands, and every farmer may discover ere long that thirty tons of mulberry leaves per acre, as their brethren not unfrequently get in California, yield a very handsome profit— yet none of these efforts can surely be dignified by the name of sericiculture. Nor will such individual essays, however laudable and persevering, culminate in the speedy establishment of the great national enterprise these pages are intended to advocate, without the co-operation of some kindred or allied industry; and we are at present aware of none so nearly related to it, and in every sense so well adapted to form a twin enterprise on the same estate and under the same general management, as the cultivation and preparation of tea.

As this essay has no pretensions to be regarded as a treatise on the mysteries of tea preparation and sericiculture, the reader need not look upon these pages as a text-book; yet it is due to the importance of the subject that some little information should be given, in order that he may judge of the desirability of linking those industries together in New Zealand. It will also be judicious to confine such remarks in the meantime as much as possible to Chinese methods and practice, as in that country chasericiculture had its earliest commercial home, and has there attained its widest development. With this necessary introduction we shall now say

### Something about Green Tea.

One of the chief approaches to the green tea district of Moyuen is the Poyang Lake, opening into the great river Yangtse-Kiang, a magnificent sheet of fresh water, about ninety miles in length with a breadth of about twenty miles. Its waters lave the towns of Yao-chow, the chief outlet for the green tea district; Neuchang, the principal centre towards which much of the black teas gravitate; Sueyhung, where the red leaf teas of the provinces of Keangsi, Ganhway, and Fokien are made up for exportation; and not far from its margin stand the world-famed porcelain factories of King-te-Ching. Four navigable rivers flow into the Poyang Lake, one of which, the Kan-Kiang, is nearly double the length of our Scottish Clyde, and the lake communicates by two separate channels of considerable depth with the river Yangtse-Kiang, one of these being at a point about 436 miles from the sea. The adjoining provinces of Keangsi and Fokien have a population of about 45,000,000 of industrious Chinese, who produce wheat, barley, rice, oranges, lemons, tea, mulberries, silk, sugar, gums, tallow, and all the metals. From these statistics it will be gathered that the neighbourhood of the Poyang Lake presents an epitome of the whole industrial pursuits and activity of the empire, and may be relied on as affording accurate glimpses of many of its industries, particularly those connected with tea.

Although several well-marked species of tea plants are cultivated in China, botanical students are by no means agreed that they may not all have originally emanated from the same plant, which is indigenous to the Wooe-or Bohea hills in the province of Fokien, and that the changes effected have been wholly due to climate and soil. Among the less known teas are some grown in Szechuen by the monks connected with the monasteries of Mount Ngomi, the infusion of which is sweet as if its taste had been assisted by the addition of brown sugar. Another kind, found growing wild in the wilderness south of Yachow, at a height of 6000 feet and higher, possesses an extremely pleasant flavour of milk—some think of butter—and has the economical recommendation that, although a shrub fifteen feet high with a stem four inches in diameter, every atom of the plant except the root is used for making the infusion. There are some other peculiar varieties met with about which little is known, but among the natives it appears to be the belief that, removal from one spot to another, where the plants meet with a marked change of climate, and especially of soil, is enough to produce the very considerable differences which have been observed. Thus it has been ascertained beyond doubt that the transfer of such plants as are cultivated for green tea in the Moyuen district, where there is little or no oxide of iron in the soil, to the highly ferruginous localities which produce the Moning and Kaisou teas of commerce, so modifies the tissues of the shrub that the better qualities of green tea could no longer be produced from it. On the other hand, it is well known that extensive areas, which formerly were devoted to the growth and preparation of very ordinary green tea, for the same reason now produce choice qualities of black. The plant itself seems to have very little to do with the result, that depending chiefly on the locality where grown and the style of manipulation, consequently this short explanation may serve to prepare the reader for a brief account of the preparation of green tea.

As soon as the pluckers arrive with their baskets of leaves, the yield is immediately spread out on bamboo trays in the sun for two hours. In this position the leaves are frequently agitated and turned over by children, and are then borne off to the curing house. Should this establishment be some miles away—the farmers seldom being also manipulators—the contents of the trays are emptied into deep baskets, each containing about fifty pounds weight, and are carried by coolies; or, packed loosely into cotton bags are taken by canal or river to their destination. But the further the leaves are removed, and the longer they remain in an unmanufactured condition, the more likely are they to deteriorate or to ferment, which last is a fatal occurrence to any crop intended for green tea. Under favourable circumstances the leaves should reach the hot pans in about two hours after they have been plucked, where the workman keeps them in motion for five minutes, then scoops out the whole contents and transfers them to the rolling table, around which a number of manipulators are seated. The first grasps as many leaves as his two hands can hold, working them into a ball with considerable pressure, and rolling the mass about on the table. It is then passed to the next man who gently bruises the ball, rapidly twisting the leaves between the fingers and thumb of both hands. Gathered up again by the next into a ball with pressure and rolling, the original quantity passes from one to another, undergoing the same alternate treatment, and is finally rubbed between the hands of the last operator into a basket, which, when full, is poured once more into the heated pan. During this second roasting, which is conducted under a less degree of heat than the first, the general superintendent goes the round of the pans and tables, and decides by the appearance of the leaves upon their future treatment; the larger leaves, according to quality, being made into gunpowder, imperial and twankay, whilst the smaller become young hyson, hyson, &c. Meanwhile the furnaces are livened up and the pans heated just short of redness, their contents being roasted, with continual motion, for about an hour. When no more vapour arises, and the leaves have assumed a fixed, dull green, they are considered safe from fermentation if kept from damp, and may be permitted to remain unfinished for twenty-four hours, or till all the pluckings on hand have been similarly manipulated. Next morning the tea is classified after passing through the winnowing machine, graduated sieves, and been carefully picked by women and girls, when the final grades are fixed and are roasted from one to four times, the colouring pigment being applied at the second last panning. It may be said in passing that the colouring of China green tea is done solely to please the European eye. No tea for native use is similarly treated, nor would a Chinaman use such if given him as a present. The practice, however, enables him to palm off old, withered leaves for those which ought to be young and fresh, and so long as the people of this and other countries are willing to be gulled, the Chinese manipulator is perfectly content to furnish the sophisticated article. Fortunately there is nothing deleterious in use for helping the colour of green tea, the ingredients being a very pure lime, soft indigo, and a little turmeric, so that the old stories, at one time in vogue of the green colour being produced by drying in copper pans or on hot plates, may be dismissed as inapplicable now.

The powder being in readiness, the workman scatters it over the contents of the pan in the proportion of about one ounce to fourteen pounds of tea, and the leaves not being yet quite dry, and even slightly sticky, the pigment readily adheres, and the final firing fixes it. So far completed, the tea is thrown into bins, where each sort or grade is kept separate until a sufficiency of one kind is collected to form what in China is called a " chop," and in this country a " break." The chop may consist of only a few chests, or it may embrace two hundred or more, but whether it be large or small, the bulk is always subjected to a last heating, and is quickly packed and soldered down in that condition ready for exportation.

It will be noted from this brief account of green tea preparation—

1. That the plants intended to produce the leaves to be made into green tea should be grown in soil containing little or no iron.

2. That plants removed from a green tea district to a ferruginous soil lose their value for producing the green tea of commerce.

3. That areas formerly devoted to the production of ordinary green tea now yield choice black qualities.

4. That green tea manufacture involves a comparatively short exposure to the sun's rays, but a considerable amount of manipulation.

5. That it should not be allowed to undergo any fermentation.

6. That although green tea is coloured for the purposes of sophistication and pleasing the European eye, the materials used are not deleterious.

7. And that it is invariably packed in a hot condition.

### Something about Black Tea.

With the exception of flowery pekoe and caper, all black teas are subjected to much the same kind of manipulation as green; and without exception they all pass under a longer or shorter period of fermentation, which, indeed, forms the chief distinguishing feature between the two sorts. Flowery pekoe, consisting as it does of the youngest and most fragrant buds, is only collected by skilled pluckers, whose baskets, in order to prevent mistakes, are usually of a different shape. Being covered with delicate, silvery hairs, such leaves are never rolled in handfuls, but are carefully though loosely twisted and curled leaf by leaf. Caper, the other exception, in addition to the usual rolling and curling, consisting as it frequently does of broken leaf and dust, is treated with gum and plumbago, and is worked into its characteristic spherical form by the aid of little flat boards attached to the workmen's hands, and sometimes by being put into bags or skins and manipulated with their feet.

The ordinary black teas of commerce are produced thus :—A morning's pluckings are spread out loosely on bamboo trays to wither in the sun for a period of twelve hours, under the protection of sheds with movable roofs. Should the weather be favourable, this preliminary exposure is considered sufficiently effective to justify the removal of the leaves to considerable distances, and, as sun-dried tea becomes an article of commerce among the natives, although as yet it has developed none of the qualities or fragrance of the finished leaf. In this condition it is packed in bags, and finds its way from great distances in the interior to Hankow, Canton, Hong Kong, Amoy, Ningpo, Shanghai, and other ports, where facilities exist for roasting, manipulating, firing, and packing. On arrival, the sun-dried leaves are thinly spread out as before, on large shallow trays or mats, under partial cover, and are frequently moved and tossed about in the sun's rays. The result is, that the tea, having been grown on a ferruginous soil, the formation of the tannic acid which ensues, united to the combined action of the sun and air, speedily darkens the leaf and develops the tannin on which the strength of the infusion and value of the article ultimately in a great measure depends. It is usual, in what may be designated "the oxygenising shed," to have manipulating tables at hand, so that the leaves may be subjected to alternate exposure to the sun and a series of tossings, curlings, and rollings. In the chamber adjoining, it passes into the hands of the regular manipulators, who subject it to precisely the same handling they give green tea, except that up to this point no artificial heat has been applied. Although apparently dry at the commencement of the process, it has now become, from frequent fingering, moist and flaccid, and in a favourable condition to be piled in little heaps in the fermenting chamber. Unlike the generality of Chinese apartments, this one is kept scrupulously clean both outside and in, and is provided with flue arrangements for stove heat if necessary. Fermentation is rarely long delayed, the first visible effect being a decided darkening of the leaves, caused by the chemical action of the oxygen of the air upon the tannin of the leaves and the iron distributed through their tissues. This symptom is shortly followed by the emission of a fragrant odour, which marks the formation of the volatile oil upon which the future flavour of the tea depends, increasing as the fermentation advances. From one hour to one hour and a half is usually necessary to produce the desired chemical transformation, and so critical is this process as it nears its close, that the slightest neglect or delay in arresting it at the proper moment, and the immediate removal of the particular heap, may result in the ruin of the whole contents of the chamber. The Chinese possess no certain test for the estimation of this crisis, but trust entirely to experience and watchfulness; the period for withdrawing the leaves being dictated partly by their colour, partly by the degree of heat evolved, ascertained by plunging the hand in the heap, and partly by the strength and pungency of the fragrance exhaled. Nevertheless, their patient skill is such that errors rarely occur, and sour tea, at one time so common and annoying in connection with our Indian gardens, is never met with. Should

the fermentation be only slightly overdone they can mitigate the
evil during the next process, although, were they acquainted with
the action of permanganate of potash in similar cases, they might
easily save themselves both trouble and anxiety.    From the
fermenting chamber the trays of leaves are quickly borne into
the manipulating room, where any that may seem a little overdone are immediately transferred to the heated pans.    Further
acidity is thus arrested, but at the expense of contracting a
burnt, and sometimes even a tarry flavour, which is apt to lessen
the value in the London market.    Should the fermentation have
been checked at the proper moment, the leaves are rolled, twisted,
and passed from hand to hand, shaken violently on sieves, and
frequently tossed up in the air as confectioners do when making
comfits.    They are now ready for roasting, and are poured into
the heated pans, and constantly stirred for five minutes ; the
furnaces being maintained at a steady glow by means of an in-
genious little blower, with wind chest and double pistons attached to each.    From the pans the rolling and twisting process
is repeated and continued for about half an hour, when the
leaves are again exposed for three hours in the oxygenising
shed.    Sunshine is not considered now so necessary ; indeed,
at this stage the Chinese profess to prefer simply a dry and
moderately cool atmosphere, so that every leaf may be affected.
Deprived as they now are of most of their moisture, the leaves
show signs of frailty, and must be more tenderly handled when
once more consigned to the heated pans for five minutes, and
then rolled slightly and twisted.    Yet with all the care that can
be bestowed, a portion of the leaves get much broken, and some
are reduced to powder, which, if permitted to remain, would
materially detract from the market value of the result.    Accordingly the whole is passed at intervals through a winnowing
machine, which roughly separates the tea consigned to it into
three classes, namely, good leaf, broken leaf, and fannings, the
dust being wafted off and separately secured during the operation.    Of the two latter products a large proportion is exported
at the end of each season, to swell the accumulations in the
London docks, the remainder being worked up into caper, brick-
tea, and to impart an appearance of truth to the curious con-
coction the Chinese themselves term "lie tea," expressly prepared for adulteration.    Perhaps as lively a picture as any connected with the preparation of tea in China, is to be seen at this
stage, when the finer kinds of black tea are carefully picked by
hand.    Seated on low benches, in large airy halls capable of
containing with comfort from five hundred to a thousand individuals, the pickers may be seen at work, singing and chatting
over their pleasant and light employment.    Every encouragement is given to the grouping of families together ; a mother

and daughters, with probably a little boy or two, take their places, when a couple of coolies deposit in their midst a basket containing a picul of tea (133½ lbs.). Presently their nimble fingers are at work among the leaves, which they usually separate into three classes, often to a vocal accompaniment of the melody Moh-li-Hwa, or Jasmin Flower, a great favourite throughout the tea districts. When the quantity served out has been picked, it is taken by the coolies, accompanied by one of the family, to the overseer, who, if satisfied, pours each quality down its appropriate shoot, hands over another picul to be operated on, and pays for that which he has passed. Consigned once more to the roasting pans for five minutes, the leaves are now exposed to the strongest heat they are capable of enduring without being injured, followed by a final and very careful manipulation on the rolling table, and by the process of firing. A series of tubular baskets, shaped like gigantic' hour-glasses, are placed over subdued open charcoal fires, made in little scooped-out hollows all over the firing shed. Sieves, in which about a couple of inches of tea have been deposited, are placed on the tops of these baskets, the tea being often stirred, and as frequently taken away for a few minutes to receive a kind of finishing twist or curl. When in the sieves over the fires it is necessary to see that not even a single leaf drops through, otherwise the flavour of the finished tea would be permanently injured by a smoky taint.

It may be desirable to remark in this connection that, on account of the difficulty of preventing small broken leaves or dust from falling through into the fire beneath, the Chinese method of drying tea is now all but abandoned in India, and has been superseded by others attended with no such risk. There are several plans at present in operation there, among which Jackson's may be quoted as a good type. The fire as well as the tea are wholly enclosed and separated by plates of iron. The tea reposes upon a series of shelf-sliding trays, placed one above another, and, in the language of the patentee, " by a convenient arrangement of shields and shoots the small tea which may fall from the trays in the drying chamber is immediately ejected outside the apparatus altogether, thus freeing it from all risks in burning, together with relieving the attendant from much tedious attention in the working."

The original gathering of leaves has now become finished tea as regards colour and curl, but it is not yet perfectly dry, and the rich aroma so characteristic of the finest Moning and Kaisow descriptions is not fully developed. Experience has taught that the teas possessing the most delicate natural flavour are produced not only in the northerly districts, but also at a considerable height above the level of the sea. Indeed, Chinese writers and tea manipulators are unanimously of opinion that the natural fragrance of the mountain-grown article is superior to that of any scent which art can communicate; nevertheless we find that some of the costliest sorts in use among themselves are artificially flavoured, although never coloured. Examples of this are to be seen in the finest specimens of Chulan, or pearl-flower, sometimes called cowslip hyson, and Loong-tsing, or hyson-pekoe, used by the wealthy Chinese as presents among each other, both of which owe their delicious aroma to the flowers of the *Chlorinthus inconspicuus*. The following are the methods adopted for

### Scenting Green Tea.

After the final roasting a portion of the tea to be treated is taken hot from the pan and poured into a hyson chest to the depth of about two inches, over which a handful or so of the freshly-plucked flowers of the *Chlorinthus inconspicuus* is strewn. Another layer of tea is added, succeeded by one of the flowers, and so on until the box is full, which is then placed aside in a warm corner and left undisturbed for twenty-four hours. At the end of that time the contents are turned out, thoroughly incorporated together, and fired for about two hours, or until the flowers become crisp and brittle. Their function being now ended, they are sifted out, and the tea thus scented becomes as it were the leaven, and is used in the proportion of one part in twenty to impart its fragrance to the stock.

### Scenting Black Tea.

Communicating an artificial aroma to black tea is differently managed, and indeed the plan adopted varies in different districts, as well as the flowers used. Under ordinary circumstances the choice of blossoms lies between the *Chlorinthus inconspicuus, Gardenia florida, Olea fragrans*, and *Jasminum-sambax*. One or other, or a mixture of these flowers, is placed in a sieve under that containing the tea to be scented, and the whole is set over a charcoal fire for two hours, when the flavour is generally found to have been imparted. The chief modifications occur in cases where the Chulan flavour is wanted in a chop of souchong or caper, or where fragrance is required for a special quality of tea for native consumption, which is subjected to very little heat. In the former the previously dried flowers, reduced to powder, are freely sprinkled over the tea whilst in the roasting pans, and in the latter the heated aromatic flowers in little crape bags are kept in contact with it during the whole process of manipulation. It may also be interesting and useful to note that, with one exception, whatever flowers are chosen, they are plucked whilst in full bloom, the exceptional example being the *Jasminum sambax*, named by the Chinese Moh-li-wah, which is used in the bud, as experience has shown that its fragrance when in that early stage is greatly augmented by heat.

Very naturally at this point the reader may ask, Why should all this trouble be taken if the natural aroma, as already stated, is really superior to any which can be imparted? The objects to be gained are these :—Long attention to the subject has shown that tea possessing the most delicate natural aroma is the produce not only of a northerly district, but is grown at considerable altitude. Thus the Moyuen district, in the province of Hwang-chow, celebrated for its green tea, lies in N. lat. 29° 56', E. long. 118° 15', at a height of nearly nine hundred feet above the sea-level, with a temperature ranging between 24° Fahr. in January, to 74° in August, and the climate of Woo-e-shan, in the province of Fokien, celebrated for its black tea, is likewise temperate, and the shrub is successfully cultivated at the height of 1000 feet. The teas produced in both these districts are noted for their exquisite flavour. It so happens, however, that the gardens which yield such naturally scented tea, like the well-known Johannisberg and Steinberger vineyards, are comparatively limited in extent, but their produce having acquired a reputation, the farmers nearer the valleys naturally desired to emulate their success, which they ultimately accomplished so satisfactorily, by processes of scenting, that the valley tea, on account of its greater strength, is now really preferred. There is, however, another most important end to be gained, by communicating an artificial aroma to tea, which may not be generally known. It has been found that newly-prepared tea is remarkably susceptible of adjacent influences, and is almost as greedy an absorbent of smells, whether evil or pleasant, as charcoal is of organic foulness, caustic lime of chlorine gas, or raw silk of water. Accordingly, in order to counteract the contaminating endosmose of objectionable gases, the tea is previously garrisoned, so to speak, with a subtile and lasting perfume. As further precautionary measures, China tea is carefully packed in lead, surrounded with soft absorbent paper, protected outside by means of papered and varnished hardwood packages. That such care is far from unnecessary may be inferred from the fact that the coolies who carry the packages from the farms to the various shipping ports, sometimes occupy several weeks on the journey, and they may often be seen dropping their burdens for a time in the fields or on the roads, and squatting or sprawling at full length over them when the mid-day sun demands a halt for wearied frames, glistening with perspiration. Under such circumstances it will readily be understood that unless the contents were thoroughly protected by exosmose, or the evolution of the perfume from within, the tea would inevitably acquire an earthy taint from the damp ground on which the packages may rest; a repulsive flavour from the strong cookery of the villages where the coolies stop for the night, and even retain an unpleasant memento of the unclean skins of the bearers. Indian tea, not being usually transported any considerable distance by coolie labour, runs less risk of contamination from this sort, but it was at one time, and may even now, be occasionally threatened by a still more formidable foe, unknown to consignments from China. In anticipation of the season there, a number of our finest steamers are generally in port ready to load, and as they get full cargoes of tea without the necessity of embarking other produce, contamination, except from stress of weather or leakage, can scarcely occur. But tea being comparatively a small product among the numerous industrial fruits of our Indian empire, it is of necessity sometimes associated on the voyage home with a miscellaneous cargo, such as hides, horns, gums, hemp, jute, linseed, and other strongly-smelling animal and vegetable substances, which are apt to ferment during the passage and even to decay. The fetid gas arising therefrom permeates the ship's hold, and the earliest and principal victim is any tea which may be stored there. Thus, Indian tea, like human beings, may suffer deterioration from evil companionship, and not being fortified by a powerful perfume like its Chinese rival, falls an easy prey to foul vapour which the other, armed with its rich scent, successfully defies. It will be evident, therefore, that perfuming tea is due to commercial prudence and forethought for its future condition on the part of the Chinese, quite as much as from any desire to enhance its value.

Suppose the scenting process complete, each sieve is now heaped up with tea and placed on the top of the firing basket. During the progress of this final heating, which lasts for two hours, the workman frequently stirs the tea, and at length makes an opening in the centre of the mass to facilitate the radiation of heat and escape of vapour. Sometimes a paper cone is likewise introduced to act as a chimney, but this seems necessary only when the air happens to be loaded with moisture.

It would be impossible to secure uniformity of quality in a chop, consisting of say from one hundred to five hundred packages, unless the whole had been previously mingled together. Tea is so exceedingly susceptible to outward influences, as has just been shown, that scarcely two chests would turn out precisely alike, even although the leaves had been plucked from contiguous bushes in the same garden, and manipulated by the same workmen, under the same apparent circumstances, if packed at once on leaving the firing chamber. The necessity for carefully bulking will be all the more obvious when it is explained

that a chop may be composed of leaves collected from hundreds
of separate gardens scattered throughout a whole district, and
that a single bush may produce at different periods within a few
days flowery pekoe, orange pekoe, pekoe, souchong, congou, and
even bohea. The few tender buds which, plucked to-day, may
form flowery pekoe, will, if left a little, take no higher rank than
ordinary congou, and at the end of the week may perhaps be
scarcely fit to be called bohea. This is an extreme case, which
is seldom allowed to occur to any extent, through the unceasing
vigilance exercised during the leaf harvest, aided by a vigorous
and fearless system of pruning; but it gives an idea how varied
any one plucking of leaves may be, and how necessary for the
homogeneity of the result that the whole should have been
thoroughly mingled together. Accordingly, attached to every
Chinese tea factory there is an extensive bulking chamber,
capable of containing from thirty to fifty tons of tea in bulk,
with ample floor space left for turning over. During the short
time the tea remains here a strong heat is maintained, and the
seasoned packages being in readiness, it is immediately packed
in a hot condition, covered with soft paper, and the lead at once
soldered down, This is done with a flat iron bolt, about a quarter
of an inch thick, four inches broad, and six inches long. The
bar of solder, dipped from time to time in the flux, which is
usually in a state of solution, is held against the front of the
bolt, when the workman dexterously runs it along and seals up
the packages in less time than it takes to describe the process.
Nothing now remains to be done beyond heading up the chests,
pasting on the ornamental edging around the lids, strapping with
split bamboo, and despatching to the shipping port.

To epitomise the foregoing information, it will be seen

1. That with the exception of flowery pekoe and caper, all
black tea is manipulated in a similar manner to green tea; but,

2. That unlike green tea, black tea undergoes a period of fermentation.

3. That whereas green tea is allowed only two hours' exposure
to the sun's rays before being roasted, black tea gets twelve hours
exposure.

4. That this lengthened exposure, combined with growth on a
ferruginous soil, fermentation, and prolonged manipulation, con-
fer or rather elicit its characteristic colour and properties.

5. That the scenting of green tea and black tea are differently
managed; that a greater variety of fragrant flowers is employed
for the latter; and that perfuming is a protective measure as
much as a means of enhancing value.

6. That all China tea intended to form a chop is bulked and
mingled together before being packed.

7. And, that black tea, equally with green, is packed whilst
hot.

*Something about Silk.*

Probably the best illustration of what the indoor department of sericiculture is will be seen by following the progress of a single brood of silkworms from the egg to the finished cocoon. Having procured healthy seed from some district untouched, or little molested with disease, the first object is to time the incubation with the first bursting of the mulberry into leaf. Not many years ago there were difficulties in the way of this, as the little worms usually appeared at the accustomed season, unless it happened to be uncommonly inclement, whether there was food for them or not. If the hatching occurred too soon ere the mulberry buds had appeared, the brood perished from famine; if too late, when the leaves had become somewhat tough and leathery, it either died of indigestion or struggled through a short term of life, only to collapse before spinning, or to produce a limited and inferior return in silk. This we believe to have been the main reason why sericiculture on a commercial scale has been so long in taking root in inviting spots in the British Islands; the worm generally appears before its food is ready, whereas in China and other parts of the world, their advent is simultaneous. Various devices have been resorted to in order to solve the enigma, such as storing for food in a dried and powdered condition, some of the youngest mulberry leaves of the previous season; keeping the eggs in bottles under water so as to maintain them at a uniformly low temperature, &c.; but the refrigerating method now in vogue in Italy and France, and at present practised with success by Captain Mason, of Yately, Farnborough, Hampshire, seems to have at length provided the means of rendering sericiculculture not only possible, but perhaps remunerative wherever the mulberry can be coaxed to grow in the open air. By this means, through the agency of ice, the vivifying of the silkworm's eggs can be retarded for long periods without in the least impairing their vitality, so that they may be sent to the most distant regions of the world in safety, or kept in an ordinary refrigerator during backward seasons, until the mulberry has commenced to bud. That no evil effect follows such an apparently unnatural expedient, was proved a few years ago by this gentleman upon a scale of some magnitude. He found that the worms hatched from 5 ounces of eggs, previously removed from an ice chest where they had been deposited during the progress of his hay harvest, not only developed rapidly, but in the fourth period of their existence, managed to devour 6155 lbs. of mulberry leaves in the course of a fortnight. So satisfied indeed are some of the Continental sericiculturists of the value of this retarding expedient, that in many places great central refrigerating establishments, capable of dealing with 50,000 ounces of eggs, have been erected.

Under normal circumstances, as soon as the mulberry bushes show signs of budding, the silkworms' eggs required to be hatched are placed in the magnanerie or nursery, where a commencing temperature of 60° Fahr. is maintained, but is gradually raised during the following nine days to 80°. About the tenth day the worms appear, and are immediately supplied with the youngest leaves cut into shreds, so that numerous raw edges may be presented to their appetites. A drop in the temperature of 5° is now recommended, the range being afterwards kept between 70 and 75°. The strictest cleanliness must be observed both inside and outside the magnanerie, as well as in the persons of the attendants, and the worms require to be fed every six hours throughout the twenty-four with freshly chopped leaves. Noises and smells should equally be suppressed, and the worms should not on any account be touched with the bare fingers. At the end of this period the consumption of food for every ounce of eggs hatched will have been from 7 to 15 lbs., when the worms pause for twenty-four hours, apparently because gorged into insensibility, but really in order to throw off skins which have become too small for their augmenting corpulence. This suspension of functions is known as the first sickness.

On the old integument being fairly sloughed, the worms are tenderly removed to clean trays of more ample dimensions, and fed as before on food not so finely shred for about four days, when the quantity devoured will probably have been from 20 to 30 lbs. Again the little creatures apparently feel the discomforts of gluttony, and once more, during their second sickness, their skins are abandoned. The endurance of the third period is usually about a week; and on the eleventh day or so from incubation, a third sickness overtakes them after having eaten from 60 to 80 lbs. of leaves, when their skins are cast anew. Another moulting occurs about the seventeenth day, and from this time onward the capacity for food shown by the rapidly growing worms is simply amazing. According to one Chinese author, each healthy worm now devours about ten times its own weight of leaves per day, so that the utmost vigilance and promptitude are required on the part of the attendants in maintaining conditions of purity, both for their own comfort and the health of their interesting charge. The fourth period is usually completed by the twenty-second day, when the worms will probably have consumed from 120 lbs. to 160 lbs. of leaves. During the fifth period, which lasts about ten days, the worms will likely have consumed from 1100 to 1200 lbs. of leaves, after which a feeling of restlessness takes possession of the little revellers, and they begin to move off in various directions in search of convenient spinning corners, which ought to be in readiness in the form of miniature hedges of common broom, about eighteen inches high,

fastened around and across the trays in which the worms have
had their last meal.   Some silk farmers provide square shallow
boxes partitioned off into little spaces like a draft-board ; others
use short bundles of straw tied round the middle and well spread
out at the two ends ; whilst many are content to supply only
small bunches of beech twigs with the withered leaves still adhering.   This seems to be more a matter of convenience to the
sericiculturist than importance to the silkworm, as it usually commences to spin immediately it finds some suitable support for
the first few threads it emits.   It happens occasionally that individuals, even after having selected a nook, return again to the tray
for more food.   This should be at once supplied, as it is well known
that the more heartily they have eaten within certain limits
of time, the better and more profuse will be their yield of silk.
On this point an ancient Chinese writer says :—" The reason why
they (the farmers) take so much pains to make these little insects
eat so much and so often, is to forward their growth and make
them spin the sooner, the great profit which they expect from
these creatures depends upon this care.   If they come to their
full growth in twenty-three to twenty-five days, a hurdle covered
with worms whose weight at first was a mass (that is little more
than a drachm), will produce 25 ounces of silk, whereas, if for
want of proper care and nourishment, they do not come to perfection in less than twenty-eight days, they will produce but 20
ounces: and if they are a month or forty days in growing they
will yield only about 10 ounces."   It is indeed considered a fair
test of what is termed "a proper education," that the worms
hatched from 1 ounce of eggs should at this period have
finished at least 1500 lbs. of fresh mulberry leaves.   About the
thirty-second day the cocoon and the sixth period of the silkworm's career are begun, the former being usually completed in
four days, when the caterpillar, under the protection and privacy
of its elastic armour, becomes a chrysalis.   Four days more are
generally allowed, when the cocoons are removed ; and if the
education has been successful, the worms have proved healthy,
and all have survived, the harvest should be about 120 lbs. of
cocoons for each ounce of eggs hatched.   Probably in no other
instance in nature could such experiments as the foregoing be so
accurately and satisfactorily conducted, and the result arrived at
with such exactness and precision.

It is the main objection to sericiculture, in the minds of tender-
hearted or sentimental persons, equally with the Buddhists of
China and some sects in India, that so much sacrifice of insect
life is involved, as, except the cocoons kept for reproduction, all
the others are usually subjected to a decree of heat which stifles
the chrysalis within.   Were it possible to unwind the whole of
the cocoons before the little hermits had had time to perforate

their silken prisons, there would then be no need for any stifling process, and the result would be that the harvest of eggs would be enormously increased. There is a hope that something of this kind may be accomplished ere long, and it is encouraging to find that in Syria, where it is practised to a small extent, the rapid unwinding of such cocoons as can be overtaken in the limited time and without sacrifice of life, yield 50 per cent. more silk than an equal number in which the insects have been killed.

The cocoons selected for reproduction are always chosen from among the best-looking and firmest in texture; those containing males are smaller, thinner in the middle, and having more pointed ends than those spun by females. Double cocoons, or those which by some accident of crowding contain two or more moths are usually rejected, although there is no good reason why. They are not liked by reelers, as the filaments being much interlaced they are unwound with difficulty. When selected, the floss silk is removed, and the cocoons are attached with gum to cardboard or cloth. In the course of five or six days the moths apply a softening or solvent liquid to the silk which enables them to push their way out, and having fluttered to the cards or other material upon which their eggs are to be laid, find partners for six hours, and spend the two or three following days in laying eggs, of which each female deposits from three hundred to double that number. Their little lives of forty days having now been accomplished, and as no food has been taken since the commencement of their cocoons, they die. It is found that on an average one pound of good cocoons yield moths which produce 1 ounce of eggs, and, as already stated, the worms from 1 ounce of healthy eggs should spin 120 lbs. of cocoons.

For export or home-reeling purposes the cocoons are subjected to sufficient heat to destroy the chrysalis, either by exposure to the sun's rays, by fire or steam heat, or by being stowed, as in some parts of China, in jars under layers of salt and leaves, with a complete exclusion of air. But in whatever way the life of the insect may be sacrificed, the after desiccation must be so effectual that the remains become crushed to powder when the cocoons are press-packed. The loss in weight by drying is, of course, very considerable, amounting to 66 per cent., 4 lbs. of desiccated cocoons being equivalent to 12 lbs. of undried. Packing, however, does them no injury, as when placed in hot water previous to being reeled they expand and resume their original form, and yield their filament as readily as if unwound immediately after having been spun.

Although silk-reeling in China is not carried nearly to the pitch of perfection the art has reached in Europe, yet it is everywhere practised; and considering the rudeness of the machinery employed, the results are very surprising. During, and for weeks after the silk season, the traveller can scarcely enter a farmhouse or peasant's hut without seeing one or more girls seated before caldrons of hot water covered with bobbing cocoons, busy unwinding the golden threads; and the money they earn in this manner during a comparatively short period forms no inconsiderable portion of the family's yearly income. In some of the regular sericicultural establishments, particularly in parts of the district of Kiangnan, still further operations are undertaken. In rear of one of these may be observed a series of sheds arranged round a shallow tank, where the floretta is cleansed previously to being passed on to bleachers and dyers. He may then follow it through other stages, all in the same premises, until it is seen exposed for sale as thread, floss for embroidery, or woven into fabrics possessing all the colours of the rainbow.

A summary of the preceding information will show—

1. That the timely use of ice enables the sericiculturist to retard the hatching of silkworms' eggs, thus allowing them to be conveyed to distant countries, or kept during inclement seasons until the natural food of the worms is ready.

2. That this expedient is practised on the Continent of Europe, and has within the last few years been verified, on a large scale by Captain Mason, to be attended by no evil results.

3. That the silkworm passes through six distinct and well-marked epochs from the egg to the cocoon, during which the most scrupulous cleanliness should be maintained, and an unstinted allowance of periodically fresh food supplied.

4. That the worms from 1 ounce of eggs, having devoured 1500 lbs. of mulberry leaves, should yield a harvest of 120 lbs. of cocoons.

5. That cocoons quickly reeled, without destroying the chrysalis within and before it has had time to perforate its prison, yield 50 per cent. more silk than the same number would after the insect had been stifled.

6. That the sexes of the imprisoned moths are known by the shape of the cocoons.

7. That 1 lb. weight of good cocoons should yield moths capable of producing 1 ounce of grain, each female laying from 300 to 600 eggs.

8. And that the loss in weight cocoons suffer through desiccation is over 60 per cent.

If these few particulars connected with tea and silk preparation have conveyed the impression intended, the reader will probably be inclined to accept without much question the belief of the writer that those industries are peculiarly well adapted to be conducted together on the same estate by much the same staff of workers and under the same general management. In silk, produced by itself, the farmer would have a product whose brief harvest and period of manipulation can hardly be expected even at the most sanguine estimate to endure beyond three months, after which a reign of almost unbroken idleness for the employés must ensue. In tea, on the other hand, he would, in confining himself to the production of this commodity—which is in constant and increasing request within the colony and in Australia—have the advantage of a more protracted season, beginning, as it likely would, after the bustle of the silk crop was nearly over, and lasting for eight or nine months. In the one case there would be a period of unproductive idleness of about nine months, and in the other of only about twelve weeks; but in the combined practice of the two industries the chasericulturist has a promise of uninterrupted and lucrative employment for himself and his entire staff "all the year round." Again, the proposal to cultivate and prepare tea by itself is met by the substantial objection that, as three or four years must elapse from the time of planting ere any appreciable pecuniary return need be expected, there would occur a heavy outlay without any immediate income; whereas, allied with sericiculture there might be a handsome income from this source during the second year. Once more, the extensive prosecution of the two industries in union would tend to influence a wider range of skilled labour from Europe and elsewhere than the pursuit of either separately on a small scale could possibly effect, with the result, doubtless, that whatever the cost of production might be at the commencement of the enterprise, the outlay as time wore on would sensibly diminish rather than the reverse. For a few years, perhaps, no local manufacturing demand for the cocoons or silk produced might be experienced; although for a decade or two, probably, every pound of tea prepared would be eagerly purchased for consumption within the colony. This absence of home inquiry for silk would, of course, necessitate its being consigned, in the first instance, to European or other markets; but whenever it became widely known that the raw material was being regularly and copiously yielded in New Zealand, the issue, according to the experience of older countries, would likely be that sooner or later all the kindred trades and professions which in Britain, France, and Italy cluster around the great centres of silk production, would speedily group themselves there also.

## The Philanthropic Aspect of Chasericulture.

In the hope that the query propounded at page 181—What reason is there to believe that the cultivation and preparation of tea and silk are at all suited to the climate of New Zealand?—has been convincingly disposed of, and before dealing with the pros-

pects of pecuniary success, we shall now allude to what may
with truth be termed the philanthropic features of the proposed
enterprise, which ought, perhaps, to be surveyed with minds
rising for the moment above the mere metallic considerations of
ordinary business.   When a commercial crisis—whether owing
to depressed commerce, infatuated overtrading, the recklessness
of bank directors, or war—bursts, numbers of delicately nurtured
and well-educated women and girls, wholly innocent of contri-
buting to the disaster, invariably suffer, and are either thrown
destitute or are forced to become the unwilling, and often
unwelcome, recipients of charity.   Those of the reduced whose
natural abilities and acquirements are above the average may,
perhaps, become governesses, teachers in public schools or private
academies, journalists, or artistic professionals; but the greater
number have usually to contemplate a dismal future of grinding
poverty, armed with no more effective weapon than the needle.
A few years ago the writer, having occasion to inspect a property
in the north-east, with a trim little mansion-house upon it, for a
probable purchaser, was conducted through the beautiful but
deserted chambers all uncarpeted, the furniture—including
several musical instruments, and the pictorial and tapestried
offspring of deft and industrious feminine fingers—lotted and
ticketed ready for the auctioneer's hammer the following week.
He had seen through every room, as he believed, from the attics
to the hall, and was about to retire, when the conductress,
habited in the drapery of woe, and apparently the only domestic
left, tapped at a door, and, turning round with eyes full of sym-
pathetic moisture, said, "The library, sir; you haven't seen it
yet."   Until that moment the visitor merely knew that the
owner of the little estate had been a sufferer by a gigantic
commercial fraud then occupying public attention, which had
ruined many hundreds, and brought not a few to untimely graves.
A whisper, and the opened door revealed some more of the
terrible reality, for there, bending over a small work-table at the
further end of the noble apartment, dressed in deepest mourning,
sat two beautiful girls—children almost—plying their needles
and mingling their curls and their tears.   Slain by the knavery
of a syndicate of thieves, their father, succumbing to the crushing
blow of his losses, combined with torturing anxiety about his
forlorn daughters, had a few days before been laid to rest in his
final narrow bed, and those two helpless orphans were shortly to
go out into the cold unknown world and commence the struggle
for existence.

This reminiscence illustrates one of the philanthropic objects
the proposed enterprise might accomplish.   During the operations of a chasericultural company in New Zealand numerous
openings would undoubtedly occur in the more delicate manipu-

lations connected with both tea and silk for females of education
who, like those interesting girls, through no fault of their own, had
been suddenly plunged from positions of comfort, if not of afflu-
ence, into the depths of hard, grinding poverty.    Every year
numbers of such delicately-nurtured sisters are thus reduced, yet
who, although unable to support themselves becomingly in the
old country, and probably unfitted physically to cope with the
robust activity of a purely agricultural life in any colony, might
nevertheless prove most valuable assistants in a tea hong or
manganerie.    Such objects of compassion have not hitherto been
much in demand anywhere, consequently their opportunities for
emigration and means of livelihood at the Antipodes, even did
they succeed in getting there, have as yet been limited.    But
in a chasericultural company's employment many of these forlorn ones would ultimately find a comfortable and independent
refuge, an important measure of relief would be given to the
higher branches of female labour at home, nearly always so
painfully overstocked, and the company would probably reap
a well-deserved reward through the engagement and hearty
co-operation of numerous, intelligent, and well-educated members of the gentler sex.    In order that any merits these views
possess may be properly appreciated, it will be useful to draw
attention shortly to such of the manipulative operations connected with chasericulture as are in other countries undertaken
by women, when we trust it will become evident that similar
duties might be more efficiently undertaken by lady emigrants
without detracting in the least from their natural dignity or
social status.

In China, as in Britain, April is a month of showers, and
although it does not herald the commencement of the tea harvest,
it witnesses more activity among the pluckers than occurs during
the previous four weeks, as then the bushes throw out their
second great flush of young verdure.   Directly the rain has given
place to sunshine, and drying winds have absorbed each leaflet's
tears, the leaf gatherers sally forth at dawn, singing and dancing
(or at least showing every sign of enjoying themselves, dancing,
as we understand the pastime, not being as yet a common amuse-
ment) as they trip to their pleasant employment.   The earliest
glimpses of daylight sees hundreds, it may be thousands, of pretty
black-eyed black-haired young damsels, marching gaily along the
narrow footpaths separating the paddy fields towards the tea
gardens among the hills, those with unmutilated feet assisting
on either side their less independent sisters ; and when the
refreshment gong sounds, if they are too far from their homes,
they retire in merry groups among the bushes to eat their frugal
meals.   It is not without some show of reason that previous to
and during the tea harvest the pluckers are dieted somewhat

sparingly as regards strong and flavoury food, because the delicacy
of the young leaf is such that the Chinese farmer deems extraordinary precautions necessary in order to prevent deterioration
through the acquisition of any objectionable taint.  In promotion
of this object the girls are required to have passed through a
season of hygienic precautions and training immediately prior to
the commencement of the harvest; and during their employment
they are altogether debarred the use of garlic and other herbs or
condiments of which all classes of Chinese are fond.  Reaching
the scene of their labours, each detachment, accompanied by
coolies to bear away the pluckings to the central drying-shed or
manipulating hong, begins upon a separate plot of tea bushes,
and in a few hours a due proportion of the flushes have been
carefully removed.  In the conscientious performance of this
first operation of the tea harvest, simple as it may appear, much
of the subsequent high character and value of the finished
article depends.  In the early days of some of our Indian tea-
plantations the blameworthy habit of stripping the branches—
that is, grasping them at their junction with the main stem, and
drawing the closed fingers sharply along, thus clearing them at
one sweep of every bud and leaf—was too often practised.  It
was a most reprehensible custom, and was only indulged in by
unscrupulous pluckers when safe from the eye of the superintendent, in order to save themselves trouble and quickly to
augment the contents of their baskets, thereby completing the
day's "task" in the shortest space of time.  The practice damaged
the tea-bushes, and proved eminently detrimental to the value of
the finished tea, which, under such rough initial manipulation
never gave a satisfactory result.  In China, the indigenous home
of tea-farming, such serious but quite preventible practices could
scarcely happen; and it may be asserted with every confidence
that where British ladies and girls of even the most ordinary
education were employed, as in a New Zealand garden, such
wilful yet stupid bungling would be next to an impossibility.

Some of the indoor duties connected with tea manufacture,
which in China are performed by women, have already been
noticed; and as those of that department of sericiculture which
are conducted under cover are everywhere acknowledged to be
specially suited for them, we shall refrain from recapitulation
and change the scene to the margin of one of the enchanting
lakes of New Zealand.

Let the reader in imagination now follow us there to a model
chasericultural farm of the future, in order to see how we propose employing educated women upon whom fortune may have
frowned at home, and whose friends have aided in reaching the
Antipodes.

It is about the beginning of September, the first month of

spring in New Zealand, and the white mulberry bushes are about to burst into leaf. Inside the magnaneries, or silkworm nurseries, everything is in readiness : 600 ounces of eggs have been exposed for the past nine days and nights to incubating heat, and the worms are expected on the morrow. By dawn the field and other employés are at their posts, and the night having passed free from rain, a quantity equal to about three-quarters of a ton of mulberry leaves is brought to the chopping shed and one-half immediately reduced to fine shreds, thrust loosely into large baskets, and quickly taken to the magnaneries. Here the trays, which the previous evening showed nothing but a thin scattering of minute eggs, are alive with myriads of tiny, dark-coloured worms, eager to begin their month of almost constant feeding, and each few trays have their appropriated lady and girl nurses in addition to the general porters who bring in and distribute the food. As the worms must be fed every six hours throughout the twenty-four, the nurses are relieved after the expiry of the first quarter, to be replaced by an equal number, who in turn yield their charge to others, and they to a fourth band, when the first detachment again go on duty. By this arrangement each lady nurse and her attendants perform six hours continuous work out of the twenty-four as long as the silk harvest lasts. The other half of the mulberry leaves brought in are dried in the sun, reduced to fine powder, and packed by girls into large earthenware jars, to serve as food at the opening of the following year's silk season, in the event of a partial failure or tardy budding of the shrubs. The same routine, with rapidly increasing quantities of leaves, goes on from day to day until the cocoons are commenced, when a partial lull ensues. Meanwhile fresh incubations of eggs are promoted as long as any are left to hatch, and as long as the resources of the plantations can produce seasonable food.

In this scene of activity probably two months have passed, and the tea bushes are showing promise of flushing abundantly. A brilliant November morning—corresponding with April in China—has dawned, and the neighbouring hills are ringing with the joyous shouts of hundreds of the bright, bold, ruddy children of British emigrants, intermingled, perhaps, with troops of laughing little Maoris, and not a few sedate and solemn-looking tiny Celestials, all engaged in tea-plucking, superintended by ladies and girls from home; some on foot, and others mounted on strong Australian palfreys, bustling about the plantations and directing the busy crowd. To some of our languid beauties in this old country, on whose features an unmodified sunbeam rarely beats, such a scene would appear simply one of horror. Yet those who have already spent many years in New Zealand's delightful climate, and whose experience of other fair regions has not been

P

limited, agree that, except perhaps in the Sandwich Islands, nowhere else is the toll of freckles exacted by the sun less aggravating, and an open-air life more enjoyable.

Not only in the field are the services of the fair sex required, but in our model tea factory they are utilised also. It is well known to travellers and residents in China that the finest and most expensvie tea of that country is never exported, because, being only sun-dried, and scarcely fired at all, it cannot stand the voyage to Europe or America, but would decay on the way and arrive in a state of decomposition. But although incapable of enduring a long carriage, the few days occupied in reaching Australia from Auckland would probably inflict no appreciable damage, so that this exquisite tea might readily be enjoyed for a few weeks every season by our relatives in Sydney, Melbourne, and the other parts of that continent. Accordingly, the preparation of this charming article, the samples of which are never seen in Mincing Lane, is left almost wholly in the hands of the ladies connected with our New Zealand Chasericultural Company, as, there being no rolling, fermenting roasting, and very little firing necessary—only a little curling, exposure to the sun, and loose packing in small canisters or jars—such trifling yet careful manipulation is undertaken by even the least robust among them, and seems more like pastime than labour. The ladies have also the satisfaction of knowing that this effort of their fair fingers commands an exceptional price, not unlike a kindred tea in China alluded to by Mr. Simmonds in his *Commercial Products of the Vegetable Kingdom.* "For delicacy," he says, "no teas approach those called 'Mandarin teas,' which being slightly fired and even damp when in the fittest state for use, will bear neither transport nor keeping. They average twenty shillings per lb., and are in request among the wealthy." In the preparation, too, of brick and tile tea, powder tea after the Japanese formula for native Asiatic use, compressed tea, and concentrated essence from the broken leaves and dust for the convenience of the army, navy, and travellers, many situations are available for the deft fingers of the fair; whilst at the termination of every harvest employment in producing tea-seed oil and oil-cake from the refuse is ready for hundreds of more robust although uneducated women and children.

In the midst of the dust, heat, and noise of the manipulating and firing chambers it is hardly to be expected there would be openings for ladies, but in the weighing and packing departments their artistic taste comes into play in the supply of decorative designs and sketches of native scenery and character wherewith to ornament the packages.

Meanwhile the silk harvest for the year has been obtained in the shape of 72,000 lbs. of green cocoons fed upon 100 acres of white mulberry leaves, showing a gross value, after deduction of 66 per cent. for desiccation, of probably £33,624, being the likely return from 600 ounces of eggs costing in Europe about £450. These figures are of course based on the assumption that the ladies of the establishment have not yet learned the art of reeling silk, and that it is obligatory to export to Europe all the cocoons produced. But at some future date, when this delicate branch of sericiculture shall have become understood and be in practice among them, the gross proceeds from the mulberry area, as at first obtained, will probably be quadrupled. Even this estimate is perhaps destined to be exceeded when the economical lesson already alluded to as taught in Syria has been mastered, as there, cocoons which are smartly unwound before the developed moths have had time to perforate their silken prisons, yield 50 per cent. more silk than after the little creatures have been stifled. But the climax of economical sericiculture will have been reached when a curious device, now under consideration, of obtaining silk direct from the spinnerets of the worm, without the intermediate form of a cocoon and without compromising the comfort and safety of the little creature during its transformation shall have been perfected. As soon as this grand triumph has been achieved, it is scarcely necessary to say that further solicitude as to the difficulties of reeling after the method now in use will disappear, for the process will no longer be required. In place of only a very small percentage of the moths being saved, the whole hatching would become available to complete their natural functions and term of life, the yield of silk would soon be so startingly augmented as almost to rival that of cotton itself, and the quantity of eggs produced so enormous, that the disease-ridden magnaneries of Europe might annually be fully replenished from the New Zealand Chasericultural Company's nurseries alone.

It is unnecessary, perhaps, to add another word in illustration of the numerous lucrative, honourable, and attractive openings which await the applications of educated although reduced women and girls once the proposed company has fairly been launched; so we shall now turn to another of the philanthropic features embraced in the enterprise, which may be explained in a few sentences.

There can be very little doubt that, in consequence of the keen and annually increasing competition of Continental and American farmers, united to the uncertainty of our climate, the position of the home agriculturist does not improve, but rather seems to get worse as the century advances. That rents have in many cases been excessive probably few will question, and that even no rent at all in some localities may have left the farmer a loser during late years. At the same time it is quite possible that the English and Scotch farmer's panacea of "mitigated rents," and the Irish cure of "no rents," are powerless to remedy the evil, and that the bane of the British farmer lies elsewhere. We humbly think that high rents are not so much to blame as the comparatively small size of the farms, the lack of chemical knowledge on the part of cultivators and their servants, insufficient capital, and the very partial use yet made of both permanent and shifting machinery. It is not to be wondered at, considering the average size of farms, that landlords object to the expense of adding to their fixed engines; but were half a dozen holdings thrown into one, and fitted with the best machinery of the period, so as to tempt men of capital and experience to embark in the business of farming over several thousand acres, the rents might be safely increased and the British farmer might again hold his own in the face of foreign competition. Meanwhile what is to become of the smaller men who shall have been displaced? To this important query an answer will be found in the last few pages of this essay.

The third of the philanthropic objects the enterprise now advocated has in view is that of attempting to wean the natives from sloth, by opening up to them vistas of usefulness, in which they might be engaged in a manner not uncongenial to their habits. Some authorities who have been consulted think that there is every hope of persuading the Maories to assist in industries which, to native ideas, have nothing menial about them, especially as in a few districts they have already, to a small extent, taken to sericiculture on their own account. Others unhesitatingly condemn the aborigines as being utterly untrustworthy, and that their labour, even if willingly given, would be dear at any price. "The Maori is a noble specimen of man," said Sir Julius Vogel, late Agent-General for New Zealand, addressing the Royal Colonial Institute, London, on the 19th March 1878. "The Maori was not an utter savage when we first knew him, and it is far from improbable that he would have worked out to a great extent his own civilisation. He wanted the knowledge that has been handed down to civilised man from past ages. He was not without an appreciation of the value of labour. The missionaries found him of a reverent nature, and eager to imbibe their teachings. The wars which from time to time desolated the colony threw the Maori back, for in time of war, alas! the sword is the only medium of education. . . . The greatest efforts are now made to educate Maori children, and especially they are taught the English language." The Hon. Judge Bathgate, of the Supreme Court, Dunedin, in his pamphlet on the resources and prospects of New Zealand, published by the Messrs. Chambers in 1880, at page 18, says :—"The Maories are now as quiet and orderly as their white neighbours. The idea of another Maori war is, in the eyes of a colonist, ridiculous. . . . The establishment of English-speaking schools is changing the habits of thought in the rising generation. . . . The land which could produce and maintain so noble and handsome a race as the Maoris undoubtedly are, must be admirably adapted for the support of a population having capital and skill to turn its resources to profitable account." Fortunately we are not limited to Maori sinews so long as there are several thousands of industrious Chinese already settled in New Zealand, and with the option of importing, under proper regulations, as many coolies as may be required from India, China, or Polynesia. It is the native element, however, which would in the first instance be tried. If the Maoris will take to the industries in question, and allow their women and children to assist as the seasons come round, a great mutual benefit would result. Looked at simply in the light of an efficient engine of civilisation, chaseri-culture amidst this interesting race, fifteen or twenty years ago, would doubtless have speedily effected that which thousands of soldiery, armed colonists, and the terrors of law only partially accomplished; and it is surely not very presumptuous to believe that the succesful establishment of tea and silk farming now would rapidly complete the humanising and refining process.

## Some Details of the Proposed Enterprise.

The patient reader who has thus far followed our line of argument with any degree of interest, will now be prepared to learn something concerning the details of the enterprise as it has been proposed to be conducted in New Zealand. Its leading features may accordingly be thus briefly sketched:—(1) It has been suggested that a syndicate should be collected together and incorporated under the Companies' Acts of 1862 and 1867, under the title of The New Zealand Tea and Silk Company (Limited), or, The New Zealand Chasericultural Company (Limited), or some other suitable designation, with an authorised capital of £150,000 in 6000 shares of £25 each, fully paid up on allotment, with power to issue mortgage debentures for £50,000, at the end of two years, or immediately after the financial result of the first silk crop shall have been ascertained; and to issue further debenture bonds for £50,000 on the expiry of four years, or directly the first tea crop has been realised. (2) That the Company be administered in the United Kingdom by a Board of Directors, and in New Zealand by a Manager assisted by a Board of Advice. (3) That the special aims of the Company be the acquisition of eligible lands, forests, and running streams for water power; the erection of suitable buildings and machinery within the province of Auckland, or elsewhere in New Zealand, for the purpose of conducting the farming and production of tea and silk, and any other articles of commerce which may be found suitable to the climate. And (4), keeping in view the circumstance that the successful establishment of such a group of industries in any district would probably raise the value of all adjacent lands, that, in order to obtain a share of the anticipated advance, the functions of a Land Settlement Association be assumed, by the further acquisition of a surrounding area of perhaps 30,000 acres, to be secured, if possible, on similar terms to those granted to the corporation in the district of Rangitikei, known as the Manchester settlement (page 215, Official Handbook, 1875).

The initial operation would consist in arranging for the food requirements of the settlement, supposing it to be planted beyond easy reach of an already cultivated area, by the tillage of 250 acres or so as a permanent cereal and root farm for the comfortable maintenance of the employés and draught animals on the estate. Contemporaneously with the establishment of the farm, tea and mulberry planting, at the rate of one or more hundred acres of each per annum, might be prosecuted, a considerable portion of suitable land thrown into wheat, let temporarily for grazing and other agricultural and stock-raising purposes, and some of it devoted to the objects presently to be described, whilst a proportionate area of forest would necessarily be retained for the supply of timber, firewood, and charcoal. Meanwhile the erection of the buildings required,—houses, cottages, and other tenements for the employés; stables, barns, granary, and outhouses connected with the farm ; and sawmills, workshops, tea-houses, laboratory, magnaneries, and stores essential for chasericulture,—would be undertaken, and the whole work so timed that the arrival of special apparatus from home, would be as nearly as possible coincident with the completion of the premises for its reception, and with the dawn of the period for its employment.

It would answer no useful purpose at present were we to enter minutely upon the various items of expenditure necessary ere the company's special estate of about three thousand acres, partly under tea and mulberries began to yield an income (beginning in the second and continuing through subsequent years) from silk, and commencing during the fourth and fifth years from tea. These items, however, have been carefully calculated in conformity with the experience of the cost of production in China, India, and Australia, as already given in previous pages of this essay, and in unison, as far as can be ascertained, with colonial rates. Yet, whilst particulars are withheld as liable, at this early stage of the enterprise, to prove misleading, and as requiring too much space, it may not be undesirable to lay before the reader a kind of rough balance sheet of four years anticipated chasericultural outlay and returns, to serve as an outline of what the reality may eventually be.

*Pro forma* balance sheet of the proposed New Zealand Chaser-cultural Company (Limited), showing the probable outlay and return from year to year until the fifth year on the chasericultural department only, when both tea and silk industries might be expected to be in active operation, and the tea gardens had yielded their first crop.

### First and Second Years.

| Return. | | Outlay. | |
|---|---|---|---|
| To Capital, | £50,000 | By Cost of land and interest, | £6,300 |
| „ Gross yield from Farm, | 2,493 | „ Spent on Farm, | 4,200 |
| „ „ Tea Gardens, | nil. | „ „ Tea Gardens, | 2,905 |
| „ „ Mulberry, | nil. | „ „ Mulberry, | 12,075 |
| „ „ Spare land, | 29,517 | „ „ Spare Land, | 3,230 |
| | | „ „ Buildings, | 4,049 |
| | | „ „ Promotion and Management, | 5,220 |
| | | „ Carried to extension fund, | 5,000 |
| | | „ Dividend on £50,000, 12½ per cent., | 6,250 |
| | | „ Balance to next year, | 32,781 |
| | £52,010 | | £82,010 |

### Second and Third Years.

| | | | |
|---|---|---|---|
| To Balance from last year, | £32,781 | By Farm, | £1,050 |
| „ Farm, | 2,587 | „ Tea Gardens, | 2,905 |
| „ Tea Gardens, | nil. | „ Mulberry, | 14,947 |
| „ Mulberry, | 9,344 | „ Spare Land, | 7,770 |
| „ Spare Land, | 36,587 | „ Wages generally, | 3,255 |
| | | „ Buildings, | 5,250 |
| | | „ Management, | 4,398 |
| | | „ Extension fund, | 5,000 |
| | | „ Dividend, 15 per cent., | 7,500 |
| | | „ Balance, | 29,224 |
| | £81,299 | | £81,299 |

### Third and Fourth Years.

| | | | |
|---|---|---|---|
| To Balance, | £39,224 | By Farm, | £1,050 |
| „ Farm, | 2,837 | „ Tea Gardens, | 5,675 |
| „ Tea Garden, | nil. | „ Mulberry, | 14,175 |
| „ Mulberry Garden, | 18,688 | „ Spare Land, | 6,930 |
| „ Spare Land, | 32,637 | „ Wages, &c., | 5,355 |
| | | „ Promotion and Management, | 5,836 |
| | | „ Extension fund, | 5,000 |
| | | „ Dividend, 20 per cent., | 10,000 |
| | | „ Balance, | 29,365 |
| | £83,386 | | £83,386 |

*Fourth and Fifth Years.*

| Return. | | | Outlay. | |
|---|---|---|---|---|
| To Balance, | £29,365 | By Farm, . | | £1,050 |
| „ Farm, . | 2,837 | „ Tea Gardens | | 5,706 |
| „ Tea Gardens, | 2,000 | Mulberry, | | 15,750 |
| „ Mulberry, . | 28,032 | Spare Land, | | 6,090 |
| „ Spare Land, | 28,687 | Wages . | | 3,255 |
| | | Management, | | 6,156 |
| | | Extension fund, | | 5,000 |
| | | Dividend, 25 per cent., | | 12,500 |
| | | Balance, . . | | 35,414 |
| | £90,921 | | | £90,921 |

To Balance with which to commence the fifth and sixth years, £35,414.

In this statement it will be seen that a sum of £5000 a year or £20,000 is laid aside in aid of future extensions; dividends, amounting to £36,250 are earned and debited to the company; a balance of £35,414 is carried over for the purposes of the fifth and sixth years, when large additions, especially to the income from silk, may be anticipated; the whole being accomplished within the limits of the capital supposed to have been originally subscribed.

It will of course be understood that these results are only to be regarded as tentative in illustration. Whilst every item of a liberal outlay has been as far as possible anticipated, any tendency at exaggeration of the income has been repressed. Indeed, the return is far more likely to meet with adverse criticism on account of its modesty, seeing that, according to well-authenticated experience, a thoroughly well-managed mulberry plantation, started with five-year-old shrubs, doubles its yield by the time the fifth season *in situ* has been reached. As the cultivation of such an estate progresses and the tea and mulberry bushes approach robust maturity, unless very material extensions are undertaken, the annual outlay, after the fifth year, must necessarily bear a diminishing proportion to the out-turn; so that by the time the whole of the original area secured and planted has reached a period of full bearing, the net income of the company promises to require a pleasing row of probably six figures to represent it.

So much for what may be termed the immediate and special objects of the New Zealand Chasericultural Company (Limited); but the subsidiary purposes to which portions of their spare land are proposed to be devoted should not be overlooked. In the course of time these will no doubt multiply both in number as well as in importance, but at present reference need only be made to six—small fruit, such as currants, cherries, &c., honey, sugar, oranges, vines, and olives—all of which, being usually more remunerative than the returns from ordinary farming, might dispute the place of cereals on portions of the company's spare land. One of the witnesses examined last year by the New Zealand Industries Commission stated that an ordinary crop of small fruit would be about six tons per acre. At the nominal price of three-halfpence per pound for preserving purposes, such a crop would yield a net return of £50 per acre. He likewise remarked that were fruit-preserving factories established, one man attending to three acres of small fruit—which he could easily accomplish—would be better remunerated than the farmer of fifty acres in grass or under the ordinary crops. At present, for lack of such factories, immense quantities of the finest cherries, peaches, currants, brambles, and other fruits in favour for preserving, annually rot on the trees and bushes; and whilst the New Zealand public are paying over £90,000 a year in the home and Australian markets for similar tinned and bottled luxuries, these could be produced at a vast saving at their own doors. In the growth and preservation of small fruit, therefore, or in giving encouragement to persons to settle on their land and pursue this profitable occupation, the company might eventually see a favourable opening for the employment of many of their, less well-informed female applicants.

Bee-farming in New Zealand may be reckoned in its infancy as compared with the achievements of apiculture in the United States. Even in our inclement north bees managed upon the humane "non-swarming" system, by which the objectionable practice of stifling is rendered unnecessary, sometimes yield as much as 79 lbs. of honey per hive per season. The motto in this case is—"Give your bees plenty of room at the right time, then plunder them at your leisure." In the Ukraine (Polish Russia), it is by no means an uncommon circumstance for the peasants to own as many as five hundred hives apiece, and even to boast occasionally that they realise more profit from their bees than the farmers do from their crops. At Mount Ida in the island of Crete, Narbonne in France, and Chamouni in Switzerland, apiculture has long been extensively prosecuted, the value and fame of their honey being recognised all over Europe. It is in America, however, that this interesting and lucrative industry is to be seen at its best. From an article in the *Times* of January 14, 1879, we learn that bee-keeping is conducted in the United States by means of large capital, many firms owning from 2300 to 5000 swarms of bees, and in the case of Messrs. Thurber, of New York, 12,000 swarms. These apiculturists, indeed, in 1878 forwarded to Great Britain 300,000 lbs. of honey, being part of a product all over the States that year of 35,000,000 lbs. Their method of administration is curious. Proprietors of orchards and farmers at three or four miles interval are bargained with, either at a fixed rent or for a share of the produce, when, probably, 100 swarms of bees are boarded with each. At regular periods trained servants go round and remove all saturated combs, clean in and about the hives, and destroy all obnoxious or useless insects. Thus the farmer or gardener has very little responsibility; and as each suitable acre is capable of maintaining twenty-five swarms, and the insects on four acres can be attended to by one man, the pecuniary result at the end of favourable seasons is very satisfactory. Indeed, no more need be urged to show the remunerative nature of the industry than to mention that in America the seven years ending with 1879 exhibited an average annual harvest of 90 lbs. of honey per hive, which realised about tenpence per pound, or, exclusive of the value of the wax, a gross return of £93 per acre. Every attention has, of course, been paid to the selection of the finest queen bees for the improvement of the indigenous species, and with this object specimens have been drawn from the most celebrated honey-producing districts of Europe. Some specially fine individuals among these, only a few years ago, sold readily in New York for as much as £10 each; but owing to subsequent success in rearing the royal insects, the price has dropped, and queens of long pedigree and other attractions may now be purchased there at from one to five dollars apiece. But our American cousins have not been contented merely to improve the breed; they have also sought with success to economise the time of their meliorated species through the adoption of a modified German idea. It has been calculated that about two-thirds of the working lives of bees are expended in comb building, so in order to leave them more leisure to collect honey, perforated walls of wax are set up in the hive, which the insects eagerly take possession of and complete. A very remarkable phase of the industry, as well as an apt illustration of this and another plan for saving time, is that branch of apiculture which is conducted afloat. During early spring a suitably fitted steamer loads a certain number of hives occupied by swarms, probably at New Orleans. Slowly steaming against the current of the Mississippi, the ship with its humming freight reaches and leisurely passes through Louisiana, Arkansas, Missouri, Tennessee, and Kentucky; during which period the glories of the Indian summer appear, and are in full splendour when the gorgeous flower-carpeted prairies of Illinois, Iowa, and Wisconsin are reached. For a short time the steamer probably remains at Minnesota, or until the captain is admonished to commence his homeward voyage by the deepening tints of autumn, when he lingeringly drifts and steams through apparently boundless plains glowing with floral opulence and grace, and so with the waning year reaches his destination ere the icy breath of winter has commenced. Thus the bees, by an eminently practical expedient, are daily, indeed hourly, introduced to an ever-diversified panorama of vegetable brilliance and inexhaustible stores of sweetness; their vigour is economised, as their flights are essentially limited although frequent; the shining hour is improved to the utmost, the storage of honey being continual, and its pillage by the watchful attendants correspondingly maintained; whilst the grand result of the season's operations is the usual harvest of two hundredweight of honey per hive.

On a small scale, a similar scene may be witnessed each autumn on the Clyde, with the difference that in this case the steamer's duties are limited to the conveyance of hives and swarms to and from the moorland districts adjoining the Frith, where the bees enjoy the blooming heather for a time.

It is no doubt well known, yet the circumstance will bear repetition, that the bee, particularly the Italian insect, is one of the farmer's best friends. Apart from its great size, robustness, prolific character, untiring industry, its greater production of honey, and its being able to revel in luxury where the ordinary small bee to which we are accustomed starves; its superior length of proboscis enables it to reach the nectaries of red clover and some plants besides, where other bees fail, so that fertilisation ensues whenever Italian bees have been roaming over red clover fields. This important function the Ligurian bee performs will not seem less valuable when it is mentioned that in ordinary seasons in New Zealand a red clover crop is reckoned as profitable to the farmer as one of wheat. Sufficient, probably, has now been said in advocacy of apiculture as one of the minor industries proposed to be taken under the wing of the New Zealand Chasericultural Company; and those who were privileged to witness the fearless and expert artificial swarming of bees and handling of Italian queens by young ladies in the tents of the Caledonian Apiarian and Entomological Society at the last meeting of the Highland and Agricultural Society at Stirling, will not likely suffer any doubts to remain as to bee-farming in one of its branches being well-suited to the gentler sex.

Beet-cultivation for sugar has been successfully tried in New Zealand, and thirty tons per acre of first-class roots obtained; but the much more profitable *durra millet* or *sorgho* grass of Asia and Africa, although doubtless well-suited to the soil and climate, appears not yet to have been attempted on a commercial scale. This long-neglected source of sugar, after having been carefully tested for some years in the United States, and found to answer admirably and pay well, now menaces the position occupied by the sugar-cane, the sugar-maple, and the beet. Sorgho has from time immemorial been cultivated as a cereal both in Asia and Africa; towards the latter division of the globe it stands indeed in the same position of its principal corn yielder as rice occupies in the former.   In the South of Europe sorgho is also produced, but in the more northern countries, such as Germany, Holland, Belgium, and Britain, the summer heat is neither so great nor so protracted as to bring this plant to perfection.   Up till the year 1857 sorgho was unknown in America, but since its introduction the cultivation has spread until now it has extended as far north as the State of Maine, where it is grown almost entirely on account of the large proportion of sugar it yields.   In favourable climates, such as that of Illinois, 384 gallons of rich syrup per acre have been obtained, which yield 10 lbs. per gallon of good crystals.   Specimens of this syrup have been subjected to analysis by Mr. M'Murtrie, chemist to the U.S. Department of Agriculture, with the following result:—

| | |
|---|---|
| Cane sugar (saccharose), . . . | 88·893 per cent. |
| Grape sugar (glucose), . . . | 5·610 „ |
| Water (by drying at 110° C., . . | 5·125 „ |
| Unaccounted for, . . . . | 0·372 „ |
| | 100·000 |

Comparing this statement with the 2800 lbs. or 3000 lbs. of sugar per acre obtained from beet in Germany and France, it will be seen that the advantage is greatly in favour of sorgho. Indeed, only a few years ago some of the farmers in Maine stated that the profit they derived from the sugar obtained from one acre of maize—which yields one-fifth less saccharine matter than sorgho—was equal to the gain from the sale of thirty acres of wheat.   The sorgho sugar industry, it need scarcely be added, is rapidly spreading in the United States, where it is not likely to be dropped so long as the profit it realises keeps near its present figure.

It is well known that no cultivated fruit surpasses the orange as a remunerative crop, even allowing that nine or ten years may elapse between seed planting and securing the first harvest, where grafting is not resorted to.   Oranges and lemons, as already stated, grow luxuriantly in different parts of New Zealand, where one hundred trees per acre may be profitably cultivated.   A moderate estimate gives from 1000 to 1600 oranges as the annual yield from each tree after the tenth year, which, at the small value of one penny three farthings per dozen, shows a yield of nearly twenty shillings per tree, or a gross return of over £96 per acre.   But the capabilities of New Zealand have not usually been reckoned much inferior to those of New South Wales, where, in certain orange groves, the gross return is estimated at £500 per acre from orange trees, individuals of which for more than twenty years have yielded three hundred dozens of the most superb fruit per annum.

The merits and attractions of Scotch marmalade are too well known wherever civilised man has penetrated to render it necessary to expatiate upon the subject here; so it need only be added that with such facilities for its production by the company as could easily in time be developed, a most important auxiliary would be added to chasericulture, also affording numerous openings for both educated and crude female labour.

A difference of opinion exists regarding the desirability of cultivating olives and vines together upon the same farm; but happily the feeling is unanimous in ascribing entire suitability to parts of New Zealand for both products. On this point an Italian authority (Mr. G. B. Federli, of the Survey Department, New Zealand, in his evidence printed by the Colonial Industries Commission, p. 40) says:—"The cultivation of the vine requires the identical kind of soil that is necessary for the olive, and the same treatment in planting, consequently when they are cultivated together the labour is at least lessened one-third, and without the slightest disadvantage to either. One more important item is that, if it should occur that the olive trees fail for one year—as is the case sometimes in the countries where it is cultivated—the vines assist in lessening the loss, it being rarely the case that both fail. In this way the plot of land will never be unproductive; in fact, the practice of cultivating olives and vines together is now much extended in Italy."

On the sericicultural industry this gentleman, in the same communication to the commissioners, thus writes:—"The mulberry is far more easily cultivated than the olive, and almost every kind of soil is suitable for its growth. I have every reason to believe that the cultivation of silkworms can be introduced not only in the North but also in the Middle Island. This tree, when once properly planted, requires no more attention. Regarding the cultivation of silkworms, there is no doubt that it requires some skill, but that can easily be acquired. In Italy and France it is well known that, where the climate is suitable, this industry is extended to a very large scale. Hundreds of thousands of families who possess not a palm of soil obtain support from this cultivation. Every landowner, as a rule, grows more mulberry trees than he requires for his own production, and the surplus is given to those people who are willing to cultivate a certain quantity of silkworms; the owner receives half the value of the produce contained in the cocoons in exchange for the leaves. This industry is not only carried on by the lower, but also by the better classes. This cultivation requires some care and attention, and is well adapted for women, and generally ladies of good standing also take great interest in this important and fascinating industry. . . . I am prepared to assert that a woman, without neglect of her domestic duties, can cultivate as many silkworms as produce 100 lbs. of cocoons in thirty-five days; and, considering the average actual price paid in Europe, she would make 2s. per hour for the time employed in that cultivation, and I consider that a good return. The mulberry tree has two other advantages, namely, in autumn the fallen leaves make excellent food for fattening sheep during winter, and the timber is considered one of the best for making receptacles for wine, spirits, &c."

Such, then, are the subsidiary industries which it is proposed should be grafted upon the stem of the more important chaseri-culture, with the double purpose of securing economy in working the whole estate, and with the view of attracting to the colony as wide and varied a circle of immigrants as possible. There are other useful yet disregarded plants which time will doubt-less add to the list of ancillary products, such as cinchona, cork, dye-saffron, dyer's madder, the Japanese chestnut, the persimmon, medicinal rhubarb, and tallow trees of China, besides many more; all fairly hardy, and no doubt well adapted to thrive in the climate of Auckland.

The fourth of the leading features alluded to at page 230 now falls to be expiscated:—The land settlement proposal on the lines of the Rangitikei colony. This interesting experiment was commenced in 1871 by The Emigrant and Colonists Aid Corporation, presided over by the Duke of Manchester, from whom the new community obtained the name of the "Man-chester Special Settlement." A block of land twenty miles in length and about eight miles broad, containing 106,000 acres, was purchased at 15s. per acre, and paid for by bills bearing 5 per cent. interest, maturing at different dates over a space of ten years. On the one hand the corporation undertook to settle on the land some 2000 people within six years, and on the other part the Government promised to provide free pas-sages for the immigrants from England, and to find work in the formation of a railway through the property, or in connec-tion with other public works in the neighbourhood for a current number of 200 labourers. The Provincial Government made a conditional agreement to expend annually for five years a sum of £2000 to assist in forming bye-roads. On arrival in port the immigrants are taken by steamer and tramway car to the boundary of the settlement without charge, and are there looked after by the corporation, and eventually settled in township two-roomed cottages, each standing on an acre of land, or on country blocks of 40 to 100 acres, the wages to be earned meanwhile at wood-cutting, carpentering, bricklaying, and saw-mill work being from 7s. to 15s. a day. Against the immigrant the charges made by the corporation are:—In the townships, 7s. per week for the rent of his cottage and land, with the certainty of both becoming his own property, if the payments have been kept up, at the end of three years; and for the farmer an annual rent of 2s. 6d. per acre up to 100 acres, with the option of absolute purchase at the end of seven years or before at the rate of £3 per acre. It may be mentioned, also, as having an important bearing upon the enterprise which has called forth this essay, that the Manchester Company relies for its profit on the enhanced value given to the remainder of their lands through the influx of population and the construction of railways and roads. Although this grand scheme hung fire for a little, it speedily got into notice, and latterly there was even a pressure to obtain the company's available land at £2 or £3 per acre for cash, whilst large numbers of township sections have been disposed of at £10 per acre outside townships to £25 per quarter of an acre in central spots.

This short review of the Manchester settlement paves the way for allusion to a similar enterprise, but on a much smaller scale, proposed to be combined with the operations of the New Zealand Chasericultural Company. It has been suggested that this corporation, when formed, should be prepared to grapple with the duties connected with a land settlement association, and acquire an additional area of perhaps 30,000 acres. The responsibility would be considerable, but so, no doubt, would be the return. It is well known that the local Government profess anxiety to promote the establishment of new industries at the Antipodes, and it is believed that encouragement, as in the present case, may not be withheld when the arrangements are further advanced. One of the early results of the successful establishment of chasericulture there would be an immediate influx of the numerous kindred and other trades and professions which elsewhere invariably gather around the centres of great industries. In order to accommodate these, and to reap some immediate advantage to the syndicate from the accompanying demand for space, and the consequent enhancement in the value of the adjoining land which must certainly follow, it is proposed, as above stated, that a large surrounding or adjacent expanse should be secured. It is at this point, also, that the promise made a few pages back (having reference to agriculturists who may have lost or been obliged to abandon their farms in the old country on account of the amalgamation of lesser holdings into others of greater dimensions) may be implemented. By way of encouragement to such to immigrate, advantages might be held out to selected farmers of proved ability and some means, along with labourers and others of good character, corresponding somewhat with those offered on the Manchester settlement. A good and firm foundation of well-understood industrial activity would thus be laid, a fair certainty of having always at hand a sufficiency of food for the infant colony wherever it might be planted would be felt, and an ever-increasing supply of both juvenile and adult labour for emergencies would be secured.

### IS CHASERICULTURE IN NEW ZEALAND LIKELY TO PAY?

The last, although perhaps not the least, important inquiry connected with the proposal to farm tea and silk in New Zealand —Will it pay?—although to some extent anticipated and answered already, still remains to be practically dealt with.

In advocating the commencement of a new industry in a new country there must always be many important points to be considered, and the promoter naturally endeavours to give his proposal as favourable a complexion as possible; yet he that would blazon forth all the apparent or expected advantages whilst carefully ignoring or suppressing all impediments or hindrances to success, would prove no true friend to this or any other enterprise, to the country in which it was proposed to be conducted, to those he desired to interest in the scheme, or to himself. Accordingly, it is but fair that, having already dwelt chiefly upon the bright side of the picture, we should now take a peep at the reverse. Fortunately, there is only one small speck to arrest the eye there, but that little blot is important, and may be called "deficient and expensive labour." We have already seen what the average wages are in other chasericultural districts of the world, and the fact is forced upon our consideration, whether we like it or not, that in New Zealand at present rates, probably from four to five times more money would be required. It is well, however, to reflect that the quantity of work performed in the latter country under all the advantages of its delightful and exhilarating climate—set against the more meagre results obtained amidst the rain deluges, the fierce heat, the scorching winds, and the terror produced by the proximity of beasts of prey in Assam—might, after all, be such as to minimise the apparent difference in wages. It should be recollected, also, that the hitherto high rate of wages paid at the Antipodes has been owing to the sparse population viewed in connection with the vast amount of heavy work to be done; but as immigration gradually peoples the soil with miscellaneous labourers and their families, and as the openings for female industry, which this chasericultural enterprise proposes to inaugurate, increase and become widely known in Europe, there can be no question that the rates of remuneration will be more equably adjusted than they are now. Again, if the average individual wages paid in China are small, the total expenditure by the planters and manipulators cannot be insignificant because comparatively little

machinery, and that of the rudest construction, is employed.
The work is done, however; but, like the erection of Egypt's
pyramids and other vast monuments of antiquity which for
centuries have taxed the ingenuity of experts to explain, is
acomplished simply by numbers, where, with the aid of suitable machinery, far fewer human hands would suffice. The
Indian tea planters early became alive to the value of proper
mechanical appliances and adopted them, thereby enabling them
materially to reduce the number of their employés. In Ceylon,
where the conditions for tea culture and preparation are on the
whole not superior to those possessed by India, the result has
been, considering the short period the industry has existed there,
even more encouraging. Wiser in her generation, and profiting
by the errors of her big neighbour, Ceylon has without excitement, gambling in bogus gardens, or at any sacrifice whatsoever,
quietly added tea planting to her older avocations of producing
coffee and cinchona, and is now intent in pushing her products
into the various markets of the world. From the mistakes of
India there would be no excuse if New Zealand failed to keep
clear. On the contrary, having the united experience of China,
India, Europe, Ceylon, and Australia to guide her, with a magnificent climate and every other advantage to boot, there seems good
reason to predict success. We have already given expression to the
antagonistic opinions which prevail regarding the likelihood of
getting the Maoris to work for reasonable wages, or indeed to
work at all. Without leaning to either side in the meantime, it
is satisfactory to know that there are many hundreds of industrious Chinese already settled in New Zealand whose co-operation
in congenial industries might be had, and whose services and
experience—acquired in many instances, doubtless, at the great
centres of tea and silk production in their native country—could
scarcely fail to be eminently valuable. As an extreme measure,
resort might be had to the importation of labour direct from
China, as experience has taught that the offer of a few pence per
day over the sixpence or ninepence the Asiatic has hitherto been
toiling for at home, is not one likely to remain long neglected.
The difficulty with the sons of the yellow race has not hitherto
been to induce them to leave their homes for places where, under
strong legal protection, fair wages were to be earned. Rather
has it been to keep them away, or, having swarmed like locusts,
as in California and some parts of Australia, to prevent and
quell the riots occasioned by their underbidding the American
and European workman, and threatening to drive them altogether out of the labour market. Of such a contingency, however, there is no near prospect, as the New Zealand Government
have decided to place a tax of £10 a head upon every Chinaman
landing on the islands, which will probably weed out from

amongst intending immigrants all except the most industrious.
There is also the wide field of India from which moderately-
priced labour may be drawn, not to mention the vast human
resources—savage as yet, to be sure—of Papua or New Guinea.
In the thousand islands of Polynesia, also, splendid hives of
untamed human sinews exist, which would only require the
exercise of prudent management to turn into useful and willing
workmen.    Unfortunately, the presence of the white man in
search of labourers there (entirely through the misbehaviour of a
few ships' crews) is not very welcome at present; but with the
introduction of humane regulations, a system of voluntary but
limited servitude under Government supervision might easily be
established, which would prove mutually beneficial and agreeable
to both employers and employed.    Lastly, we should not overlook the prospect that in the course of time, when the value of
the inducements to take service under the company shall have
become known, hundreds, perhaps thousands of respectable girls
from home will flock to its standard, feeling that a colonial life
in such an exquisite climate possesses irresistible attractions as
securing health, comfort, and independence.    Altogether, therefore, the opinion seems reasonable that tea and silk farming in
New Zealand will be placed at no serious disadvantage as regards
labour and wages when compared with the seats of similar
industries elsewhere.    If the use of human muscles be at present
somewhat costly there, this objection in the ordinary course of
events must gradually alter in favour of the farmer.    Meanwhile,
by the introduction of superior machinery, driven where suitable
by the copious water-power so largely available, by a carefully
matured system of divided labour, and by the employment of
only the best superintendence to conduct all scientific, manipulative, and commercial operations, little doubt is entertained that
the average cost of production to the New Zealand Chasericultural Company will not exceed the average outlay of the tea
planters of India and Ceylon, and the silk farmers of Europe and
Asia, whilst the splendid capabilities of the climate and the
comparatively short distances any of the farms are likely to be
from a shipping port, will enable the company's invoices, at no
distant date, to compare favourably with theirs.

If these and previous remarks have proved satisfactory in
removing the only objection to the enterprise which has hitherto
been urged, it must be evident that chasericulture in New
Zealand, even from the first, is likely to pay well; that after
the fifth year it must pay handsomely; and that when all the
subsidiary industries which shall have nestled and grown up
under its wing are in full operation the Company's annual income
will probably be enormous.

## THE STEPS WHICH HAVE BEEN TAKEN.

The queries propounded at page 181 being no longer in the way, the reader may now welcome any information we may offer touching the steps which have been taken to emancipate the contents of this essay from the unsubstantial realms of suggestion and place them on the rock of accomplishment.

On the 3rd July 1879 a correspondence was commenced with the New Zealand Government through the Agent-General in London, in the course of which an epitome of the proposed enterprise was from time to time sent as it became developed. During the following year it was deemed necessary that the public both here and at the Antipodes should also be made aware of the scheme; accordingly several letters on the subject appeared in the columns of the *Glasgow Herald* and *New Zealand Public Opinion*, last year articles were printed in *Chambers's Journal, The Colonies and India*, in *The British Trade Journal*, and on the 31st January 1882 a paper in advocacy of the establishment of chasericulture in New Zealand was read before the Society of Arts, London. Thus there has been a degree of simultaneous action in the attempt to excite public interest in both hemispheres. Several objects were sought to be attained by this method of procedure. The proposal to cultivate tea and silk as a combined industry in New Zealand being a novelty, it was felt that every possible source of information available ought to be probed and utilised, and that following the approaches to the New Zealand Government there should be appeals to the general public, so that a wholesome action and reaction in the shape of favourable and adverse criticism might result. The plan answered every expectation, many useful suggestions were elicited, neither propitious nor antagonistic analysis were withheld, although by far the more important expressions of opinion, both as regards number and weight, have hitherto been eminently friendly, and some even enthusiastic. In the early stages of publicity not much was expected from the colonial authorities beyond information and a little moral encouragement, but a great deal was anticipated from intelligent colonists, many of whom were in this country at the time, who might stamp the scheme with their approval, should it seem to them to possess the elements of success, or subvert it with their adverse criticism if found unworthy. Here, again, no disappointment was experienced as the Agent-General undertook to communicate on the subject with his Government, and many returned colonists responded to the calls for their candid opinions with the utmost promptitude and in the most favourable terms. Still, something was looked for from Government, if not at an early stage, a little further on, in the promise of support, pecuniary or in kind, after the manner of the India and continental powers, which for many years had been aiding tea or silk farming, or both, in their respective countries out of public funds. As an assistance in arriving at a conclusion the Government of New Zealand, through their Agent-General, were informed that the openings for aid might be as follows :—

### For the Tea Industry.

1. The necessary supply of one-year-old tea plants and fresh seed from China, Ceylon, Assam, the Neilgherries, and Darjeeling, delivered at the nearest port to the proposed plantations at cost price or free.

2. Facilities for the importation of labour from China, India, or elsewhere, and reasonable legal protection to the planter against the non-fulfilment or evasion of labourer's engagements.

3. A proportion of forest-land to the acreage purchased or rented, at a reduced cost or free.

4. The admission by the customs, without duty, of all material, implements, tools, and machinery necessary in tea cultivation, manufacture, and packing, for a short term of years.

5. Freedom from duty or excise impost for all tea grown and prepared in the colony for the first ten years.

### For the Silk Industry.

6. The necessary supply (400 plants per acre) of five-year-old white mulberry bushes grafted on black mulberry stocks, or other approved kinds and seed from Sydney or elsewhere. Also the needful quantities of any other silkworm-feeding shrubs—such as the castor-oil plant, the terminalia and jujube trees, the ailanthus, &c., delivered at the nearest port to the proposed plantations at cost price, or free.

7. Facilities in regard to labour, land, and freedom from duties as in the tea industry.

8. And such encouragement generally as might lead to the speedy settlement of skilled reelers from France and Italy, silk throwsters from England, and the purchase in time of the mechanism required in the higher branches of the silk industry.

These hints as to the apertures through which Government succour might usefully flow were of course simply made in the form of suggestions, to be increased, diminished, or modified hereafter.

There is a feeling in many minds that no national industry is worthy the name which needs Government assistance, and we are quite of this opinion when expressed towards one which has been already to some extent established. Nevertheless, let the well-known authority on silk culture, M. Robinet, be consulted, when his opinions will be found to be these:—"In a new country the sericiole industry cannot be expected to take deep root unless it is initiated by a large model establishment, which is a nursery not only for plants, but for worms of the right sort, and at the same time a training school for reelers and breeders. . . . This opinion is corroborated by facts. If we follow, step by step, the history of sericiculture, we find that in every country where it is flourishing—where, as in France and Italy, nine-tenths of the silk produced comes from within the walls of the cottage—we find that this industry invariably originated in a model establishment, formed and supported by public money." Mrs. Bladen Neill of Victoria, already alluded to in this essay, in quoting the above remarks of M. Robinet in the course of an eloquent paper on sericiculture in Australia, read before the British Association at Bristol in 1875, said:—"If a nation so industrious as the French, if in a country where the sericiole industry has been flourishing for three centuries, and gives employment and bread to millions, if among producers whose silk is considered the best in the world, the Government still find it advisable to take this step, I leave it to the public to decide what the Government of new countries ought to do."

Many even acute persons have fallen into the error of believing that tea farming and sericiculture have been essentially cottage industries at their first commencement in a district; that these eminently scientific undertakings, in the countries where they are at present found, have risen from the blundering experiments of the peasant to the dignity of the vast establishments we now see. Any one who cares to dip into the literature of China will quickly be disabused of the fallacy as regards both tea and silk, and M. Robinet and other continental authorities dissipate the chimera if attempted to be thrown around the latter product. Indeed, it may be accepted without question that in a new country, all that the untaught cottager without industrial traditions to guide him can hope to accomplish is simply to grow indifferently well the bushes which form the basis of the important twin industries under review. Technical education is absolutely required whenever the tea and mulberry cultivator seeks to pass the merely agricultural stage, and it is at this point, if not previously given, that Government aid is desirable and has been ungrudgingly and sometimes lavishly bestowed in all countries in which the industries have reached a high pitch of perfection. It was the Government of India that in 1834 and afterwards planted and conducted the first experimental tea gardens in the Seebsaugur and Debroghur districts, thus founding the present vast tea trade now annually passing through Calcutta. Not until 1839 and 1840 was it that the bulk of these gardens became the property of the Assam Company. By both local and supreme governments in India sericiculture was afterwards, in 1862, most liberally fostered, particularly in the Punjab, and although, through some erroneous computations regarding temperature and rainfall, the early experiments were disappointing, the authorities were not deterred from making subsequent trials there and in other districts with gratifying results. In America, too, the first important silk harvest, obtained in California some years ago, was the development of a government grant. It is well known that for centuries the Governments of China, Japan, Italy, France,—and in some measure Russia, Turkey, Switzerland, and Austria might be included,—have been aiding to develop their sericicultural industries, and have cherished them in every possible way when once established. The grand result has been that out of the total import of raw silk into Great Britain per annum (probably, in round numbers, over 10,000 tons) nineteen-twentieths come from foreign countries, and only the remaining twentieth, or say 500 tons, is the produce of our own possessions reared by our own people. Vast as is, or rather was, the annual silk crop of France, through the paternal encouragement the industry has received from every successive occupant of the Tuileries, it might at this moment have been enormously greater but for the spread of various diseases among the silkworms, and a little event of a few hours' duration which decided whether the Middle Island of New Zealand should in future be French or British soil. Intimation having in 1840 been sent to Governor Hobson of the North Island that sixty French emigrants in the whaling vessel "Compte de Paris," escorted by the frigate "L'Aube," were about to land and form a settlement at Akaroa, he ordered off Captain Owen Stanley (elder brother of the late popular and distinguished Dean of Westminster, who relates this anecdote in his memoirs of his father and mother) in H.M.S. "Britomart" to anticipate and forestall the French by attaching the island to the British Crown. The captain started at once, disembarked on the spot, formed a hasty encampment on the beach, and held a court of petty sessions under a tree, whilst the French frigate was slowly working into the harbour. When the emigrants landed they found themselves under the shadow of the British flag, and it has since been freely alleged, with probably some degree of truth, that had the circumstances been reversed and the French Government become the masters, every suitable yard of land in the Middle Island would long ago have been clothed with vineyards, mulberry and olive plantations.

But enough has probably been said to show the desirability of a little judicious fostering at first on the part of the New Zealand Government. Such support out of the public purse, or an equivalent in concessions similar to those already indicated, need only be temporary, enduring for merely a few years at the outside, as the essence of the enterprise lies in its mutually-co-operative and reciprocally-supporting design.   Once fairly started, even with a very moderate capital, the twin industries would become so inter-changeably combined and interlaced in labour, experience, and results, that the one could scarcely fail to buttress the other at all times, especially during periods of commercial depression in either; but, on the other hand, if launched with a capital and staff commensurate with the importance of the undertaking, Government aid in any form would probably cease to be an element worthy of further consideration.

With the leading points in this essay the New Zealand authorities, through previous and present agents-general, have already been made acquainted.   As the executive has hitherto professed a willingness to promote and encourage new local industries, the queries have been asked:—" Are you prepared to give assistance of any kind to tea and silk farming within the colony?   If so, in what direction is such aid likely to flow?" So far the direct replies received have scarcely been of that definite and substantial character which the actual existence of an influential company would doubtless have elicited.   The officials are cautious, as all well-trained and properly-conducted officials certainly ought to be; and these gentlemen are not likely to earn a reprimand from headquarters on account of being too communicative; nevertheless taciturnity in matters of this kind may not always be the best policy.   The government has evidently missed the opportunity of taking the initiative in the inaugura-tion of chasericulture in its territory, and the period will probably soon elapse when it will be of any importance what steps are officially taken.   Some fear of this sort has apparently, according to recent colonial newspapers, begun to stir in the Executive mind.   The *Littleton Times* of 24th May 1881 informs us that the Hon. the Minister of Lands, in reply to the Industrial Asso-ciation (of Christchurch) wrote:—" I am of opinion that with proper care it (sericiculture) should be made a thriving industry in this colony.   In order to give the experiment a fair trial, the Government has—at Mr. Federlis's suggestion—ordered by the outgoing mail a number of silkworms' eggs, mulberry trees, seeds, and cuttings.   It is hoped the eggs will arrive early in October so as to give an opportunity of at once starting the industry with the mulberry trees which are immediately available in the colony, leaving the better class of trees to follow from Japan at the proper season.   An order has also been sent to Sydney for white mulberry trees (*Morus alba*) to be sent at once, so that a start may be made before next spring."   The same newspaper has a paragraph, dated Wellington, May 25, as follows:—" The Government sent by last San Francisco mail an order through Mr. Creigton for a large consignment of silkworms' eggs of the green, orange, and white cocoon varieties, and for a quantity of the white mulberry trees on which the worms feed. At the same time an order was sent to Sydney for 500 white mulberry trees, two years old. The intention is to establish silk culture in New Zealand, in accordance with the idea which was *initiated* by Mr. Federli, of the Survey Department, who is an expert in that branch of industry." It will be seen with a feeling of regret that the eminent services rendered to practical sericiculture eleven years ago in New Zealand by Mr. T. C. Batchelor of Nelson, and Mrs. Bladen Neill's able advocacy of the same industry for both New Zealand and Australia before the British Association at Bristol in 1875, are thus being quietly ignored. It is hopeful, however, to find that the Government has really made a commencement, and that one of their own officials is getting the credit of reviving an industry which at the present moment might have been as important to the colony as wool is now if more attention had been paid to the actual results obtained by Mr. Batchelor, and to the eloquence of Mrs. Neill. As the matter at present stands there is ground for hope in colonial sericiculture but very little upon which to congratulate the executive. It has already been shown that the industry, conducted by itself without some natural ally alongside of it to divide the expense of production, cannot possibly pay. Yet this is the groove in which it is being directed. Every resident in New Zealand and thousands at home who have paid attention to the subject knew, many years ago, that the mulberry grows luxuriantly in many parts of the colony, and that silk of good quality has already been obtained ; there is, therefore, no further necessity for the indulgence of mere experiment. The time for vigorous action has surely arrived. Here is a colonist's idea of what the Government is credited with having done, quoted from *The Press*, Christchurch, 6th June 1881 :—" A Wanganui nursery-man, writing to the *Chronicle*, expresses surprise that the Government should have decided to send for 500 white mulberry trees, and adds that *for years past large numbers of these trees have been grown in the nurseries of the colony*, but there being but little demand the supply has fallen off. He is, however, in a position to supply a considerable number, and believes that as many thousands could be got as the hundreds now asked for. To persons who contemplate making a trial of silkworm culture such a statement should be highly gratifying." By all means let the Government encourage the colonial nurserymen to culti-vate the mulberry in quantity, which would probably be the cheapest and most popular way they could devise of giving initial aid to sericiculture ; let them, if they prefer it, themselves establish nurseries for the supply of every known species of silk-worm-feeding shrub, not forgetting an equal breadth of ground covered with tea plants, or, what would probably be of most value ultimately to the colony and to chasericulture, let them make it worth while, and hand over both the responsibility and the profit to the coming New Zealand Chasericultural Company.

Our story is told. If we have succeeded in advocating the claims of this great enterprise to any purpose, there need surely be little difficulty or hesitation experienced on the part of New Zealand statesmen and colonists in deciding to support it. The company's proposed operations are clearly for the benefit of their adopted country quite as much as for this. A stream of prosperity irrigating one portion of Her Majesty's dominions cannot fail sooner or later to extend its fertilising influence even to the most distant shores. If the prosecution of chasericulture at the Antipodes is calculated to unlock a fresh coffer of wealth to the colonists, this can be all the more pleasantly achieved by drafting off hundreds, perhaps thousands, of willing workers from home to help in the operation and enjoy a share of the boon. On the other hand, let the colonists recollect how many millions of idle capital there are in this rich old Britain which the owners are ever trying with eagerness to invest safely and profitably ; let both our New Zealand friends and those nearer home keep in view that large and increasing army of well-born, well-educated, but reduced females already alluded to, to whom employment in a tea and silk company's factory would seem, and indeed be, a Heaven-sent blessing ; let us not forget the atmosphere of joy and cheerfulness such agricultural openings as the company would have to bestow, must carry to the firesides of hundreds of small, struggling farmers and labourers in the old country—let us examine with unbiassed judgment all these highly probable results of this enterprise, and then say if it be not worth promoting and encouraging, as likely to rank among the most conspicuous of the philanthropic and mercantile institutions of this marvellous nineteenth century.

---

## ACCOUNT OF THE SHOW OF THE HIGHLAND AND AGRICULTURAL SOCIETY HELD AT STIRLING IN 1881.

THE fifty-fourth Show of the Society was held at Stirling on the 26th, 27th, 28th, and 29th July.

The Society had visited Stirling on three previous occasions—namely, in 1833, the year in which the Society celebrated its jubilee; in 1864 on a requisition signed by 720 proprietors and tenants connected with the district of the Show; and in 1873, when the yard was for the first time kept open for four days, a custom ever since observed.

The Show in 1881, as well as those of the three previous meetings at Stirling, was held in the King's Park. The ground enclosed occupied about thirty acres, and a more convenient site it would be impossible to find.

The arrangements were as nearly as possible the same as on former occasions: the judging took place on Tuesday; the general meeting of members and public banquet were held on Wednesday; and the ball on Thursday.

The public banquet was held in the Golden Lion Hotel. The Earl of Mar and Kellie, Vice-President, in the absence of the Duke of Richmond and Gordon, the President, occupied the chair and Sir James Ramsay Gibson-Maitland, Bart., acted as croupier. Lord Mar was supported by Provost Anderson; Sir James H. Gibson-Craig, Bart.; Sir Robert Menzies, Bart.; Sir G. Graham Montgomery, Bart.; Rev. Dr. Grant, chaplain to the Society; Mr Irvine of Drum; Colonel Gillon of Wallhouse; Mr Mackenzie of Portmore; Mr Pott of Dod; Colonel Williamson of Lawers; Colonel Hare of Calder Hall. The Chairman, in proposing the toast of the evening—The Highland and Agricultural Society— said nobody could deny that the Society had done an immense amount of good towards the agriculture of this country. Almost all the improvements that had taken place in agriculture had really had a certain amount of impulse from the Highland Society. It was started pretty late last century with only 160 members, while now there were nearly 5000. A great deal had been said lately about agricultural depression, and it was an unfortunate fact that they had all felt the effects of it, both land- lords and tenants. The present show of the Highland Society did not look as if Scotland was going down under the effects of the agricultural depression. The Clydesdales did not seem to have suffered much. He thought the farmers of Scotland were going to weather the storm, and he did not think they were so badly off as their neighbours in the South. That might be owing in a certain extent to the education afforded by the agricultural societies. The President of the Society, the Duke of Richmond, would have been at the show, but he was obliged to go to Good- wood, not to see the races, but to perform his duty toward the heir-apparent to the throne of entertaining his Royal Highness. They would all allow that that was a paramount duty which his Grace could not escape from. In conclusion, he gave the toast of the evening, coupled with the name of the Duke of Rich- mond. Among other toasts were—The Judges, given by the chairman, and replied to by Mr. Wood, Ripon; The Successful Competitors, by Sir Graham Montgomery, and responded to by Mr. Bruce, Burnside; The Secretary, by Mr. Irvine of Drum, and acknowledged by Mr. F. N. Menzies.

The exhibition consisted of the following entries in the different classes of stock :—

### Cattle.

|  | Bulls. | Cows. | Heifers. | Oxen. | Total. |
|---|---|---|---|---|---|
| Shorthorn, . . . . . | 37 | 10 | 19 | ... | 66 |
| Ayrshire, . . . . . | 27 | 30 | 18 | ... | 75 |
| Polled Angus or Aberdeen, . . | 23 | 12 | 35 | ... | 70 |
| Galloway, . . . . . | 16 | 5 | 17 | ... | 38 |
| Highland, . . . . . | 19 | 10 | 30 | ... | 59 |
| Fat Stock, . . . . . | ... | ... | 3 | 20 | 23 |
| Extra, . . . . . . | 2 | 1 | 1 | 1 | 5 |
| Totals, . | 124 | 68 | 123 | 21 | 336 |

### Horses.

|  | Stallions. | Entire Colts. | Mares. | Fillies. | Geldings. | Total. |
|---|---|---|---|---|---|---|
| Agricultural Horses, . . | 20 | 71 | 21 | 50 | 4 | 166 |
| Hunters and Roadsters, . | ... | ... | 12 | ... | 22 | 34 |
| Ponies, . . . . | ... | ... | 9 | ... | 3 | 12 |
| Extra, . . . . | 3 | ... | ... | ... | ... | 3 |
| Totals, . | 23 | 71 | 42 | 50 | 29 | 215 |

### Sheep.

|  | Tups. | Ewes. | Gimmers. | Lambs. | Wethers. | Total. |
|---|---|---|---|---|---|---|
| Blackfaced, . . . | 65 | 35 | 41 | 35 | ... | 176 |
| Cheviot, . . . | 20 | 3 | 6 | 3 | ... | 32 |
| Border Leicester, . . | 44 | 15 | 30 | ... | ... | 89 |
| Leicester, . . . . | ... | ... | ... | ... | ... | ... |
| Cotswold and Lincoln, . | 6 | 6 | 3 | ... | . . | 15 |
| Short-Woolled, . . | 24 | 12 | 15 | ... | ... | 51 |
| Extra Sections, . . | ... | ... | ... | ... | 30 | 30 |
| Totals, . | 159 | 71 | 95 | 38 | 30 | 393 |

### Swine.

|  | Boars. | Sows. | Pigs. | Total. |
|---|---|---|---|---|
| Large Breed, . . . . | ... | 2 | ... | 2 |
| Berkshire Breed, . . . | 8 | 9 | 12 | 29 |
| Small Breed, . . . . | 1 | 4 | 3 | 8 |
| Totals, . | 9 | 15 | 15 | 39 |

*Collie Dogs.*

|  | Dogs. | Bitches. | Total. |
|---|---|---|---|
| Long-Haired, . . . . . . | 16 | 4 | 20 |
| Short-Haired, . . . . . . | ... | 1 | 1 |
| Totals, . | 16 | 5 | 21 |

Poultry, . . 294 Entries, 365 Head.

Implements, . . 2001 „ 163 Exhibitors.

The following is a comparative view of the exhibition of stock and implements, the premiums offered, and the receipts (gate money and catalogues) at each of the shows at Stirling:—

| Year. | Cattle. | Horses. | Sheep. | Swine. | Poul-try. | Imple-ments. | Pre-miums. | Re-ceipts. |
|---|---|---|---|---|---|---|---|---|
| 1833 | 288 | 68 | 160 | 54 | ... | 22 | 553 | 211 |
| 1864 | 397 | 181 | 614 | 76 | 252 | 973 | 1350 | 1729 |
| 1873 | 406 | 297 | 622 | 96 | 534 | 1400 | 1860 | 3140 |
| 1881 | 336 | 215 | 393 | 39 | 365 | 2001 | 2340 | 2577 |

In consequence of the Privy Council Orders prohibiting the import of animals from England into Scotland, owing to the existence of foot-and-mouth disease in England, the actual number of stock in the yard was rather fewer than stated above. About 23 head of cattle, 11 of sheep, and 16 of swine, were made by English breeders, in the expectation that the Directors would induce the Privy Council to relax the Order. The Directors, however, abstained from urging the relaxation of the Order, which was made partly at their own request, and the entry-money or stall-rent was returned.

The health of the stock was reported good, no case of disease having come under the notice of Principal Williams, or of Mr. Stewart, V.S., Stirling, who were in attendance throughout the show.

## CATTLE.

Of Shorthorns the exhibition was less numerous than would otherwise have been had English exhibitors been allowed to bring their "plumes" across the Border.   But although the number of animals forward was fewer than at some former exhibitions, the general character and quality of the stock shown was very creditable, considering the present position of agriculture.   Aged bulls were a good useful lot, and although differing considerably in individual character and shapes, several of them showed good style, symmetry, and substance.   Two-year-olds were neither so large nor so good as the aged or yearling bulls.   The latter section was fairly represented and possessed one animal of considerable merit.   The cow section was not large, but was fairly good ; two or three animals showed excellent character and substance.   Two-year-old heifers were a small section and middling in quality.   Yearling heifers were a fair section, but from their varied individual forms and character were more difficult to judge than any other section.   Several of the animrls showed good style and breeding.   A marked and a greatly improved feature of the shorthorns exhibited was the absence of over-feeding.   Exhibitors should be encouraged to bring forward breeding stock for exhibition in a more natural condition, over-feeding having proved very prejudicial, especially to the heifer sections.

The show of Ayrshires was pronounced very good.   The aged bulls were a very fine lot, and contained some animals of great merit.   In the section for two-year-olds there were two or three good specimens.   The yearlings were a very large and fine section. The aged and three-year-old cows in milk were fair animals, while the cows in calf were a large and remarkably fine section. Among the two-year-old heifers were some extra good animals. The yearling heifers were a large and very fair display, but not so good as the two-year-olds.

The Polled Angus or Aberdeen Breed was exceedingly well represented, being almost entirely devoid of coarse or inferior animals.   The aged bulls, although not numerous, were a very creditable section and all good specimens of the breed, the first-prize animal in particular being of extra quality.   The two-year-old bulls were scarcely so well represented as in the former section, the first and second prize animals, however, deserving special notice.   The one-year-old bulls were a well brought out, fair lot, but, except the first prize one, were not possessed of any great excellence.   The cows were all good useful animals, those placed especially being of great substance and fair quality, partaking, however, of somewhat different character.   The prize-takers in the two-year-old heifer section were particularly good, the first prize heifer being of extra style and substance ; the other winners being all worthy of special notice. The section for yearling heifers was the strongest in point of numbers, and was altogether a meritorious section, those placed being extremely good, and so equal in general excellence that more difficulty was experienced in placing them than in any of the other sections.

Of Galloways there was a fair display, and the quality of the animals in almost all the sections was of a very high order. The exhibits of both sexes in the aged sections were specially good, and it was satisfactory to find the representatives of the breed maintaining their best qualities after coming to maturity. The aged bulls included several very superior specimens. The first prize bull was a massive, compact animal of grand quality, with a capital back and ribs; the second was a full brother of the first, and both are possessed of the high quality so desirable in breeding animals; the third prize was a lengthy bull, with superior fore-quarters but deficient in his hind-quarters. The two-year-old bulls were not so good as the aged ones. The bull to which the first prize was awarded showed good quality and superior hair; the second seemed an improving animal, whose bone was a little rougher than was desirable; the third had straight lines and massive frame, but his head was rather coarse; and the others in the section were fairly good specimens. The yearling bulls were inferior to the other males exhibited. The first prize bull had well-sprung ribs; his weak points being the two extremes of his body. There were only five animals in the section for cows, but their merit was of a very high order; indeed it is seldom that such a specially select lot of Galloway cows meet in competition. The first was a beautiful cow of prime quality, and had she been slightly larger would have been almost a model Galloway. The two-year-old heifers were a good section. The first prize one possessed great substance and good quality; the second and third were pretty promising heifers, but manifesting a tendency to be patchy. The yearling heifers were also a good section. The first prize animal was a sweet, well-proportioned youngster, whose hair was a little too wiry; the second showed good quality, with a slightly plain head, and her rump was a little too strong; the third was also possessed of nice quality, but her head was slightly faulty, and she was developing a little patchiness at the tail root.

As might have been expected in a town so conveniently situated for their exhibition, Highlanders proved a very important and attractive feature of the show, nearly all the celebrated herds in Scotland being represented. The aged bulls, though not numerous, were a meritorious section, the first prize animal being of great style and quality. The three-year-olds were exceptionally good, and the competition very close in the first three animals. The two-year-olds do not call for special remark. In the female section cows were an excellent show.   The three-year-old heifers were a numerous and very superior section.   The two-year-olds were unusually numerous and of fair merit.

In the sections for Fat Stock there were no animals except the Highlanders calling for special notice, though as a whole the class was very creditable.

## HORSES.

Of Horses for Agricultural Purposes the first in the section for aged stallions was a genuine type of the Clydesdale, having good feet and legs, free action, and was an easy winner.   The second was also a very meritorious animal; indeed, all the horses placed in this section were of great merit.   In the three-year-old section the first, although low in condition, was an exceedingly good horse, having grand size and substance, uncommonly good feet, and fine feathery legs, good action, and could not fail to be a valuable sire.   The second and third had also great merit, and the section generally good.   The two-year-old colts were not so equal, although the prize-takers were of fair merit.   The yearling colts were a very good display, there being a great many very meritorious animals in the section.   The first, a big, stylish colt, is sure to be a winner again: the second, though not so big, was symmetrical: the third, a big, strong-boned colt, is likely to make a good sire.   The horses gaining prizes were generally good, and cannot fail to maintain the standard of the valuable breed of Clydesdales.

The turn-out of mares and fillies was fairly numerous in the aged sections and very numerous in the younger, and the quality all over was very good.   The mares with foals at foot were comparatively few in number, but those forward were excellent specimens of draught mares, the one placed at the top of the prize-list being specially worthy of commendation.   The contest in the yeld mare section was close and keen, several of the best possessing high quality and great style.   In the section of three-year-old-fillies the two animals placed first were animals of immense substance, but their quality was not quite so good.   The one to which the third prize was awarded appeared out of bloom, especially in the state of her legs, and her under-size, as compared with the most of the others in the section, told against her.   The others placed were highly creditable fillies.   The two-year-old fillies formed a fairly meritorious section on the whole, the first prize one, however, being decidedly the best.   But the yearling fillies were not only the most numerous but also the most meritorious animals submitted to the inspection of the judges.   A large proportion of the animals entered made a capital appearance as they were paraded in the ring, and they gave every promise of growing up into massive, symmetrical, well-bred mares. Awarding the prizes in the section was a matter of considerable difficulty, and some of those sent out without tickets would have made creditable prize-takers had there not been what were considered superior animals in the section.

Of Hunters, Roadsters, and Ponies there were in all 49 entries. In the section for brood mares there was a good display; the first prize mare with foal at foot showed good quality. The section for aged mares and geldings suitable for the field produced a poor lot on the whole, both as regards numbers and quality, there being only one fairly good horse in the lot that could be called a hunter. In general, the hunting classes at the Society's shows do not come up to many of the local shows; and this by some is attributed to the number of days they have to remain on the ground. The section for young mares and geldings for the field was fairly represented. The hackney section was good, but the jumping prize was a complete failure, as only three animals competed for it; and it would be well for the Society to discontinue it. The ponies were particularly well represented in every section, the first size animals possessing great merit. The extra horses do not call for any remark.

## SHEEP.

The strength of the show in the sheep sections lay in the Blackfaced Breed, and the display was superior throughout. The prize aged tups were strong-boned, well ribbed and coated. It is noteworthy that the animal which gained the first prize also secured the same honour as a two-year-old at Kelso and shearling at Perth. Shearling tups were not only very numerous, but meritorious, well-faced, of great strength, quality, and symmetry, and splendidly woolled. Ewes and lambs were well represented, and of very good style and quality. Gimmers were also a good show, strong-boned, well-woolled, and fine-faced. The family section being shown for the first time could hardly be expected to arrive at a very high standard. The turnout, however, was very creditable, and augured well for the prosperity of a class which deserves support at the hands of the Society and sheepbreeders.

Of Cheviot Sheep the show was limited in extent. Tups above one shear were a fair lot, although they might have been a little more hardy in appearance and had less hair in their coats. Shearling tups were only a middling lot, except those the prizes were awarded to. Ewes and lambs were only middling, while the gimmers were a bad lot.

As a whole, the exhibition of Border Leicesters was not calculated to call forth a great amount of commendation. There were, however, in each section animals fully sustaining the prestige of former shows. The first prize aged tup was a very fine specimen of the breed. possessing fair size, fine style and quality, and lacking in nothing but wool. In the shearling tups the first prize sheep was an exceptionally fine animal, having good substance, true symmetry, and a rare covering of wool of the fashionable sort. The second, although also of good quality, was inferior to him in his head, and especially in his wool, and did not come up to the owner's usual type of sheep. In the ewe sections there was nothing of high merit; but in gimmers the first prize for size, substance, wool, and general conformation was a treat to look at; and not only a long way in front of anything else in the sections, but decidedly the best of any section that came before the judges.

In the sections for Leicesters, Cotswolds, and Lincolns, only Cotswolds were exhibited. They were fair good specimens, but none of any great merit.

The entries in the four sections for Short-woolled sheep numbered 33 (29 Shropshires and 4 Oxfords); but, unfortunately, through the stringent orders of the Privy Council, several pens were vacant. In the aged tups the first prize was awarded to a two-shear of good character; long, low, and wide, somewhat round in his rump, and his fleece scarcely close enough. The second prize sheep was a good sort, had a capital fleece, but was bad in his rump and rather effeminate. The third prize had a good fleece and skin. The shearling tup to which the first premium was awarded was a straight sheep of nice quality, capital shoulder-top, but wanted strength. The second and third were strong, useful sheep with good heads, but not as square on their legs as could be wished. The highly-commended sheep showed good breeding, but was wanting in bone and muscle. The aged ewes do not call for any special mention; but the two prize pens of shearlings were a credit to the country, especially the one placed first. The third was also useful. Northern breeders ought to be very careful in introducing close fleeces into their flocks, as the climate seems to have a tendency to grow the wool rather more open than is desirable.

## SWINE.

The pigs were very inferior, and not up to the proper type in any of the sections. The falling-off can only be attributed to the Privy Council orders prohibiting animals from England being exhibited.

## COLLIE DOGS.

The Collies exhibited (sixteen dogs and five bitches) were a fair class, and were regarded with much interest.

R

## POULTRY.

The exhibition of Poultry was excellent in quality, particularly the Dorkings, Brahmas, Scotch greys, and game.

## IMPLEMENTS.

The number of implements exhibited was considerably greater than on any former occasion at Stirling. Special premiums were offered for artificial manure distributors, potato lifters, and turnip lifters. By the regulations the Society was to provide ground near Stirling at a suitable season, and the premiums were not to be awarded without thorough and exhaustive open and competitive trials. The trials accordingly took place on the farm of Hillhead, near Stirling, kindly granted to the Society by Mr Peter Dewar, the tenant.

The Manure Distributors were tried on 18th October 1881. Four machines came forward for trial. The judges—Messrs. Munro, Fairnington; Dewar, King's Park; and M'Laren, Sauchie—tested the machines for three hours, working by hand before they were taken to the field, one manure used being dissolved bones. They were afterwards taken to the field, when 1¼ cwt. of the four following manures, namely, dissolved bones, Peruvian guano (riddled), fossil guano phosphates, Kainit salt, were distributed. The judges did not consider that any of the machines were entitled to the first prize (£15), but they recommend the directors to award as follows :—2nd prize (£10), Ben. Reid & Co., Aberdeen; 3rd prize (£5), to Shaw & Williamson, 130 Pleasance, Edinburgh.

The Potato Lifters were tried on the 18th and 19th October 1881. The judges—Messrs. Mylne, Niddrie Mains; Swinton, Holyn Bank; and Paterson, Plean—reported that they considered the trial very satisfactory both to judges and exhibitors, and that it was conducted in a thoroughly exhaustive manner. The field was very suitable for the trial, having a variety of soil, with a good crop of potatoes and light and heavy land. Every facility for conducting the trial was afforded by Mr Dewar, the tenant. Eleven machines appeared on the ground; the work, on the whole, was satisfactory, but the draught was in the opinion of the judges a great drawback to the whole of the machines, the lightest draught being 4¼ cwt. up to 6 cwt. under very favourable circumstances of soil. The judges would draw the attention of the makers of these machines to this objection. The judges recommend to the directors that the prizes should be awarded as follow :—1st (£15), J. D. Allan & Sons, Culthill, Dunkeld; 2nd (£10), Wm. Dewar, Strathmartine, Dundee; 3rd (£5), John Wallace & Sons, Graham Square, Glasgow.

The Turnip Lifters were tried 1st November 1881. The judges—Messrs. Mylne, Niddrie Mains; Munro, Fairnington; Swinton, Holyn Bank; Paterson, Plean; and Buchanan, Whitehouse—tried the machines on a crop of swedes; but, in consequence of a snowstorm having prevailed during the trial, it was resolved to allow the exhibitors to ask the directors to hold another trial in the neighbourhood of Edinburgh. The directors having agreed to the request of the exhibitors, the adjourned trial was held on 22nd November on Mr. Hope's farm of East Duddingston. The judges present were Messrs. Mylne, Niddrie Mains; Swinton, Holyn Bank; and Hope, Duddingston. All the machines (five in number) were first tried on an excellent crop of swedes, the land being light loam and dry and in good condition. On this crop the machines made very creditable work, leaving the turnips in a fair state for storing. They were then tried on a field of yellow or hybrid turnips, when the topping was in some places deficient and some extra labour would be required before storing, the machines being more liable to choke among the yellow turnips. The draught of the machines was remarkably light, any of them being light work for one horse. The work of the whole was such that the machine would be a valuable adjunct on a farm where labour was scarce; and the price was moderate, being £4, 10s. for a single machine and £9, 9s. for a double machine. Without drawing any distinction between the single and double machines, the one being adapted for a small and the other for a large farm. The judges, after full consideration and exhaustive trial, found that the machines of Thomas Hunter, Maybole, and G. W. Murray & Co., Banff, were so nearly equal that they recommended to the directors that the first and second prizes (£15 and £10) should be divided equally between them, and that the third prize (£5) should not be awarded. A considerable advance has been made on these implements during the last few years, but the judges considered there was room for further improvement.

---

## IMPLEMENT DEPARTMENT OF THE SOCIETY.

On the occasion of the General Show at Perth in 1879 it was arranged that the Society should offer three premiums of the value of £20, £10, and £5 for approved reports on the best method of arranging the implement department.

Five reports were lodged in response to the Society's advertisement; and at a meeting of committee held on 21st July 1880, it was decided to award the whole prizes, although the reports did not contain much that had not previously been often considered by the committee.

The gentlemen found entitled to the premiums were—(1) William Wallace, 7 Graham Square, Glasgow; (2) Joseph Parsloe, 7 Brereton Road, Bedford; (3) Alexander Leslie, Cherryvale, Aberdeen.

The following observations contain the principal recommendations in the prize reports:—

### EXTRACT FROM MR. WILLIAM WALLACE'S REPORT.

In reviewing the past history and the present position of the various agricultural societies, and also their position towards the implement trade, I think it unnecessary to review the systems of trials and awards that have hitherto been adopted by the Highland and Agricultural Society of Scotland. Not that they have been so conducted as to warrant my taking no notice of them, but I consider that the disadvantages which belong to the systems already mentioned will in a great measure be found in those lately carried out by the Highland Society. It has had the competitive trial system with awards, the system of judging implements in the showyard and awarding medals without any trial whatever, and also the system of selecting what had been entered as new inventions or radical improvements upon implements already in practical use, and testing such by themselves and giving awards. The two last-mentioned systems have been fruitful sources of discontent amongst implement exhibitors, and have also failed to be of any assistance to farmers in enabling them to select the best implements.

In seeking to profit by the experience of the past, I think the Highland Society could now take a stride in advance of all other existing societies by adopting a system of trials and awards as suggested by the advantages and disadvantages of the systems hitherto carried out; and, after thorough consideration, I would recommend the following systems:—

*First* (*a*)—Offer substantial prizes for labour-saving machines which are wanted by agriculturists, and which do not at present exist in a marketable state of excellence, such as binders, turnip lifters, &c.

(*b*) Let the premiums be offered at least two or three years before they are to be competed for, so as to give inventors opportunities of perfecting their implements.

(*c*) No premium or part of a premium should be awarded unless the Society consider the implement or machine of sufficient merit. This will insure that the money is judiciously expended.

(*d*) No awards should be made until the implement has been subjected to a thorough and exhaustive trial.

(*e*) Let the premiums offered be sufficient to induce all grades of inventors to compete for a binding machine. I would recommend a premium of not less than £200, and for other implements premiums in proportion to their labour-saving value.

By offering substantial premiums, and thus encouraging new inventions, the Society will be strictly fulfilling one of the objects for which it was instituted ; and by strictly adhering to the offering of premiums for new inventions only, it will reduce to a minimum the labour and expenditure devolving upon the Society in its thorough exhaustive testing. In recommending this system to the Highland Society, I am aware that the offering of handsome premiums is not new to it, for in 1837, and until 1843, the substantial premium of £500 was offered for steam-cultivating machinery, and I have, therefore, greater confidence in anticipating that it will be adopted.

It is only by such a system of trials that the Society can now expect to have the co-operation of the implement trade, and be of service in assisting in the encouragement and diffusion of new labour-saving machines.

*Second.*—If at any future time the Society should think it necessary to test what might appear as a great and radical improvement upon any implement or machine formerly in practical use, let both the old and new inventions be subjected to a competitive trial together.

*Third.*—Have working exhibitions of such implements and machines as practicable during the time of the Society shows, the Society providing the lands and crops *free*, and making all the necessary arrangements for trials.

The Highland Society's circuit shows are specially adapted for this system of trials. They would afford agriculturists in the several districts an opportunity of seeing various machines at work, which are only brought together by such a meeting as the Highland Society.

The success which has attended this working exhibition system in the Bath and West of England Society is a sufficient guarantee that it will meet with the approval and support of both the implement makers and agriculturists of Scotland.

*Fourth.*—Showyard arrangements. I should recommend that the Society adhere to the showyard arrangements as carried out at Perth in 1879, which gave universal satisfaction. A new "miscellaneous section" might with profit be added, so that all articles not exclusively agricultural be excluded from the implement yard, and exhibited by themselves.

Having thus briefly given my opinion of the position our Scottish National Society should take towards the implement trade in trials, premiums, and shows, I hope it may in some small degree be productive in helping to develop the agricultural interests of our country.

### EXTRACT FROM MR. JOSEPH PARSLOE'S REPORT.

In order to test and demonstrate the value of new implements and machines, the Highland Society might, as circumstances would permit, invite manufacturers to submit their productions for trial. The machines entered could be first exhibited in operation at the annual show, and then be placed in the hands of well-known farmers and worked during a period sufficiently long to test their capabilities both as to performance and durability. Still better would it be were the Highland Society to establish in some central position a model farm, at which trials could be conducted, and where could be demonstrated the science and practice of agriculture in all its branches. Such an establishment might be developed into a National College of Agriculture. After the expiration of a given time, the machines might be placed in the hands of the judges of the Society for final trial and dynamometrical test. Then, instead of awarding prizes first, second, third, I would suggest that a number of the best machines—say three—be selected for specially detailed reports (the remainder might be briefly noticed), pointing out the results of the trials. It would be of advantage for the special reports to be accompanied by illustrations of the machines, which the manufacturers would doubtless be glad to supply. The reports might then be published as the awards of the judges, for the use of the makers as well as agriculturists generally.

I have thus tried to indicate how by a system of reports, in preference to the award of prizes, the enterprise of the manufacturers may be supplemented by the action of the Society. Such reports would prove a valuable guide to purchasers, and would be of much general interest as permanent and continuous records of the progress of improvement.

The requirements of the times in which we live call for the adoption of every appliance for farm purposes which shall economise time and money. The progress made hitherto has been great indeed, but we have not reached the final stage of perfection; and whilst there is the native disposition of the manufacturers to progression, their exertions may in the future be greatly aided, as they have been in the past, by the co-operation of our great agricultural societies.


### EXTRACT FROM MR. ALEXANDER LESLIE'S REPORT.

If we inquire what position the National Society should take towards the implement trade in the encouragement and development of new inventions, we arrive at the conclusion that the trade should be granted every facility for exhibiting their wares.

"Give implement makers encouragement," say Messrs. Clayton and Shuttleworth, "by reducing (or abolishing) charges for shedding, paying cartage of implements to and from railway stations, as the cost of carriage of goods, assistance, and men's expenses are very heavy, and must press much upon small makers, and thus limit their exhibits. Implements attract large numbers of people to shows, and firms should therefore have every encouragement in exhibiting their productions. Invention would thereby be stimulated and inventors remunerated."

Facilities ought also to be afforded to the exhibitors of field implements for showing them at work at specified times, so that farmers attending the shows might have better opportunities for forming a judgment for themselves.

With regards to trials and awards, it is desirable that no award be made without a thorough trial, and that in the case of every award the grounds on which it rests be distinctly and specifically stated.

Manufacturers ought to have the option of exhibiting at all shows without being obliged to compete for prizes. The manufacture of agricultural implements and machines is now carried on on so large a scale that a money prize is of trifling importance, and manufacturers prefer to rely on the substantial merits of their manufactures in effecting sales rather than on the opinions of judges who may be inexperienced or prejudiced. In order to induce them to submit their implements to trials, it is necessary that these trials be not too frequent, that they be conducted with the greatest care and impartiality, and that they be reported with sufficient detail, and with positive, and not merely comparative, results, duly stated.

In a letter addressed to the writer, Messrs. Ransome, Sims, & Head, the oldest firm connected with the agricultural implement manufacture, write:—"In our opinion the very best thing that the Scottish Agricultural Society could do towards the encouragement and development of the implement trade would be to give up offering any prizes for implements, but to afford every facility for the exhibition of implements and machines at their shows; also, not to tax exhibitors so highly as at present for the space required for the exhibition of their goods. So far as our experience goes, purchasers at the present day are guided more by the success of machinery that has been sold and worked than by the prizes it has won, and manufacturers are bound for their own credit's sake to see that what they send out is thoroughly adapted for the purpose for which it is intended. Instances have been known where machines have gained the first prize at a show, sales have been made in consequence, and the machines afterwards returned on the maker's hands. There is no doubt in the past the prize system has had a stimulating effect on the manufacturers of agricultural implements; and its object having been attained by the present high standard which has been reached by the principal makers of agricultural machinery, we think it might with advantage to all parties be discontinued."

## THE CULTIVATION OF PRICKLY COMFREY, AND ITS USE AS A FODDER PLANT.

By DAVID W. WEMYSS of Newton Bank, St Andrews.

*[Premium—The Medium Gold Medal.]*

Prickly Comfrey (*Symphytum asperrimum*) is now extensively grown, especially in England, as a fodder plant, both for horses and cattle, and is noted for its mucilaginous produce and emollient properties. It is a perennial plant, and produces a most useful and profitable crop, and one which, no doubt, in a few years, will be more generally grown throughout the British Isles. It is relished by all animals, horses being frequently kept through the winter on it, without hay, and only a moderate allowance of oats, which has the effect of giving them fine coats of hair. When given to milk cows, it not only produces a full yield of milk, but the butter made possesses the quality and natural rich colour of the best summer butter. Young cattle also thrive well upon it, with or without turnips. Sheep do not eat it so freely, unless being compelled by much snow being on the ground. Should cattle at first be found not to take it readily, their dislike to it will probably be caused by the roughness of the leaves; for this reason they should be withered before being given. But this does not often happen, as all animals, as a rule, eat comfrey readily.

Previous to use, it is necessary to put the comfrey through a chaff-cutting machine, along with some hay or straw, so as to cut it into short lengths. Mixed in equal quantities, two pecks morning and evening, is the allowance that ought to be given either to horses or cattle, with a moderate allowance of other food; when a little salt is added they will relish it better, and will thrive well on it.

No plant can be more easily propagated and cultivated than comfrey, and, as formerly stated, there is no plant yet discovered that yields such milk-producing qualities. Its medicinal properties also cannot be overlooked, it having been found to be a curative as well as a preventative in cases of foot-and-mouth disease; and it has been affirmed that cows fed on comfrey have escaped this disease, while others in the same dairy not fed on it had the disease badly. Having these qualities, there is every reason to believe that comfrey will be more generally known and more extensively cultivated than at present. If a commencement was made and a proper variety selected, there is no doubt but its cultivation would gradually extend.

Comfrey is propagated by cuttings of the root, or crowns, like horse-radish sets, and may be planted at any time except during hard frost, or when the land is otherwise not in working condition, it being one of the most hardy plants cultivated; but the spring is undoubtedly the best time for planting. If planted before the month of May, a heavy crop may be taken the same summer. It will grow well on any soil except chalk. The distance at which the sets should be planted depends upon the depth and richness of the soil. In a well-trenched rich soil lines three feet apart, and sets two feet from each other, will be a proper distance; but on light or poor land they may with advantage be set much closer. The ground should be prepared in the ordinary way for any crop, by digging and manuring. When properly levelled, a line strained across the ground, and holes dibbled two or three inches deep, about two feet apart, and the sets placed into them, and covered up one inch underground, like planting potatoes, is the proper and simplest way of planting. Once planted, it will remain for any number of years, and only requires keeping clean and heavily manuring to produce eighty to one hundred tons of fodder per acre per annum. The simplest way of manuring is to burn the last crop of the season, the ashes of which will form an excellent manure, and young shoots will spring out early the following spring.

Comfrey should be cut when it is about half-grown, as stock like it better then, and it springs up again quicker; besides, when cut at that time, four or five crops may be taken in one year. But if cut just before the flower-buds open, it should not be cut closer to the crown than two inches. It is usual to reap it with a sickle, the crop from one root being as much as a man can get his arm round when set close. However, it may be mown with a strong scythe.

In various parts comfrey is specially cultivated as green food for stock during the winter months; and as the young shoots are cut regularly every year, the plant is never allowed to become hard and woody. When an increase of sets is wanted for extending its growth, the simplest way of obtaining these is to take up a few plants, and carefully divide the roots with a sharp knife, so as to have sets each with a single crown.

An imperial acre of well-grown young comfrey which is regularly cut will keep four or five horses or cows during the winter and early spring months with very little assistance in the shape of hay or roots.

The proper kind of comfrey to cultivate is *Symphytum asper-*

*rimum,* or the Caucasian variety. It is a native of Caucasus, and was introduced into England about the end of last century. This is one of the most productive and nutritious varieties, and yields from seventy to eighty tons of forage an acre per annum, according to the soil, and grows from three to four feet high, and bears bells of a whitish yellow or straw colour. True Caucasian comfrey, *S. asperrimum,* has a large rough leaf, with a number of prickles on the under surface; hence its name " Prickly Comfrey."

Before the introduction of this improved variety into this country, the varieties grown were *Symphytum officinale* and *S. tuberosum,* or tuberous-rooted comfrey, which were the native species, but which now may be considered useless varieties. For a long time the name of the improved variety was confounded with these native varieties, which retarded its cultivation. One of the many advantages of *S. asperrimum* is that it can be cut earlier and later than any other variety, commencing in April and continuing to November.

When the British varieties, *S. officinale* and *S. tuberosum,* were first introduced into this country, they were chiefly grown as ornamental plants, being remarkable for their graceful bells of bright-blue flowers. Still, these and the new foreign species, *S. asperrimum,* are all relished by cattle, and they seem to contain much the same chemical principles. Common or English comfrey grows wild in this country; it has a rather smooth leaf, bears a whitish or yellowish flower, but is of no use for cattle fodder.

When comfrey is to be planted, the first thing necessary, in order to avoid disappointment, is to get the proper kind, and the one which will grow to the best advantage and yield the heaviest crop. There are two kinds which might be planted to advantage, and which are considered the best, namely, *S. asperrimum* and the solid-stemmed variety. The advantage of the solid-stemmed over *S. asperrimum* is that it grows to a larger size, a greater weight of produce per acre is obtained, is somewhat quicker and earlier in growth, although not so nutritious, and can be propagated from stem-cuttings as well as from root-cuttings. Sets planted in spring will afford one or two moderate cuttings before winter; the next year, when well established, they will give from four to six cuttings, according to the season and soil.

They require to be planted a yard apart each way, which will, of course, take 4840 plants to plant an imperial acre, and which will cost about fifty shillings. When once planted they will remain for any number of years, and will only require keeping clean and manuring to produce from 100 to 120 tons of good fodder per acre per annum. The cultivation of comfrey, under any circumstances, is very simple; but where it is intended to have a permanent " comfrey meadow," seeds might be sown along with oats, after a well-manured root crop, at the rate of 6 lbs. per acre, in the month of March or April.

On deep, rich arable land, where heavy crops of white and green crops are annually grown, it might not be so profitable to convert it into a " comfrey meadow"; but as it will grow on the poorest of land, it would undoubtedly be the most profitable crop for waste lands, and will yield food for an additional number of cattle, where formerly it yielded little or nothing.

Being so common a plant, the value of comfrey is not so generally appreciated as it ought to be, but there is every reason to believe that in a short time it may be more extensively grown, seeing that it is such a useful and profitable crop, and one which requires so little trouble and attention, as well as little expense, after once planted. All these ought carefully to be considered nowadays, as it is principally to stock-raising and cattle-feeding that the farmer has to look forward to and depend upon his profit.

No doubt there is considerable trouble attending the preparation of comfrey before it can be given to stock, but its plentifulness and little value for other purposes would on a large farm well repay that trouble.

## EXACT PROGRESSIVE MEASUREMENT OF TREES.

By Sir ROBERT CHRISTISON, Bart., M.D., D.C.L., LL.D., Hon. V.P.R.S.E.

In accordance with a suggestion from the directors of the Highland and Agricultural Society, I beg to submit a summary of the inquiries I have made during the last three or four years relative to the scientific and practical bearings of the exact measurement of trees. I do so in the hope that, through the influence of the Society, forest-owners and foresters may be induced to adopt the method of measurement which I have recommended, in place of the vague, and for the most part profitless, methods hitherto pursued by practical men.

It was these vague methods, useless for most scientific as well as practical objects, that first led me to consider whether a more precise and more delicate system might not be advantageously introduced, and without such refinements as would be beyond the reach of the majority of British foresters. I found, in fact, that the existing methods presented no uniformity; that they did not follow any general principle, or even any arbitrary rule; that measurement was made at a great variety of heights from the roots, and that the height was often not mentioned at all; that no adequate means were taken to secure that a subsequent measurement after an interval of some years should be taken at precisely the same line as the first; and that there was sometimes reason to suspect careless and inaccurate observation. In illustration of the last serious criticism, it may be stated that when I applied for fresh measurements of certain somewhat noted trees, whose trunks had been many years ago measured at given levels from the ground, the information received in reply made out that the girths indicated by the measurement of eleven different great trees all came to exactly so many feet, without fractions. On account of these several reasons I had little satisfaction in referring, for comparison in the present day, even to the old measurements of Dr. Walker, or to the vast accumulation we owe to the industry of Loudon, as displayed in his *Arboretum Britannicum,* or to the long official catalogue published by our Society in 1866. But on consideration it also appeared probable that, by substituting for the coarse methods hitherto followed in forestry something of the more delicate modes of inquiry pursued in cultivating the sciences, there might be attained far greater nicety, exactness, certainty, and speed, and consequently results of much more practical value. The experience of the last four years has amply confirmed these expectations.

It has proved that measurements may be made, in the case of most trees even of large size, to the accuracy of the tenth or even twentieth part of an inch, with confidence in their exactness; and that the trunk-growth of many trees is such as, by following the system recommended, may supply in the course of a single year, or even in three months only, results applicable to immediate practical treatment. For proof I refer to several papers which have appeared during the past two years in the *Transactions of the Botanical Society of Edinburgh,* giving the result of observations made in 1878, 1879, and 1880, in the Botanic Garden and Arboretum, and in the woods of Craigiehall and Cammo, near Cramond, on upwards of eighty trees, young and old, and belonging to thirty species. The results thus obtained are the following:—

1. After the first measurement and marking, in the way to be described presently, all subsequent observations are made with great ease, certainty, and speed.

2. There is no growth of wood in leaf-shedding trees during the seasons of winter and spring. This, of course, might have been readily foretold; but it appeared right, nevertheless, to settle the point by positive observation.

3. There is no growth of wood during the same seasons in evergreen trees. This result, for obvious reasons, could not have been foretold with the same confidence; and, in fact, when I consulted a knot of able botanists on the subject, none of them

could give an answer confidently, though most of them were inclined to think that, as all such trees were covered with perfect leaves, they must continue to form wood in winter, when that season is not unusually harsh. It is not so, however: there is no growth of wood in evergreen trees in this climate in winter and spring.

4. The growth of wood in leaf-shedding trees is confined in ordinary years to the three months of June, July, and August. In May their juices are employed in developing their leaves, without which wood cannot be formed. In September the juices are required for forming the buds for the following year, and for ripening the young twig wood. At least I cannot see any other explanation of the undoubted fact, which at first surprised me, that in fine Septembers there is, with very few exceptions, no growth of wood in leaf-shedding trees. It may be presumed that when an unusually favourable spring develops the leaves early in May, this month will be added to the wood-growing months of the year. But no such spring has occurred since my observations were begun.

5. In evergreen trees the growth of wood is limited at the end of the season by the same month as leaf-shedding trees; but many seem to find the advantage of possessing a full foliage at the advent of fine weather, and begin to form new wood a month earlier than leaf-shedding trees,—that is, during the month of May.

6. In fast-growing trees it is easy to trace their increase from month to month. Thus a thriving young Hungary oak (*Quercus pannonica*, var. *conferta*), 27·1 inches in girth at 5 feet from the roots, increased from April 30, 1880, to May 31, 0·3; from May 31 to June 30, 0·4; from June 30 to July 31, 0·4; from July 31 to August 31, 0 3; from August 31 to September 30, 0·0—in all, 1·4 inches in four months. These increments are easily measurable in a smooth-barked tree, if the simple precautions be observed, which will be noticed presently. It will be observed that this fine species added the month of May to the usual period for leaf-shedding trees growing their wood. The reason is that in 1880 its leaves were fairly developed in the middle of May instead of the beginning of June.

7. Everyone knows that of our acclimatised trees different species are variously influenced by incidental inclement seasons, some being killed outright, others more or less injured in their foliage and twigs, and others indifferent to all weathers, except, perhaps, the visitation of an Arctic winter. Now, by minute measurement the extent of this influence may be settled with a speed and certainty, and according to a practical scale, unattainable in any other way.

The year 1878 was, on the whole, favourable to the growth of wood; 1879 was much the reverse. Spring was backward, though not otherwise unpropitious; summer and autumn were unprecedentedly cold and sunless, and September was especially so, hindering thereby the ripening of young wood and buds for the following year. The early winter of 1879–80 was distinguished by a severity of frost of which there had been no record in this country. The spring of 1880 was again backward, and the summer under average for sun and heat, but superior in these respects to 1879. August was a fine month, and September, equally fine in all respects, was highly favourable to budding, and to the ripening of young wood. But the winter of 1880–81 set in with a severity surpassing that even of the previous year. The spring of 1881 was for a third time backward; the summer and autumn were cold and sunless, except the month of September, which, in the west country at least, was favourable. In one or more of these four conditions for vigorous growth—a fine September, a winter of no great severity, a forward spring, and a genial summer and month of August—the last three years have been more or less seriously faulty. The following consequences have been indicated by the test of exact measurement :—

Of seventeen leaf-shedding trees in the Botanic Garden and Arboretum, comprising four of beech, two of lime, two of sycamore, a sweet chestnut, a horse chestnut, a flowering ash, a tulip tree, a hawthorn, a birch, a Turkey oak, an American red oak, and a hornbeam—all of them in 1878 healthy vigorous trees, from about 40 to 130 years of age—the aggregate trunk-growth in that favourable year was 12·8 inches, and in 1879, 1880, and 1881, 6·9, 5·6, and 9·4 inches. I do not know how to explain their partial and considerable recovery during our late cold summer and August except by reference to the fine budding season in the preceding September and the absence of any severe frosts during last spring; in consequence of which, I presume, it was that forest trees generally were well clothed with fine foliage. It is not, of course, to be understood that each species followed in its growths each year the ratio of these aggregates; far from it. But the number of observations on the several species has been too limited to justify the separation of any of them. One species, however, I have detached on account of its anomalous growth and resistance to severity of climate. This is the Hungary oak (*Quercus pannonica*, var. *conferta*). In the spring of 1878, a tree of this species, planted out in 1865 on a northern slope, exposed to direct north and north-west winds, but not to the north-east and east, was 23·6 inches in girth at the narrowest part of its trunk, 3 feet 4 inches from the roots. In October 1881 it was 30·3 inches. Its increments in the last four successive years have been 1·8, 1·7, 1·4, and 1·8 inches. As two other younger trees not measured till the spring of 1880 and then found to be 13·5 and 16·45 inches at very nearly the same elevation, have since added, during the last two unfavourable years, one of them 1·10 and 1·55, and the other 1·10 and 1·75, to their girth—a great increase at their age—I cannot but conclude that this beautiful oak is the hardiest of our leaf-shedding trees, whether native or acclimatised, so far as I have yet examined them.

I have also made observations on twenty-nine evergreen trees —yew, ilex, pinus, picea, araucaria, deodar, sequoia, and cypress. But the details are so vitiated by collateral influences, such as injury from storms, peculiar locality, and undiscoverable causes of failure, that it is not possible to attach confidence to the results. I have been surprised, however, to find that numerous specimens of sequoia, araucaria, and deodar have suffered little injury during the last three years, and very much less than they appear to have sustained in other parts of Scotland. On the other hand, the Scotch fir has been a great sufferer. One tree in the Botanic Garden, two on the high east ground of the Arboretum, a fine one, nearly 8 feet in trunk girth, on the low south-west ground, and one (the finest of all I have seen around Edinburgh), on the lawn of Camino House, near Cramond Bridge, have ceased entirely, or nearly so, to make wood for three years past, and their heads have shown every successive year more and more failure in foliage.

8. When trees are grown for profit, and doubts are entertained whether certain of them have not ceased to add to their wood, the point may be settled with precision by an exact measurement at the beginning and end of a single growing season of three or four months.

Since these results, expressed numerically, have been so easily obtained, simply by patient observation,—results which are unattainable by any other method yet known,—it follows that by the same means information of greater value in a practical point of view may be arrived at in regard to the influence of soil, subsoil, altitude, exposure, climate (as constituted mainly by heat, cold, sunshine, and rain), transplanting, thinning, pruning, and especially manuring. This work, however, must be consigned to forest owners, who alone can conduct it; and they will meet with their reward if they will combine, form themselves into a committee of this Society, teach and encourage their foresters to observe, and offer prizes for the ablest reports.

I mention manuring particularly, because the subject has been hitherto almost entirely neglected. But from inquiry it will appear that a forest does not differ in this respect from a farm. If we examine the section of the trunk of a tree some ninety years old, reared in a hill forest with thin soil, we find that for forty years its wood has grown at a pace scarcely less than in a much lower altitude and finer climate; but that between its fortieth and sixtieth year this rate ceases, and not gradually, but rather suddenly. In three or four years the width of the annual layers of wood is reduced to one-half or a third of what it was. The reduction goes on increasing, and at last the rings are so narrow that they can scarcely be counted. I can see no explanation of these curious facts so reasonable as that, the scanty soil being exhausted of those saline matters, which are in part essential for the formation of leaves and wood, growth must become less vigorous, and even cease, long before the natural limit in more favourable circumstances. The question then will be, what saline matter is lost by the soil and appropriated by the trees, and what sort of manure will replace the loss?

But foresters must be taught to observe minutely, and to record with accuracy. For this purpose I reproduce the recommendations recently adopted by the Meteorological Society of Scotland.

The observer should note :—

1. The elevation of the site above sea-level.
2. Whether it is on a hill slope, steep or gentle, or on a terrace on the slope, or on a level plain, or in a narrow gorge.
3. If on a hill slope, the direction of its face by compass, and whether there is protection from direct winds by heights above or around.
4. Anything peculiar in the meteorology of the district, and differing from that of the adjacent country.
5. The nature of the soil, its depth, and the nature of the subsoil.
6. Whether the wood has been subjected to timely and judicious thinning or pruning.
7. Whether it has undergone any nutritive or stimulating treatment.
8. Twenty trees should be chosen growing near one another, and not at the very verge of the wood.
9. All ill-thriving trees should be rejected, and had better be felled, but otherwise selection is not advisable.
10. Scotch fir, larch, spruce, and oak will probably be the standard subjects of observation, but any other species may be usefully observed also.
11. Any change of treatment during the period of observation, or any injury from storms, insects, &c.
12. Trees whose bark is apt to scale off are obviously unsuitable. In others the bark is apt to crack and start up, in which case the elevation should be levelled with the knife or rasp.
13. The measurement should be made usually about five feet from the roots. But, in more general terms, the place of measurement should avoid the swelling at the base, and that under the spring of the chief branches.
14. All lumps should be avoided, and little excrescences in the line of measurement should be levelled with the knife or rasp, if this can be done without injury to the tree.
15. The tape should be applied as level as possible if the trunk be erect, but at right angles to the line of the trunk if it be a little inclined. Trees much inclined may be excluded.
16. The tape should be long enough to go round the whole trunk. It should be of a material that does not easily lengthen by stretching. The

most convenient is an eight-foot tape, but divided progressively by inches, and with a single inch at the beginning in the opposite direction from zero, divided into tenths of an inch. It is easy to see that with this contrivance it is unnecessary to subdivide any other part of the tape.

17. The tape being applied, and before it is removed, a few small short lines made with white oil-paint should be put upon the bark all round, at distances of twelve or eighteen inches, and close to the upper edge of the tape. Thus a fixed line will be obtained for all subsequent measurements.

18. A number should be painted upon every tree.

19. A book should be kept in which each measurement should be noted before proceeding to another.

20. An assistant is advisable, both for celerity and for checking the measurement; but a single observer can manage by thrusting a strong brass pin through the ring of the tape obliquely into the bark.

21. While the information derived by the Meteorological Society will be mainly confined to young trees, and such others as an eight-foot tape will girth, it is also a matter of interest to measure individual trees of greater size and age, regarding whose rate of growth little is at present known.

N.B.—The first measurements should be taken on or before the 1st of May, and the subsequent ones at any time in October.

(*Specimen.*)

SEQUOIA GIGANTEA.—Edinburgh Royal Botanic Gardens. 1. Fifty to eighty feet. 2. An undulating plain. 3. A low height, with old trees to west and north-west. 4. No peculiarity. 5. Sandy loam, about deep, with subsoil of pure sand. 6. None. 7. None. 8. Four trees only, at two places, with other young trees around, but not very near. 9 to 20. All attended to.

| | May 1, 1878. | Oct. 1, 1878. | Oct. 1, 1879. | Oct. 1, 1880. |
|---|---|---|---|---|
| No. 1. | 23·95 inches. | 25·10 inches. | 25·90 inches. | 26·90 inches. |
| „ 2. | 23·95 „ | 25·70 „ | 27·35 „ | 29·15 „ |
| „ 3. | 18·95 „ | 20·80 „ | 22·30 „ | 23·80 „ |
| „ 4. | 23·85 „ | 25·10 „ | 26·80 „ | 28·35 „ |

# EXPERIMENT IN CATTLE FEEDING.

By JOHN MILNE, Mains of Laithers, Turriff.

[*Premium—The Medium Gold Medal.*]

AN accurate knowledge of the progress made by farm stock at the different ages, and from an ascertained weight of food of the different kinds, would be of much value to the stock farmer; yet, notwithstanding the recognised importance of this knowledge in a pecuniary sense, there is perhaps no branch of every-day farm practice of which we are so ignorant. This is shown from the very few reliable feeding experiments on record, and the widely different practice of practical farmers in regard to the use of cattle feeding stuffs. One farmer uses a large quantity of these, and supposes that without the use of such it would be impossible for him to pay rent, or keep his farm in improving condition. His next neighbour perhaps does not use a ton of these

s

stuffs in twelve months, and yet gets on fairly well. All over Scotland, however, the use of cattle feeding stuffs is rapidly increasing, and they enable the farmer to turn out his usual number of finished cattle even in years in which the turnip crop is very deficient, as it was in 1877 and 1879. If the manure value scale of Drs. Voelcker and Lawes is to be trusted, the use of some kinds of feeding stuffs is undoubtedly one of the cheapest methods of increasing and maintaining the fertility of the soil.

In regard to cattle feeding, practical experience shows that if they are supplied with a sufficiency of grass of very good quality, an addition of feeding stuffs does not much hasten the process of maturity or fattening. If, however, the grass is of inferior quality, feeding stuffs will very much promote their growth and fattening. On all inferior pastures, if the cattle kept are of an improved breed, some feeding stuffs should invariably be given along with the grass, and nothing in cattle feeding will pay so well. The quality of the turnip crop is greatly influenced by manure, soil, and climate; and wherever from any cause the quality is inferior, feeding stuffs to make up the deficiency ought to be given. When turnips are of very fine quality and the fodder good, cattle can be made quite fat with these alone, and it becomes a question of relative cost whether it is judicious to use feeding stuffs or otherwise. Where turnips are of good quality it would seem, from some experiments made by Mr Hunter, Dipple, Fochabers, and others, that it is unprofitable to use linseed cake or grain, and at the same time give a full allowance of turnips; since very few turnips are saved the cost is much greater, while the increase is not in a corresponding ratio. It would seem that an animal can digest only a certain quantity of the constituents of food, yet it will eat of some articles at least a greater quantity than it can digest and assimilate. Hence if economy is studied when feeding stuffs are given, an equivalent quantity of turnips should be withheld.

In cattle feeding the profit or loss depends greatly upon the age of the animals. For the last two years I have practised weighing all my cattle and sheep once every four weeks, and from this have had my opinions as to the unprofitableness of keeping old animals fully confirmed. The improved breeds, if well fed, increase in live weight at almost the same rate per month from birth until thirty months old, and as the ox of six to nine months old will consume scarcely one-third of the food required by the same ox when twenty-four to thirty months old, it is evident that the younger animal will pay three times as much as the older animal for the food consumed. An ox over thirty months old will, as a rule, pay for its keep only if it has been previously poorly fed and is in low condition, or if between buying and selling the price of meat advances. I am induced to make these remarks, as they have a very direct bearing upon the profit or loss of using feeding stuffs. Last season I carried out an experiment to test how far some of the more commonly used feeding stuffs could profitably take the place of turnips in cattle feeding, and the most advantageous kinds to use. The number of articles tried in a single experiment must necessarily be limited by the number of suitable cattle of equal breeding, age, and sex upon a farm, and the number that can be properly attended to by an individual. When most of the food has to be weighed twenty cattle are all that one person can attend to, and as each lot should contain at least four animals, the number of lots and the number of articles tried are necessarily limited to five.

The cattle selected for the experiment were twenty well-bred Irish steers about twenty months old at the beginning of the trial, and two years old at its close. They had been upon the farm for twelve months previously, and were a good and equal lot in thriving condition. They were bought on 13th November 1879 at £4, 10s. each; they then weighed on an average 3 cwts. 3 qrs. 23 lbs., and consequently cost 2·438d. per lb. live weight. At the commencement of the experiment on 9th December 1880 they weighed on the average 8 cwts. 3 qrs. 27 lbs., being an increase of $10\frac{1}{10}$ lbs. per week. At the end of the experiment, on 14th April 1881, they weighed on an average 10 cwts. 2 qrs. 22 lbs., being an increase of $10\frac{1}{2}$ per week. On 2nd September 1881 they weighed on the average 12 cwts. 7½ lbs., being an increase of only $7\frac{2}{10}$ lbs. live weight per week. They were then sold at 71s. per cwt., and as, when killed, they averaged 57 per cent. of meat to live weight, the price they made per lb. live weight was 4·311d. At the end of the experiment, 14th April, all the lots were quite fat, and would have brought as much per cwt. as when sold. There was a considerable loss by keeping on until 2nd September; younger animals would have made much more weight for food consumed. They were fed alike up to 9th December 1880, when they were divided into five lots of four each, and fed as follows:—Lot 1 received 150 lbs. of sliced swedes daily, divided into three feeds of 50 lbs. each; lot 2 got 50 lbs. sliced swedes and 5 lbs of good pure linseed cake; lot 3 got 50 lbs. sliced swedes and 5 lbs. of American decorticated cotton cake; lot 4 got 50 lbs. sliced swedes and 5 lbs. bruised oats; lot 5 got 50 lbs. sliced swedes and 5 lbs. finely ground maize daily. The turnips and other feeding stuffs were equally divided into three lots, and given at three times daily. Straw, which was not weighed, was supplied, but no difference could be detected in the quantity used by the various lots. Water was also given as required. The turnips were grown upon good land, and were apparently of good quality; they were in fine condition until 20th January 1881, after which, owing to the very severe weather, they sometimes had to be drawn from the field in middling condition; they were, however, always washed in fresh water and sliced. The low temperature at which the turnips were sometimes given did not seem specially to interfere with the progress of the lot fed wholly upon turnips. The byre in which the cattle were fed was very comfortable and well-ventilated, and although the temperature outside stood for several days below zero, ice about the thickness of a penny was found in the water-pails only on one morning. The cattle were well combed daily, comfortably littered, and were marked by different numbers clipped on the rump. The opposite table gives the results obtained.

If nothing is counted on the straw consumed, and if we assume that the 50 lbs. of turnips used in each of the experiments produced one-third of the gain obtained by the use of 150 lbs., the following quantities were required to produce—

|  | 1 lb. live increase. | 1 lb. of meat. |
|---|---|---|
| Turnips, . . . | 96·30 lbs. | 169·00 lbs. |
| Linseed cake, . . | 4·00 ,, | 7·00 ,, |
| Decorticated cotton cake, | 5·00 ,, | 8·77 ,, |
| Oats, . . . . | 6·55 ,, | 11·50 ,, |
| Maize, . . . | 5·32 ,, | 9·33 ,, |

If we deduct interest on the value of the animals say on £20 at 5 per cent., and cost of attendance at sixpence per week, the value of the different feeding stuffs, without reckoning the straw consumed, and the manurial value of excrements would be as follows :—

| Turnips (swedes), . . . | £0 | 6 | 5¼ per ton. |
|---|---|---|---|
| Linseed cake, . . . | 8 | 4 . 3 | ,, |
| Decorticated cotton cake, . . | 6 | 1 | 2 ,, |
| Oats, . . . . . | 4 | 5 | 1 ,, |
| Maize, . . . . | 5 | 13 | 4 ,, |

If we add to the above feeding value the manurial value of the excrements according to Lawes' scale, the combined values are as follows :—

| Turnips (swedes), . . . | £0 | 10 | 8½ per ton. |
|---|---|---|---|
| Linseed cake, . . . | 12 | 16 | 9 ,, |
| Decorticated cotton cake, . . | 12 | 11 | 2 ,, |
| Oats, . . . . . | 6 | 0 | 1 ,, |
| Maize, . . . . | 7 | 4 | 4 ,, |

From these results it will be seen that, unless something is allowed for the increased value of manure, none of the feeding

EXPERIMENT IN CATTLE FEEDING.

| Daily Allowance. | No. | Weight at Dec. 9, 1880. cwts. | qrs. | lbs. | Weight at Jan. 20, 1881. cwts. | qrs. | lbs. | Increase in 42 days. lbs. | Average Increase lbs. | Weight at Mar. 3, 1881. cwts. | qrs. | lbs. | Increase in 42 days. lbs. | Average Increase lbs. | Weight at April 14, 1881. cwts. | qrs. | lbs. | Increase in 42 days. lbs. | Average Increase lbs. | Increase in 126 days. lbs. | Average Increase in 126 days. lbs. |
|---|---|---|---|---|---|---|---|---|---|---|---|---|---|---|---|---|---|---|---|---|---|
| Lot 1. 150 lbs. Swede Turnips sliced, . . . | 17 | 8 | 1 | 22 | 9 | 0 | 19 | 81 | 69¼ | 9 | 2 | 12 | 49 | 39½ | 10 | 1 | 23 | 95 | 87½ | 225 | 196¼ |
| | 18 | 9 | 3 | 22 | 10 | 2 | 0 | 62 | | 10 | 2 | 22 | 22 | | 11 | 2 | 5 | 95 | | 179 | |
| | 33 | 8 | 3 | 11 | 9 | 2 | 0 | 73 | | 9 | 3 | 16 | 44 | | 10 | 2 | 5 | 73 | | 190 | |
| | 34 | 8 | 2 | 2 | 9 | 0 | 7 | 61 | | 9 | 1 | 22 | 43 | | 10 | 0 | 25 | 87 | | 191 | |
| Lot 2. 50 lbs. Turnips, . . 5 lbs. Linseed Cake, | 15 | 8 | 2 | 21 | 9 | 1 | 16 | 79 | 91 | 9 | 3 | 14 | 54 | 65 | 10 | 1 | 24 | 66 | 67½ | 199 | 223½ |
| | 16 | 9 | 1 | 6 | 10 | 0 | 22 | 98 | | 10 | 2 | 0 | 34 | | 11 | 0 | 24 | 80 | | 212 | |
| | 19 | 9 | 1 | 18 | 10 | 0 | 22 | 88 | | 10 | 3 | 19 | 81 | | 11 | 3 | 2 | 95 | | 264 | |
| | 20 | 8 | 3 | 13 | 9 | 3 | 0 | 99 | | 10 | 2 | 7 | 91 | | 10 | 3 | 8 | 29 | | 219 | |
| Lot 3. 50 lbs. Turnips, . . 5 lbs. Decorticated Cotton Cake, . . | 21 | 9 | 1 | 20 | 9 | 3 | 16 | 52 | 58 | 10 | 2 | 3 | 71 | 67½ | 11 | 0 | 11 | 64 | 64¼ | 187 | 189¾ |
| | 22 | 8 | 3 | 26 | 9 | 1 | 7 | 37 | | 9 | 3 | 12 | 61 | | 10 | 1 | 12 | 56 | | 154 | |
| | 29 | 8 | 2 | 19 | 9 | 1 | 8 | 73 | | 9 | 3 | 15 | 63 | | 10 | 1 | 23 | 64 | | 200 | |
| | 30 | 8 | 1 | 12 | 8 | 3 | 26 | 70 | | 9 | 2 | 17 | 75 | | 10 | 1 | 6 | 73 | | 218 | |
| Lot 4. 50 lbs. Turnips, . . 5 lbs. Oats, . . . | 23 | 9 | 0 | 22 | 9 | 3 | 0 | 62 | 51¾ | 10 | 1 | 2 | 58 | 55¼ | 10 | 2 | 17 | 43 | 54½ | 163 | 161½ |
| | 24 | 8 | 3 | 6 | 9 | 1 | 13 | 63 | | 10 | 0 | 2 | 73 | | 10 | 2 | 8 | 62 | | 198 | |
| | 27 | 8 | 3 | 3 | 9 | 0 | 12 | 37 | | 9 | 2 | 7 | 51 | | 10 | 0 | 4 | 53 | | 141 | |
| | 28 | 9 | 1 | 2 | 9 | 2 | 19 | 45 | | 10 | 0 | 2 | 39 | | 10 | 2 | 6 | 60 | | 144 | |
| Lot 5. 50 lbs. Turnips, . . 5 lbs. Maize, . . . | 25 | 9 | 0 | 7 | 9 | 2 | 13 | 62 | 63¾ | 10 | 0 | 0 | 43 | 48¾ | 10 | 2 | 11 | 67 | 71¼ | 172 | 183¾ |
| | 26 | 9 | 1 | 7 | 9 | 3 | 13 | 62 | | 10 | 1 | 1 | 44 | | 10 | 3 | 15 | 70 | | 176 | |
| | 31 | 8 | 3 | 22 | 9 | 2 | 5 | 67 | | 10 | 0 | 10 | 61 | | 10 | 3 | 12 | 86 | | 214 | |
| | 32 | 8 | 3 | 24 | 9 | 2 | 4 | 64 | | 9 | 3 | 23 | 47 | | 10 | 2 | 1 | 62 | | 173 | |
| Average increase, . | ... | ...... | | | ...... | | | ... | 66¾ | ...... | | | ... | 55¼ | ...... | | | ... | 69 | ... | 191 |

stuffs experimented upon quite paid the cost price, which in every case was somewhat higher than the value of the meat produced. When Lawes' scale of manurial values is added the results are different, each of the articles, with the single exception of oats, produced a value of manure and meat together considerably over the usual cost price. Linseed cake would leave a profit of from £2 to £3 per ton; decorticated cotton cake, a profit of about £5 per ton; on oats there would be a loss, as the price is seldom so low as 17s. per qr., which seems about their value for feeding cattle; maize would leave a profit when the price is under £7 per ton. Upon younger animals the pecuniary results would have been more favourable; while upon the older animals they would have been worse. The experiment shows that 4 lbs. of linseed cake, or 5 lbs. of decorticated cotton cake or maize, are about equal to 100 lbs. of swedes; and that, if we compute the manurial value by Lawes' scale, linseed cake and decorticated cotton cake are of much better value as cattle food than either oats or maize.

## THE COMPARATIVE VALUE OF MANURE MADE WITH AND WITHOUT COVER.

By JOHN AINSLIE, Jun., Hillend, Loanhead.

*[Premium—Fifteen Sovereigns.]*

PROBABLY few occupations are so subject to the disappointments and failures that are common to all human employments as that of the agriculturist, and this results not only from the vicissitudes of the seasons as from the want of sufficient and necessary practical information and management.

I believe, however, that there are other causes in existence that in no unimportant way help to produce the too frequent grand total "Failure," and one of these causes I hold to be the "waste" of the farm.

"Wilful waste makes woeful want"; "Waste not, want not," are well known proverbs; but are they not too frequently ignored in the management of the farm? Amongst the wastes of the farm let us place, first, as most important, the management of the farmyard manure. The value of liquid manure cannot be overrated. I believe that the late Mr. Michi had for many years made a most valuable fertiliser for his farm, with bones reduced in his liquid manure tank. At various times he had pointed out the profits resulting from covering manure, instead of allowing it to get soaked by the rains or dried by the sun, as is generally done. When rough sheds have been built to cover the manure-heap, the crops fertilised by this pile have been increased in productiveness sufficient to pay for the shed-covering the first year. I have never seen any exact figures of the proportionate value of covered manures that I remember until the following, which I have heard, and believe to have been tested by Lord Kinnaird, a Scotch landowner and farmer. They present the best statement possible, I think, of the advantages of the plan.

Four acres of good soil were measured, two of which were manured with ordinary farmyard manure, and two with an equal quantity of manure from the covered shed. The whole were planted with potatoes. The products of each acre were as follows:—Potatoes treated with farmyard (uncovered) manure, one acre produced 272 bushels; one acre produced 292 bushels. Potatoes manured from the covered sheds, one acre produced 442 bushels; one acre produced 471 bushels. The next year the land was sown with wheat, when the crop was as follows:—Wheat on land treated with farmyard (un-covered) manure, one acre produced 41 bushels 18 lbs. (of 61 lbs. per bushel); one acre produced 42 bushels 38 lbs. (of 61 lbs. per bushel). Wheat on land manured from covered sheds, one acre produced 55 bushels 5 lbs. (of 61 lbs. per bushel); one acre produced 58 bushels 47 lbs. (of 61 lbs. per bushel). The straw yielded one-third more upon the land fertilised with the manure from the covered stalls than upon that to which the ordinary manure was applied. These experiments are, I presume, sufficient evidence of the value of manure that has been covered. The points are these—No urine should be lost, either by sinking through the byre and stable floors when voided from the animals, or by allowing it to run into open drains in the farmyard, to mingle with the manure heap as best it can. The floors of all the stables should be so secured, and supplied with "covered drains," that all the urine may be conveyed into a covered tank made of stone, or, better still, fire-brick, here to be stored for future use. The urine contains more nitrogenous matter than the solids, and should, therefore, be mixed with the litter and solid substances, unless treated with sawdust, char-coal, peat mould, dry earth, or some other absorbent.

Remember, Peruvian guano itself is the excrement of birds. The quantity of manure made and wasted on a farm is immense. You can calculate what your farm makes from the following estimate:—A horse voids more than five tons of solid matter and 25 cwt. of urine in one year. A cow 8½ tons of solid and 4 tons of liquid matter in one year. A sheep about ½ ton solid and liquid matter in one year. A pig 25 cwt. solid 6 cwt. liquid matter in one year. Of course much depends upon the size and condition of the animal, the quantity and quality of the food; but, so far as we can gather, these figures are within the mark. Of course, in addition to these quantities, the bedding, &c., has to be added.    Doubtless, we will be told that the straw absorbs the urine, and that the cry of "waste" is a groundless alarm. Will any one try for himself if the litter absorbs all the urine? In a trial made to arrive at some conclusion on the point, it was found that 14 lbs. of straw absorbed 22½ lbs. of urine.    Take one stone of straw as the daily amount of litter you give to your cow and 79 lbs. as the daily urine voided during 210 days of winter, and 59 lbs. daily for 155 days in summer, we have a total of 25,735 lbs., or nearly 11½ tons.    This is higher than the approximate quantity assumed above, but this being stall-fed, gave higher results.    To litter this cow we allow one stone of straw per day, which absorbs 22¼ lbs. of urine, or 8212 lbs. in one year, leaving 17,538 lbs., or nearly 8 tons, to flow into the tank, horse-pond, open drains, &c.

In reference to the above, I have practised it to some extent for a few years, and always found it a great advantage.    I, however, thoroughly tested it for two succeeding crops.    In the spring of 1878, I manured part of a field in the drill for Swede turnips.    The field is of medium good land, with stiff clay sub-soil, about 500 feet above the level of the sea, and four miles south-west from Edinburgh; was in good condition, and fairly well drained.    After a good crop of oats it was ploughed in good order, with a pretty strong furrow about the end of November, after which the winter set in very long and most severe.    I put some cattle into a house, which I do generally every year about the beginning of November, and also some into an open court, the latter of course having an open shed to go under as they choose. The court was cleaned out several times during the winter, and laid on a dunghill in the field till ready to put on the ground.    The house was cleaned out in the middle of January, and put into a heap on the field, and kept till the spring for this experiment.    The cattle were put away in the middle of April, but the manure then was not removed from the house until required for the turnip drills.    I then took off a few carts of the driest stuff from the top, and kept it aside when I got into the good made manure.    I then applied it to the turnip drills.

Commencing on the 8th of May 1878, beginning with the manure taken straight from the house, I put 15 tons per imperial acre, with 3 cwt. of dissolved bones, and 2 cwt. Peruvian guano to the first acre.    There was an acre measured just beside it, and the dung which was taken out from the house in January applied to it.    In the same manner with the same artificial manure, and on the same day the turnips were also sown, just behind the plough. Also on the same day I manured an acre next to them, with the manure from the open court, which had been lying for some months in a large heap on the field. The dung was equally well made; each acre got the same quantity, and also the same amount and quality of artificial manure. The turnips came away very well, and were all singled on the 13th of June. They were at that time splendid plants, being all very equal and healthy. They were all worked at the same time, and in the same way, getting all the same chance in every respect. They were furred up with the double furred-plough in the middle of November, then left till about the middle of February 1879, when the three different parts were lifted and carefully weighed. Some of them were sold at 22s. per ton when lifted, the others being used on the farm No. 1, or the acre which was manured with the dung taken straight from the house, weighed 22 tons 4½ cwts., calculating at the price obtained at the time, namely 22s. per ton, which comes about £24, 9s. per imperial acre, being £1, 19s. 9¼d. more than the lot No. 2, which was manured with that taken out of the house in January, and left on the dung-hill in the field for about four months, and applied to the turnip drills in a similar manner. No. 2 was lifted and removed from the field at the same time, as the former was weighed accurately, and only made 20 tons 9 cwts., being 1 ton 15½ cwts. less than the manured part, which was driven straight from the house.

No. 3, or the part dunged from the open courts next to the others, was lifted and weighed similarly; it was, however, much the smaller crop, being only 17 tons 5¼ cwts., making it 3 tons 3¼ cwts. less than No. 2, and 4 tons 19 cwts. less than No. 1, or that which was manured straight from the covered house, making £5, 9s. less than No. 1, and £3, 9s. 2¾d. less than No. 2. Examples No. 1 raised 22 tons 4½ cwts. at 22s. per ton, £24, 9s. per imperial acre; No. 2 raised 20 tons 9 cwts. at 22s. per ton, £22, 9s. 2¾d.; No. 3 raised 17 tons 5¼ cwts. at 22s. per ton, £19.

It will be seen by the foregoing the great importance of covered courts for manure making alone, besides the decided advantage to feeding. The cattle really feed very much better and quicker than they do in the open courts, the heat being such a benefit. The year 1878 was an exceptional good season for turnips in this district, but as they all got the same chance in every respect, the different ways of manure-making was the only difference in the three separate parts hereby tested.

In reference to the barley crop the next year, the house-made manure was considerably the better. The No. 1 came again to the front; but 1879 being a very wet, backward, bad year, the barley was a poor crop, as well as very bad quality. It was sown on the 16th of April, and cut on the 29th of September.

There was a most decided difference hereto referred.  The No. 1 looked certainly best; No. 2 lot considerably better than No. 3. They were all got in good order at the same time, and stacked and well kept till the month of February 1880.  When thrashed and measured separately, No. 1 thrashed out 4 quarters 1 bushel, weighing 15 stone 10 lbs., at 40s. per quarter, making £8, 5s. ; No. 2, 3 quarters 7¼ bushels, 15 stone, 10 lbs. at 40s., £7, 17s. 6d. ; No. 3, 3 quarters 2 bushels at 40s., £6, 10s.  No. 1 thereby showing an increase on the others, of 1¼ bushels per acre on No. 2, or 7s. 6d. more money, and about 7 bushels more than No. 3, and £1, 15s. more money per imperial acre.  As regards the straw there was also considerable difference, but as I had it all thrashed at the same time with the travelling mill, I did not keep it separate.  The barley was all much the same quality, and was put through the fanners altogether and mixed.  The whole produce of the field was sold in Edinburgh market as one sample on the 18th February 1880 at 40s. per quarter.  Even the second year there was an advantage.  Some people may think there is not very much difference, perhaps not worth putting up houses for; but if they have 200 or 300 acres arable land it will pay itself the first year.  Of course we cannot expect that the tenants should put up buildings, especially in these hard times; but if some of the landlords in this country would build feeding-houses, they would thereby assist the tenant both in feeding and manure-making, improving their own property at the same time to a great extent, besides keeping up the condition of the land.

An experiment like this might be of great advantage to many people who really take an interest in agriculture.  It might encourage landlords to build, and assist their tenants considerably. Should the landlords not assist their tenants in one or other way, most farmers may require to give up their farms altogether if there is not some change soon.  It appears as if it would be "the man with the largest purse who will stand out the longest."  The hay crop the third year I could scarcely make any comparison, as I tried two different kinds of artificial manures on the ground referred to; but I could not help thinking that the oats this year when growing, were heavier where the manure was brought straight from under cover; a good many were lying down and twisted, while the rest of the field had only spots here and there.

In conclusion, I would like to recommend farmers to make and keep as much of their home-made manure under cover as possible until applied to the land.  They would soon come to see for themselves the great advantage of covered courts.  In wet weather the best of the manure is washed away.  Of course many people collect the liquid manure and apply it in a different manner, but that is still reducing the quality of the farmyard manure to a great extent. If the courts were covered, and the rain all run off, the sewerage would be mixed along with the dung, thus the greater strength would be obtained. A great deal of ammonia must be lost from the dung when the sewerage is all run away, which must assist the crops for the first year at least; and I have invariably observed that one good crop follows another even with the same treatment.

## EXPERIMENTS ON POTATOES WITH DIFFERENT MANURES.

By Russell Swanwick, M.R.A.C., Cirencester, and E. W. Prevost, Ph.D. F.R.S.E., late Professor of Chemistry in the Royal Agricultural College, Cirencester.

*[Premium—Two Medium Gold Medals.]*

### PART I.

THESE experiments were conducted by Dr. E. W. Prevost and myself jointly, he kindly undertaking the lion's share of the work—namely, the whole of the chemical and analytical work, amounting to not less than twenty-five complete analyses, which in many cases were made in duplicate; also all the weighings and preparation of the various manures for each plot, an account of which appears in the second portion of this report. My bailiff (Mr. Rutherford) assisted in the applications of the manures, and superintended the weighings of the potato crop with most minute care.

Thirteen years of potato-growing on this farm, and many previous experiments, lead me to suggest certain combinations of manures calculated to be most useful, and to supply a crucial test as to which would produce the best results; others were added by Dr. Prevost as having some scientific as well as practical interest, and as likely to effect the composition of the tuber. When Dr. Prevost suggested the great interest and value of a careful estimate of the starch in samples from each application I imagined it could be easily done by determining the specific gravity, and I had no idea of the large amount of labour he was entailing upon himself in making an actual complete analysis of fifteen samples of potatoes. The interest of these chemical results, however, has quite recompensed for the labour. I regret, on my part, that I did not keep samples of the various plots to test their cooking and eating qualities, for, with a difference of 3 or 4 per cent. in the starch, it would certainly have been perceptible. When considering these experiments, it was determined that they should be tried on a variety of potato which had hitherto been comparatively exempt from disease—

namely, the Champion—so as to avoid as much as possible complications which would arise when a portion of the crop was lost through disease, and thus enable the effect of ammoniacal manure on the increase of the crop to be tried undisturbed as far as possible, as, with non-disease-resisting varieties, it is well known that ammoniacal dressings increase the tendency to disease.

Three sources of phosphoric acid have been employed so as to test in which it is most available for the potato. Thus, so-called bone superphosphate—made to all appearance half with bones and half with ground coprolite—was tried against coprolite superphosphates and also against ground coprolites, each in such quantity that the dressing contained between 88 lbs. and 89 lbs. of phosphoric acid per acre. As there was a small quantity of undecomposed nitrogenous compounds in the bone superphosphates, an equal quantity of nitrogen in the form of sulphate of ammonia (35 lbs. per acre) was added, so that the bone superphosphate should have no advantage on account of its nitrogen over the other two. This constitutes the first series, which may be called for convenience the "unaided phosphates," though there can be no doubt that even this small quantity of nitrogen has had a material effect.

The second series consists of No. 1 series, plus an addition at the rate of 2 cwts. per acre of sulphate of ammonia to each of the three.

The third series consists of No. 2 series, plus 2 cwts. of kainit.

The fourth series consists of No. 2, plus 56 lbs. of potashes substituted in place of the kainit.

Thus, it will be observed, the three phosphates are tested against one another under four varying conditions—alone; in conjunction with sulphate of ammonia; in conjunction with sulphate of ammonia, plus kainit; and in conjunction with sulphate of ammonia, plus potashes.

The effect of sulphate of ammonia is tested by comparing the results of the three unaided phosphates with the same plus sulphate of ammonia. The effect of kainit is tested three times over by comparing members of the second series with the corresponding members of the third series. That of potashes by comparing members of the fourth series with members of the second series; and by comparing the fourth with the third series the two forms of potash are compared with one another three separate times. Besides this, each manurial application is tried in triplicate, so that the phosphates are tested against one another twelve times, and the sulphate of ammonia nine times, kainit nine times, potashes nine times.

The field chosen is perhaps the best potato soil of any on the farm. The experimental piece is slightly too heavy rather than too light, and though very even for the Oolitic [*] formations, there is considerable variety in the same half-acre of land.   It was therefore determined to try every dressing as above stated in triplicate, the different plots of each triplicate being carefully distributed so as to counterbalance irregularities.   The size of the plots were $\frac{1}{12}$ of an acre, or 51·8 yards' run of one potato drill.   This plan of small plots in triplicate has been repeatedly found to give the most accurate results, far more so than when large plots of half an acre are tried singly.

On April 21st the furrows on the whole piece having been split open with the double mould board plough, the various dressings were applied as on the main crop, with great care down the central portion of the furrow.   The sets were then carefully planted so as to ensure perfect regularity, and at once covered in.

As the crop grew it was observable that those plots to which the 2 cwts. of sulphate of ammonia had been applied looked the most vigorous; but as they ripened these same plots showed most disease on the shaws.   It may be mentioned that a crop of Regent potatoes which had been planted on the side of the prevailing and dampest wind were very much diseased, and it is probable that the accelerated spread of the disease amongst the Champions was due to this, as they turned out more diseased than was anticipated.   The latter part of June and July was remarkably wet, as also was September, and the disease manifested itself in the Regents at the end of July, so that the disease was throughout all the potato crops over an average.

The potatoes were dug and weighed on 18th October, and the weights on each plot are seen in Table I., which also shows the distribution of the plots and the weights of the manures per acre.   Table II. column 1, contains the average result of each manuring obtained by adding together the weights of the three triplicates, and then dividing the sum by three.   This result is stated in column 1, and it will be seen that the whole of the bone superphosphate results are averaged, also those of the whole of the coprolite superphosphates, and those of the whole of the ground coprolites; and from this it is seen that the yield from bone superphosphates exceeds that from coprolite superphosphates by 13 cwts., and that from ground coprolite by 1 ton 13 cwts.   It must be remembered that in each of these quantities, each tried in triplicate, the total quantity of nitrogen applied is equal; therefore, it is evident that the soluble phosphates produce the greatest crop, and of the two kinds the bone superphosphates surpasses the coprolite superphosphates when in conjunction with sulphate of ammonia.

_____

* The Oolitic formation is a variety of limestone, consisting of minute spherical grains.

TABLE I.—*Showing the position of Potato Plots, also the Applications and the Weight which they would amount to per Acre. The yield of Potatoes, both of Large, Small, and Diseased, is given in lbs. per Plot, which is equivalent to cwts. per Acre, each Plot being the 1/112th of an Acre. Each Application is in Triplicate.*

NORTH.

| | | | | | | | | |
|---|---|---|---|---|---|---|---|---|
| **1.**<br>Cwt. lb.<br>5 0 cop. super.<br>0 85 sul. am.<br>Large............124<br>Small............ 46<br>Diseased........ 20<br>Total......190 | **6.**<br>Cwt. lb.<br>6 85 bone super.<br><br>124<br>29½<br>15<br>168½ | **11.**<br>Cwt. lb.<br>2 8½ ground cop.<br>0 85 sul. am.<br><br>117<br>34<br>13<br>164 | **16.**<br>Cwt. lb.<br>5 0 cop. super.<br>2 85 sul. am.<br>2 0 kainit.<br>161<br>58<br>35½<br>254½ | **21.**<br>Cwt. lb.<br>6 85 bone super.<br>2 0 sul. am.<br>2 0 kainit.<br>168<br>67<br>37<br>272 | **26.**<br>Cwt. lb.<br>2 8 ground cop.<br>2 85 sul. am.<br>2 0 kainit.<br>158<br>25<br>15<br>198 | **31.***<br>—<br>112<br>35<br>10½<br>157½ | **36.***<br>—<br>112<br>35<br>10½<br>157½ | **41.***<br>—<br>112<br>35<br>10½<br>157½ |
| **2.**<br>5 0 cop. super.<br>2 85 sul. am.<br>Large............178<br>Small............ 37½<br>Diseased........ 40<br>Total......255½ | **7.**<br>6 85 bone super.<br>2 0 sul. am.<br><br>165<br>41<br>34½<br>240½ | **12.**<br>2 8½ ground cop.<br>2 85 sul. am.<br><br>150<br>23½<br>15<br>188½ | **17.**<br>5 0 cop. super.<br>2 85 sul. am.<br>0 56 potashes.<br>139<br>52½<br>53<br>244½ | **22.**<br>6 85 bone super.<br>2 0 sul. am.<br>0 56 potashes.<br>185<br>52<br>25½<br>265½ | **27.**<br>2 8 ground cop.<br>2 85 sul. am.<br>0 56 potashes.<br>143½<br>24½<br>18½<br>186½ | **32.**<br>Cwt. lb.<br>5 0 cop. super.<br>2 85 sul. am.<br>2 0 kainit.<br>174<br>83<br>84<br>263 | **37.**<br>Cwt. lb.<br>6 85 bone super.<br>2 0 sul. am.<br>2 0 kainit.<br>180<br>51<br>33½<br>264½ | **42.**<br>Cwt. lb.<br>2 8½ ground cop.<br>2 85 sul. am.<br>2 0 kainit.<br>162<br>28<br>30<br>220 |
| **3.**<br>5 0 cop. super.<br>2 85 sul. am.<br>2 0 kainit<br>Large............186<br>Small............ 38½<br>Diseased........ 34½<br>Total......259 | **8.**<br>6 85 bone super.<br>2 0 sul. am.<br>2 0 kainit.<br>170<br>58<br>41<br>269 | **13.**<br>2 8½ ground cop.<br>2 85 sul. am.<br>2 0 kainit.<br>161<br>23<br>20½<br>204½ | **18.**<br>5 0 cop. super.<br>0 85 sul. am.<br><br>150½<br>30½<br>15½<br>196½ | **23.**<br>6 85 bone super.<br><br>169<br>29<br>11½<br>209½ | **28.**<br>2 8 ground cop.<br>0 85 sul. am.<br><br>136<br>37<br>10<br>183 | **33.**<br>5 0 cop. super.<br>2 85 sul. am.<br>0 56 potashes.<br>205<br>56<br>15½<br>276½ | **38.**<br>6 85 bone super.<br>2 0 sul. am.<br>0 56 potashes.<br>191<br>49<br>18<br>258 | **43.**<br>2 8½ ground cop.<br>2 85 sul. am.<br>0 56 potashes.<br>189<br>30½<br>16½<br>236 |
| **4.**<br>5 0 cop. super.<br>2 85 sul. am.<br>0 56 potashes.<br>Large............119½<br>Small............ 50<br>Diseased........ 14½<br>Total......184 | **9.**<br>6 85 bone super.<br>2 0 sul. am.<br>0 56 potashes.<br>163½<br>63<br>24<br>250½ | **14.**<br>2 8½ ground cop.<br>2 85 sul. am.<br>0 56 potashes.<br>198<br>35½<br>15<br>248½ | **19.**<br>—<br>102<br>31½<br>8<br>141½ | **24.**<br>—<br>114<br>32<br>10<br>156 | **29.**<br>—<br>101<br>42<br>9½<br>152½ | **34.**<br>5 0 cop. super.<br>2 85 sul. am.<br><br>188<br>29½<br>17½<br>235 | **39.**<br>6 85 bone super.<br>2 0 sul. am.<br><br>181<br>86<br>16½<br>283½ | **44.**<br>2 8½ ground cop.<br>2 85 sul. am.<br><br>186<br>25<br>11<br>222 |
| **5.**<br>—<br>Large............103¼<br>Small............ 49½<br>Diseased........ 11½<br>Total......164½ | **10.**<br>—<br>94½<br>34½<br>7½<br>136½ | **15.**<br>—<br>114<br>38½<br>5½<br>158 | **20.**<br>5 0 cop. super.<br>2 85 sul. am.<br>186<br>47½<br>14½<br>248 | **25.**<br>6 85 bone super.<br>2 0 sul. am.<br>207<br>76<br>22<br>305 | **30.**<br>2 8 ground cop.<br>2 85 sul. am.<br>158<br>39½<br>24<br>221½ | **35.**<br>5 0 cop. super.<br>0 85 sul. am.<br>148<br>45½<br>14<br>207½ | **40.**<br>6 85 bone super.<br><br>144<br>37½<br>9<br>190½ | **45.**<br>2 8½ coprolite.<br>0 85 sul. am.<br>159½<br>33½<br>12<br>205 |

SOUTH

* 31, 36, 41 were all weighed together, and therefore the average is put in each plot.

In column 2, Table II., the unaided phosphates are brought into prominence. In column 3 the same phosphates, plus sulphate of ammonia, are brought into prominence, and averaged. If we compare the two, it is seen that the sulphate of ammonia has increased the average crops by 1 ton 6 cwts. The addition of kainit (see column 4) has lessened the crop by 10 cwts. per acre, and the potashes (see column 5) has lessened it by 5 cwts.

TABLE III. *Shows the Value of the Crop per acre at £3 per Ton, the Cost of each Manurial Application, the value of the Crop after deducting this and the Profit produced over and above the Value of Crop with no Manure.*

| Application | Weight of crop per acre in tons and cwts. | Value of crop per acre. | Cost of manures | Value of crop after deducting cost of manures | Clean profit, after deducting cost of manures and value of crop with no manure, viz., £21, 12s |
|---|---|---|---|---|---|
| Bone super., . . | 8 17 | £26 11 0 | £1 18 0 | £24 13 0 | £3 1 0 |
| Bone super.+sul. am., | 12 12 | 37 16 0 | 4 0 0 | 33 16 0 | 12 4 0 |
| Bone super.+sul.am. +kainit, . . | 11 11 | 34 13 0 | 4 5 0 | 30 8 0 | 8 16 0 |
| Bone super.+sul.am. +potashes, . . | 11 14 | 35 2 0 | 5 8 0 | 29 14 0 | 8 2 0 |
| Cop. super., . . | 9 1 | 27 3 0 | 1 7 0 | 25 16 0 | 4 4 |
| Cop. super.+sul am., | 11 3 | 33 9 0 | 3 9 0 | 30 0 0 | 8 8 0 |
| Cop. super.+sul. am. +kainit, . . | 11 4 | 33 12 0 | 3 14 0 | 29 18 0 | 8 6 0 |
| Cop. super.+sul. am. +potashes, . | 10 13 | 31 19 0 | 4 16 0 | 27 3 0 | 5 11 0 |
| Ground cop., . . | 8 13 | 25 19 0 | 1 2 0 | 24 17 0 | 3 5 0 |
| Ground cop.+sul. am., | 9 15 | 29 5 0 | 3 4 0 | 26 1 0 | 4 9 0 |
| Ground cop. + sul. am.+kainit, . | 9 3 | 27 9 0 | 3 9 0 | 24 0 0 | 2 8 0 |
| Ground cop. + sul. am.+potashes, . | 10 7 | 31 1 0 | 4 5 0 | 26 16 0 | 5 4 0 |
| Blank, with no manure at all, . . | 7 4 | 21 12 0 | ... | 21 12 0 | ... |
| Dung, 10 tons per acre, | 10 2 | 30 6 0 | 3 0 0 | 27 6 0 | 5 14 0 |

It is to be noticed that the three so-styled "unaided phosphates" have produced nearly equal crops; but, owing probably to the slower assimilation of the undecomposed nitrogen in the bone super-phosphates than of the 35 lbs. sulphate of ammonia added to the coprolite superphosphates—to equalise the nitrogen—the former produces rather the smaller crop. When, however, 2 cwts. of sulphate of ammonia are added to each, the bone superphosphates then shows a great superiority, giving nearly 1½ tons more. This looks as if some form of nitrogen ready for immediate use by the plant were necessary to its early growth, and a more slowly decomposing form of nitrogen were necessary to carry on the later growth. Sulphate of ammonia is seen throughout to have had a remarkable effect, especially when in conjunction with a soluble phosphate, having increased the crop with bone superphosphates by 3 tons 15 cwts. above bone superphosphates alone, and by 2 tons 2 cwts. with coprolite superphosphates above coprolite superphosphates (almost) alone; whereas with ground coprolites it has only increased the crop by 1 ton 2 cwts. above the ground coprolites (almost) alone.

Table III. speaks for itself, and shows the monetary results. The price of £3 per ton is taken as under the price obtained on the average for Champions in this neighbourhood when taking the large and small together. The diseased potatoes have not been valued, but have been given in for luck to pay for extra expense in sorting the heavier crops.

At the bottom of the tables, and independent of the experiments, the result of 10 tons of farmyard dung is given. It is not an actual part of the experiments, because it was not analysed, and it must only be taken for rough comparison.

## PART II.

After the description of the agricultural portion of the experiments, it becomes necessary to describe somewhat fully the chemical results, and to give an account of the materials which brought about those results.

The following figures represent the composition in parts per 100 of a carefully selected sample of the dried soil:—

*Analysis of Soil (calculated on the dry).*

| | |
|---|---|
| Silica, . . . . . . | 62·00 |
| Phosphoric acid, . . . . | 0·286 |
| Carbonate of lime, . . . . | 11·30 |
| Peroxide of iron, . . . . | 7·04 |
| Alumina, . . . . . | 8·114 |
| Magnesia, . . . . . | 0·62 |
| Potash, . . . . . | 0·704 |
| Organic matter, . . . . | 9·55 |
| (Containing nitrogen equal to ammonia, | 0·390) |
| | 99·674 |
| Soluble salts, . . . . . | 0·575 |

T

It will thus be seen that the soil was not remarkably rich, but contained a fair proportion of ammonia, potash, and phosphoric acid, and also a moderate supply of plant food in a soluble condition, such as is most necessary for the growth of crops. It will be unnecessary to give a detailed analysis of the manures employed, for although all the substances present were estimated, yet, by reason of the very small quantities of many of them present, they could have no influence on the results; therefore the amount of the principal constituents only will be found in the following tables :—

PHOSPHATES.

| Insoluble "Curaçoa phosphate," ground to an impalpable powder. | Soluble Phosphates. | |
| | "Bone superphosphate." | "Mineral superphosphate." |
| --- | --- | --- |
| | Per cent. | Per cent. | Per cent. |
| Insoluble phosphate of lime (tricalcium phosphate), . . | 85·51 | 5·56 | 7·12 |
| Soluble phosphate of lime (monocalcium phosphate), . . | ...... | 16·39 | 20·77 |
| "Soluble phosphate" equivalent to bone earth made soluble, | ...... | 21·84 | 27·61 |
| Sulphate of lime, . | 2·7 | 30·57 | 34·06 |
| Sand and insoluble matter, . . . | 0·46 | 7·69 | 9·40 |
| Organic matter and combined water, . | 1·53 | 32·74 | ...... |
| Containing nitrogen equivalent to ammonia, . . | ...... | 1·26 | ...... |

The sample of kainit was found to contain 27·21 per cent. of sulphate of potash (=14·7 $K_2O$); the sample of "potashes" prepared from crude tartar contained 59·77 per cent. of potash (52·05 per cent. being present combined in the form of carbonate of potash); the sulphate of ammonia, a fine white sample, contained 96·44 per cent. of pure sulphate.

In accordance with calculations based on these analyses, the manures were carefully weighed, so that all the plots should have equal weights of *phosphoric acid*, whether in the soluble or insoluble condition, as also of ammonia and of potash, no matter in what form it was employed. The mixtures having been made in the laboratory, they were placed in bags, and the bags on their respective plots, so that no mistake should occur in their application; the manures were then sown personally by myself, aided by two skilled assistants, in as even a manner as it was possible.[*]

TABLE IV.—*Quantities applied in Pounds per Acre.*

| Plots. | Potash ($K_2O$). | Phos. Acid ($P_2O_5$). | Nitrogen. | Equivalent to Ammonia. |
|---|---|---|---|---|
| 2, 20, 34 | ... | 88·8 | 52·94 | 64·27 |
| 3, 16, 32 | 32·92 | 88·8 | 52·94 | 64·27 |
| 7, 25, 39 | ... | 88·3 | 53·15 | 64·54 |
| 8, 21, 37 | 32·92 | 88·3 | 53·15 | 64·54 |
| 12, 30, 44 | ... | 89·0 | 52·94 | 64·27 |
| 13, 26, 42 | 32·92 | 89·0 | 52·94 | 64·27 |
| 1, 18, 35 | ... | 88·8 | 7·14 | 8·77 |
| 6, 23, 40 | ... | 88·3 | 7·35 | 8·92 |
| 11, 28, 45 | ... | 89·0 | 7·14 | 8·77 |
| 4, 17, 33 | 33·0 | 88·8 | 52·94 | 64·27 |
| 9, 22, 38 | 33·0 | 88·3 | 53·15 | 64·54 |
| 14, 27, 43 | 33·0 | 89·0 | 52·94 | 64·27 |
| B | 32·9 | 55·95 | 4·7 | 5·7 |

When the time arrived that the crops should be lifted, the samples for determination of the composition of the potatoes as affected by the manures, were chosen from those plots which stretched in a band across the field, viz., plots 2, 7, 12; 3, 8, 13; 18, 23, 28; 33, 38, 43; and 24 (see Table I., these plots are enclosed in black lines). Some of the tubers were reserved for the estimation of the specific gravity, which is generally considered as an indication of the amount of starch present, others were employed for the direct estimation of the starch, nitrogen, fibre, moisture, and ash. The amount of starch was estimated by Siegert's process, as this, when done in duplicate, was found to give the most accurate results, as, for example, No. 33, according to two analyses of the dried sample, was found to contain 76·9 and 76·6 per cent. of starch.[†]

[*] This does not apply to plots A and B.
[†] Siewert's process (*Landw. Vers. Stat.*, xxiv. 427), in which the potato meal is heated in sealed tubes with tartaric acid to 115° C., was tried, but the results were so discordant that it was abandoned in favour of the above-mentioned method, in which sulphuric acid is employed at 95° C. for eight hours, and then after filtration, the solution being first diluted, is again heated with more acid ; the resulting glucose was estimated by Pavy's ammoniacal Fehling's copper solution

TABLE V.—*Showing the average Composition of the Tubers.*

| Plot | 18 | 23 | 28 | 2 | 7 | 12 | 8 | 8 | 18 | 28 | 28 | 43 | 24 | A | B | C |
|---|---|---|---|---|---|---|---|---|---|---|---|---|---|---|---|---|
| Manures applied | 5 lbs. copr. super., and 5 oz. sulph. am. | 6 lbs. 5 oz. bone super. | 2 lbs. ½ oz. coprolites, and 5 oz. sulph. am. | 5 lbs. copr. super., and 2 lbs. 5 oz. sulph. am. | 6 lbs. 5 oz. bone super., and 2 lbs. sulph. am. | 2 lbs. ½ oz. coprolites, and 2 lbs. 5 oz. sulph. am. | 5 lbs. copr. super., 2 lbs. 5 oz. sulph. am., and 2 lbs. kainit. | 6 lbs. 5 oz. bone super., 2 lbs. sulph. kainit. | 2 lbs. ½ oz. coprolites, 2 lbs. sulph. am., and 2 lbs. kainit. | 5 lbs. copr. super., 2 lbs. 5 oz. sulph. am., and 7·5 oz. pot-ashes. | 6 lbs. 5 oz. bone super., am., and 2 lbs. sulph. 7·5 oz. pot-ashes. | 2 lbs. ½ oz. coprolites, 2 lbs. 5 oz. sulph. 7·5 oz. pot-ashes. | No manure. | Farmyard Manure. | 4 cwt. bone super, and 2 cwt. kainit. | Diseased. |
| | % | % | % | % | % | % | % | % | % | % | % | % | % | % | % | % |
| Moisture, | 69·64 | 69·02 | 73·57 | 68·76 | 69·87 | 78·52 | 72·24 | 69·87 | 71·90 | 70·43 | 70·68 | 70·76 | 71·97 | 71·50 | 70·55 | 76·28 |
| Total solids, | 30·36 | 30·98 | 26·43 | 31·24 | 30·13 | 26·48 | 27·76 | 30·03 | 28·10 | 29·57 | 29·32 | 29·24 | 28·03 | 28·50 | 29·45 | 23·72 |
| In 100 parts of potato, (Mean results):— | | | | | | | | | | | | | | | | |
| Starch, | 24·98 | 23·60 | 21·98 | 25·1038 | 24·050 | 21·1280 | 23·86 | 23·00 | 22·50 | 28·07 | 24·23 | 23·45 | 23·10 | 24·52 | 24·87 | 18·66 |
| "Albuminoids," | 1·7122 | 1·845 | 1·8918 | 2·2020 | 1·9884 | 2·0714 | 1·834 | 1·904 | 1·92 | 2·04 | 1·688 | 1·72 | 1·248 | 1·884 | 1·664 | 1·687 |
| "Albuminoid" nitrogen, | 0·2708 | 0·2946 | 0·2198 | 0·8478 | 0·818 | 0·8267 | 0·278 | 0·8009 | 0·3084 | 0·324 | 0·253 | 0·269 | 0·197 | 0·2186 | 0·268 | 0·263 |
| True albuminoids, | 1·978 | 0·9653 | 1·0487 | 1·1501 | 1·873 | 1·0488 | 0·848 | 1·188 | 1·1485 | 1·18 | 1·019 | 1·044 | 1·177 | 0·844 | 1·398 | 1·3809 |
| (True albuminoid nitrogen) | 0·179 | 0·1578 | 0·1649 | 0·1867 | 0·2169 | 0·1681 | 0·1886 | 0·204 | 0·1809 | 0·1789 | 0·181 | 0·165 | 0·188 | 0·1017 | 0·221 | 0·215 |
| Oil, &c. (By difference,) | 1·949 | 1·48 | 0·503 | 2·004 | 1·385 | 2·6887 | 0·834 | 8·198 | 0·9913 | 2·664 | 1·677 | 2·804 | 1·988 | 0·936 | 1·371 | 1·840 |
| Fibre, | 0·696 | 0·878 | 1·07 | 0·691 | 0·799 | 0·6116 | 0·518 | 0·72 | 0·6239 | 0·643 | 0·617 | 0·949 | 0·719 | 0·658 | 0·561 | 0·719 |
| Ash, | 1·128 | 1·176 | 1·306 | 1·2997 | 1·820 | 0·9771 | 1·089 | 0·61 | 1·085 | 1·153 | 1·078 | 0·917 | 6·995 | 0·982 | 0·934 | 0·884 |

In plants there exist certain compounds which contain nitrogen, and these may be divided into two classes: the coagulable (capable of curdling) and the uncoagulable. These in the potatoes were estimated in duplicate, and by two processes, viz., the precipitation by carbolic acid, and the combustion with soda-lime. By the first process is obtained the true amount of the coagulable nitrogen compounds, called albuminoids or flesh-formers, and by the latter the whole of the nitrogenous matters, which are generally considered as albuminoids or flesh-formers, but are in reality a mixture of the true albuminoids, with other nitrogenous substances, such as solanine, &c., that are not at present considered to be of any feeding value.

I have, therefore, inserted in the table of analyses these so-called "albuminoids," as distinct from the amount of the true albuminoids; I have also added the amount of nitrogen as obtained by the two processes, for the albuminoids are only calculated by multiplying the quantity of nitrogen, which analyses show them to contain, by 6·33. The difference between the two figures representing the nitrogen, as obtained by the two analytical methods, may be considered as the measure of nitrogenous matters present in the potato in forms other than coagulable albuminoids, and these may be termed "amides." Fibre was estimated by the "acid and alkali" process, being generally done in duplicate; the "fat, &c.," being in so small a quantity and of little importance was calculated by "difference."

Table V. shows the composition of each of the various crops, as well as the amount of manure applied in each individual case; and for greater convenience of reference the mean of the specific gravity determinations are placed side by side in the subjoined table with the percentage of starch.

TABLE VI. *Showing Specific Gravity and Percentage of Starch.*

| Plot. | Sp. Gr. | Starch. | Plot. | Sp. Gr. | Starch. | Plot. | Sp. Gr. | Starch. |
|-------|---------|---------|-------|---------|---------|-------|---------|---------|
| 28 | 1·1357 | 21·96 | 12 | 1·1240 | 21·13 | 7 | 1·1205 | 24·65 |
| 18 | 1·127 | 24·98 | 13 | 1·1238 | 22·50 | 2 | 1·120 | 25·103 |
| 43 | 1·127 | 23·45 | 8 | 1·122 | 23·60 | 33 | 1·11 7 | 23·07 |
| 36 | 1·1255 | 24·22 | 3 | 1·1210 | 23·36 | | | |
| 24 | 1·1255 | 23·10 | 23 | 1·1212 | 25·60 | | | |
| A | 1·1205 | 24·52 | B | 1·1250 | 24·87 | C | 1·122 | 18·66 |

No relationship seems to exist between the specific gravity of the tubers, and the percentage of starch. Attempts to estimate the amount of dry matter and starch, by the aid of the tables published by Heidepriem (*Landw. Vers. Stat.*, xx.) * were fruitless, as the results were far from the truth, and therefore unreliable; as, for example, tubers of specific gravity 1·127 should

* See also Fresenius, *Jour. Chem. Soc.*, 1881, p. 932.

contain, according to the tables, 21·69 per cent. starch, and 28·9 dry matter, but in reality I found by analysis that the actual amounts were 24·98 and 30·36 (Plot 18).

Again, no definite relationship exists between the starch and the amount of nitrogen (see Table V.), whether we consider the nitrogen in the form of coagulable albuminoids, or the total nitrogen present in the other compounds, as well as in the albuminoids; but, on the whole, a reduction of starch is accompanied by an increase in nitrogen.

TABLE VII.—*Showing Average Percentage of Starch obtained with various Manures, and an Analysis of the Aggregate Averages.*

| Plots. | Manures. | Average Percentage of Starch | Phosphates with small quantity of Nitrogen. | Phosphates and Ammonia. | Phosphates, +Ammonia +Kainit. | Phosphates, +Ammonia +Potashes. |
|---|---|---|---|---|---|---|
| 23 | Bone superphosphate, | 25·60 | 25·60 | | | |
| 7 | Bone super.+sul. am., | 24·65 | ... | 24·65 | | |
| 8 | Bone super.+sul. am.+kainit, | 23·60 | ... | ... | 23·60 | |
| 38 | Bone super.+sul. am.+potashes, | 24·22 | ... | ... | ... | 24·22 |
| | Total, | 98·07 | | | | |
| | Average of all the bone super. plots, | 24·52 | | | | |
| 18 | Coprolite superphosphate, | 24·98 | 24·98 | | | |
| 2 | Cop. super.+sul. am., | 25·10 | ... | 25·10 | | |
| 3 | Cop. super.+sul. am.+kainit, | 23·36 | ... | ... | 23·36 | |
| 33 | Cop. super.+sul. am.+potashes, | 23·07 | ... | ... | ... | 23·07 |
| | Total, | 96·51 | | | | |
| | Average of all the cop. super. plots, | 24·13 | | | | |
| 28 | Coprolites, | 21·96 | 21·96 | | | |
| 12 | Cop.+sul. am., | 21·13 | ... | 21·13 | | |
| 13 | Cop.+sul. am.+kainit, | 22·50 | ... | ... | 22·50 | |
| 43 | Cop.+sul. am.+potashes | 23·45 | ... | ... | ... | 23·45 |
| | Total, | 89·04 | 72·54 | 70·88 | 69·46 | 70·74 |
| | Average of all the ground coprolite plots, | 22·26 | 24·18 | 23·63 | 23·15 | 23·58 |
| | Farmyard manure, | 24·52 | | | | |
| | 4 Bone super.+2 kainit, | 24·87 | | | | |
| | Unmanured, | 23·10 | Average of Unaided Phosphates | Average of Phosphates and Ammonia | Average of Phosphates and Kainit | Average of Phosphates and Potashes. |

A cursory glance at the table of averages shows that bone superphosphate, alone or mixed, produced tubers with a higher percentage of starch, the mean results being for bone superphosphate 24·52 per cent., mineral superphosphate, 24·13 per cent., and "coprolites," 22·26 per cent, so that there was a gain by employing the dissolved phosphate; and it should also be noticed that the maximum amount was produced when the

superphosphates were used alone. All other additions appear to
have acted prejudicially on the quality of the potato, excepting, however, when undissolved phosphate was employed, and
then we find that additions of other manures were beneficial.

The reduction of the amount of starch was produced by the
sulphate of ammonia, but not to so great an extent as when it
was in combination with kainit, which last admixture is evidently
most unsatisfactory, when the aim of the agriculturist is to produce a starchy potato; and in these experiments we find that
those tubers which grew on the unmanured plots contained as
much starch as if they had been treated with ammonia and
kainit.*

"Potashes" and ammonia do not seem to be quite as prejudicial as the kainit, but the slight gain in starch over the
unmanured plot (24) is not commensurate with the additional
outlay, unless the yield be large. As the kainit was put in with
the other manures, and not as Völcker recommends, at an earlier
period, it is possible that the percentage of starch might have
been raised, if this plan had been followed. As soon as this
deleterious effect of kainit was perceived, we determined that
in the succeeding set of experiments (which were commenced
June 4, 1881), we would employ such manures as should aid us
in determining which ingredient it was that caused this reduction in starch, whether it was the large amount of sulphuric acid
added in the kainit and sulphate of ammonia, or whether it was
the magnesia. However, a paper by A. Meyer (*Landw. Ver.
Stat.*, xxvi. 77, and *Jour. Chem. Soc*, 1881, p. 459) has in part
answered our inquiries, for it is there shown that bases combined with mineral acids (such as sulphuric acid), are not so
readily assimilated as if they had been in combination with
organic acids, as carbonic acid, &c., so that here we may have an
explanation of the effect produced by "potashes" as compared
with that produced by the potassium in kainit.

*Effect on the amount of Nitrogen* (Table V.).—Under this
heading the nitrogen present in the form of coagulable albuminoids, and that in any other form such as "amides," &c., are to
be considered, and not only these two separately, but the proportion which one bears to the other. As the ordinary "soda-
lime" method of analysis does not give always the absolute
quantity of nitrogen present, the figures which represent the
"Total Nitrogen" must be considered only as an approximation
to the true quantity, therefore the difference between the two
"Nitrogens" which represents the "amides" is also but an
approximation.

Noticing firstly the true albuminoids present, I find that the

* Kainit and superphosphate alone (Plot B) being, on the other hand, satisfactory.

action of ammonia has been to raise the quantity of albuminoids, but this influence is counteracted by the addition of potassium manures, and more especially when potashes were employed; as was the case with starch, so with albuminoids, the action of the three kinds of phosphates has been very dissimilar, and when in one set we find "Cop. Super" (3) with low albuminoids, we find it elsewhere with high albuminoids (2); still, looking at it as a whole, the effects of ammonia and potash are as above stated, the unmanured plot shows the smallest quantity of non-albuminoid nitrogen.*

As might perhaps be expected, "amides," &c., were present in greatest quantity in these potatoes manured with ammonia (average=0·1399 per cent. N.), but this quantity was greatly reduced by the addition of potash as kainit (average=0·1212 N., plots 3, 8, 13), and it was further reduced when potashes were employed (average=0·1127 N., plots 33, 38, 43), and the amides were in greater quantity than when "supers" were used alone (average=0·097 per cent. N.). Probably this figure would have been still lower if there had been no ammonia at all present with the phosphates. If any conclusion may be drawn from B, it is that the non-albuminoid nitrogen has been reduced to a minimum by the increased ratio of potash to superphosphate.

*Effect on the Ash.*—The influence of the manures on the ash was very indefinite, as the quantity produced by the variation of the phosphate employed was so different. It appears, however, that the highest ash was produced by phosphates and ammonia (average of plots 2, 7, 12=1·31), while the addition of potash in any form reduced the quantity of mineral matter (plots 3, 8, 12=0·914, and 33, 38, 43=1·047 per cent.) and when the superphosphate was applied in smaller amounts (plot B), we find 0·561 as the percentage of ash, closely approximating that found in Plots A and 24. Fleischer (*Bied. Centr.*, 1880), considers that phosphoric acid and kainit increase the ash by 100 per cent.; I have not found so great an increase, but certainly the results obtained by us point in the same direction. What has been said concerning the ash, also holds good concerning the fibre.

*Total Solids.*—As regards "total solids," under which heading are included the small percentage of fat, &c., it appears, firstly, that insoluble phosphates have had a depressing influence on the yield of dry matter, but that soluble phosphates have been advantageous, and that as regards their source but little influence is decernible. Taking the average yield of each separate class, we obtain (plots 18, 23, 28) 29·26 per cent.; (plots 2, 7,

* The supplementary Plot A shows but a low percentage of albumin, while in B it is found to be high, whereas the "amides" are present in but small amounts.

12), 29·31 per cent.; (plots 3, 8, 13), 28·63 per cent.; and (plots 33, 38, 43), 29·37 per cent. All of them are above plot 24 (unmanured), 28·03 per cent., and plot A, 28·5 per cent. It is clear, then, that the addition of any soluble manure has been productive of good effects, when considering only the solid matter. Fittbogen (who introduced the manure into the soil three weeks before placing his "sets") found that the "super" lowered the dry matter, and that kainit, with or without superphosphate, produced tubers containing the smallest amount of dry matter. Reference to any of the plots (except 28, 12, 13), and comparison with 24 and A and B, will show that our results are very different; but I find that ammonia and superphosphate alone have given better results than when kainit has been added. The effect of potashes has been good when considering the average amount, but the maximum amount is considerably below the maximum of the other plots.

*Summary.*—Bone superphosphate has produced in all cases the most valuable tuber, whether the phosphate was used alone (which was the most satisfactory) or when mixed with ammonia or potash, or with both, the starch being generally in the largest quantity, and the water in least. The addition of ammonia slightly detracts from the percentage of starch, and adds a little to the water; but, on the other hand, the nitrogenous matter is distinctly increased,—however, in a form of no value as regards feeding. (See Table V.)

Insoluble phosphate does not appear to advantage as regards starch, with but one exception (43), and it seems generally to have increased the albuminous matter, and to have decreased the ash and the fibre when in conjunction with other manures; but seeing that these two last are very subordinate constituents of a potato, its use could not be especially recommended in further trials. That bone superphosphate should have produced the best results is somewhat remarkable, as like quantities of nitrogen were present in both superphosphate applications; and in the case of the "mineral superphosphate" it was in a more advanced stage for assimilation by the plants, and according to Mürcker (*Bied. Centr.*, 1880, 409) ammonia, to produce its effects, must first be converted into nitric acid; hence it was to be expected that the nitrogen in the bone superphosphate would act more slowly and produce its effects more tardily than the nitrogen in the added sulphate of ammonia. Whether the sulphuric acid present has had a retarding influence is a matter yet to be determined.*

* Although Plot B has been frequently quoted in this report, it must be distinctly understood that no great importance can be attached to the results obtained, as no special care was taken in its preparation, it being quite an afterthought, was made at a later date, and was not intended to have been introduced into this report. The analyses of its produce are, however, of value.

A word may perhaps be said concerning the diseased potato. (C.) The great difference between the composition of this and that of any other, but healthy tuber, appears to be in the amount of water and starch present, the former in much larger, the latter in much lesser quantity. The nitrogenous matter does not seem to be in higher quantity, but consists almost wholly of coagulable albumin. Of course, the higher ratio which the albumin bears to the starch in this than in a healthy potato accounts in part for the peculiar character possessed by diseased tubers.

It remains now, after having discussed the merits of the various manures, as affecting the composition of the tuber, to examine the value of the total crops which they have produced. In Table IV., Part I., the value of the crops are there calculated from a definite fixed standard of £3 per ton, no allowance being made for the quality. I have therefore prepared the following somewhat similar Table (VIII.), in which the market value of the average yield is affected by the quality; the standard employed is 1d. for each pound of starch present in the whole crop.

TABLE VIII.—*Showing the Value of the Experimental Crops as calculated from the Percentage of Starch.*

| Plots. | Manures. | Gross Value of Crop. | | | Value of Manure. | | | Nett Value of Crop. | | |
|---|---|---|---|---|---|---|---|---|---|---|
| | | £ | s. | d. | £ | s. | d. | £ | s. | d. |
| 7 | Bone super. + sul. am., | 28 | 19 | 9 | 3 | 19 | 10 | 24 | 19 | 11 |
| 2 | Cop. super. + sul. am., | 28 | 4 | 3 | 3 | 8 | 6 | 24 | 15 | 9 |
| 38 | Bone super. + sul. am. + potash, | 26 | 10 | 1 | 5 | 7 | 5 | 21 | 2 | 8 |
| 3 | Cop. super. + sul. am. + kainit | 24 | 8 | 11 | 3 | 13 | 6 | 20 | 14 | 5 |
| 8 | Bone sup. + sul. am. + kainit, | 25 | 9 | 4 | 4 | 4 | 10 | 20 | 4 | 6 |
| 23 | Bone superphospate, | 21 | 4 | 1 | 1 | 17 | 10 | 19 | 6 | 3 |
| 33 | Cop. sup. + sul. am. + potashes, | 23 | 0 | 5 | 4 | 16 | 1 | 18 | 4 | 4 |
| 43 | Coprolites + sul. am. + potashes, | 22 | 14 | 8 | 4 | 11 | 11 | 18 | 2 | 9 |
| 12 | Coprolites + sul. am. | 19 | 15 | 6 | 3 | 4 | 4 | 16 | 11 | 2 |
| 13 | Cop. + sul. am. + kainit, | 19 | 5 | 11 | 3 | 9 | 4 | 15 | 16 | 7 |
| 28 | Coprolites, | 17 | 15 | 1 | 1 | 2 | 4 | 15 | 12 | 9 |
| 18 | Coprol. super., | 16 | 3 | 1 | 1 | 6 | 6 | 14 | 16 | 7 |
| 24 | ... ... | 14 | 12 | 11 | | ... | | 14 | 12 | 11 |
| A | Farmyard, | 23 | 2 | 3 | 3 | 0 | 0 | 20 | 2 | 3 |
| B | Bone super. and kainit, | 22 | 18 | 2 | 1 | 9 | 0 | 21 | 9 | 2 |

It will be noticed that the two tables agree remarkably well, when we remember that the points from which the calculations start are so widely different.

The deductions to be drawn from these calculations, which have reference solely to the value of the manures as measured by the total amount of starch produced on the acre, are almost self-evident. Phosphates unaided are but of small advantage to a potato crop, as, with one exception, the increase over the unmanured crop is very small, although the amount of starch in each tuber is raised; insoluble phosphates are not productive of good results, but aided by ammonia their value is increased. Bone superphosphates takes precedence of "mineral" superphosphates (with small additional ammonia); ammonia and superphosphates alone are better than when potash is employed, either as kainit or as potashes, not only in gross but also in nett value.

## MANURES AND THEIR APPLICATION.*

### By Dr. A. P. AITKEN, Chemist to the Society.

THERE was a time not so far gone but that many here may remember it when artificial manures were almost unknown, and when the only manure the farm had to rely on was that which was produced on the farm. In some favoured places in the neighbourhood of towns additional supplies were obtainable, but on the great majority of farms the land supplied its own manure. In order to grow grain it was necessary to feed stock, and to the feeding of this stock by far the greater portion of the land was devoted. Crops of grain were grown on one part of the farm by means of the farmyard manure derived from other parts of it. There was no importation of manure, and no addition made to the riches of the soil, but simply a transference of these from one part of the farm to another. On a well-managed farm the parts of the farm supplying the manure and those receiving it were so arranged that periodically every part of the arable farm received in its turn an application of manure derived from the rest. This system of local transference is what still prevails almost everywhere. It constitutes what may be called the *lateral system* of the farm.

But there is another system of transference going on on a farm which may be called the *vertical system*—a transference of the riches of the soil from below upwards. This is accomplished in various ways. The hay, straw, oats, and fodder plants, which go to nourish the stock of the farm, derive their substance not only from the thin layer of soil which comes under the action of the plough but also from greater depths, from the subsoil into which

* A lecture delivered at Berwick to the East Berwickshire Agricultural Association, 5th November 1881.

the roots of plants penetrate and absorb nourishment, which they carry up into their stems and leaves. This part of the riches of the soil having served as food finds its way in whole or in part into the manure heap, and in due time is spread upon the surface of the land. There are other agencies at work which determine this transference from below upwards, some of them due to the work of the farmer and others quite independent of his exertions. Among the former may be mentioned drainage, subsoil cultivation, and others which I shall refer to hereafter; while among the latter are capillary attraction, by which salts in solution are carried up from considerable depths and concentrated upon the superficial soil, and the slow but constant working of the humble earthworm, whose castings, derived often from great depths, have recently been shown by Darwin to be capable of renewing in a few years the entire surface of the soil.

It will be seen that in the lateral and vertical transference of the soil no addition whatever is made to the total amount of wealth it contains. There is a certain amount of nitrogenous matter brought down to the soil from the air by rain, but the mineral matter which forms so important a part of the food of plants receives no increment; on the contrary, it is being continually diminished. All that the farmer puts into or expends upon the soil is his work. He ploughs, harrows, and cultivates his land, and thus increases the amount of the surface of the soil which is exposed to weathering—that is to say, to the solvent and ameliorating action of air, rain, sun, and frost, which hastens the disintegration and decomposition of the soil, and causes its locked up treasures to become more readily suitable for the nourishment of crops. His whole energies are devoted to extracting from the soil as rapidly as possible all its available wealth for the production of corn, beef, mutton, milk, cheese, poultry, eggs, or other saleable products. If the soil were inexhaustible, this kind of farming might go on for ever; but common experience teaches us that there is a limit to the fertility of soils, and that in the case of our long-cropped soils that limit is easily reached. We know that if we go on cropping land continually we shall soon have a crop not worth lifting, and reason tells us that though we adopt ever so many expedients for extending this term of fertility the end must come some time. Forty years ago Liebig brought this fact very forcibly before the attention of farmers, and there was no place where his warnings were better understood and regarded than in this country.

But there are still very many who do not believe this fact, and who maintain that a judicious system of rotation and husbanding of the resources of the farm is quite sufficient to enable agriculture to be carried on, and that progressively. Where a soil is deep and its resources undeveloped, and where, under the ordinary operations of tillage, the weathering of the soil goes on more rapidly than is necessary to supply the demands of agriculture, such an opinion is quite natural, but it may seem strange that it should be entertained by those who are farming the old worn soils of this country. If we consider, however, the great reforms which have taken place in agriculture during the last forty or fifty years, we shall find that while they have all tended to the more rapid and thorough exhaustion of the riches contained in the soil, they have also tended to postpone the time when that exhaustion would become apparent. The most notable of these reforms was the system of "thorough drainage," introduced by Deanston about the year 1835, a system which has had an immense effect upon our agriculture. From small beginnings it rapidly extended, and under the stimulus of the Government loan of 1845 enormous sums of money were expended on deep draining and tile draining, which had then come into use.

The effect of deep draining is to remove the water in the soil to a lower depth, and thus greatly to increase the area into which the atmosphere can gain access, and carry on the process of weathering which renders the soil fit to be the habitation of the roots of plants. By the adoption of thorough draining the crops on the farm were enabled to send their roots down to depths where formerly they had not been able to penetrate, and thence to draw up stores of nourishment which had hitherto been unavailable; just as a coalmaster, finding that the seam of coal he has been working is nearly exhausted, digs deeper and finds a lower stratum of accumulated wealth waiting to be developed. The practical effect of drainage is to greatly increase, perhaps to double the area of crop-producing land, and that as certainly as if it had been doubled in superficial extent. The increase of soil in contact with the roots of crops means an increase in the amount of plant-food carried from below upwards, and this causes an increase in the amount of farmyard manure, by which the upper layer of the soil is enriched at the expense of the lower, and the evil day of exhaustion is pushed a few years further back. But exhaustion still goes on; the land will eventually become barren; the new seam will be worked out just as the old one was. Besides the increase in the amount of arable soil vertically, it was found that thorough drainage enabled the former also to increase the breadth of his arable land, for by its means thin, poor soils, which formerly would not pay the expense of cultivation, were deepened and fitted for bearing remunerative crops. The system proved to be a great immediate gain both to proprietors and farmers in increasing the value of the land and the amount of its produce.

Subsoil cultivation was another important step in the same

direction, and all improvements that have taken place in the implements of cultivation from Small's swing plough to the Darby digger are important as they enable the farmer to render his soil more suitable for the nourishment of crops by hastening the processes of weathering, which makes the riches therein available for rapid assimilation by the plant, or in other words, as they enable the farmer the more rapidly to exhaust the riches of the soil.

None of the improved methods referred to did anything towards increasing the total amount of plant-food contained in the soil; on the contrary, they all went indirectly towards decreasing it. There was, however, one substance which was imported upon the farm in considerable quantity, viz., lime. Lime is a part of the food of plants, and essential to their growth, and in so far as it was applied to soils deficient in that constituent, liming was an important addition to the wealth of the soil. But it was, and still is, customary to apply lime in greater quantity that is necessary for plant-food, and to apply it to soils which are in no way deficient in that material. The application of lime was found, among other things, to cause an increase of the crops, but this increase was not directly due to the lime itself, but to its very complex action in the soil, whereby it assisted weathering, and rendered the plant-food in the soil more readily available.

The old system of farming then meant exhaustion of the land, and though by the introduction of one improvement after another the exhaustion was less apparent, and the farming of Scotland attained to a very high standard of excellence, yet we see that it contained within it the elements of its decay. The time must come, however it might be temporarily retarded by a few great radical improvements, when the land would be no longer able to be cultivated to the same extent, and be capable of raising the same amount of food for the people.

It was therefore a great new era for agriculture when it was found to be practicable to augment the riches of the soil by the application of imported and artificial manures. Shortly before the time of thorough draining, bones began to be experimented with in small quantities, and the results were so beneficial, that their use increased from year to year, so that about 1840 somewhat over 1000 tons were in use. The annual consumption is now over 40,000 tons, giving an average increase of 1000 tons annually. About the same time Peruvian guano began to be imported, and in twenty years the annual consumption rose to 50,000 tons, and though a considerable falling off occurred thereafter, it is once more rapidly rising into favour.

Chemical analysis showed that the powerful fertilising effect of these manures was due to their containing chiefly two substances, phosphates and nitrogenous matter, and it showed also that these were the materials which were being lost to the soil by the exports of the farm, and that it was a due supply of them that was needed to maintain the farm in its fertility and even to increase that fertility if desired.

The demand for artificial manures containing these ingredients increased very rapidly, until now about a million sterling is annually expended by farmers in Scotland in the purchase of bones, guano, superphosphate, nitrogenous and potassic manures.

The effect of this enormous importation of fertilising materials upon the land, has been to entirely change the face of agriculture, and to bring about a revolution whose effects we are only now beginning to feel.

In addition to this importation, there is another one of great magnitude and scarcely less important, viz., the importation of feeding cakes and feeding stuffs of all kinds. Their consumption on the farm adds to the fertility of the soil, as surely and perhaps even more economically and permanently than their equivalent of artificial manure.

I have compared the old method of farming to the working out of a mine, where the riches were in the soil, and only required to be brought out by an expenditure of labour. But in the new method of farming the riches are not in the soil except to an unprofitable amount, and they require to be imported. The soil is now in the position of a workshop furnished with the means of converting the raw material supplied to it in the form of manure into the finished article of corn, beef, mutton, or other produce.

The ready availability of artificial manures, the ease with which they can be applied and the rapidity of their action, enable the farmer, who is not otherwise restricted, to enjoy a freedom of cropping and manipulating of his farm that was quite impossible under the old system. There is no doubt that this has, in many cases, been attended with the happiest results, while in others, although the energy with which the farmer has taken advantage of his freedom may be creditable to his enterprise, the results have frequently been profitable neither to himself nor to his landlord.

I shall just mention a few of these. He has been enabled to extend the amount of his arable land often far beyond the limits indicated by the amount of farmyard manure that can be made on the farm, even with the increased value of that material derived from the consumption of artificial food. The success of this change depends very much on the natural strength of the land and on the climatic conditions to which it is exposed. With a good soil and a fair climate the alteration may be a profitable one, but if the soil be poor and the weather unfavourable there is likely to be a loss rather than a gain. It is one great disadvantage of artificial manures that their success is much dependent on the weather ; during a wet season a considerable proportion of them is carried down through the soil and run off by the drains, while if the season be very dry they are in great measure prevented from coming into operation.

In increasing the proportion of arable land it has also frequently happened that old pastures on hillsides have been broken up which should never have been touched. The steepness of the land and the great wash to which it is subjected during the winter fallow make it very ill suited for cultivation even at the best. There is no doubt that much of the land which has been so treated has during the succession of bad seasons we have just experienced proved a great loss to our farmers on the Border, and it is likely that it will prove still more so in the future, for the vigour of the virgin soil has now been cropped away, and to maintain the land in its fertility will take a large expenditure of manure, and in many cases be more costly than putting it back into pasture.

Another disadvantage attending the use of artificial manures is that it has enabled the farmer to work the land down to a lower state of fertility than was permitted under the old system. The facility with which a crop can be produced on a poor soil by the action of a few hundred-weights of manure does not impose upon the farmer the same necessity for keeping his land in high condition—that is to say, in a condition in which a large reserve of available nourishment is lying stored up in the soil— as was necessary under the old system of farming.

What the average amount of depression in the fertility of the soil amounts to per acre I have not been able to determine, owing to the want of accurate statistics, but that a marked depression does exist there can be no doubt. It must be familiar to many of you that the effects of artificial manure applied in these days is feeble in comparison with what it was forty years ago. This is a sure sign that the land has been reduced in condition.

Again, it is unfortunate that the use of artificial manures has in the minds of many diminished the importance of farmyard manure so much that its manufacture and preservation do not receive the amount of care and attention that they ought to do. Not only so, but it has come to be the fashion in some quarters to regard farmyard manure as an antiquated, barbarous kind of application, and even books are not wanting, enjoying a wide circulation which treat of artificial manures, as if they were the only scientific manures. They formulate and measure out the doses of each particular ingredient for each particular crop with the nicety of an apothecary, as if differences in soils and climate did not exist, while farmyard manure, the king of all manures, is looked upon somewhat as a necessary evil and a nuisance. This is indeed a strange doctrine, and those who run after it will have all the way to run back again. A deeper truth and a truer science teach us that farmyard manure ought to be the one on which most attention should be bestowed, and that artificial manures should be used chiefly as adjuncts and supplements of this great manure. It is in this respect that artificial manures are so beneficial. They can be used to supply the deficiences of farmyard manure, and by their judicious employment they are capable of greatly enhancing the value of a crop, and often by their timely application even rescue it from failure.

While I should be sorry to undervalue the great services rendered to agriculture by artificial manures, where judiciously and economically applied, yet when I consider their costliness, their susceptibility to weather influence, the ease with which they can be misapplied, and the great want of knowledge which prevails regarding their qualities and their proper and precise application, I can see that in relying too much upon their help, farmers are running considerable risk, and that as the use of these manures is becoming more and more extended, it is of the utmost importance that efficient means should be adopted to prevent their being used indiscriminately or wastefully. Of equal, or even greater importance, is the exercise of economy and care in the production and accumulation of farmyard manure.

I would like to say a few words regarding farmyard manure. In the abundance of the discussion which has been going on all around us recently regarding various forms of artificial manures, the claims of farmyard manure have been somewhat overlooked. The great difference between it and artificial manures is its great bulk and the large amount of organic matter it contains. This is frequently cited against it as a disadvantage, but this very bulkiness is a characteristic which contributes largely to its usefulness as an ameliorator of the soil. The effects of short dung upon light soil and of long dung upon heavy soil are to improve greatly the physical character of each, and upon sharp, cold soils the large amount of organic matter imported by a liberal application of farmyard manure, is attended with the greatest benefit. Organic matter, although it has fallen into disregard during these days of phosphate of lime and nitrate of soda, is a very valuable constituent in a soil, and though it is not directly absorbed by the roots of such plants as form our crops, it has nevertheless very important functions to perform in the soil. It forms a soft kindly bed for roots to ramify in, and it is sufficiently retentive of moisture to prevent the crop from suffering much from drought. By its decomposition it yields carbonic acid, which has the power of decomposing various minerals in the soil, and setting free their

U

constituents to serve as food for plants. Our forefathers had great faith in organic matter, and though chemistry has shown that they were wrong in supposing that it formed directly the food of plants, yet their faith in it was not so ill-founded as the supporters of what is called the "mineral theory" so vehemently maintained. There is usually a kernel of truth in all doctrines which for a time have received the assent of thoughtful men, and the more we know of the work going on in the soil the less we are inclined to undervalue the effects of organic matter. It is a constituent predominating in garden soil, and in all fertile soils. Consisting as it does of the decaying remains of a former race of plants, it contains a considerable amount of nitrogenous matter, which is slowly made available as plant food. Recent researches have discovered that it is teeming with minute forms of life, consisting of microscopic germs which have the power of converting the nitrogenous matter it contains into nitric acid, and that it is in the form of nitrates that the roots of plants absorb the nitrogen required to form the albuminoid matter of their tissues.

We must no longer regard the fertile soil as a dead thing, but rather as a world of which every cubic inch is the home of myriads of living organisms busily engaged in converting the decaying remains of a former generation of plants into a form suitable for the nourishment of a new generation. Farmyard manure is the nursery of those minute germs, which may be called the leaven of the soil. The whole heap is swarming with them, and every drop of the brown liquid which flows away from a manure heap contains countless thousands of germs which if allowed to fall upon a soil containing organic matter carry on the great work of nitrification.

Yet how careless we are of this living wealth. Every farmer knows that in leaving manure heaps exposed to the rain in this moist climate he is losing in the constant wash that silently drains away a large proportion of the best part of his manure, and yet how seldom do we find any means used to prevent it. Compared with the great bulk of the heap, that which flows away may seem small, but it is not so small as it seems, for it is the concentrated essence of the manure.

It is difficult to estimate its value, but there are certain data which enable us to form some approximation to it.

Here is a short condensed statement showing at a glance the main results of an elaborate series of analyses of farmyard manure which were carried out by Dr. Vœlcker many years ago.

A well-made manure heap was divided into three parts, one part was made into a heap and left exposed to the weather, another part was covered, and the third part was spread upon the land.

Samples of these three parts were taken and analysed at intervals of six, nine, and twelve months, and the weights of the three parts when fresh and at the intervals stated, are seen in the first table.

| | I. Exposed. | | II. Covered. | | III. Spread. | |
|---|---|---|---|---|---|---|
| | lbs. | loss per cent | lbs. | loss per cent. | lbs. | loss per cent. |
| Fresh (November), . . | 2438 | ... | 3258 | ... | 1652 | ... |
| After 6 Months (April), . | 2026 | 28·8 | 1613 | 50 4 | 1429 | 13·4 |
| „ 9 Months (July), . | 1994 | 29·7 | 1297 | 60·0 | 1012 | 38·7 |
| „ 12 Months (October), | 1974 | 30·8 | 1235 | 62·0 | 950 | 42·4 |

The loss of weight was in each case very considerable, and was most in the case of the heap under cover. An examination of the next table shows that most of the loss was due to the escape of water, but that in heaps I. and III. there was also considerable loss of other important ingredients. Limiting our attention to four constituents of the manure, viz., water, organic matter, nitrogen, and ash, we find that the percentages of these constituents at the various dates were as follows :—

| | | Water. | Organic Matter. | | Nitrogen. | | Ash. |
|---|---|---|---|---|---|---|---|
| | | | Total. | Soluble. | Total. | In the form of Ammonia. | |
| | | per cent. | per cent. | per cent. | per cent. | per cent. | per cent. |
| Original Manure (Fresh) | | 66·17 | 28·24 | 2·48 | ·64 | ·12 | 5·59 |
| I. | After 6 Months, | 65·95 | 23·50 | 4·27 | ·80 | ·09 | 10·55 |
| | „ 9 „ | 75·49 | 15·15 | 2·05 | ·60 | ·05 | 9·36 |
| | „ 12 „ | 74·29 | 13·63 | 2·74 | ·65 | ·05 | 12·08 |
| II. | After 6 Months, | 56·89 | 30·06 | 4·63 | 1·19 | ·07 | 13·05 |
| | „ 9 „ | 43·43 | 30·14 | 4·13 | 1·27 | ·12 | 26·43 |
| | „ 12 „ | 41·60 | 33·06 | 5·87 | 1·51 | ·17 | 25·28 |
| III. | After 6 Months, | 80·02 | 12·62 | 1·16 | ·53 | ·05 | 7·36 |
| | „ 9 „ | 70·09 | 11·05 | ·49 | ·41 | ·06 | 18·86 |
| | „ 12 „ | 65·56 | 10·36 | ·42 | ·39 | 03 | 24·08 |

We see from the first column that the proportion of water contained in heap II., which was under cover, gradually diminished, and that there was a corresponding increase in the proportion of organic matter, and especially of nitrogenous matter, and more especially in the soluble part of these ingredients; the manure not only became more concentrated but it also became more matured, more capable of acting immediately as plant food. Heap I. deteriorated from the beginning but especially after six months, and at the end of nine months about half of its valuable ingredients had disappeared; they had gone to enrich the soil immediately around the heap. Heap III. lost quality to a still greater extent, but its valuable constituents went to enrich the whole soil over which it was spread.

These heaps were small, and the loss which occurred was proportionally great, but even in the case of large manure heaps exposed to the weather, the loss sustained is very considerable.

The above analyses and many others show that ordinary farmyard manure contains nitrogen equal to nearly 1 per cent. of ammonia, and that at least a quarter of this is soluble and easily washed away. Experiments in this country and elsewhere have also shown that in about six months the half of the soluble ingredients may be washed away. In a heap of 1000 tons there may be therefore a loss of more than a ton of ammonia, whose value is nearly £100. But analysis of the wash shows that a large amount of phosphoric acid and potash is also being lost which may represent somewhere between £50 and £100. In a large and well-compacted manure heap the loss may not be so great as I have indicated, but it seems highly probable that the ordinary loss is not less than £10 for every hundred tons or £1 for every 10 tons of manure. Surely some sort of covering, even sheds of a portable kind, could be made at little expense to prevent this great waste.

We hear of means being adopted to fix the ingredients of manure heaps, but no means are of any avail unless the manure is under cover. With the manure under cover it is possible to prevent almost all waste. Many experiments have been made to discover the best means of preserving the valuable constituents of a manure heap.

Here is a very interesting experiment made by Prof. Wolff of Hohenheim, to whose valuable researches agriculture is so greatly indebted. Operating with small quantities he divided a well-made sample of manure into five parts, one was exposed and four were covered, and to three of the covered portions he added charcoal, gypsum, and slaked lime respectively, and the table shows the percentages of ingredients remaining after the experiment had gone on for fifteen months.

| | Exposed. | Covered. | | | |
|---|---|---|---|---|---|
| | Nothing added. | Nothing added. | Charcoal added. | Gypsum added. | Lime added. |
| | per cent. | per cent. | per cent. | per cent. | per cent. |
| Moist dung, . | 46·9 | 18·8 | 45·2 | 47·6 | 41·1 |
| Dry substance, . | 34·2 | 42·0 | 42·7 | — | — |
| Organic matter, . | 25·2 | 33·8 | 34·8 | 40·0 | 44·0 |
| Nitrogen, . . | 44·1 | 67·6 | 71·0 | 77·5 | 92·5 |
| Water, . . | 52·1 | 51·3 | 45·1 | 46·2 | 33·9 |

Here again we see from a comparison of the first two columns how great is the advantage derived from merely covering the manure. The increased proportion of organic matter and nitrogen in the other three columns shows that all the substances added had the effect of preserving the manure. The amount of charcoal added was about one quarter per cent., of gypsum a little more, and of lime about a half per cent. Gypsum is seen to have a very marked effect in preserving the manure, and there are many other experiments that might be noticed confirming the very beneficial action of this substance as a fixer of the valuable ingredients of a manure heap; but what is most remarkable in this experiment is the unexpected result, that the best preservative is a small dose of lime. The amount of lime thus added must be very small, not more than one ton to two hundred of manure, and it must be added when the manure is fresh, and layered into the heap during its manufacture. To add lime to a rotten manure heap would cause a great loss of ammonia from the decomposition of the ammonia salts which have been formed during the rotting of the heap, but in fresh dung there are no ammonia salts, and thus the addition of lime occasions no loss, but, on the contrary, preserves the nitrogen of the manure. The rotting of the heap goes on, but not quite so rapidly as if no lime had been applied. In the ordinary rotting of a manure heap, a large amount of carbonate of ammonia is formed, and it is that which smells so pungently when a heap is being turned over, but in this case ammonia salts are not found in the heap; the nitrogen is converted largely into nitric acid, and this is found in combination with the lime. This formation of nitric acid is no doubt due to the busy work of the germs I have already alluded to as occurring in fertile soil, and we thus see that by this method of treating manure, the changes which go on in the soil have been anticipated in the manure heap. There is much yet to be learned regarding the preservation of manure, but until we abandon the wasteful method of exposure at present in use nothing that we can learn can be of much use.

Among the mineral substances applied to the soil, lime is the one which has been longest in use, and has been applied most abundantly. I have already referred to it when speaking of exhaustion, and have stated that it promotes the exhaustion of the soil by liberating potash from its compounds in the soil, and otherwise enabling the roots of plants to find their food more easily. I have said that the action of lime in the soil is a very complex one. It affects the soil both physically and chemically, but to enter into detail on this subject would take me far beyond the limits of this paper. I will content myself with mentioning one or two of its functions which are perhaps not so commonly known.

The effect of lime on the mechanical condition of clay land is very remarkable. It has been shown by Schlœsing that lime tends to coagulate clay soil into fine particles, rendering it easily permeable by water. If some clay soil is put in a funnel and water allowed to flow steadily through it, it will drop through bright and clear for some time, but by and by the drops become muddy and continue so until the clay is all washed away or the funnel is choked up with mud which refuses to let the water flow. If while the muddy drops are falling a little lime is sprinkled on the surface of the soil the drops soon begin to fall clear again and continue to do so until the lime is again washed out, when the clay will once more flow away rendering the water drops muddy. This is a little experiment which any one can try for himself, and it conveys a great amount of information. When rain falls continuously on clay land it soon ceases to be absorbed; if the land is flat it becomes covered with muddy pools, but if it is steep the water runs down in streams, carrying the finely divided soil along with it. What has occurred here is exactly what occurred in the experiment referred to. The excess of rain has washed away the lime and other salts from the superficial layer of the soil, and its porous granular condition has been changed into a muddy one, and long after the rain has ceased, this muddy condition remains until, by capillary attraction, lime salts come up from below and cause the mud to cohere into fine granular masses, through which water can once more drain away freely. Other salts also possess this character to some extent, but none to so great an extent as lime.

Lime is a strong base and has a powerful affinity for acids. In the soil are to be found various acids with which it may unite, and notably carbonic acid. Carbonic acid is always being formed during the decay of organic matter, and anything which takes away carbonic acid hastens that decay. Whenever any chemical action is going on, if the products which are being formed are not taken away, the action very soon ceases, but as soon as the products are taken away, the action goes on again. Hence it is that lime, by taking away carbonic acid, hastens the progress of decay, and lime is, therefore, an excellent thing to apply to old fogged-up pastures and moory or peaty land overcharged with organic matter.

But there are other acids produced in the soil. I have already told you that there are myriads of germs in the soil converting the nitrogen of organic matter into nitric acid. Lime seizes hold of the nitric acid thus formed, converting it into nitrate of lime, and thus clears the way for the production of more nitric acid, and still further hastens the process of decay. Not only so, but when nitrate of soda is added to a soil containing lime salts, a chemical action takes place between these, and nitrate of lime is formed. Nitrate of lime is a very soluble salt, and during wet weather it soon finds its way down through the soil and subsoil and escapes into the drains. That is the reason why nitrate of soda is so transitory in its effect.

It is unfortunate that one of the results of liming should be to hasten the loss of nitric acid, and it is important that we should endeavour to diminish that waste as much as possible. The only way to catch the nitrate in its downward progress is by means of the roots of plants which absorb it into their tissues. It is therefore very beneficial, as Dr. Lawes pointed out some time ago, to have the ground covered with vegetation. Any kind of green growth is better than bare soil, and thus it is that summer fallowing is necessarily a wasteful practice, which is happily going fast out of fashion.

The thicker the vegetation and the more closely the roots of a crop possess the ground, the less chance is there of a loss of nitrate. There is no crop which is thicker than a grass crop, and you are all familiar with the fact that of all crops on the farm there is none so "grateful" (to use a common expression) for the application of nitrate of soda as a grass crop.

This, I think, will also explain the unexpected result obtained by Dr. Voelcker in his recent experiments with farmyard manure, that it is more economical and therefore more advantageous to apply farmyard manure to the grass crop than to the root crop as is the usual custom.

It may be asked why, when lime is apt to carry away the most valuable constituent of the soil, its employment is still recommended. That has been partly answered already, but there are other reasons, one of which is that there are other acids in the soil, whose presence is not so desirable as nitric acid, such as muriatic acid and sulphuric acid, not to mention several organic acids. In a very instructive paper recently published by Professor Mayer, he has given the results of some experiments with kainit and other salts, consisting mostly of sulphate and muriate of potash, carried out with the view of discovering the cause of the frequent failure of these forms of manure. His experiments led him to the conclusion that their potash was more rapidly taken up by the roots of plants than the sulphuric and muriatic acids with which it was combined, and thus an excess of these acids was left in the soil and the land became soured. He found that when he used lime along with kainit and allied salts, their action instead of being injurious was very beneficial. Recent experiments show that these potash salts do best in soils well supplied with lime, and that they ought to be applied in the autumn and not in the spring, so that the lime may have time during the winter to enter into combination with the sulphuric and muriatic acids they contain, and carry them down out of the reach of the roots of the crops. Lime takes some time to exert its influence upon the soil, and, therefore, the benefits of liming are not usually felt until the first or second year after its application. It is, therefore, strongly to be recommended not to apply lime immediately to the crop which it is intended to benefit, but to put it on the land one or two years previously.

As regards the mode of liming, it is questionable whether we are right in the practice which prevails of putting on the land large doses at rare intervals. There are, no doubt, occasions when a large dose is necessary, but with land in ordinarily good condition I incline to think that the method of liming gently year after year would accomplish its object more economically and without the great tear and wear and subsequent loss of a heavy liming.

It is a frequent matter of complaint that lime finds its way so rapidly out of the soil, and this is in some measure due to the extravagant method of heavy liming at rare intervals. I have already explained that it is necessary that lime should find its way into the drains if it is to perform some of its most important functions, but it is also desirable that lime should be present in the soil in the place where it is most wanted, and this, I think, will be best attained by applying at least some portion of the lime frequently in small doses.

Frequent application in small doses is also strongly to be recommended for nitrate of soda. Owing to its own great solubility and to the rapidity with which it is decomposed by lime and carried down through the soil, it frequently happens that a heavy flood carries away a large part of that valuable and very expensive manure, and therefore to sink it by drilling it in with other manures is a mistake. It should be used lightly and superficially as a top-dressing. It is most beneficially applied to the braird, and as I have already indicated, the deeper and wider the roots of the crop have ramified, the less chance is there of the nitrate escaping them and running into the drains. Sulphate of ammonia does not escape so rapidly. It is retained by the soil until it is converted into nitrate, and then it flows down easily through the soil and subsoil.

Nitrate of soda, apart from its manurial properties, has, like lime, a very beneficial action upon the physical condition of the soil and subsoil, tending to open it up and make it more porous.

There is a very common belief that nitrate of soda is not, properly speaking, a manure ; some call it a *stimulant*, and consider that its function is simply to exhaust the land—a kind of purge which does not itself contribute to the making of a crop. This is a very inaccurate view to take of the action of nitrate of soda. I have already explained that all nitrogenous matter in the soil is being converted into nitrate, and in [this form it is taken up by roots. In manuring with nitrate of soda we simply give to the soil nitrogenous plant-food ready made and in larger quantity than can be supplied by the soil itself during the time in which it is wanted. If the addition of this nitrogenous food causes a large increase in the crop, that is a sign that there is a want of nitrogenous matter in the soil, or that what is there is not being rapidly enough decomposed. Thus when a soil is rich in phosphate and other mineral plant food, but the plant is unable to make use of these for the want of nitrogen, the mere addition of nitrate by presenting the plant with the nitrogenous food it requires enables it to take out of the soil all the other constituents it requires for its growth. It is said that nitrate of soda has been applied to some soils until they have been reduced to poverty. That is no doubt a misfortune for the land, but it is not because of the addition of nitrate that the land has suffered, it is because phosphates and perhaps potash and other manurial matters were not added in due proportion. If a man becomes reduced to a state of bodily poverty from eating nothing but potatoes, it is not the potatoes that are to blame ; they have done their best ; it is the want of the concomitant roast beef or other nourishing food.

Coming now in this very cursory sketch to the various forms of phosphatic manure, whose employment in ever increasing quantity has during these latter years done so much to alter the whole conditions of agriculture, I will endeavour to be very brief. The form of phosphatic manure which first was tried in this country was bones—and that was just about half a century ago. They rapidly rose into favour, and have never lost the good opinion that was formed of them. The old method of using them has happily fallen into disuse. It was customary for a good many years to use half-inch bones, which meant fragments of bone in size from two inches downwards. I have seen some of these which had been sown about fifteen years before, turned up by the plough in a state of very good preservation    No tenant-farmer in using half-inch or coarsely crushed bones need hope to reap the benefit of the application during the term of his lease.

Bones are valuable on account of the phosphate and also of the ammonia they contain.   Good bones contain about 50 per cent. of phosphate of lime, and 4½ per cent. of ammonia, and should be used in the form of bone meal *ground down to as fine a powder as possible*.   The expense of extra grinding is far more than compensated by the greater certainty and rapidity with which the manure comes into operation.

There are two ways of reducing bones to a state of extreme fineness; the one is by laborious grinding, and the other is by dissolving them with sulphuric acid.  Bones, in their natural state, can be only partially dissolved with sulphuric acid, so as to obtain a manure which is dry enough to be spread upon the land, and though manure manufacturers have acquired great skill in the dissolving of bones so as to be able to produce a sample of genuine dissolved bones containing a much higher percentage of soluble phosphate than was formerly able to be obtained, there is no doubt that a large proportion of what is sold as dissolved bones, containing a high average of soluble phosphate, is really a mixture of bone phosphate with some other phosphate of mineral origin.   There is no form of manure so easily sophisticated as dissolved bones, and it is often impossible to tell by analysis or otherwise whether what is called dissolved bones, is dissolved bones, or whether it is in part a dexterous imitation.   There is an old prejudice in favour of dissolved bones, rather than any other dissolved phosphate; and as a high percentage of soluble phosphate is usually demanded, manufacturers have been forced into the production of a superphosphate, consisting more or less of bone, and have sold it under the name of dissolved bones, in order to satisfy this popular predilection.

The difference between dissolved bones and other kinds of dissolved phosphate, is that the former contains or ought to contain from two or three per cent. of ammonia, while superphosphates usually contain none at all.   It is, therefore, quite unfair to compare the manurial effect of equal weights or of equal values of these two forms of manures.   Where both phosphates and ammonia are required to enrich the soil, no amount of phosphates will ever compensate for the want of ammonia; and it is an entire fallacy to suppose that the fine grinding, or dissolving, or any other treatment whatever, of a phosphate, is equivalent to the addition of a certain quantity of ammonia.   My own experience, and the experience of all unbiassed experimenters with whose work I am acquainted, show clearly that there is no special virtue in dissolved bones, but that the same, or even better results, can be obtained by the use of superphosphate and sulphate of ammonia mixed in proportions to imitate the composition of dissolved bones.

Considering the enormous quantity of mineral phosphates which are now available for the manufacture of superphosphate, I am strongly of opinion that it is a mistake to dissolve bones, and that they are put to a much better use by applying them in their natural state in as finely ground a condition as they can possibly be got. The germ life in the soil, and in the bone, will very rapidly convert the whole into a form available for the nourishment of plants, but to dissolve bones in sulphuric acid is to kill out the germ life within it, and retard the delay of any nucleus of bone it may contain. The fashion of vitriolating bones is in my opinion open to the same, or to still greater objection, for not only is the germ life in the bone destroyed, but after the superficial layer of dissolved bone is removed, there remains a kernel of bone which will remain undecomposed in the soil for a very long time.

Regarding mineral phosphates, considerable discussion has taken place of late as to whether it is better to dissolve them into superphosphate, or to use them in their natural state, but ground down to an impalpable powder. It is an interesting question, and one that may easily be discussed impartially and without acrimony.

From all that I have been able to learn either by experience or by reading, I am forced to the conclusion that when equal quantities of phosphate of lime are used in the dissolved and in the undissolved state, the advantage is clearly in favour of the former in four directions—firstly, in the certainty of its action; secondly, in the rapidity of its action; thirdly, in the amount of crop it is able to produce; and fourthly, in the earliness of the maturing of the crop. These are four weighty considerations, and in this uncertain climate the last is perhaps the weightiest of all. But there are other circumstances to be taken into account; there is a certain amount of expense involved in the dissolving of a phosphate—there is the work of dissolving it and the cost of the sulphuric acid employed; and shilling for shilling it may be found that to use the undissolved phosphate is the cheaper in the end. Moreover, I have seen experiments conducted with great care in Forfarshire, where the crops produced were markedly in favour of the undissolved phosphate, apart altogether from the cost; and I am forced to the conclusion that this is not a question to be decided *ex cathedra*, or by any one man operating on any one soil, but that each district must determine for itself what is the most appropriate and economical form of phosphate to employ. In a country like ours, with such a wide range of soil and climate, it is the duty of every district to determine for itself what are the best forms to employ, not only of phosphate, but of all other kinds of manures—how to employ them, when to employ them, and in what amount, so as to secure the most reliable, economical, and excellent return for the large amount of money which is annually expended by our farmers in the purchase of artificial manures.

The experiments which are at present being conducted in Scotland show very various results, making it evident that nothing but local experiments, and these more and more localised in each particular district, will ever give farmers that certainty of information which they require in order to prevent their spending their money for that which is not bread and their labour for that which satisfieth not, for if ever that may be said with truth of anything, it may be said regarding the misapplication of valuable artificial manures.

Among the many causes to which the present unfortunate depression in agriculture is to be ascribed, I think a prominent place should be given to the large amount of money indiscriminately invested in artificial manures and feeding stuffs, much of which has been misapplied. That our soils have been brought down to a low condition, requiring the aid of fertilising materials borrowed from the soils of other lands, constitutes a severe strain upon our agriculture, and brings us face to face with a condition of affairs which has had no precedent in our history. It is, therefore, of the utmost importance that this great new expenditure in the purchase of fertilising and feeding materials should be wisely directed, and I appeal to you who are members of this Association to set an example to all other agricultural associations in Scotland by choosing from among your number one or two who have the ability and inclination for the work, to begin a few experiments upon your own soils in order to determine for yourselves what are the directions in which the money you annually expend upon manures and feeding stuffs can be most economically invested. Put to yourselves the question, What is the cheapest method by which I can now grow a bushel of wheat, barley, or oats, and produce a pound of beef or mutton? and do not rest until you have answered it. If that question were taken up by every agricultural association in Scotland, and worked out with scientific accuracy, there would be an advance in the agriculture of Scotland such as it has never yet known.

## EXPERIMENTAL STATIONS.—REPORT FOR 1881.

### By Dr. A. P. AITKEN, Chemist to the Society.

### EXPERIMENTS AT HARELAW AND PUMPHERSTON.

THE crop on the experimental stations during the past season was oats. The manures described on pages 329 and 330 were applied to both stations under the most favourable conditions, and no accident of any kind occurred to interfere with the success of the experiments. The season throughout was cold, wet, and sunless, and was one which will long be remembered by farmers as the gloomiest of the cycle of disastrous seasons which have had so depressing an effect upon our agriculture. The inclemency of the weather told most severely upon white crops, and upon no crop more than upon oats. The harvesting was not begun till far on in November, and successive showers of rain while the crops were in the stook made it late before the whole was securely stacked. In the following tables are contained the statistics of the crops at both stations.

Despite the unpropitious character of the season, the crop obtained at Harelaw was a very heavy one. As much as ten quarters per acre was obtained on several of the plots, and two even exceeded that amount. Three crops had been removed from the field without any application of manure, in order to reduce its fertility, and while there was noticed a considerable falling off, yet there is still a large amount of unexhausted wealth lying in the soil. For experimental purposes it is desirable to operate upon a soil in low condition, in order that it may respond more readily and decidedly to the manurial treatment it receives. We have to consider, however, that the object of our experiments is a practical one, and is meant to convey information regarding the relative value of various forms of manures when applied to soils in ordinary cultivation, whether rich or poor, and on that account it is rather an advantage than otherwise that we have in our two stations subjects differing so widely in their fertility and general character.

It is satisfactory to find that although the average crop here is high there are yet considerable differences in the produce of the various plots, so that the high condition of the soil does not seem to interfere with its utility as a subject for experiments. If we direct our attention in the first place to the table of results obtained at Pumpherston, we find that the figures show a great range of difference. As years go on the characters of the various plots become more and more marked, and we are enabled now to trust with confidence to the information conveyed by the various plots, as they year after year report the same story in language ever more emphatic.

## Oat Crop, 1881—Harelaw.

| | No. of Plot. | Bushels per acre | Weight per bushel. | Heavy grain per acre. | Light grain per acre. | Total grain per acre. | Straw per acre. |
|---|---|---|---|---|---|---|---|
| | | | lbs. | lbs. | lbs. | lbs. | cwts. |
| Phosphates | 1 | 58¾ | 41½ | 2438 | 326 | 2764 | 37 |
| | 2 | 80 | 44 | 3520 | 156 | 3676 | 36 |
| | 3 | 55½ | 40¾ | 2257 | 300 | 2551 | 38 |
| | 4 | 80 | 44 | 3520 | 144 | 3664 | 36 |
| | 5 | 74¾ | 43¾ | 3270 | 168 | 3438 | 36 |
| | 6 | 80 | 44¼ | 3540 | 112 | 3652 | 34 |
| | 7 | 72 | 44¼ | 3186 | 180 | 3366 | 37 |
| | 8 | 71¼ | 43¾ | 3120 | 128 | 3248 | 37 |
| | 9 | 73½ | 44 | 3234 | 224 | 3458 | 36 |
| | 10 | 80 | 44 | 3520 | 188 | 3708 | 36 |
| | 11 | 78½ | 40 | 3140 | 184 | 3324 | 34 |
| | 12 | 59 | 44 | 2596 | 156 | 2752 | 24 |
| Nitrogen. | 13 | 83¾ | 43¼ | 3622 | 208 | 3830 | 35 |
| | 14 | 74 | 44 | 3256 | 184 | 3440 | 30 |
| | 15 | 80½ | 44½ | 3582 | 160 | 3742 | 32 |
| | 16 | 67½ | 44¾ | 3020 | 180 | 3200 | 28 |
| | 17 | 54 | 44¾ | 2416 | 156 | 2572 | 24 |
| | 18 | 64½ | 42¾ | 2757 | 344 | 3101 | 36 |
| Potash | 19 | 78 | 44½ | 3472 | 252 | 3724 | 30 |
| | 20 | 76¾ | 45 | 3453 | 196 | 3649 | 32 |
| | 21 | 68½ | 42¼ | 2928 | 260 | 3188 | 32 |
| | 22 | 57 | 45 | 2565 | 104 | 2669 | 24 |
| Guanos | 23 | 71¼ | 45 | 3206 | 160 | 3366 | 28 |
| | 24 | 75½ | 44¾ | 3378 | 180 | 3558 | 30 |
| | 25 | 74½ | 44¼ | 3296 | 148 | 3444 | 32 |
| Unmanured | 26 | 54 | 44½ | 2403 | 152 | 2555 | 22 |
| | 27 | 52 | 45 | 2340 | 134 | 2474 | 22 |
| Superphosphates | 28 | 75¼ | 44¼ | 3352 | 174 | 3526 | 30 |
| | 29 | 75¼ | 44¼ | 3352 | 196 | 3548 | 32 |
| | 30 | 63 | 43 | 2709 | 220 | 2920 | 32 |
| | 31 a, b | 80 | 43½ | 3480 | 172 | 3652 | 34 |
| | 32 a, b | 80 | 43 | 3440 | 216 | 3650 | 36 |
| | 33 a, b | 77 | 44 | 3388 | 168 | 3556 | 32 |
| | 34 a, b | 80½ | 43½ | 3502 | 184 | 3686 | 32 |
| | 35 a, b | 69 | 44¼ | 3053 | 140 | 3193 | 28 |
| | 38 a, b | 71 | 43½ | 3088 | 204 | 3282 | 32 |

Plot 27, which has remained unmanured (see scheme of experiments, p. 330), has produced the smallest crop on the station, viz., 13¾ bushels of oats per acre. Next to it is plot 22, which has been regularly manured with potash salts alone. The result is that it has produced only one bushel more per acre, showing us plainly that potash is not the ingredient that is most wanting in that soil. Next above that is plot 12, whose annual allowance is bone ash alone. It has produced only three bushels per acre more than the unmanured plot, although enough of phosphate was applied to supply the wants of a crop of oats of 60 bushels per acre; that is to say, only one-twentieth of the phosphate has been used by the crop, and nineteen-twentieths remain unappropriated in the soil. It is evident from the crops obtained on these plots that to use potash salts alone or phosphates alone on Pumpherston is to bury money, much of which may never be found again. Even when we apply the two together, as shown on plot 17, the crop is a failure, only 18½ bushels per acre, or scarcely five bushels more than the unmanured plot. How different is the result obtained by the application of nitrogen. Plot 18 has all along received only nitrate of soda, and the crop this year is about 34 bushels, and a very large proportion of straw, viz., 24 cwts., showing that there is in the soil a considerable reserve of phosphates and potash salts, but for the want of nitrogen the plant is unable to make use of them. The amount of nitrogen applied to plot 18 (in common with all the other plots which received nitrogen) is 40 lbs. per acre, and that is just about the quantity of nitrogen contained in 34 bushels of oats and 24 cwts. of straw.

When to this nitrogenous manure there are added phosphates, as in plot 21, there is a very slight increase in the amount of grain, although there is not so much straw. When to the nitrogenous manure there is added potash, as in plot 11, the increase of grain is very considerable, but there is no increase in the amount of straw. Lastly, when all these are combined, and a well-balanced manure containing nitrogen, potash, and phosphates is applied, the best results are obtained both in the quantity of grain and of straw.

An instructive plot is No. 26, which formerly had applied to it a mixed manure which was a kind of imitation guano, and its produce compared not unfavourably with other guano plots. For two years the manure has been discontinued, and the result is that this year it has yielded less than half a crop, thus showing that the soil of this station is in poor condition and dependent for its fertility upon the immediate application of manures.

If we compare these results with those obtained at Harelaw station we find very similar indications, only that as the latter has practically been manured for the first time, the differences are not quite so marked. The two unmanured plots, 26 and 27, and plot 17 which received no nitrogen are the lowest. Plot 22, which received potash salts alone, is very little better and plot 12, which received undissolved phosphate alone in the form of bone-ash, has produced a very poor crop. In plot 18, the immediate effect of a nitrogenous manure in increasing the produce of grain, and especially the produce of straw, is again noticed; and plots 21 and 11 bear corresponding testimony to the advantage obtained by adding phosphates and potash respectively to the nitrogenous manure, while the largest crops on the station are borne by plots all of which received an equal application of nitrogen, phosphoric acid, and potash, as described on the scheme already referred to.

Plots 1 and 3 have this year borne smaller crops than others of the same class at both stations, but especially at Harelaw where they have been less productive than some of the plots which received incomplete manures. Thus far we see that a very similar story is told by corresponding plots on these two very different stations, the one with a one-year old, and the other with a four-year old experiment.

The results obtained upon the first ten plots, which are designed to test the relative value of soluble and insoluble phosphates, show very markedly the great inferiority of the latter form of phosphate on these soils. A considerable number of experiments have been carried out during the last few years to determine whether soluble or insoluble phosphates are the more economical form of manure, and the results obtained have been various. In Aberdeenshire and also in other parts of the country it has been found that finely ground insoluble phosphates may be employed with advantage, while in others they have been found to be comparatively useless. The results hitherto obtained at the Society's stations lie somewhere between these extremes. The following are the results obtained at both stations with the oat crop this year:—

UNDISSOLVED PHOSPHATES (PUMPHERSTON).

| Plot | Kind of phosphate. | Bushels per acre. | Weight per bushel. | Heavy grain per acre. | Light grain per acre. | Total grain per acre. | Straw per acre. |
|---|---|---|---|---|---|---|---|
| | | | lbs. | lbs. | lbs. | lbs. | cwts. |
| 1 | Bone ash . . . | 32 | 42¼ | 1368 | 148 | 1516 | 29 |
| 3 | Ground coprolites . | 31½ | 41¼ | 1298 | 92 | 1390 | 27 |
| 5 | Bone meal . . | 34 | 43¾ | 1479 | 92 | 1571 | 23 |
| 7 | Phosphatic guano . | 39 | 43¼ | 1686 | 136 | 1823 | 27 |
| 9 | Ground mineral phosphates . . . | 34½ | 43¼ | 1492 | 208 | 1700 | 24 |
| | Average . . | 34·2 | 42·8 | 1465 | 135 | 1600 | 26 |

DISSOLVED PHOSPHATES.

| Plot | Kind of phosphate. | Bushels per acre. | Weight per bushel. | Heavy grain per acre. | Light grain per acre. | Total grain per acre. | Straw per acre. |
|---|---|---|---|---|---|---|---|
| | | | lbs. | lbs. | lbs. | lbs. | cwts. |
| 2 | Bone ash . . | 38 | 41½ | 1681 | 252 | 1933 | 30 |
| 4 | Ground coprolites . | 40½ | 44 | 1774 | 280 | 2054 | 30 |
| 6 | Bone meal . . | 47¼ | 42 | 2005 | 128 | 2133 | 29 |
| 8 | Phosphatic guano . | 45¼ | 43¾ | 1980 | 156 | 2136 | 30 |
| 10 | Ground mineral phosphates . . | 42 | 44¼ | 1858 | 260 | 2118 | 28 |
| | Average . . | 42¾ | 43·7 | 1859 | 217 | 2075 | 29½ |

UNDISSOLVED PHOSPHATES (HARELAW).

| | | | lbs. | lbs. | lbs. | lbs. | cwts. |
|---|---|---|---|---|---|---|---|
| 1 | Bone ash . . | 58¾ | 41½ | 2438 | 326 | 2764 | 37 |
| 3 | Ground coprolites . | 55½ | 40¾ | 2257 | 300 | 2551 | 38 |
| 5 | Bone meal . . | 74¼ | 43¾ | 3270 | 168 | 3438 | 36 |
| 7 | Phosphatic guano . | 72 | 44¼ | 3186 | 180 | 3360 | 37 |
| 9 | Ground mineral phosphates . . | 73½ | 44 | 3234 | 224 | 3458 | 36 |
| | Average . . | 66¾ | 42¾ | 2877 | 239·6 | 3115 | 36 |

DISSOLVED PHOSPHATES.

| | | | lbs. | lbs. | lbs. | lbs. | cwts. |
|---|---|---|---|---|---|---|---|
| 2 | Bone ash . . | 80 | 44 | 3520 | 156 | 3676 | 36 |
| 4 | Ground coprolites . | 80 | 44 | 3520 | 144 | 3664 | 36 |
| 6 | Bone meal . . | 80 | 44½ | 3540 | 112 | 3652 | 34 |
| 8 | Phosphatic guano . | 71½ | 43¾ | 3120 | 128 | 3248 | 37 |
| 10 | Ground mineral phosphates . . | 80 | 44 | 3520 | 188 | 3708 | 36 |
| | Average . . | 78¼ | 44 | 3444 | 145·6 | 3589 | 36 |

If we examine the figures in these six columns, and compare
the produce of the plots with undissolved and with dissolved
phosphates, we see very well marked differences. The dissolving
of the phosphates has increased the bulk of grain at Pumpherston about 8¼ bushels per acre, which is an increase of nearly 25
per cent., and at Harelaw 11½ bushels per acre, which is an
increase of 17 per cent. The quality of the grain, as seen by
the weight per bushel, has also been improved by the dissolving
of the phosphates. At Pumpherston the bushel is increased in

weight by nearly 1 lb., and at Harelaw by 1¼ lb. In consequence of this two-fold superiority, there is an increase in the
weight of heavy grain at Pumpherston of 3½ cwt. per acre, and
at Harelaw of 5 cwts. per acre, which is an increase of 27 per
cent. and 19½ per cent. respectively. So far the results obtained
at the two stations corroborate each other; but when we examine
the figures of the fourth column, indicating the amount of light
grain produced by the use of soluble and insoluble phosphates, we
find that the results are entirely at variance with each other. At
Pumpherston the effect of dissolving the phosphates has been
extraordinarily to increase the yield of light grain, while at Harelaw the effect has been still more extraordinarily to decrease it.
Conflicting as these results are, they admit of a very satisfactory
explanation if we consider the great differences of soil and
climate at the two stations, and also the very exceptional
character of the summer of 1881. At Pumpherston we have a
thin exhausted and retentive soil, a high exposed situation, and
a comparatively wet and cold climate. In such circumstances
we must expect that the proportion of light grain, that is to say,
of ill-nourished and unripened grain, will be very considerable
even at the best; but when we consider further the cold, moist,
sunless character of the past summer, we can quite understand
that the application of a manure which increases the amount of
the crop will more especially increase the amount of unripened
grain. Moist weather during the growing season increases the
amount of straw, and in a less degree the amount of grain; but
warm dry weather is wanted during the latter part of the summer to check this growth, and accelerate the ripening process.
But the prevalence of wet dull weather during July and August
greatly protracted the growing season and interfered with the
ripening of the grain. On the other hand, at Harelaw, with a
fine porous and fertile soil and a warm dry climate, the application of manure did not produce so marked an increase in the
bulk of the crop, and the use of soluble phosphates in this early
district was favourable to the large crop produced there in
accelerating the time of ripening, and thus enabling a larger proportion of grain to be ripened than was possible on the plots to
which the slower-working undissolved phosphates were applied.
A very instructive lesson is thus conveyed by the disproportionate
amount of light grain produced at those two stations, for it shows
us very forcibly how much the effects of manuring are dependent
on the conditions of soil, climate, and season, and how cautious
one should be in drawing conclusions derived from experiments
conducted in one particular place at one particular time, and it
also shows us how necessary it is for the farmers of each district to study for themselves the special kind of manurial treatment most suited to the conditions of their soil and climate. The

total amount of grain produced on these two stations is considerably modified by the unequal proportion of light grain, so that the total increase of grain per acre is reduced at Harelaw to 15 per cent., while at Pumpherston it is increased to about 30 per cent.

Lastly, if we regard the amount of straw produced by the application of these two forms of phosphate, we again see results which are dissimilar, though to a less extent. At Pumpherston the dissolving of the phosphates caused an increase of 3 cwt. per acre of straw, but at Harelaw it produced 1 cwt. per acre less.

The soil and climatic conditions of Pumpherston are more favourable to the production of straw than of grain; and we find that the proportion of straw to grain at that station is greater than at Harelaw. Roughly speaking, the proportion of straw to grain at Pumpherston is about 10 to 6, while at Harelaw it is about 10 to 8. The proportion of straw to grain, while it is thus shown to be much under the influence of soil and climate, is also powerfully affected by manuring, and the phosphate plots form a good illustration of this.

PROPORTION OF STRAW TO GRAIN.

| | | For 1 cwt. of Straw there was produced of Grain— | | | |
|---|---|---|---|---|---|
| | | At Pumpherston. | | At Harelaw. | |
| | | Undissolved. | Dissolved. | Undissolved. | Dissolved |
| | | lbs. | lbs. | lbs. | lbs. |
| 1 and 2. | Bone ash | 52·3 | 64·5 | 74·7 | 102·1 |
| 3 and 4. | Coprolites | 51·5 | 68·5 | 67·1 | 101·8 |
| 5 and 6. | Bone meal | 68·3 | 73·5 | 95·5 | 107·4 |
| 7 and 8 | Phosphatic guano | 67·5 | 71·2 | 91 | 87·8 |
| 9 and 10. | Mineral phosphates | 70·8 | 75·7 | 96 | 103· |
| | Average, | 62·1 | 70·7 | 86·9 | 100·4 |

We see from these figures that one very marked effect of the application of phosphates in the soluble form is to increase the proportion of grain to straw. At Pumpherston the increase is nearly 14 per cent., while at Harelaw it is 15½ per cent., and it would have been nearer 20 per cent. at the latter station but for the great falling off on plot 8, a circumstance which is explained by the very insoluble form of nitrogenous manure which this plot received four years ago. This is a difference which will rapidly disappear, and it is remarkable that it has persisted so long.

The increase in the proportion of grain to straw has a very

important meaning. It means not only the production of a crop which is in itself more valuable, but it also means that the time of the filling of the ears has set in earlier, and that the crop has arrived sooner at maturity, thus confirming the observation frequently made on these stations that one marked effect of the use of dissolved phosphate is to hasten the time of ripening, and advance the harvest by about ten days or a fortnight. In our uncertain climate an advance of ten days in the time of harvesting is an advantage which farmers are not likely to underestimate.

Among the nitrogenous manures (plots 13 to 18) the most remarkable thing to notice is the large crop obtained on plot 15, which was manured with horn dust. This plot had hitherto received its nitrogenous manure in the form of shoddy, but the manure had proved so entire a failure that it was thought useless to continue the application of a substance which, in its natural state scarcely deserves to rank as a manure. It is used by manufacturers as a source of nitrogen in dissolved manures such as ammoniacal superphosphate and dissolved bones, and in such combinations may furnish a nitrogenous material quite as effective as the nitrogen contained in pure dissolved bones, but in its natural state it is so protected by grease and the mechanical condition in which it is supplied that it does not come into operation as a nitrogenous manure. Accordingly a slow-acting nitrogenous manure was sought for to take the place of shoddy on plot 15, and horn dust was selected. Horn is a substance which has the composition of hair and wool, and is indeed just a kind of solid agglutinated hair. It is known to be a very insoluble substance, and pieces of it remain in the soil for many years with very little change. It was therefore a great surprise to find how remarkably effective a nitrogenous manure it has proved itself to be. The appearance of the plot shortly after brairding was not very promising. In bulk and general vigour it was much behind plots 13 and 14, which received nitrate of soda and sulphate of ammonia respectively, but as the season progressed it put on a very vigorous growth, and was shot nearly a week before the neighbouring plots. It tillered well and assumed a very handsome appearance, and it ripened early and in the end was the best of the nitrogenous plots at Pumpherston and the second best at Harelaw. The explanation of this unexpected result must be looked for in the very fine state of division of the horn dust. It is supplied in the form of exceedingly fine saw-dust, and the result attained affords a striking instance of the great advantage secured by the fine grinding of manures which are not rapidly soluble. Nitrate of soda showed itself superior to sulphate of ammonia in its effect upon the oat crops in every way except in the weight per bushel of grain.

Other nitrogenous manures experimented on were dried blood, rape cake dust, cotton cake dust, all of which are insoluble and none of which are ground to the fineness required for the success of insoluble manures, especially when applied to a cereal crop whose period of growth is short. Accordingly we find that the dried blood on plot 16 has not come into operation, and the amount of crop is quite comparable with those which received no nitrogenous manure at all. Dried blood is supplied in a form consisting in great measure of very hard, corny particles, which are capable of being ground to a very fine powder, and until this is done dried blood cannot be considered a profitable manure to apply directly to the soil, especially for a cereal crop. Cake dust, like dried blood, contains a considerable amount of oil, which retards its decomposition, and the resinous matter contained in these substances has a similar preservative effect.

As regards potash manures only two were employed—the sulphate and the muriate—and while the former maintains the superiority it has shown in former years in the yield of grain, the differences otherwise are not so well marked as to call for special notice here.

The guano plots show an interesting difference from former years. The chief peculiarity is the great improvement shown by the plot manured with fish guano, and it is accounted for in two ways. In the first place, and chiefly, because the kind of fish guano employed was that improved form now being imported which has been in great measure deprived of its fatty matter and is thus rendered much more active. The inferiority of the crop produced on this plot (No. 24) four years ago was attributed to the fatty nature of the manure, and the correctness of that explanation seems borne out by the result obtained this year. In the next place, we may assume that the favourable action of the manure this year may also in some measure be due to the long-delayed action of the less soluble form of fish guano employed in former years. The improvement in the manufacture of fish guano is undoubtedly a very important matter for agriculture, especially for the future of agriculture in this country; for while we are in sight of the time when the supplies of Peruvian guano will be exhausted, and while we know that the supply of Ichaboe guano must necessarily be always very limited, we have in fish guano a source of manure which is inexhaustible, and is capable of restoring to the land in an indirect manner that large amount of manurial wealth which our extravagant system of sewer drainage is continually carrying down from our large cities into the sea. It is therefore much to be desired that the quality of this manure should continue to be improved until it rival the real ammoniacal guanos in the rapidity of its action, and provide us with a manure which in constancy of composition and certainty of action may even be superior to these.

The superphosphate plots at Pumpherston have shown results in favour of the more highly dissolved superphosphates; but taking these in conjunction with the experience of former years, we are not entitled to draw any very definite conclusions. In such an experiment much must no doubt depend on the nature of the phosphate from which the superphosphate is made, its softness and friability, and the fineness of its state of division, and it will take some time before we are able to speak with certainty upon the results of these plots.

### $\frac{1}{12}$ Acre Plots.

The crop on these plots this year was barley. At Harelaw the crop was sown again without a manure, but at Pumpherston the manures were applied for the first time to a soil which had been mixed and laid down so as produce a uniform piece of ground for these small experiments. The plots are numbered according to the numbers of the large plots of which they are duplicates. Plots 11a and 12a are not duplicates of 11 and 12, but are two additional phosphate plots, where Curaçoa phosphate has been applied in the undissolved and dissolved state respectively.

| | No. of Plot. | Grain per Plot. | Total Grain per acre. | Straw per acre. |
|---|---|---|---|---|
| | | lbs. | lbs. | cwts. |
| Phosphate Plots, | 1 | 19½ | 2184 | 29¼ |
| | 2 | 22½ | 2520 | 35¼ |
| | 3 | 23 | 2576 | 34½ |
| | 4 | 21 | 2352 | 31½ |
| | 5 | 23½ | 2632 | 31 |
| | 6 | 23½ | 2632 | 35½ |
| | 7 | 26½ | 2996 | 40 |
| | 8 | 30½ | 3416 | 42 |
| | 9 | 28½ | 3192 | 42 |
| | 10 | 28 | 3136 | 40 |
| | 11a | 27½ | 3080 | 37 |
| | 12a | 30½ | 3416 | 37½ |
| Nitrogen Plots, | 13 | 27 | 3024 | 38½ |
| | 14 | 31 | 3472 | 41 |
| | 15 | 26½ | 2962 | 39½ |
| | 16 | 27½ | 3080 | 37½ |
| Potash Plots, | 19 | 22 | 2464 | 32½ |
| | 20 | 26 | 2912 | 38½ |
| Superphosphate Plots. | 28 | 20 | 2240 | 27 |
| | 29 | 20¼ | 2324 | 30½ |
| | 30 | 29 | 3148 | 37½ |
| Unmanured, | ... | 14 | 1568 | 20 |

The preceding table shows the quantities of grain and straw produced.

It cannot be said that these results corroborate those obtained in the large plots, and careful examination shows that there are anomalies that can scarcely be explained except on the ground of inequalities of soil. It is perhaps too much to expect that results obtained upon an artificial soil such as this should be quite reliable the first year, and we shall probably have to go on for a year or two before we shall find much help from the cropping on these miniature plots.

Owing to the extreme lateness of last season, and to the unavoidable delay which occurred in the fitting up of the Society's laboratory, the chemical analysis of the oat crop is far from complete; but the full details of this, along with a resumé of the experiments during the first rotation, will appear in the next report.

### EXPERIMENT ON THE MARQUIS OF TWEEDDALE'S HOME FARM OF YESTERMAINS.

#### Turnip Crop 1881.

The six experiments reported below are a repetition of those which were reported in the last year's volume of the Transactions, and they are duplicates of six phosphate plots upon the Society's stations. The object of the experiments is to test the value of soluble and insoluble phosphates as a manure for the turnip crop upon the soil at Yester. The results of last year's experiments were very decisively in favour of soluble phosphates, the increase of crop obtained by their use being nearly 50 per cent. As no other experiments recently carried out in Scotland showed so great a difference in the crop-producing value of these two forms of manure, it was considered expedient to repeat the experiments this year on another part of the farm. The manures employed were bone meal, coprolites, and mineral phosphate dissolved and undissolved, and the following are the weights per acre produced, as communicated by Mr. Swinton, under whose care the experiments were put:—

|  | Undissolved per acre. | | Dissolved per acre. | |
|---|---|---|---|---|
|  | Tons. | Cwts. | Tons. | Cwts. |
| Bone Meal, . . . | 1 | 10 | 10 | 12 |
| Ground Coprolites, . . | 1 | 18 | 12 | 8 |
| Ground Curaçoa Phosphate, . | ... | 14 | 12 | 2 |
| Average, . . . | 1 | 7¼ | 11 | 14 |

The extent of the plots was half an acre each, and the soluble and insoluble phosphates were applied on alternate ridges in the middle of a turnip field whose soil was fairly uniform. No comment is required upon these figures; they speak for themselves. The season was a very unfavourable one. The produce with dissolved phosphates was half a crop, while that with undissolved phosphates was an utter failure. These experiments have settled the question as to the kind of phosphates required at Yester, but it is the intention of the Marquis of Tweeddale to perform another experiment on these plots with the succeeding crop, in order to see what is the unexhausted value of the manures upon them.

SCHEME OF EXPERIMENTS AT THE EXPERIMENTAL AGRICULTURAL STATIONS OF THE HIGHLAND AND AGRICULTURAL SOCIETY OF SCOTLAND, COMMENCED MAY 1878.

At each station there are 10 acres under experiment, divided into 40 plots of 1 rood each. The cropping is a rotation of turnips, barley, grass, and oats. The chief object of the experiments is to determine the crop-producing value of the various forms of the most important manures. The manures on each plot contain—

| | |
|---|---|
| Phosphoric Acid, . . . . . | 80 lbs. per acre. |
| Potash, . . . . . | 60 ,,      ,, |
| Nitrogen, . . . . . | 40 ,,      ,, |

Plot.                    PHOSPHATIC MANURES.

1. Bone Ash, . . with mixed Potash Salts. Nitrate of Soda.
2.   ,,     dissolved, . .
3. Ground Coprolites, . .
4.   ,,        dissolved,
5. Bone Dust, . . .
6.   ,,     dissolved, . .
7. Phosphatic Guano, . .
8.   ,,        dissolved,
9. Ground Mineral Phosphate,
10.   ,,        dissolved,
11. No Phosphates, . .
12. Bone Ash alone.

NITROGENOUS MANURES.

13. Nitrate of Soda, . . with Superphosphates. Mixed Potash Salts.
14. Sulphate of Ammonia,   ,,      ,,      ,,
15. Horn Dust, . . .   ,,      ,,      ,,
16. Dried Blood, . .   ,,      ,,      ,,
17. No Nitrogen, . . .   ,,      ,,      ,,
18. Nitrate of Soda alone.

*Rape Cake and Cotton Cake, see Plot 35.*

POTASH MANURES.

19. Sulphate of Potash,　　.　　. with Nitrate of Soda. Superphosphate.
20. Muriate　　„　.　　.　　.　　„　　„　　„
21. No Potash,　.　　.　　.　　.　　„　　„　　„
22. Potash Salts alone.

GUANOS.

23. Peruvian Guano, ( with Bone Ash and ) Containing about 10 per cent.
24. Fish　　„　{　Potash Salts and } Ammonia and 10 per cent.
25. Ichaboe　„　(　Nitrate of Soda. ) soluble Phosphate.
26. No Manure, formerly imitation Guano.

27. Unmanured continuously.

SUPERPHOSPHATES.

28. 10% Soluble Phosphate of Lime. Sulphate of Ammonia. Muriate of Potash.
29. 20%　　　„　　　„　　　„　　　„
30. 40%　　　„　　　„　　　„　　　„

VARIOUS QUANTITIES.

31. Same as Plot 1. { a. $\frac{3}{4}$ quantity per acre.
　　　　　　　　　 { b. $1\frac{1}{3}$　　　„
32.　　„　　„　2. { a. $\frac{3}{4}$　　„
　　　　　　　　　 { b. $1\frac{1}{3}$　　„
33.　　„　　„　14. { a. $\frac{3}{4}$　　„
　　　　　　　　　 { b. $1\frac{1}{3}$　　„
34　　„　　„　20. { a. $\frac{3}{4}$　　„
　　　　　　　　　 { b. $1\frac{1}{3}$　　„
35. { a. Rape Seed Dust.　　Superphosphates. Potash Salts.
　　 { b. Decorticated Cotton Cake.　　„　　　„
36. $\frac{1}{14}$ Acre Plots.
37. Unmanured.
38. Duplicate of Plot 7 { a. with 1 cwt. Supersulphate.
　　　　　　　　　　　　 { b.　„　2　„　　„
30, 40. Unmanured.

EXPERIMENTS ON PLOT 36, VIZ., $\frac{1}{14}$ ACRE PLOTS.

*These Plots are duplicates of the Rood Plots, with corresponding numbers.*

Plot.
1. Bone Ash,　.　　.　　.　　. with mixed Potash Salts. Nitrate of Soda.
2.　　„　　dissolved, .　　„　　„　　„
3. Ground Coprolites,　.　　„　　„　　„
4.　　„　　　dissolved, „　　„　　„
5. Bone Meal,　.　　.　　„　　„　　„
6.　„　　dissolved,　.　„　　„　　„
7. Phosphatic Guano,　.　„　　„　　„
8.　　„　　　dissolved, „　　„　　„
9. Ground Canadian Apatite,　„　　„　　„
10.　　„　　dissolved, „　　„　　„
11a. Ground Curaçoa Phosphate,　„　　„　　„
12a.　　„　　dissolved, „　　„　　„
13. Superphosphate,　.　　.　„　　„　　„
14.　　„　　.　　.　　.　„　　„　Sulphate of Ammonia.
14a.　　„　　.　　.　　.　„　Muriate of Potash.
16.　　„　　.　　.　　.　„　Mixed Potash Salts. Dried Blood.
28.　　„　10% soluble, „　　„　Nitrate of Soda.
29.　　„　20%　„　　„　　„　　„
30.　　„　40%　„・　„　　„　　„

## THE CEREAL AND OTHER CROPS OF SCOTLAND FOR 1881, AND METEOROLOGY OF THE YEAR RELATIVE THERETO.

### THE CROPS.

THE following comparison of the cereal and other crops of 1881 with the previous year, has been prepared by the Secretary of the Society from answers to queries sent to eminent agriculturists in different parts of the country.

The meteorology of the year has been furnished by Mr. Alexander Buchan, Secretary of the Meteorological Society of Scotland.

The queries issued by the Secretary were in the following terms:—

1. What was the quantity, per imperial acre, and quality of grain and straw, as compared with last year, of the following crops? The quantity of each crop to be stated in bushels. What quantity of seed is generally sown per acre?—(1) Wheat, (2) Barley, (3) Oats.

2. Did the Harvest begin at the usual time, or did it begin before or after the usual time? and if so, how long?

3. What was the quantity, per imperial acre, and quality of the hay crop, as compared with last year, both as regards rye-grass and clover respectively? The quantity to be stated in tons and cwts.

4. Was the meadow hay crop more or less productive than last year?

5. What was the yield of the potato crop, per imperial acre, as compared with last year? The quantity to be stated in tons and cwts. Was there any disease, and if so, to what extent, and when did it commence?

6. What was the weight of the turnip crop, per imperial acre, and the quality, as compared with last year? The weight of the turnip crop to be stated in tons and cwts. How did the crop braird? Was more than one sowing required? and why?

7. Were the crops injured by insects? State the kind of insects. Was the damage greater or less than usual?

8. Were the crops injured by weeds? State the kind of weeds. Was the damage greater or less than usual?

9. Were the pastures during the season of average growth and quality with last year?

10. How did stock thrive on them?

11. Have cattle and sheep been free from disease?

12. What was the quality of the clip of wool, and was it over or under the average?

From the answers received, the following statistics have been compiled :—

EDINBURGHSHIRE.—Wheat, 32 bushels ; quality very inferior to last year ; quantity of seed 3 bushels.  Barley, 40 bushels ; quality very inferior to last year ; quantity of seed 3 bushels.  Oats, 50 bushels ; quality not much inferior, weight good ; quantity of seed 3 bushels.  Harvest three weeks later than average, and much prolonged by bad weather.  Quantity of hay about 2 tons, somewhat less than last year ; quality very superior.  Meadow hay much less productive than last year.  Yield of potato crop 8 tons larger than last year, but about one-third diseased of regents ; champions comparatively sound.  Turnip crop say 15 tons, much behind last year ; crop brairded fair, but much of it destroyed by fly, and large breadths resown twice or three times.  Damage by insects greater than usual.  Weeds bad.  Pastures much behind both in growth and feeding.  Stock fed slowly, but were free from disease.  Clip of wool under average.

LINLITHGOWSHIRE.—Wheat about the one-half, and very bad quality ; more straw but not so good ; would say want of sunshine, and too much rain ; seed about 3 bushels.  Barley from 12 to 16 bushels, and in the higher districts of the county much more ; straw about the same quantity but not so good quality ; seed from 3 to 4 bushels.  Oats about the same as barley ; seed from 4 to 5 bushels.  Harvest from a month to six weeks later.  Hay a light crop with few exceptions.  No meadow hay in this district.  Potato crop from 3 to 4 tons less than last year, with the exception of champions, which were about the same ; much disease, but was late in making its appearance.  Turnip crop very variable, from one-half to a third less than last year ; crop brairded well, but from both frost and fly nearly all had to be resown, and in some cases twice.  Little or no injury by insects, with the exception of turnips.  No injury by weeds.  Pastures about the same as last year, but not so good quality.  Stock did not thrive well, too wet and cold toward the end of the season.  Cattle and sheep free from disease.  Wool clip about the average.

HADDINGTONSHIRE (Upper District).—Very little wheat grown.  Barley has yielded 36 bushels of poor quality, fully 3 lbs. per under average weight ; straw average ; seed 3¼ bushels.  Oats, 36 bushels, 1 lb. per bushel under last year ; straw average ; seed 5 bushels.  Harvest began on 12th September, fifteen days later than last year.  Hay considerably under average, and some of it not well secured.  Meadow hay crop much less than last year, and the greater part of it destroyed by wet.  Potatoes little more than half a crop, and about half of that diseased ; disease appeared about middle of September.  Turnips on good loamy land about two-thirds of a crop, which has continued growing all winter ; on clay land less than half a crop, but all of good feeding quality ; the crop brairded well, but was destroyed by frost and fly, part was resown three times.  Damage from insects not more than usual.  The first part of the season was very favourable for cleaning fallows, latterly the wet weather prevented turnips being scraped or hoed as they should have been.  The pastures yielded abundance of grass, but not of good feeding quality.  Stock did not feed much unless where extra food was given ; the mortality about an average.  Lambs suffered much from scour before being put on stubbles.  The wool from sheep which had extra feeding was about an average ; unfed sheep about a fourth deficient in weight.

HADDINGTONSHIRE (Lower District).—Wheat a small crop, 36 bushels, much damaged by wind on 5th August and sprout in September, a third less value than last year ; seed 3 bushels.  Barley, 36 bushels, much damaged by high winds on 5th August, no sun afterwards to ripen it ;

quality poor, 10s. per quarter less price than last season ; seed 2 to 3 bushels. Oats, 50 bushels, with average straw, both damaged by wet harvest, about a fourth less value than last season ; seed 4 bushels. Harvest commenced 29th August, fourteen days later than last year. Hay an average crop, 2 to 3 tons. No meadow hay. Regent potatoes from 7 to 10 tons, one sound to three diseased, these sold, bringing 20s per ton less than last year. Champions sound, 25s. per ton less than last season. Turnips 10 to 20 tons, half of what they were last season ; had to be resown in many cases, caused by cold frosty nights and bright sunshine forenoon. Crops were not injured by insects. Turnips were partly hurt by weeds, but the damage was not great. Pastures were a good average both as to growth and quality. Stock thrived fairly well, and were quite free from disease. Clip of wool under the average.

BERWICKSHIRE.—Wheat, 30 bushels, all damaged by bad weather ; straw, say about 250 stones ; seed sown about 3 bushels. Barley, 30 bushels, bad quality, being damaged with wet weather ; straw say about 170 stones ; seed about 3 bushels. Oats, 36 bushels ; straw remarkably light, say about 160 stones ; seed about 3 bushels. Harvest ten or twelve days later than usual. Rye-grass and clover mixed would average, say 1 ton ; crop light and short. Meadow hay very small crop and badly got. Potato crop, say 10 tons ; disease bad amongst regents, but reds and champions did not suffer much. Turnip crop 12 or 13 tons ; crop brairded very badly, had to be sown in many cases three and four times over, owing to the frost at night destroying the young plants. Turnips were injured by fly to a greater extent than usual ; other crops did not suffer anything unusual in the way of insect damage. No injury by weeds. Pastures neither of average growth nor quality with last year. Stock thrived badly, but were free from disease. Clip of wool under average.

ROXBURGHSHIRE.—No Wheat. Barley, 28 bushels ; straw shorter and more brittle ; grain 4 lbs. per bushel less weight, and altogether of inferior quality ; 3 bushels sown. Oats, 36 bushels ; straw as good as last year ; grain about 1 lb. lighter, and not so well coloured ; 5 bushels sown. Harvest about a week or ten days later than usual. Both rye-grass and clover better than last year ; about 19 cwts. No meadow hay. Potato crop 10 tons (or nearly), hardly so good as last crop, not so well grown ; little disease ; champions or rocks mostly grown. Turnip crop braird bad, injured by frost and fly, especially the early sown swedes ; resowing very general. Pastures deficient in quality and quantity. Stock did not graze well, but were very free of disease. Clip of wool good quality and average quantity.

SELKIRKSHIRE.—Almost no wheat grown. Barley a fair crop, but secured in an unsatisfactory condition, and samples of grain now on sale are mostly of inferior quality, and prices are nearly 10s. per quarter under those frequently current ; from 3 to 4 bushels is sown. Oats an average crop, both in grain and straw, but owing to the want of frost and winds the grain is wanting in condition ; from 4 to 5 bushels of oats is sown, and the average yield will be from 24 to 30 bushels. Harvest commenced about the usual time, viz., the third week in August. Rye-grass hay was an average crop, and mostly secured in fine condition ; the crop would range from 2 to 3 tons. Meadow hay was decidedly deficient in quantity to last year, as excepting the warm week about the end of May the weather was too cold and wet. Potato crop was under an average in quantity, excepting the variety known as champions, which were an average crop, and almost free from disease, and fine quality ; about 4 tons is an average crop. Turnips not above half a good crop, of sound quality, and from 10 to 12 tons. The crop brairded well, but was almost destroyed by turnip-fly, and resowing was almost general. Owing to the mild weather, the crop where not stored is running to seed. No other crop but the turnip were injured by insects. Owing to excessive rainfall weeds were numerous, especially chickweed and other annual weeds. Pastures were of average growth, but inferior in feeding quality. Stock throve only moderately, but were generally free from disease. The quality of the wool clip was under an average, owing to the extra severe winter previous, and the quantity was quite below the average, and to this has to be added a very low price, as cheviot wool has scarcely ever exceeded 1s. per lb.

PEEBLESSHIRE.—No wheat. Barley, quantity would average about 32 bushels; the yield of straw much the same as last year, but the quality of the grain very deficient, about 14 lbs. lighter per 4 bushels than last year; from 3 to 4 bushels sown. Oats fair average crop; general average about 34 bushels per acre; more straw than 1880, but rather less corn, and lighter per bushel. Harvest began about the last week of August, being about a week later than the harvest of 1880, but about an average time of the last twenty years. Hay crop lighter than previous year, about 20 cwts. Meadow hay fair crop, as good as last year. The yield of potatoes per acre would be much the same as 1880, but with little or no disease; average 6 to 7 tons per acre. Turnip crop, weight about 7 tons, in most places not more than half a crop, but owing to the mild open autumn turnips left in the field improved considerably; quality very good; the crop generally brairded well, but required three to four sowings, owing to the frost at night and the scorching sun and turnip-fly during the day. There was little or no injury done to white crops by insects. On properly farmed land there was little or no injury caused by weeds. Pastures not so rough as in 1880, and the quality of grass not so good, owing to the wet summer and want of sun. Stock did not thrive so well as usual, but were free from disease. Wool, quality inferior and under the average.

DUMFRIESSHIRE (Upper Nithsdale).— No wheat grown. Very little barley grown. Oats from 35 to 40 bushels; quality under an average, and more light grain; straw an average in bulk, but not in quality. Harvest about two weeks later than the average of seasons. Hay under an average crop; quantity from 25 to 30 cwts.; quality fair. Meadow hay considerably less productive. Potatoes from a ton to a ton and a half less than last year; fully a fourth diseased, which commenced about the middle of September. Quantity of turnip crop would be from 3 to 4 tons less than last year, say from 12 to 15 tons; quality under an average; a fair braird; swedes mostly sown a second time on account of frosty nights and parching sun through the day. Crops injured by fly rather more than usual. Weeds much as usual; crop difficult to keep clean on account of wet season. Pastures under the average, both in growth and quality. Stock did not thrive so well as usual. There was nothing more than the usual disease. Wool clip considerably under an average, both in quality and weight.

KIRKCUDBRIGHTSHIRE.—Little wheat grown. Barley, 10 bushels short; weight 5 lbs. per bushel short; quality inferior; generally 4 bushels sown; straw average quantity. Oats, quantity 10 to 15 bushels short; weight 5 lbs. per bushel short; quality inferior; straw average quantity. Harvest about five weeks later; unfavourable weather for securing crop. Hay, both clover and meadow, quality very inferior, generally below average, particularly on light soil. Potatoes full average crop; very little disease. Turnip crop very inferior quality; brairded badly; resowing almost general; quantity much below average. Turnips much injured by fly and wire-worm. Mangold much injured by mangold fly. Much injury from weeds. Wet weather prevented land being properly cleaned. Wild mustard, red shank, and couch grass on badly cultivated land most troublesome ; scrub greater than usual.  Owing to the wet season there was plenty of grass, but in consequence of the prevailing low temperature of the most important months of the year for vegetation, quality inferior, and stock generally did not fatten well.  Cattle and sheep very free from disease of all kinds.  Cows slipping calves in some dairies are reported.  Clip of wool average quantity ; quality under average.

WIGTOWNSHIRE.—Wheat about 18 bushels, of poor quality ; average about 52 lbs. ; both quality and quantity inferior to last year ; straw pretty good ; 3 bushels of seed.  Barley, quantity about 32 bushels, the same as last year, but the weight hardly 50 lbs. per bushel ; seed 3½ bushels.  Oats about 35 bushels, 3 more than last year, but weight only 40 lbs. 2 lbs. less ; seed 4¾ bushels.  Harvest was three to four weeks later.  Hay crop not quite so good as last year, which was stated at 1 ton.  Meadow hay less productive.  Potato crop about 8 tons, the same as last year ; disease hardly one-tenth, commenced in September.  Turnip crop 12 to 15 tons, 25 per cent. less than last year ; quality good ; brairded very ill, some not at all.  Early sowing had to be resown, owing to drought and fly.  Only turnips injured by insects.  No injury from weeds.  Pastures hardly equal to last year ; suffered from want of sunshine and heat.  Stock throve fairly.  Cattle and sheep were free from disease.  Clip of wool only moderate, rather under average.

AYRSHIRE.—Wheat, 38 to 40 bushels in 1880 ; 24 to 26 bushels in 1881 ; quality very inferior in 1881 ; seed about 3 bushels ; straw of all the crops generally inferior on account of unfavourable harvest weather.  Barley, 40 to 48 bushels in 1880 ; 26 to 30 bushels in 1881 ; weight and quality inferior in 1881.  Oats about 50 bushels in 1880 ; 42 to 44 bushels in 1881 ; crop very bulky on uplands of Kyle and Cunningham.  Harvest three weeks later than average.  Hay 30 to 35 cwts. ; unfavourable weather caused general inferiority of quality.  Meadow hay rather under average both in quantity and quality.  The early crop of potatoes yielded 4 to 6 tons ; when not raised till August one-fourth to one-third, and latterly more than one-half, became diseased ; crop on light coast land was better in 1881 than in 1880, but worse on heavier inland soils.  Late crop 6 to 7 tons on good land ; champions not much diseased ; finer sorts nearly one-half.  Turnip crop about 12 tons, or one-half the weight of crop in 1880 ; very much resowing ; improved greatly in autumn and winter.  Mangold was damaged by caterpillars ; the damage to mangold in that way seems to be on the increase.  There was the additional trouble from weeds which is usual in moist seasons.  Pastures fair growth and quality.  Stock did moderately well.  The make of cheese was inferior in some districts, but on whole was not much under average.  Nothing unusual of disease among stock.  Clip of wool under average both in quantity and quality.

BUTE.—Wheat, 3½ quarters ; of an inferior quality to last year ; 24 bushels, 58 lbs. in weight ; straw well got and of equal value to wheat ; very little wheat sown in Bute now ; about 4 bushels sown to the acre.  Barley, 36 bushels average to acre, of inferior quality to last year, only 51 lbs. per bushel instead of 55 lbs. ; a large acreage sown of barley in Bute ; about 4 bushels sown to acre.  Oats, 38 bushels average, of fair quality, but not so good as last year in either oats or straw ; weight about 40 lbs. ; about 6 bushels sown.  Harvest about two weeks later than usual.  Hay a small crop, about 1¼ tons ; pretty well got, but neither rye-grass or clover so good or bulky as last year.  Meadow hay greatly less productive.  Potatoes small crop, in many early soils 3 to 4 tons, and poor compared with last year ; a good deal of disease in all finer varieties.  Champions keep well, and a fair crop above 7 tons.  Turnip crop about 10 tons an acre, a small crop compared with last year.  The crop brairded pretty well on many fields, on others resown three times, cause not being known. Except to turnip braird not much injury from insects. Not many weeds; ground generally pretty clean in Bute. Pastures poor compared with last year. Stock did not thrive very well, season too cold and wet, but were pretty free from disease. Wool clip less than last year, and quality not so good.

ARRAN.—No wheat or barley. Oats about 30 bushels; more straw than last year, but quality not so good; seed about 6 bushels. Harvest about five weeks later than 1880. Hay less in quantity, and quality not so good, about 25 cwts. Very little clover. Meadow hay none in this district. Potato crop yield not so good as last year; quantity about 5 tons of champions, other kinds poor crop, and disease very bad; disease appeared about middle of June amongst early kinds. Turnips a poor crop, not nearly so good as last year; yellow about 10 tons, swedish 8 tons; did not braird well; swedes had to be resown, some of them twice, fly being the cause, and cold wet weather. No injury by insects, and none from weeds. Growth of pastures up to average, but quality very inferior. Stock did not thrive very well; cattle free from disease; sheep a good deal of rot and also braxy, rot far worse than previous years. Quality of wool not so good, and quantity under average.

LANARKSHIRE (Upper Ward).—Very little wheat grown. Barley, quantity nearly as much as last year, but quality much inferior, about 28 bushels. Oats same as barley in comparison to last year, about 36 bushels. Harvest fully three weeks after the usual time. Hay about 1 ton; quality fairly good. Meadow hay less in quantity, but good quality. Potato crop about one-third less, about 3 tons sound and 2 tons diseased; disease commenced in September. Turnip crop about 15 tons on an average; half of the fields sown twice, some three times; swedes almost a total failure. Corn crops were the better of the turnip-fly, as they completely ate up the wild mustard at the same time the turnips were suffering. Corn would be at least 12 bushels an acre more on that account; good land is very bad with it; loss as much as 20 bushels an acre by it. Grass fairly plentiful, but for want of sun bad for feeding or milking. Stock throve middling, but were free from disease. Clip of wool under average.

LANARKSHIRE (Middle Ward).—The average would be about 30 bushels of wheat; quality rather inferior; straw fair quality; seed sown generally between 3 and 4 bushels; do not know of any barley having been sown. Oats from 36 to 40 bushels; quality inferior; straw very fair. Harvest began from three to four weeks later than usual. Hay was a fair good crop, and better than last year; it would reach to near 2 tons, and the quality was good. Meadow hay was an average crop. Potatoes were not up to the average, 5 to 6 tons would be the outside yield; disease began about middle of August, and fully one-third were lost over the Middle Ward, but in some places fully one-half was diseased. Turnips in some places were obliged to be sown two or three times over, and consequently were late in brairding; swedes would not be more than 15 tons per acre, and yellows were not any better. Crops generally were injured not so much by insects but by frosts in the early morning. Greater injury by weeds than last year. Pastures about an average season. Stock throve well on light land, but not at all well on stiff land; were free from disease. The clip was fair, rather under the average.

LANARKSHIRE (Lower Ward).—Wheat, average 40 bushels, quality good; seed sown, 4 bushels; straw, 2 tons 10 cwts. Barley, none grown. Oats, good, 54 bushels, good quality; seed sown, 5 bushels; straw, 2 tons. Harvest three weeks later. Hay, quality good, above average, 2 tons; rye-grass and clover well fixed. No meadow hay. Potato crop, average 9 tons, one-third diseased beginning of August.  Turnip crop 18 tons, good braird, one sowing.  Greater damage by weeds than usual.  Pastures, average growth and quality.  Stock throve well, and were very free from disease.  Clip of wool good and an average.

UPPER WARD OF RENFREWSHIRE.—No wheat grown ; no barley grown. Oats, average crop of straw, but both were deficient in quality, on account of the wet season.  Straw is all consumed on the farms here, and is never weighed.  About 20 cwt. and 30 bushels grain ; 5 bushels for seed.  Harvest three weeks after last year.  The hay crop was more deficient in quality than quantity—the average yield 1 ton 12 cwt.  Meadow hay is very much deficient in both quantity and quality—the frost in May and June hurt the growth of it.  Potato crop—Champion potatoes would average about 7 tons ; earlier sorts, about 3 tons of dressed ones ; the later is very deficient in quality, on account of so much rain and little sunshine.  The disease would start about the beginning of September, and the half of them unsound. Turnips would want a third on well-manured light land, but on heavy and wet land they would want a half.  They brairded well, but the frosty nights withered them away, and about the half would be sown a second time. More injury done by the frost than by the fly.  Owing to the wet season, there were weeds among the crops than usual.  Grass was both deficient in quality and quantity.  Stock did not thrive so well as last year, and milk cows had to get feeding along with the grass.  Cattle and sheep have been free from disease.  Wool was deficient both in quality and quantity.

RENFREWSHIRE (Middle Ward).—Wheat about 20 bushels, of very inferior quality ; straw about 2 tons; seed sown about 4 bushels—last or 1880 season 40 bushels would be as general as 20 this season, and 5s. per bushel as easily got as 3s. this year.  Unless the bad season when wheat was all or nearly so sprouted before being got secured, this is the worst wheat season in this district in my remembrance.  Barley is not grown to any extent in this district, but the crop of 1881 was under average in quantity and quality, about 30 bushels per acre ; quality secondary or inferior ; straw about 2 tons ; seed sown about 4 bushels.  Oats, a fair crop as to quantity; quality inferior; about 40 bushels as against 45 former season ; straw about 2 tons; seed sown about 6 bushels.  Harvest about three weeks later, not general till about September 20th.  Hay about 2 tons, nearly one-half heavier than last season, and most secured in good condition.  Meadow hay similar to last year, perhaps rather better.  Potato crop about 7 tons, unless among new varieties, such as champions, magnum bonums ; disease made sad havock, in my own case, except the two varieties mentioned ; there was not above one-fourth of sound potatoes, and many others were similar; about one-half sound would perhaps be near an average ; disease was late in appearing, about end of September.  Turnip crop about 15 tons; quality superior to last season ; brairded bad generally ; where first sowing did an excellent crop was the result, from 20 to 25 tons; sown repeatedly, at least three-fourths sown twice, and some places three and four times sowing before a sufficient braird was obtained.  Damage by insects greater than I ever remember ; besides damage by insect, frost had also very much to do with the destruction of the young plants where they did braird.  Crops injured not by weeds as a cause, in solitary cases of mustard probably as an effect. Pastures not of average growth or quality; with frost nearly always ; when dry not only was growth prevented, but substance extracted from the pastures.  Stock throve imperfectly, but were remarkably free from disease. Wool cannot be considered a staple commodity of this district.

RENFREWSHIRE (Lower Ward).—Barley is little grown in the district ; quality inferior.  The oat crop of 1881 is deficient in quantity, and will

Y

not yield more than 6 bolls; the weight per bushel too is below the average, and on high grounds both grain and straw in very bad condition. The harvest commenced late, fully three weeks after the usual time, and was in all respects tantalising from the unfavourable weather; as a rule rain prevailed, and if a dry day occurred there was no drought, and thus little or no progress was made in winning; the crops were ultimately secured after a fight with the elements. Hay crop was inferior to 1880, 15 to 20 cwts. would be about the average. Meadow hay was less productive by about 20 per cent. than in 1880. Early potatoes were a complete failure; the champions maintain their character as to withstanding disease better in a wet season, and the yield of this sort per acre will average 7 to 8 tons. They are extensively grown, and the potato trade in the district has undergone a change in consequence. Turnip crop was a failure; the fly was more prevalent than in any former year, and sowing was repeated in some cases for the third time. In exceptional cases where the fly did not destroy the first sowing entirely, the plants were strong; but in no case is the yield above a fourth of the average, and in many cases the crop was lost altogether. No crop injured by insects; wire-worm did not prevail. Indigenous weeds were difficult to keep under in consequence of the wet season. Pastures were deficient; the continued frost of last winter retarded an early growth, and it was quite evident that grasses generally did not throughout the whole season attain to a luxuriant growth; in addition to this cause, the excessive wet, and continued with the absence of sun, prevented pastures as in also other crops from reaching maturity. Stock throve very middling, but were free from disease. Clip average.

ARGYLLSHIRE (Parishes attached to the district of Oban).—No wheat grown in the district. The little barley grown was of good quality, in fact was the best crop of the season; yield about ten returns. Oats were a fair crop, but not equal to 1880; quality of grain and straw middling, owing to wet and cold season; crop greatly damaged by severe storms previous to shearing; seed sown per acre about 5½ bushels; yield about 26 bushels. Shearing of oats commenced at Bonaw on 10th September. Rye-grass a short and thin crop, owing to the severe frost of winter and the dry and frosty nights of May; not very well secured, as the weather was most unsuitable. Meadow hay was about equal in quantity with that of 1880, but not generally secured in such good order, as the season was wet. Potato crop pretty good, yield being about an average. About 40 per cent. of the finer varieties were in some localities diseased. In Skerrie Blues there was little or no disease, and the yield was about equal to the whites; but generally the quality of all kinds was excellent. Turnips were not at all good, as the season was most unsuitable for such a tender crop; on level and ill-drained land there was no crop at all, but on high and dry soils there would be a crop of about 14 tons per acre. No injury to any considerable extent by insects, and not more than usual. Oxeye, daisy, and such weeds were seen in some fields, but damage not more than usual. The pastures were under an average, and not equal to the previous year. Stock throve moderately well, but did not get up to the condition of the previous year; were free from disease. The quality of the wool was very good, and the quantity was about an average, the preceding summer and autumn having been favourable.

ARGYLLSHIRE (Parishes attached to district of Lochgilphead).—No wheat grown, nor barley. Oat crop not more than one-third thrashed, but it is inferior to last year's both in quantity and quality, the averages being, 1880, 6 bolls to acre, 41 lbs. per bushel; 1881, 5 bolls or a little more, 39 to 40 lbs. per bushel. Harvest was late; a month later than last year, and a fortnight later than usual time. Rye-grass crop much behind last year in both quantity and quality; cannot state exact quantity. Meadow hay less productive. Potato crop averaged about 9 tons per acre, this year not more than 6 tons; there was not much disease, but the crop was sadly injured by frosts in June, and never recovered. Turnip crop average this year 16 or 17 tons, last year about 20 tons; crop brairded badly owing to frost and fly, and a second sowing was necessary in some cases. Pastures not nearly so good. Stock throve badly. Cattle were free from disease, and sheep also, with the exception of braxy; the losses among hoggs from this disease have been very heavy. Wool was under the average in quantity and quality, but cannot say how much.

ARGYLLSHIRE (District of Cowal).—No wheat sown. The crop of barley generally was about 30 bushels, or about 6 bushels less than last year, and the weight was 6 lbs. per bushel under last year; the crop was fairly well got, but neither the quality of straw or grain equal to last year; seed sown about 4 bushels per acre. As regards bulk the oat crop would be an average one, but for want of sunshine it did not ripen well, and both grain and straw were deficient in quality; the crop, though bulky in appearance, did not thrash more than about 30 bushels, and the weight per bushel not over 39 lbs; seed sown 5 bushels per acre. General harvest would be about twenty-eight days later than last year, and in some cases even more. The weather during harvest was very broken, but crops were generally well secured, except in a few instances where there was some sprouting of the grain. The hay crop was about the same as last year, say about 20 cwts., but the quality is not equal to last year; both this and last year have been under an average in bulk, and this from the exceptional dry and cold month of May and part of June. The crop of meadow hay would be about the same as last year, and though fairly well secured the quality was not so good; want of sunshine may be attributed for this, the same as in every other crop. The yield per acre of potatoes would not be more than 6 tons against 8 or 10 last year, but there has not been much disease, which appeared in some places about 20th August; the crop is to be a losing one for the farmer, prices are so low. The average turnip crop will not exceed 14 tons against 20 last year; did not braird well, though only in a few cases had they to be sown a second time; quality not up to the average. No crops were injured by insects. No crops were injured by weeds, though green crops required more labour to keep them clean than last year. There was neither an average growth or quality of pastures as last year. Stock did not fatten so well as last year, and the produce of dairy cows was under an average. Both cattle and sheep have been free from disease, except that young sheep have been more subject to braxy than any former year. In many cases as much as 50 per cent. have died from this disease. No reason can be assigned except the continued wet and stormy weather. The clip of wool was less than last year, and the quality was not quite so good. The crop of lambs were also under an average, and hill stocks generally were in low condition.

ARGYLLSHIRE (Islands of Islay, Jura, and Colonsay).—I only saw one field of wheat in Islay, and it was quite green in the month of October. When it was sown I do not know. Barley not an average crop, the wet weather supposed to be the cause. Oats an average crop, from about 40 to 48 bushels per acre; weight from 40 to 43 lbs. per bushel. Straw not so bulky as last year, but a fair good crop. Harvest fully a fortnight later than last year, no doubt owing to the wet weather. The quantity and quality of hay was much the same as last year, not a heavy crop, but got saved in good condition, from 1 ton to 1½ ton. Meadow hay rather a heavier crop this year. The champion and magnum bonum potatoes were as good this year as last, and as free from disease, but the rocks and earlier sorts in many farms were almost a complete failure; disease began about the middle of July. The weight of swedes was 16 tons 5 cwts.; yellows, 17 tons 10 cwts., and never were fresher and better turnips; on several farms they were resown; braird supposed to be killed by frost; on some farms there will not be 7 tons. The crop brairded very well, but was longer of being thinned, and after thinning was long before they began to grow much. Mangold, as far as I know, was the only crop damaged by insects. The insects did not leave one with myself, and with some others as bad. The insects looked like a small clock or small insect with wings and black; the damage was much the same as last year. Crops were not injured by weeds. The pastures were of average growth with last year, but not at all the quality, owing to so much rain. Cows went back in their milk very much when the rain came on. Stock did not thrive so well as last year. Cattle have been free from disease, but sheep have not; very many sheep have died from fluke, louping-ill, and braxy. The clip of wool was about an average, and the quality good.

ARGYLLSHIRE (District of Inveraray).—No wheat or barley grown. Oats rather a light crop both in straw and grain compared to last year or ordinary years. Harvest was considerably later than usual, but crop very little damaged considering the time it stood in stook and the boisterous wet weather. The weather was cold. The usual seeding is 6 bushels, would not like to hazard yield. Harvest considerably later at least a fortnight. There being not much cultivation in this district, there was not much land under clover and rye-grass, but both crops and meadow were rather lighter than usual, unless the last cut of meadow. Cannot give weights, but ordinarily well saved. Meadow hay crop less on the whole. Potatoes are a plentiful crop and above average, though not quite up to crop 1880. Some fields and varieties of potatoes were slightly affected with disease shortly before digging time, but the crop is generally sound and plentiful. Turnips are a light crop all over the district, had to be sown two, three, and in some cases four times. It is supposed here that it was frost spoiled the first sowings. Quality sound; cannot give weights; perhaps about three-fifths an average crop. No injury by insects. Turnips and potatoes were more weedy than usual, the crops not getting up timeously. Pastures scarcely equal to last year for want of summer heat. Stock throve as well as usual, not having been so much troubled with heat and flies; were quite free from disease, except that braxy has been heavy about the end of the year. Clip of wool an average.

DUMBARTONSHIRE.—Wheat, this year 26 bushels; last year 36 bushels; quality poor this year, last year fine; the cause of indifference this year the want of sunshine and continuous rain; the quantity of seed sown about 3 bushels. Barley, this year 28 bushels; last year 36 bushels; the same cause for poor quality; but not much grown in this district; the quantity of seed sown about 2¼ bushels; quite unexceptional crop; above estimate was furnished by one of the few who have tried it. Oats, this year 46 bushels; quality fair; much about the average, but last year specially fine; the quantity generally sown 4 bushels. Harvest, this year about the 12th September; last year a month earlier. Hay crop, this year 2¼ tons; hay is softer this year than last, owing to the unusual quantity of clover and the heavy rainfall while it was growing; generally harvested in fair condition. Meadow hay crop, scarcely any grown in this district; there would be more weight but scarcely so well got as last year. Potato crop, this year 5 tons; last year 10 tons; disease commenced about the end of August in the first earlies and regents; very little disease in champions; there would be 7 tons of this variety. Turnip crop, this year 12 tons; last year 24 tons; the crop did in this district generally with the one sowing, but in many instances the braird was very defective, owing to cold weather and fly. No damage from insects to speak of. Slow to start on account of the cold wet season. Turnips were the only crop affected by insects, as stated above. Crops not particularly injured by weeds, nor any particular kind. Damage not greater than any usual wet season. Pastures—in the district there would be more grass, but quality not so nutritious, owing to continuous rain and want of sun. Stock did fairly well. Cattle and sheep in this district particularly free from disease, with the exception of sheep-scab, which is reported as rather prevalent in some districts of the county. Clip of wool—Quality fair, but barely up to the average.

STIRLINGSHIRE (Western District).—No wheat grown. The oat crop of 1881 was quite as bulky as that of 1880, but the yield of grain deficient and the quality inferior ; the average yield would be about 40 bushels per acre, and 40 cwts. straw ; the quantity of seed sown about 5 bushels. Harvest about fourteen days later than usual. Hay rather more bulk than in 1880, but in general not so well got ; the average yield would be about 1 ton 15 cwts. Meadow hay about an average crop of fair quality. Potato crop fully 3 tons less than last year ; the yield would be about 6 tons, about one-half diseased, which began about the 1st September. Turnips very inferior crop, about a third of 1880, say 7 tons, large extent required to be sown more than once from the braird being eaten by fly. Crops injured by fly to greater extent than usual. The weather being cold and wet, and weeds of all kinds very abundant, the damage on that account was greater than usual. Pastures of average growth but inferior quality. From the long continued wet the pasture was inferior, and cattle did not thrive well. Both cattle and sheep have been very free from disease during the past season, sheep being very lean from the effects of a severe and long-continued winter. The clip was considerably under the average.

STIRLINGSHIRE (Eastern District).—The severe winter damaged the wheat crop of 1881 badly. Portions of the fields were drifted bare of snow, and the long-continued frost afterwards threw out the wheat entirely on these bare portions, some farmers replacing it with barley or oats, while others ploughed up the fields entirely ; and where it escaped damage by winter severity, it suffered from want of summer sunshine, so that, speaking generally, wheat may be said to have been a failure, although on some exceptionally good farms there was a fair crop. The district average is estimated at 24 bushels ; seed, 2¼ to 3 bushels. Barley was a fair crop in 1881, though it can hardly be said to be up to an average, and the quality turned out only middling, mainly owing to too much wet and too little sunshine. Average is estimated at 30 to 35 bushels ; seed, 3 bushels. Oats were also a fair crop in 1881, though not quite equal to that of 1880. Average is estimated at 40 bushels or thereby, and quality fair; seed about 4 bushels. The harvest began about the usual time, but it was not a good harvest, and it was long and tedious, owing to broken weather. Wheat suffered to a certain extent. The hay crop was again deficient, nor was the quality quite equal to last year. Crop about 20 cwts. on the average ; second crop also short. Little or none of meadow hay. Potato crop good, probably about 10 tons; but disease attacked it about lifting time, and caused much loss then and after, in some cases a third or even a half gone. On the Carse the turnip crop was good, only one sowing was required, while on dry field farms it was not so good, several sowings having been necessary, owing to the interference of fly. Average estimated at 15 tons. No insects worth talking about except the turnip-fly in the dry field land already alluded to. Except some trouble in keeping down chickweed, &c., in the turnip fields, weeds were not more than usual. The pastures did fairly well during the season, although in some cases there occurred partial failures in the early part of the season, owing, it is thought, to frosty nights. Stock did very well upon the whole. Both cattle and sheep perfectly free from disease. Wool—what there was of it—may be taken as about the average. Beans, which are an important crop, were good in 1881, there being a great bulk of straw and fair quality of bean, although the bushels per acre may not have been up to a full average. Average estimated at 24 bushels. Upon the whole the greatest failure has been in the wheat crop. The severe winter and sunless summer were the features of the year, and the low prices, combined with a short crop, render the returns very unremunerative to the husbandman.

FIFESHIRE (Eastern District).—Wheat, 24 bushels ; 1½ tons straw; 3 bushels sown.. Barley, 32 bushels ; 18 cwts. straw ; 3 bushels sown. Oats, 42 bushels ; 22 cwts. straw ; 4 bushels sown. Harvest three weeks after the usual time. Hay crop, 1 ton ; rye-grass, fair quality ; clover very deficient. No meadow hay grown. Potato crop, 25 per cent. less than last year, 5 tons, about one-third diseased ; disease commenced in middle of September. Turnip crop 30 per cent. deficient, 10 tons, brairded badly ; had to be resown on account of frost. No injury by insects. Pastures more growth and less quality. Stock throve fair, and were free from disease. Quality of wool good, quantity under an average.

PERTHSHIRE (South-West District).—Comparatively little wheat sown ; average produce about 30 bushels. Quantity of straw much the same as previous year, but quality inferior. Produce per acre rather less than above stated on clay land, say 28 bushels, and weight not more than 58 lbs. on average. Barley, quantity of grain much less than previous year, and quantity of straw greater. Weight of grain 3 or 4 lbs. per bushel lighter than usual. Produce 4½ qrs., or 36 bushels. Grain dark in colour, about 4 bushels per acre sown. Oats, average quantity, 30 bushels, and straw much the same as previous year. Weight of grain 3 lbs. lighter than previous year. About 6 bushels sown in dry field, and 5 bushels in Carse land. Harvest about a fortnight later than usual in the earlier districts, and much more in the late. In fact, the glens were a month later, and in some localities the farmers have had no harvest weather at all. Hay about 25 cwts. on an average, and fair good quality. More clover this year. Meadow hay much less productive, and the quality inferior. The potato crop was quite equal in quantity to that of 1880, but disease was more virulent, and the quality was not so good. The disease commenced a few weeks before maturity. The turnip crop was not more or much more than half that of the previous year, but the quality was good. The crop brairded badly, and had to be resown more than once owing to the ravages of the beetle. Turnip crop was much injured by the beetle ; in some localities ruined entirely. The green crops were not easily hoed or kept clean, owing to the wetness of the weather. Pastures were not nearly so good as usual, nor half so nutritious. Stock throve badly. Cattle perhaps never came to either market or stall in the fall in lower condition. Cattle and sheep were free from disease. Clip of wool under the average in quantity and quality.

PERTHSHIRE (Coupar-Angus District).—Very little of the wheat is thrashed yet, not being in good enough condition ; what has been thrashed is very inferior to what it was last year, and from 1 to 2 qrs. less in quantity. We generally sow in autumn 4 bushels per acre, this season fully 4 bushels, the wheat being so bad. Barley, quantity per acre from 30 to 40 bushels, less by 10 to 20 bushels from last year's crop ; quality of grain very inferior, selling at from 10s. to 15s. at less price per quarter of 8 bushels than last year ; from 3 to 4 bushels sown. Oats, from 40 to 50 bushels, about a quarter short of last year; quality inferior to last year from the wet harvest; about 4 bushels sown. Straw in these crops about an average, but generally got in in bad form. Harvest commenced generally about 1st September, or eighteen days later than last year; this is later than the usual time. Hay a fair crop; this is not much of a hay district. No meadow hay. Regent potatoes a full crop—about 6 or 7 tons, about one-half diseased; Victorias one-third; champions and magnum bonums a large crop, and no disease; disease commenced about middle of September. Potatoes almost unsaleable. The turnip crop is very varied as to bulk; some fields carry from 20 to 25 tons, whilst others carry only from 10 to 15 tons. They have improved very much since autumn when left in field. The turnips were very much destroyed by fly, and very few fields but had to be resown, sometimes twice. The insects were of the species we always suffer from, only this season the frosty weather at time of sowing retarded the growth of the plants, and gave the fly greater advantage. Not much injury from weeds. Pastures an average growth. Stock did not feed, that is, did not take on flesh very well, owing to the cold summer, but were free from disease. Clip of wool an average.

PERTHSHIRE (Western District).—There is no wheat grown in this district, and very little barley. There is not much oats sown here, it being a pastoral district; about a boll generally sown. Oats short in quantity; straw inferior. Harvest wet and very late. Crops a good deal under average in yield. Harvest about three weeks later here than usual. Corn did not ripen at all in many places hereabouts. Hay crop very short in quality. Meadow hay crop short. Potato crop about an average as to quantity, but about a third lost through disease. Turnip crop pretty good hereabouts as to quality and quantity. No injury by insects, and none by weeds. Owing to the continued wet and dulness there was no stamina in grass, therefore an ordinary stock kept pastures very bare. Stock did not thrive very well, owing to want of substance in grass through want of solar heat, but were free from disease. Wool inferior in quality; weight a good deal under average, owing to the stormy winter.

PERTHSHIRE (Perth District).—Wheat, about 3 bushels of seed sown per acre. On black land, where the plants stood the severe winter, wheats of the harder varieties, such as " square head," are turning out a good crop of about 40 to 45 bushels, but the quality is not nearly as good as last year, and 3 lbs. per bushel lighter. The straw is very brittle, owing to so much moisture. On clay soils, and all spring-sown wheats the crop is a miserable failure; from 16 to 20 bushels per acre of light grain, 56 to 58 lbs. per bushel. A great proportion of last year's winter-sown wheat had to be ploughed up, as the plants were entirely killed by the very severe frosts. Barley, about 3 bushels of seed sown per acre. Barley, where early sown and on good land, was a good crop of about 40 to 45 bushels, weighing 54 to 56 lbs. per bushel. The straw was as good as last year, but the grain wanted the golden colour. Where the crop was later it is a poor affair, about 30 bushels, and from 50 to 52 lbs. per bushel is still soft, and not improving in the stack as expected. On an average both grain and straw is 30 per cent. more than last year in both quantity and quality; too much rain and want of sunshine is the whole reason; about 4 bushels sown. Oats are the best crop of the season; excellent quality of grain and straw, 45 to 50 bushels per acre; 40 to 43 lbs. per bushel as good as last year. Harvest from a fortnight to three weeks later than usual. Hay about 1½ tons; quality nearly as good as last year. Hardly any meadow hay grown. Potatoes, from 5 to 7 tons; about one-third diseased, except in champions, where there was little or none; quality as good as last year; disease began in the middle of September. Turnip crop very variable, from 10 to 16 tons ; quality good. Bulbs swelled very much in November and December. Two-thirds of swedes sown a second time with yellows ; cause of failure mostly frosts at night, which kept back the young plants, and then the fly took them. The turnip crop was injured by fly more than usual. The wheat crop was also injured to a certain extent, but not more than usual. Not nearly so many annual weeds as usual ; the frosts seem to have killed them. Pastures were very bare during the whole summer ; not half an average, and very soft, poor quality. Stock thrived very moderately ; the ground was too cold and wet for them lying on, but were free from disease. Quality of wool clip very poor ; much under an average.

PERTHSHIRE (Highland District).—No wheat grown. Barley, quality inferior, 32 to 33 bushels ; average 50 lbs. per bushel. Straw good, average quantity sown 4 bushels. Oats, quality not so good as last, about average, very inferior in the high glens, and late in being secured ; average quantity from 22 to 34 bushels ; average weight, 37 lbs. per bushel. Straw short, and in the glens very inferior and badly secured ; average quantity sown 5 bushels. Barley harvest a fortnight later than last year. Oats three weeks later than last year in early places, and eight to nine weeks in the glens. Hay under usual average, 14 cwt., not too well secured. Rye grass thin, and killed out altogether in some places by the frost. Clover good, about 2 cwts. better than last year. Meadow hay a very inferior crop throughout the district ; 5 cwts. less than last year where cut, some parts not fit to be cut. Potato crop same as last year, about 4½ tons, some partial disease, got home well, but have not kept satisfactorily in the pits, disease showed itself about three weeks before lifting. Turnip crop about 16 tons per acre ; swedes bad and deficient ; yellows good ; very bad growth at first, made remarkable improvement in October where well laid down ; on most farms sown two or three times, as fly and frost destroyed the braird ; the braird of the turnip crop on the majority of farms in the district was destroyed by fly, damage much greater than usual ; no inquiry by weeds. Pastures under average ; season too wet and cold, and grazings not nutritive. Stock throve fairly well considering the season ; much inclination to scab in the sheep stock during the whole season, requiring constant attention ; cattle free from disease. Wool, quality dry, and 10 per cent. under average.

PERTHSHIRE (Dunkeld and Stormont District.)—Wheat 8 bushels less than last year ; quality of both grain and straw much inferior ; 4 bushels sown. Barley 4 bushels less ; quality first got in good, last much inferior ; 5 bushels sown. Oats 10 bushels less ; quality of straw and grain much inferior ; 5 bushels sown. Harvest one month later. Rye-grass and clover 5 cwts. less ; average quality good. Meadow hay equal to last year. Yield of potato crop equal to last year ; disease very slight, commenced middle of September. Turnip crop 6 tons less ; quality not so good ; braird fair, but destroyed by fly ; sown twice, in some cases three times. Oats injured by fly, damage greater than last year ; no injury by weeds. Pastures inferior to last year. Stock throve pretty fair and were free from disease. Clip of wool, quality good ; average much the same as last year.

FORFARSHIRE.—Wheat not grown. Barley about 48 bushels, plenty of straw, but grain not good quality ; seed, per acre, 4 bushels. Oats about 48 bushels, plenty of straw, but grain not good quality ; seed, per acre, 4½ bushels. Harvest much later than usual, about three weeks. Hay a light crop, about 1½ tons, and very moderate quality. Meadow hay not grown in this district. Potatoes a large crop and pretty free from disease ; weight per acre about 7 tons. Yellow turnips about an average crop, 20 tons ; swedes a very small crop, about 10 tons per acre ; crop brairded, but was eaten with fly, and had to be resown, in some cases a third sowing was necessary.  No damage done by insects except in the case of the turnips ; no damage from weeds.  Pastures not equal to last year.  Stock did not thrive well, but were free from disease.  Clip of wool about an average.

ABERDEENSHIRE (Buchan District.)—Little or no wheat grown, the principal grain crops being barley, bere, and oats, three-fourths of the land under crop being the last-mentioned cereal.  Barley this year would be about equal to last as regards quantity, but not the same weight, and bringing from 4s. to 6s. less per quarter.  Straw very fair quality.  Oats the staple crop.  On early and rocky or open bottomed soils there is not more than 3 to 4 bushels under last year, whereas on other soils the difference would be from 5 to 6 bushels, and 1 to 2 lbs. less weight.  Rather more straw than last year, of good quality.  Harvest commenced about the middle of September, and was some fifteen days later than last year.  Hay crop about the same as to bulk as last year.  Although somewhat thin in early part of the season, both the rye grass and clover closed up very much.  Very little meadow hay grown.  Potatoes not so large a crop as last year, but are keeping much better, being free from disease, of which there was scarcely any.  The yellow fleshed turnips are a little more than half the crop of last year, whereas the swedes on most farms would not be over a fourth part ; all these sown before Whitsunday as a rule brairded well in from three to five days, and went off again and had to be resown two, three, and in some cases four times.  The damage caused by insects during the first part of the season was very great.  Owing to so much resowing having been resorted to there were not many weeds during the summer, although in some cases the turnip breaks appear now somewhat tinged with weeds.  Pastures were nearly of average growth, but not of so good quality as last year.  Stock throve remarkably well during the latter end of May and beginning of June owing to the very warm weather, but did not afterwards make the progress they should have done ; they were entirely free from disease.  Clip of wool under average.

ABERDEENSHIRE (Formartine.)—Wheat not grown to any extent.  Barley and bere, or bigg, much cultivated ; was a good crop as regards both grain and straw.  This year's crop would be about equal to last year's in straw and grain, 36 bushels, but the grain not so heavy ; last year, 54 to 56 lbs., this year 52 to 53 lbs. per bushel.  Grain not nearly so plump and well filled, and not well coloured ; quantity sown 4 bushels barley and 3 bushels bere or bigg.  Oats after lea or grass land had received a check in its early stage of growth, and was not such a full or bulky crop as oats after cleaned land or green crop, which is generally sown later.  The straw of this year's crop not so abundant as last year, and the grain not so heavy ; last year, 38 to 40 bushels, grain weighing 42 to 45 lbs. per bushel ; this year, 32 to 38 bushels, grain weighing 41 to 42 lbs. per bushel.  Along the coast side during harvest the weather was drier and the crop secured in much better condition than in the interior of this district, where the harvest was wet and very protracted, and a good deal of heating took place in the stack ; quality of grain and straw in the uplands not so good as last year ; quantity sown 6 bushels per acre.  Harvest commenced last year about 20th August, this year about 9th September.  Hay crop not so heavy as last year, about 1¼ tons per acre.  No meadow hay.  Potato crop good and generally free from disease, the quality very superior, about 6 to 8 tons.  The turnip crop this year has been one of great anxiety to farmers.  Along the coast side the crop brairded and remained, coming to the hoe in regular succession as sown, no second sowing being required, while in the upper district the seed brairded and disappeared in many cases three times ; the swedish variety being altogether lost, as it was deemed too late to sow that kind after so many trials and the season so far advanced ; yellows were sown instead. The turnip fly was very prevalent during the months of May and June, and seemed to be the cause partly of destroying the young turnip braird ; the reporter, however, thinks that the frost at night and the bright sunshine by day during these months had much to do in shrivelling up and killing the young plants, and this would account for the success near the sea where the frost was less severe.  Along the coast side the crop would average from 16 to 24 tons, and in the upper district 10 to 12 tons.  No damage done by weeds.  This season has been the worst for pasture grass that has occurred for a long time, in fact, grass never was abundant during the whole season. Cattle and sheep did not do well, the season being cold, and when killed off grass turned out very bad in internal fat and tallow ; were free from disease. Clip of wool was under an average.

ABERDEENSHIRE (Garioch District).—Scarcely any wheat grown.  The yield of barley would be about 40 bushels, or same as last year ; but the weight per bushel would be 2 lbs. less, owing to absence of sunshine ; the quantity of seed sown per acre is 4½ bushels.  A portion of the oat crop was not so well harvested as last year, in consequence of heavy rainfall ; but the bulk would be about the same, and return similar, viz., 36 bushels ; seed required, 6 bushels per acre.  Harvest was commenced in the lower part of the Garioch about the 14th September, and the upper part about the 28th, which is fully three weeks later than the average time.  The hay crop was generally very light, but quality good and well mixed ; the weight is under last year by about 3 cwts. ; the weight this year may be put down at 1 ton 5 cwts.  No meadow hay.  The potato crop was somewhat less than last year, but quality exceedingly good, and free of disease ; the average yield would be from 4½ to 5 tons.  The turnip crop is considerably under last year. It is stated in the report of the Garioch Turnip Growing Association that the weight of swedish last year was 22 tons 11 cwts., and this year 10 tons 5 cwts. ; green top yellow, 22 tons 8 cwts. 2 lbs. last year, against 15 tons 17 cwts.—showing a deficiency on the former variety of 12 tons 6 cwts., and on the latter of 7 tons 1 cwt. ; the quality is excellent, and free of disease ; many fields had to be resown three times.  An insect attacked the turnip seed crop in the month of May, and almost totally destroyed it, a circumstance I never remember having occurred in any previous year.  The land is generally kept very clean, and no damage has been done under that head. Owing to the severe winter, the land was so thoroughly cooled that growth was late in starting ; and from the havoc by frost to the turnip crop, cattle had to be early put to grass, and there was not a full bite the whole season. Stock throve moderately well ; both cattle and sheep have been exceptionally free from disease.  The quantity and quality of the clip of wool would be equal to the average of former years.

ABERDEENSHIRE (Strathbogie District).—Scarcely any wheat grown.  Barley crop generally up to the average, in regard to both straw and grain ; the average yield was about 40 bushels per acre, and the weight from 52 to 55 lbs. per bushel ; the quantity of seed generally sown is about 4 bushels.  Oat crop was deficient in bulk of straw, but fully up to the average as regards yield of grain ; on well-farmed, good land, the yield was in many cases as high as 56 bushels, but the general average is from 40 to 44 bushels, and the weight from 40 to 44 lbs ; the quantity of seed sown is from 4 to 6 bushels, and in the later localities from 6 to 8.  Harvest began about the usual time—about the middle of September, and about a fortnight later than last year ; but, as the weather got very wet after the first week, harvest operations were suspended for about ten days ; complaints were general in the district of heating in the stackyards, five or six weeks after the crop was secured.  The hay crop was generally very light, unless where top dressed, and the quality fair ; the average yield is not much over 20 cwts. No meadow hay. Potato crop was very good as regards both quantity and quality, but very little breadth is grown in the district ; the quantity per acre was from 7 to 9 tons ; there was no disease to speak of in the district. The turnip crop is much under an average. The unprecedented heat during the later half of May, with sharp frosts at night, blighted the earlier sown swedes ; and after resowing the fly attacked the plant, so that there are almost no swedes in the district ; second sowing was almost universal, and, in the majority of cases, a third sowing was required. Yellow turnips are a fair crop in some localities, but the average weight per acre will not be much over 18 cwts. Unless the fly which attacked the turnip crop, there was no unusual destruction to the crop by insects. No unusual injury to crops by weeds. Pastures were generally very bare all through the season ; the cattle having to be turned out earlier than usual, owing to the scarcity of winter keep ; pastures never got to be a full bite. Cattle did not make much progress on the grass, partly owing to having been fed a good deal during the spring on artificial food, and partly owing to the scarcity of grass. Cattle and sheep have been free from disease. The quality of clip of wool was fair, but the quantity was under the average.

BANFFSHIRE (Lower District).—No wheat grown. Barley average yield —32 bushels ; quality generally inferior, owing to wet weather in harvest. Oats, 33 bushels ; quality for the most part good, but grain 1½ lb. lighter per bushel. Harvest a fortnight later. Hay crop light—18 cwts.—owing to the exceptionally hot weather in May ; clover very deficient. No meadow hay. Potato crop 3½ tons ; quality excellent, but crop considerably lighter than last year ; in this district potatoes are not grown as a crop, but for home use. Turnip crop—12 cwts.—much inferior to last year, both in quantity and quality. Turnips did not braird at all well, and the young plants having been destroyed by frost, the land for turnips had almost wholly to be sown three times. Damage by frost very great ; little destruction by insects. No injury by weeds. Grass was generally scarce in the early part of the season ; and cattle did not thrive so well on the grass as they did last year. Cattle and sheep were quite free from disease. Few sheep kept in this district.

BANFFSHIRE (Upper District).—No wheat grown. Barley grain dark coloured, and under an average, both in quantity and quality, the ripening being in many—I may say most—cases deficient ; weight of grain 3 lbs. under an average ; straw a fair bulk, but soft. Oats under an average both in grain and straw ; on some early farms the deficiency less felt, but in the late districts, and on north-lying farms over 700 feet above sea-level, the crop never thoroughly ripened ; the crop was well harvested, and although one-fifth under an average bulk, the straw is good quality and fresh ; grain 2 lbs. per bushel under an average weight. The harvest was about three weeks later than an average season. Hay generally poor, not exceeding an average of 16 cwts. ; clover generally deficient, and rye-grass thinly planted ; crop generally saved in fair condition. No meadow hay grown. Potatoes a full crop, and fine quality, the tubers being invariably well sized and numerous ; no disease ; this crop is not extensively grown for the market in Banffshire. Turnips under three-fourths of a full crop, or about 15 cwts. ; there was no fly, but owing to the frosts in the end of May, swedes were in most cases a failure, the land being resown with yellows ; where this was delayed too long, the turnips are small, but the crop is generally healthy and the quality good. No insects of any kind affected the crops during the year. Weeds were not specially numerous or injurious to any of the crops. Pastures were under an average growth, caused partly by the coldness of the season, and also by stock being too soon put on them. Owing to the cold wet season, stock did not thrive well even where pastures were a full bite. Cattle never rest well when the ground is cold and damp. There was no disease during the past season. Wool was deficient in quantity, quality, and price.

MORAYSHIRE.—The wheat crop was considerably under that of last year in every respect; the quantity per acre ranged from 1 to 5 quarters; the quantity of straw would be one-fourth under last year; grain dark in colour, and 2 lbs. per bushel under last year; straw weak and not well ripened; the causes were the extreme severity of the winter, destroying a large portion of the plants, and the low temperature, and dark sunless character of the summer throughout; the quantity of seed used per acre generally is—with the drill 3 bushels, and broadcast 4 bushels. Barley was the best crop of the season; the average quantity of grain would be 32 bushels; quality not so good as last year; colour of grain very dark, unfitting it for brewers, which greatly affected its value; the weight of grain from 54 to 56 lbs. per bushel; the quantity of straw fully an average, and rather above last year; and the quality of both grain and straw greatly injured by the extremely wet weather prevailing during the month of August and beginning of September, and the dark sunless character of the season; seed used, 3 to 4½ bushels. Oats were under an average as to bulk of straw, but rather over last year's bulk; there was an unusual large quantity of black or blasted heads in general, but in cases where a change of seed was used from a later district, there were almost none; the yield of grain would be from 3 to 6 qrs.; grain 1 lb. per bushel less than last year; the quality of the straw good. Harvest was general in the last week of August, and two weeks later than last year, which was earlier than usual; at the commencement the weather was extremely wet, which made the harvest long, and caused a good deal of the crop to be secured in bad condition. With few exceptions the hay crop was rather light, but heavier than last year; was well mixed with clover, but on account of the low temperature of the summer did not fill up well; the quality was good; average, 30 cwts. Little or no meadow hay in the county. The potato crop was quite free from disease; the yield would be about 5 tons, and 1 ton less than last year. The turnip crop would, with few exceptions, be about one-third below the weight of last year, which was considerably above the average; the brairding of the crop was perhaps the worst in the history of the plant; a large portion of the crop was sown a second, and part a third, time; most of the swedes were resown with yellows, and on account of the extremely mild autumn weather, the crop has turned out beyond expectation. With the exception of the turnip crops, none of the other crops were injured by insects; with few exceptions, the whole of the turnip braird was more or less injured by insects; many farmers were of opinion that the extreme heat of the last week of May and the first week of June, which gave all kinds of crop a start, which brought up the turnip braird very quickly, while strong frost prevailed at night, was to a large extent the cause of the failure of the turnip braird; the great heat might also have been the cause of producing an unusual number of the turnip-fly. The crop did not suffer injury from weeds to a greater extent than usual, with the exception of the wheat crop, where it was much thinned by the severe winter; in such cases it was much injured by winds. Cultivation will only be perfect where nothing grows in the land but what is sown in it. The pastures were at least one-third below the average growth, the result undoubtedly of the lowness of the temperature; the growth was less, and the quality much inferior, to last year. Stock of all kinds made exceedingly small progress in the pastures, the result, no doubt, of low temperature, more especially during the night. Cattle and sheep were almost free from disease, with the exception of one case, where a large number of very good calves died from quarter ill; in this case no cake was given to the calves; many are of opinion that a small allowance of from ¼ to 1 lb. of cake per day to each is a preventative. The clip of wool, both as to quantity and quality, was under the average, the result, no doubt, of the very severe winter.

NAIRNSHIRE.—No wheat grown.  Barley, grain and straw about the same as last year ; grain, in most part, dark in colour, but of good quality ; average per acre, say 28 bushels ; weight a good average, many samples weighing 56 lbs. per bushel ; seed sown 3½ to 4 bushels.  Oats, grain and straw under an average ; quality and colour of grain good ; weight not more than average, yield say 28 bushels per acre ; seed from 4 to 6 bushels. Harvest later than usual, and fully a fortnight later than last year.  Hay a very thin light crop, in many cases an entire absence of clover, which may be accounted for in some places by the severity of the previous winter, say 16 cwts.  No meadow hay grown.  Potatoes on an average about the same as last year, say 5 tons ; a marked absence of disease.  Turnips a fair average crop ; yellows, say 16 tons, swedes 20 tons ; quality good ; more second sowing than was ever known, especially with all early sown turnips, caused by frosty nights succeeded by bright sunshine, and in some cases fly. No injury by insects.  Weeds not more plentiful than ordinary, except where turnips were sown more than once.  Pastures scarcely of average growth or quality.  Stock throve fairly well ; cattle and sheep were free from disease. Clip of wool under an average.

INVERNESS-SHIRE (Inverness District).—Wheat about 3 quarters per acre ; quality inferior compared with crop 1880 ; about 4 bushels sown in autumn, and 3½ in spring ; very little sown during past few years in this district ; both quantity and quality much less during past six years than formerly. Barley about 40 bushels on best land, and from 24 to 32 bushels on light land ; quality very fair both of grain and straw ; quantity sown on best land about 3 bushels, and on light land from 4 to 5 bushels.  Oats from 34 to 40 bushels on best land, and from 20 to 30 on light land ; the return for oats have been less than anticipated on good land.  Harvest about the usual time, if anything later than the average of seasons.  The quantity of hay upon heavy well-drained land in good condition would average about 2 tons, while on light ill-conditioned land something like 25 cwts. would be an average upon the high ground.  No meadow hay of any consequence. The potato crop was excellent, both as regards quantity and quality ; the average yield would be from 8 to 10 tons per acre on good land well manured ; the braird of early sown swedes was damaged by frost, followed by fly on some farms to a great extent ; many farmers resowed yellows instead, and the result in most cases has been satisfactory ; there are some excellent crops of turnips ; the weight per acre varies considerably ; some fields were damaged, partly by insects, but the frost first caused the damage, which was succeeded by dry scorching weather, favourable to the development of insect life ; the damage was much worse than usual.  The injury done by weeds was not more than usual ; wild mustard abounds, and does much damage.  The quantity of grass was fairly good, but the quality was much inferior, caused by an excess of moisture and want of sunshine. Stock throve very middling, much worse than in 1880, but were quite free from disease, with very few exceptions of an ordinary nature ; one case of pleuro occurred, but was stamped out.  Clip of wool about an average ; quality very fair.

INVERNESS-SHIRE (Beauly District).—No wheat grown for some years. Barley—the quantity in 1880 would average 32 bushels; in 1881, 28 bushels ; quantity of straw in 1880 rather under 1881, and quality fully 2 lbs. per bushel lighter.  Oat crop 1880 would average 36 bushels ; 1881, 24 bushels ; bulk of straw in 1881 fully one-third under 1880 ; quality good.  Harvest began about a month later than ordinary.  The quantity of hay per acre was very unequal, some fields would average 2 tons, others only 15 cwts. ; the average this season would be 1 ton, last season 25 cwts. ; crop more equal ; clover in both seasons good.  No meadow hay.  Potato crop of this season would yield about 9 tons, and of last year 7½ ; frost took effect in some fields in the latter end of August, and disease followed, but very slight, and in some fields none.  The turnip crop of last season would average about 18 tons per acre, this season about 3 tons less ; crop brairded well, but was eaten by fly or beetles, and a great part was sown twice, and some thrice, which caused a limited quantity of swedes to be left of very poor quality. Injury by beetles greater than ever seen here.  Injury by weeds no more than usual.  Pastures under average growth, and bad quality.  Stock did little good from want of sunshine and heat, but were quite clear of disease. Clip of wool much about an average for quantity and quality.

INVERNESS-SHIRE (Skye District).—No wheat or barley grown.  Oats one-third less on account of extreme cold and wet ; straw one-fourth less, and inferior in quality.  Harvest at least three weeks later than last year.  Hay from 50 to 60 stones.  Meadow hay generally scarce, and not extra in quality. Potato crop about the same as last year, from 3 to 4 tons.  Turnip crop about 13 tons per acre, sown twice in most cases.  No damage by insects nor by weeds.  Pastures not of such feeding quality as last year.  Stock did not thrive so well as usual, but were free from disease.  Quality of clip of wool generally an average, but quantity less.

INVERNESS-SHIRE (Fort-William District).—No wheat grown, and very little barley.  Oats yield about 26 to 28 bushels ; straw and grain much like previous year's crop.  Harvest began a fortnight later than usual, and nearly a month later than 1880.  Hay about 28 cwts. ; rye-grass deficient : clover considerably better than in 1880.  Meadow hay a good crop, and secured in good weather.  Potato crop about 13 tons ; very little disease ; such disease as there was first noticed about middle of August.  Turnip crop 9 tons per acre ; brairded well ; only one sowing required, except in very few instances ; those later sown proved the best crop ; considerable injury by insects, especially to earlier sown, by grub, and finger and toe. No injury from weeds.  Pastures average growth, but probably not of average quality, owing to the dark cold season.  Stock did not thrive quite so well as usual, but were free from disease ; rather more braxy in young sheep than usual, probably due to want of constitution in lambs from severe winter and spring 1880–81, coupled with the very cold wet autumn of 1881. Clip of wool under average, owing to the severe character of the previous winter ; not much complaint against quality.

ROSS-SHIRE.—Wheat in some cases failed altogether, killed by frost ; produce in other cases low, average certainly not exceeding 24 bushels ; quality of grain and straw both inferior ; seed sown about 3 bushels per acre. Barley, quantity over an average, 35 to 40 bushels on average, but running up to 55 bushels on good lands ; quality inferior from lack of germinating powers, and below average weight ; quality of straw good ; average seed sown 3 bushels per acre.  Oats, quantity of grain deficient, average about 32 bushels ; quantity of straw deficient, quality good ; quality of grain only fair, in some cases inferior ; seed sown about 4 bushels, sometimes 5. Harvest three weeks behind usual time.  Quantity of hay deficient as compared with last year ; average perhaps not more than 25 to 30 cwts. ; generally fairly got and of average quality ; clover and rye-grass fairly mixed. Potato crop yield much superior to last year ; quantity averaging perhaps in good and bad land 6½ tons ; little disease, what there was only showed itself at lifting time.  Turnip crop much inferior to last year, which was over an average ; this year probably not above 12 to 14 tons ; brairded well, but early sowings to a large extent cut by frost, and in some cases destroyed by fly ; much resown. Not much injury from insects, except turnip-fly. No unusual injury from weeds. Pastures much inferior to last year ; grass late in coming, and, from want of sunshine, soft, and did not stand out well. Stock did not make much progress ; sheep on hill pasture never got into good condition ; no disease, but considerable loss of ewes and lambs at lambing time. Clip of wool on well-fed park sheep about an average ; on hill pasture clip very light.

SUTHERLANDSHIRE.—Wheat not grown. Barley, 3 to 4 bushels are sown, according to locality ; less quantity of grain and quality not so good owing to the wet, cold summer ; straw good, as harvest work was got over quickly. Oats, very deficient on leas in the return of grain ; grain and straw both good. Harvest rather after usual time. Hay crop, one-third less than last year. Meadow hay crop less productive than last year. Potato crop, no disease and a good crop. Turnip crop—turnips did not braird regularly, and were in many places sown twice or three times ; crop very much below an average. Turnips were supposed to be injured by fly in some places ; I think in most cases the injury was done by frost. Weeds of the usual kinds grew very strongly, owing to the wet season, and helped to keep back the turnip crop. Pastures were not of average growth and quality with last year, except on dry soils and in favourable situations. Stock did not thrive well on pasture. Cattle and sheep have been free from disease. Clip of wool, quality fair ; quantity under an average owing to the severity of the previous winter.

CAITHNESS-SHIRE.—No wheat grown. Barley, 32 bushels per acre, about 4 bushels less than last year ; seed 4 to 5 bushels ; straw an average. Oats, 30 bushels per acre, 8 to 10 bushels under last year ; straw an average ; weight of grain 2 lbs. per bushel less ; straw greater than last year ; seed 4 to 6 bushels per acre. Harvest fully fourteen days later than average. Quality of hay good ; quantity 2 to 3 cwts. per acre under former year. Little meadow hay grown ; crop secured in very good condition. Potatoes mostly grown for home use ; produce per acre not ascertained ; deficient in quantity and quality, but little disease ; potato crop about one-third less than last year. Turnip crop brairded well, but the first sowings were destroyed by frost in some cases, and fly in others, second sowing required in many instances, and a third in some. No damage from insects, except in the case of fly in turnips. An unusual absence of injury to oats by grub. No special damage by weeds. Frosts in June with the sunless weather of July and August injured growth and quality. Stock throve far from well. No disease among cattle ; some loss by rot in sheep in spring. Clip of wool inferior and under average.

ORKNEY.—No wheat and very little barley grown. Oats about 32 bushels, say 40 lbs. more straw than last year, but grain lighter. In some districts the crop much shaken by the gales on 11th and 12th October ; from 4 to 5 bushels sown. Harvest from ten to twelve days later than usual. Ryegrass much lighter than last year ; clover about the same ; quality good. Not much meadow hay. Potato crop much less, fully a half ; highest yield not over 3 tons ; small, and quality not so good, but no disease. Turnip crop not above half the weight of last year, and quality not so good ; brairded well, but did not come on well in consequance of frost ; no second sowing. No damage by insects. Injury by weeds more than usual, owing to the tardy growth of the turnip, principally runches and wild mustard. Pastures under the average, owing to the cold season. Stock did not thrive so well, but were free from disease. Clip of wool under the average ; quality not so good.

SHETLAND (Unst).—No wheat or barley grown. Bere, straw heavy and considerably more than last year, fully an average ; grain plentiful, and quite an average, but 2 lbs. lighter per bushel. Oats a very heavy crop, both as regards quantity and weight; straw very rank, and bulked quite one-third more than last year, and over an average. Harvest very late; began 21st September, three weeks later than last season, and a fortnight later than the average. The gales during the first week of October did great damage to uncut corn, of which there was a good deal. Rye-grass an average crop. Clover plentiful; quality did not turn out very good, owing to the great difficulty in curing during the continual rains. Meadow hay quite over an average, and much more than last year, but being more difficult to cure is not sound. Potato crop half of last year, which was an average crop; little or no disease heard of. Turnips about 12 tons, not much over half of last year; quality good; braird well; no second sowing; very long in getting single blade owing to cold weather in June and July. Weeds more than usual, owing to exceptionally wet weather, principally runches and wild mustard. The spring being exceptionally late and the summer very cold, pastures did not make the usual progress; quality not considered nourishing, and grass rather scarce. Stock did not thrive very well owing to the cold wet season, but were quite free from disease. Clip of wool, quality not good, and quantity about one-fourth under last year, which was an average.

## METEOROLOGY OF 1881.

THE weather of 1879 and 1881 will long mark these two years as among the most disastrous to the farming interests of Scotland in recent times. From November 1878 to October 1879, the mean temperature of the months was uniformly low without a break, and generally to such an extent that the mean of these twelve months was $3°·1$ under the average of that of previous years. Again, from October 1880 to October 1881, the temperature of each month, with the single exception of May, was under the mean, the average of these thirteen months being $3°·0$ less than the mean of previous years. The only twelve consecutive months since 1764, which show a greater mean degree of cold than these two years, are the following:—

February 1782 to January 1783, when deficiency was $4°·5$
February 1799 to January 1800,          „          „       $3°·3$
November 1815 to October 1816,          „          „       $3°·3$

If we except 1860, no other consecutive twelve months can be selected, the weather of which showed anything that can well be regarded as an approach to the above. Thus the last three years contributes two out of the six conspicuously cold years which have occurred during the past 118 years.

JANUARY 1881.—The opening month of this year had a temperature about $10°·0$ below the average of January, and was, besides, absolutely the coldest month experienced since 1764. The next coldest month was January 1814, the temperature of which was $9°·0$ under the mean. The only other winter months marked by a deficiency of temperature amounting to at least $7°·0$ were, in 1780, January $7°·3$; in 1785, February and March, $7°·0$; in 1838, February, $7°·8$; in 1855, February, $8°·0$; in 1874,

December, 7°·5; and in 1878, December, 8°·2.   The great and unprecedented cold of January 1881 was felt in a very unequal degree over Scotland, being much less in the north and west than in the south and east, and on the coast than in inland situations. Thus the deficiency was 2°·5 at North Unst, 3°·0 at Cape Wrath, 4°·6 in the south of Cantyre, and 6°·0 at the Mull of Galloway; whereas at Inverness it was 9°·7, at Aberdeen 8°·6, at Glasgow and Dalkeith 10°·3, at Lanark 11°·7, at Milne Graden 12°·1, and at Stobo Castle 13°·4.   In Shetland, Orkney, and in the extreme north of Caithness and Sutherland colder months have occurred than January 1881,—January 1867 having been on the whole colder in the northern regions, but elsewhere over Scotland January 1881 was absolutely the coldest month.   The mean temperature was lower than any previously recorded month in varied amounts up to 4°·0; this excessive degree of cold being experienced chiefly in the upper narrow valleys of the interior of the country, such as Lairg in Sutherland, Upper Deeside and Tweeddale, and the uplying valleys of the Cheviots.   The greatest absolute cold occurred generally during the night immediately preceding the great snow storm of London and the south of England on the 18th.   The lowest temperatures were −16°·0 at Springwood Park, near Kelso; −15°·0 at Stobo Castle; −13°·0 at Paxton House, near Berwick, and −11°·0 at Lairg and Thirlestane Castle.   These excessively low temperatures were all but identical with those which occurred in the same districts during the memorable frost of December 4, 1879, and on both occasions great and unexampled damage was done to our forest trees. This temperature reading of −16°·0 observed at Springwood Park in December 1879, and again in January 1881, is absolutely the lowest hitherto observed anywhere in the British Islands, with a properly protected verified instrument.

The rainfall of the month was everywhere under the average, nearly the whole of which fell in the form of snow; and though in many places railways were blocked and buried under the snow-drifts, yet nowhere was the snow so deep that when melted did the water equal the average rainfall of January for the locality.   The heaviest falls occurred in East Lothian, Berwick-shire, and Roxburghshire; but in the south and west, and in inland situations, except a few isolated districts, such as the Pentland Hills and Douglas Castle, the aqueous precipitation only amounted to from 5 to 25 per cent. of the average rainfall of the month.

FEBRUARY.—This month, though not in the same degree as January, was also exceptionally cold.   The mean temperature was 4°·6 below the average of February, and during the past 118 years there have been only eight colder Februarys.   The distribution of this cold was unusually uniform, the deficiency

z

being from 2°·0 to 3°·5 over western districts, and from 3°·5 to 5°·5 over eastern and inland districts. The snow and rainfall was singularly unequal in its distribution over the country. Over the whole of the east coast, and for at least 30 miles inland, the rain and melted snow was much above the average of February. The excess above the average was 164 per cent. at Barry, 155 per cent. at Edinburgh, 130 per cent. in the east of Fife and Haddingtonshire, and generally at least double the average near the sea from Ellon to Dunbar. The snowfall rapidly diminished inland, if we except Caithness and Sutherland, so that in all the more strictly inland situations, and westward to the coast opposite the Hebrides, the fall was under the average, the deficiency in western districts of the counties of Perth, Inverness, Ross, and Sutherland amounting to from 40 to 80 per cent. In the Hebrides and along a narrow strip of the coast from Ardnamurchan to the Mull of Galloway, and eastward along the Solway to Gretna, the rainfall was from 10 to 40 per cent. above the average.

MARCH.—The temperature of this month was 2°·6 under the average, this diminution being brought about chiefly by the cold frosty nights. The deficiency was considerably greater in the north and east than in the south and west. Thus, in the north of Shetland, it amounted to 5°·0, whereas at the Mull of Galloway it was only 1°·6; and in South Uist, while it was only 1°·0, at Aberdeen it was 3°·4. But it was the extraordinary and unequally distributed snow and rainfalls that will long make this month memorable in the annals of our Scottish weather. As regards Scotland, the snow-storms of this remarkable winter may be regarded as having culminated in the great storm of the 5th and 6th, when, on all hands, telegraph wires were broken, in some places railway trains were buried 20 and even 50 feet under wreaths of snow, and the east coast, especially from Buchanness southward, was strewn with innumerable wrecks. A sudden thaw set in on the 11th, the effects of which will not soon be forgotten by those who happened to travel at the time through the Midland counties, the low-lying grounds of Strathearn and Strathallan being converted into a chain of lakes rolling large waves and wreckage of all sorts on their lee shores. The distribution of the rainfall over the country was unequal in the highest degree. Thus, near the Solway, it was from 50 to 85 above the average, but higher up Annan and Nithsdale it was only the average. Over Galloway, Ayr, Cantyre, Islay, and the southern Hebrides it rose to from 40 to 120 per cent. above the average; but in the North Hebrides, Skye, and the coasts surrounding the Minch, the rainfall was under the average, in several cases little more than half the usual amount having been recorded. In Shetland, Orkney, and the coasts of the Moray Firth round to the mouth of the Spey, it rose generally to nearly a half more than the average. Over the whole of the north-east of Scotland, between the Spey and the Dee, the rainfall was from a third to a half deficient; whilst on the other hand, from the Dee to the Forth, some of the heaviest rain and snow falls of the season occurred. Thus at Fettercairn, the excess for the month was 183, and at Loch Leven and Cupar 122 per cent. On the south shores of the Firth of Forth the aqueous precipitation was less than the average, in several places only a half; whilst over the Pentland Hills and upper reaches of the Clyde and the Tweed there was an excess of from 64 to 80 per cent., and over the higher ground in the east of Berwick an excess of 30 to 40 per cent. occurred.

APRIL.—The temperature of this month was 2°·4 under the average of the month, the greater part of this diminution of temperature being due to the colder nights, the deficiency of which was double that of the days. The sunshine was a few hours above the average, but the continued prevalence of east and north-east winds kept down the temperature. As happens with easterly winds, especially as the spring advances, the deficiency of temperature was very much greater on the eastern slopes of the country than in the west. Thus on the Lower Tweed, the deficiency was 4°·0, but at Ardrossan only 1°·5; at Aberdeen it was 2°·5, but in Skye it was about the average; and midland districts were intermediate. Everywhere over Scotland, except the north-west of Sutherland, the rainfall was below, and very greatly below, the average. The deficiency was distributed over the country in a remarkably uniform manner, being generally about 50 per cent., falling, however, in a few isolated localities as low as 75 per cent. The weather of the month, therefore, was remarkably cold and dry.

MAY.—This month stands out as the only exceptional month to the prevalent cold weather of the year, the temperature having been 1°·8 above the average. This excess was wholly due to the greater warmth of the days; in other words, to the stronger sunshine. Indeed, during the last quarter of a century, the day temperature of May was only once exceeded, viz., in 1859, when it was 61°·7, or 2°·3 higher than last year. In May 1881, cloud was 20 per cent. less than the average: sunshine 16 per cent. above it, and as happen in such warm weather thunder-storms were greatly in excess, being nearly double the average. All these peculiarities attained a maximum during the last week of the month, when, indeed, over the greater part of Scotland, the highest temperatures for the year were recorded. The excess of temperature was very decidedly greatest in the west. Thus while at Eyemouth, Aberdeen, and Dunrobin in the east, the excess was respectively 1°·0, 1°·6, and 0°·9; at Callton Mor, South

Uist, and Scourie in the west, it was 2°·6, 2°·3, and 2°·2. The excess in inland situations closely approximated to that of the west adjoining. The rainfall, again, was unequally distributed. Over the whole of the south draining into the Solway and Firth of Clyde, the rainfall was double the average, and nearly an equal excess occurred over a somewhat broad track stretching from Cantyre to Cupar. Along a broad track from the sea inland, extending from Montrose northward to Orkney, the rainfall was largely above the average; also in the South Hebrides, in Mull, and adjoining parts of the mainland. On the other hand, a deficiency was felt in the Lews, West Ross-shire, Skye, a large part of Argyllshire, Forfarshire, East Perth-shire, East Fife, Mid-Lothian, the greater part of Berwickshire, and the upper parts of the Clyde and Tweed.

JUNE—The temperature was 2°·2 below the average, the deficiency of the days being 1°·7, whilst that of the nights was 2°·7. Clouds were above the average, and sunshine 17 per cent. under the mean. This deficiency was pretty evenly distributed, the maximum, however, being in midland districts north of the Forth and Clyde. A marked feature of the meteorology of the month was the high temperature of the first days, continued from May, and the remarkable cold which prevailed from the 5th to the 11th, which inflicted serious injury on the green crops in many parts of the country, particularly in the counties of Perth and Inverness. The rainfall was greatly in excess along the Solway, being double the average near the head of the Firth; fully a half above the average over the west from Galloway to Ardnamurchan; a third, northward from this point to Storno-way; and from a third to half in Orkney, Caithness, East Suther-land, East Aberdeenshire, Fife, West Perthshire, Dumbartonshire, and Renfrewshire. On the other hand, in Berwick, East and Mid-Lothian, Upper Tweeddale, Forfarshire, North Perthshire, Inver-ness, Moray, Nairnshire, and Ross-shire, it was under the average, the greatest deficiency being about a fourth under the average in eastern districts south of the Firth of Forth.

JULY.—The temperature was 1°·0 below the average, and all but the whole of this defect arose from the reduced temperature of the days. With this reduced temperature there occurred unfortunately 10 per cent. more cloud than is usual in July, and consequently fifty-five hours less sunshine, being 25 per cent. less than the mean. This state of things resulted from an extra-ordinary excess of south-west and west winds, which, for a quarter of a century, has not been exceeded in any July. Consequently the greatest depression of temperature was felt over the west and districts open to the westerly winds, and the least in the eastern districts. Indeed, in three separate districts, mean temperatures were even slightly, about half a degree, above the mean, these districts being about Wick, Forfarshire, and north of Fife, and Mid and East Lothian and East Berwickshire. In these districts it is noteworthy that the temperature of the days was fully above the average of past Julys. Thus in this important month, so far as sunshine and days' temperatures were concerned, the weather of the Lothians and the counties of Forfar and Fife was greatly more in favour of the growing and flowering cereals than elsewhere in Scotland. Except a small patch of Perthshire about Pitlochrie, and a larger district including the Tweed and its affluents and lower Esk, Annan and Nithsdale, the rainfall was everywhere above the average. At all places open to the west, the excess was large, generally from a half to three-fourths more, but rising in some places to more than double the usual amount. It was also equally large in eastern districts north of the Dee. If we except West Perthshire and Upper Clydesdale, the rainfall was not excessive at inland situations.

AUGUST.—August turned out to be a much worse month than July as regards the weather and crops, the temperature being 3°·5 under the average, cloud being in excess, sunshine deficient, and north-west winds considerably more prevalent than usual. The defect of temperature was about equally partitioned between the days and the nights, and was, besides, remarkably uniform in all parts of the country. On the other hand, the rainfall was most unequally distributed. Thus, if we except Dee and Donside, part of Orkney, the coasts of the Minch, Mull, and Clydesdale, the whole of Scotland to the north and west of a line drawn from Montrose round by Perth and Douglas to Kirkcudbright, had a rainfall less than the average, the deficiency in some districts, such as the shores of the Moray Firth, Strathtay, and Argyll, being from 30 to 50 per cent.; but from the Firth of Forth to the Cheviots, the rainfall was excessive, in many cases disastrously so, the excess above the mean in some parts of East Lothian being upwards of 150 per cent. Thus, then, in the important grain-growing districts of Berwick and the Lothians, the weather of August 1881 was felt far more disastrously than elsewhere. This weather may be considered to have been at its worst on the day of the great review at Edinburgh, and the low temperature of that and following days.

SEPTEMBER.—September, as regards its temperatures, its partitioning between the days and nights, and its distribution over the country, may be regarded as a fair average harvest month, not so, however, as regards its rainfall, which was most abnormal in its distribution. If a line be drawn from Aboyne, passing southwards through Perth, Cupar, Linlithgow, Bowhill, and Wolfelee, it will divide Scotland into two widely different divisions as respects the rainfall; to the east of the line the rainfall was in excess of the average, whereas to the west of it the rainfall was everywhere deficient. Over a considerable part of the rainy division the excess above the average was from 40 to 50; and again, as in August, the greater part of the excess was precipitated over the Lothians and Berwickshire. As regards the rest of Scotland, the weather was characterised by great and unusual dryness; over large and extensive breadths of country less than half the usual rainfall of September was measured. It is scarcely necessary to add that, as regards the south-east of Scotland between the Cheviots and the Forth, the weather of 1881, so calamitous to the agricultural interests, wrought there its disastrous work with a crushing completeness nowhere else experienced in Scotland.

OCTOBER —The temperature was 1°·8 under the average, the defect of the days and the nights being equal. In the north, the deficiency was small, being almost everywhere north of Aberdeen less than a degree, but it rapidly increased south of the Tay. Thus, the defect was 2°·4 at Edinburgh, 3°·3 on the Lower Tweed, 4°·4 among the Cheviots, and 4°·9 at Silloth. Again, a most unequal distribution of the rainfall characterised this month. Along Tweeddale above Melrose, and over the whole of the north-east of Scotland to the east of a line drawn from Inverness by Pitlochrie to North Berwick, the rainfall was above the average, the greatest excess being in Strathspey and Upper Deeside, where at Braemar it was 66 per cent. above the average. Elsewhere it was below the mean, being, as in the case of September, only half the average of the month over a third part of Scotland, and generally in the same districts. This month will be long remembered for the great storm which swept over the British Islands on the 14th, and burst on the east of Scotland with a furious impetuosity scarcely to be equalled by any storm of recent years, for the extensive breadths of forests which it levelled with the ground, and for the well-nigh unparalleled loss of life which it occasioned among our fishing population between the Forth and the Tweed.

NOVEMBER.—In this month a total change set in, instead of a temperature under the average which had all but persistently prevailed for thirteen months previously, the temperature now rose to a degree absolutely unprecedented for November in our Scottish records of weather. Everywhere the excess was abnormally large,—the smallest excess being 3°·5 on the north coasts and the largest in inland situations, as happens at this time of the year with high temperatures, since in such circumstances the cooling through terrestrial radiation is much less than usual in strictly inland places. The greatest excess occurred in the central districts south of the Forth and Clyde, where it rose to 6°·3 above the average of the month. During the past 118 years no such large excess has been recorded in November, the nearest to it being an excess of 5°·5 in 1818, and 5°·2 in 1792 and 1847. The distribution of the rainfall was strikingly unequal in Scotland. The peculiarities of temperature and rainfall were due to an extraordinary prevalence of S., S.W., and W. winds, greater indeed than has been experienced in any November during at least a quarter of a century. In the south of Scotland these winds were south-south-westerly, but in proceeding ou their course they became southerly in the south-east, and then south-easterly farther north. Hence on the Solway, the rainfall was fully 50 per cent. above the average, increasing to 150 per cent. of excess at Moffat, and rapidly diminishing after passing to the north of the Lead and Lowther Hills, till in Berwickshire and the Lothians the rainfall was less than the average, the deficiency in East Lothian being 50 per cent. Crossing the Firth of Forth, we meet an extensive tract reaching as far as the high grounds of the Grampians, where the rainfall was excessive, rising from an excess of fully 50 per cent. on the Fife coast to 100 per cent. at Pitlochrie, and 157 per cent. at Dalnaspidal. Again, beyond the Grampians and including the whole of the north of Scotland to north of a line drawn through the Butt of Lewis, Scourie, Forres, Ballater, and Montrose, the rainfall was below the average, the deficiency in the counties of Caithness, Banff, and the north-east of Aberdeen being 50 per cent. It is noteworthy that the foreshores of the Firth of Forth, the Moray Firth, and the Pentland Firth had a rainfall greatly under the average, and that this always occurs when the rain-bringing winds are southerly and south-easterly.

DECEMBER.—The temperature was about half a degree above the average. In Shetland the excess fully exceeded 2°·0, but in Wigtownshire the temperature was about 1°·0 below the average. Over the whole of the west, from Cape Wrath to Galloway, temperature was under the average, though only slightly so; but in the east it was above the average, the greatest excess being nearly 1°·0 from Inverness to Duncansbay Head. Over the west the rainfall was above the average, the greatest excess, about 50 per cent., being to the south of Skye; but it was under the average in all eastern and inland districts, and over the whole of Galloway and Clydesdale as far to westward as Dumbarton. The deficiency was greatest in Aberdeen, being 73 at Cluny Castle and 95 per cent. at Logie Coldstone below the average.

Since abnormalities of temperature and rainfall are brought about by the winds which prevail, the following table, showing for each month the winds which were in excess or defect of the averages of the previous twenty-four years, may not be without interest:—

TABLE SHOWING THE EXCESS OR DEFECT OF DAYS FROM THE AVERAGE OF
THE DIRECTION AND FORCE OF THE DIFFERENT WINDS IN SCOTLAND
DURING 1881.

| | North. | North-east. | East. | South-east. | South. | South-west. | West. | North-west. | Calm. | Force. lbs. to square foot. |
|---|---|---|---|---|---|---|---|---|---|---|
| January . . . | +2 | +2 | +2 | −1 | −2 | −4 | 0 | 0 | +1 | −0·53 |
| February . . . | +1 | +2 | +3 | +1 | 0 | −4 | −3 | 0 | 0 | 0·00 |
| March . . . . | 0 | −1 | −2 | +2 | −1 | −1 | +3 | 0 | 0 | +1 05 |
| April . . . . . | 0 | +2 | +2 | +2 | −1 | −3 | −1 | 0 | −1 | +0·32 |
| May . . . . . | −1 | 0 | +1 | 0 | 0 | 0 | +1 | −1 | 0 | +0·65 |
| June . . . . . | +1 | 0 | 0 | 0 | +1 | 0 | −1 | 0 | −1 | +0 82 |
| July . . . . . | −1 | −1 | −2 | −1 | −1 | +3 | +4 | +1 | −2 | +0·83 |
| August . . . | +1 | +1 | +1 | −2 | −1 | −3 | +1 | +3 | −1 | +0·80 |
| September . . | 0 | +2 | +2 | 0 | 0 | −2 | −1 | −1 | 0 | +0·10 |
| October . . . | 0 | +1 | +3 | +2 | −1 | −3 | −2 | +1 | −1 | +1·71 |
| November . . . | −2 | −2 | −2 | 0 | +2 | +5 | +1 | −1 | −1 | +2 30 |
| December . . . | −1 | −1 | −1 | −1 | +2 | +1 | +1 | 0 | 0 | +0 64 |

Thus January, which was the coldest month in Scotland of which there exists any authentic record, was remarkable for the lightness of wind and predominance of northerly and easterly winds; and November, which was warmer than any previous November as far back as 1764, was characterised by an unprecedented predominance of strong south-westerly winds.

The cutting of the harvest commenced from two to four weeks later than the average, being about a week earlier in the east than in the west. The earliest district, as compared with past years, was Tweeddale, a circumstance due to the combined higher temperature and smaller rainfall there up to the end of August. The latest district was the south-west of Scotland, where in some places harvest was five weeks later in commencing than usual.

Everywhere wheat was under the average, in some places as much as 50 per cent., the crops in some places which were not under a covering of snow being destroyed, or all but destroyed, by the great frosts and stormy winds of January, February, and March.

Barley also was under the average generally, but in a few districts, as along the south coast of the Moray Firth, the crop was an average one.

Oats were better crops, being in the majority of the districts, at any rate, the average; this was particularly the case in Shetland, Orkney, and to the south of Aberdeen and Mull. The quality and weight did not stand generally so high, though over considerable breadths at least the average weight was secured, and in several districts the weight was from one to three lbs. above the average.

As regards the cereals, next to the low summer temperature, the distribution of the rainfall most affected the returns. Thus the broken wet weather and heavy rains which prevailed on the east coast and from 10 to 30 miles inland, from the Dee to the Tweed during August, September, and a large part of October, increased the damage already sustained by the coldness of the summer, and made the season of 1881 perhaps the most disastrous in recent years to the farming interest in the important agricultural districts of this part of Scotland.

Over the same districts, these heavy autumnal rains inflicted the most serious damage on the potato crop, from one-third to two-thirds of the crop being in many places lost by disease. Champions, however, suffered little or none at all, even in these districts. On the other hand, in the north-east and north of Scotland, and in the west generally, where these late summer and early autumnal rains did not prevail, little or no disease appeared, and good crops were secured.

The frosts that occurred in the beginning of June seriously damaged the turnip crop in districts, chiefly inland situations, and the crop over Scotland generally was a very poor one, being a third, a half, and even in some places three-fourths under the average. Only two or three of the observers report a good or at least average crop for their districts. Some late growth was, however, made during the singularly open weather which closed the year.

AGRICULTURAL STATISTICS OF SCOTLAND.—RETURNED UPON 4TH JUNE 1881.—(*Extracted from the Government Returns.*)

TABLE No. 1.—TOTAL ACREAGE UNDER EACH KIND OF CROP, BARE FALLOW, AND GRASS, IN EACH COUNTY OF SCOTLAND.

| Counties. | Total Acreage under Crops, Bare Fallow, and Grass. | CORN CROPS. | | | | | | | GREEN CROPS. | | | | | | | Clover, Sanfoin, and Grasses under Rotation. | Permanent Pasture or Grass not broken up in Rotation (exclusive of Heath or Mountain Land). | Flax. | Bare Fallow or Uncropped Arable Land. |
|---|---|---|---|---|---|---|---|---|---|---|---|---|---|---|---|---|---|---|---|
| | | Wheat. | Barley or Bere. | Oats. | Rye. | Beans. | Peas. | Total. | Potatoes. | Turnips. | Mangold. | Carrot. | Cabbage, Kohl-Rabi, and Rape. | Vetches, &c. | Total. | | | | |
| | Acres. | Acres. | Acres. | Acres. | Acres. | Acres. | Acres. | Acres. | Acres. | Acres. | Acres. | Acres. | Acres. | Acres. | Acres. | Acres. | Acres. | Acres. | Acres. |
| 1. Aberdeen | 604,784 | 48 | 17,874 | 194,108 | 593 | 151 | 224 | 212,477 | 7,885 | 63,287 | 21 | 91 | 71 | 2,835 | 104,210 | 259,550 | 97,406 | 9 | 809 |
| 2. Argyle | 120,452 | 7 | 2,529 | 90,695 | 613 | 886 | 13 | 34,481 | 7,481 | 5,256 | 91 | 30 | 141 | 35 | 12,900 | 29,261 | 60,164 | — | 1,776 |
| 3. Ayr | 317,719 | 8,411 | 4,480 | 90,596 | 410 | 1,802 | 23 | 60,287 | 10,098 | 7,670 | 782 | 861 | 50 | 200 | 19,906 | 98,719 | 149,680 | — | 1,177 |
| 4. Banff | 167,709 | 806 | 8,377 | 53,110 | 109 | 166 | 44 | 61,904 | 2,081 | 25,390 | 9 | 4 | 5 | 968 | 28,935 | 67,263 | 9,268 | — | 269 |
| 5. Berwick | 194,413 | 3,886 | 21,443 | 38,043 | 20 | 1,924 | 295 | 84,317 | 3,081 | 20,068 | 161 | 13 | 278 | 823 | 34,992 | 66,050 | 86,915 | — | 329 |
| 6. Bute | 25,488 | 103 | 701 | 4,769 | 83 | 188 | 10 | 5,764 | 1,455 | 1,412 | 10 | 4 | 9 | 62 | 2,948 | 6,703 | 9,994 | — | 15 |
| 7. Caithness | 108,938 | 13 | 1,894 | 25,806 | 101 | — | 80 | 26,874 | 1,990 | 14,051 | 0 | — | 68 | 809 | 16,989 | 39,604 | 25,604 | — | 926 |
| 8. Clackmannan | 15,788 | 786 | 1,101 | 8,290 | 19 | 715 | — | 5,899 | 387 | 966 | 22 | — | 10 | 72 | 1,458 | 3,640 | 4,446 | — | 281 |
| 9. Dumbarton | 46,080 | 1,280 | 614 | 8,119 | 5 | 274 | 6 | 10,200 | 3,804 | 1,544 | 33 | 8 | 49 | 128 | 4,059 | 8,201 | 18,054 | — | 72 |
| 10. Dumfries | 233,362 | 277 | 1,646 | 49,884 | 85 | 80 | 108 | 60,494 | 5,849 | 20,247 | 69 | 28 | 174 | 131 | 26,618 | 60,298 | 98,903 | — | 104 |
| 11. Edinburgh | 134,999 | 4,459 | 11,468 | 21,980 | 29 | 987 | 9 | 38,272 | 7,392 | 12,495 | 16 | 49 | 502 | 141 | 21,484 | 81,570 | 49,403 | — | 190 |
| 12. Elgin | 103,526 | 2,628 | 14,916 | 32,023 | 606 | 56 | 39 | 40,158 | 3,516 | 12,630 | 16 | 9 | — | 1,080 | 20,684 | 38,670 | 6,611 | 7 | 106 |
| 13. Fife | 247,070 | 18,143 | 31,479 | 36,111 | 1,024 | 1,818 | 37 | 84,944 | 10,165 | 27,547 | 17 | 88 | 66 | 487 | 48,204 | 63,147 | 60,768 | — | 1,474 |
| 14. Forfar | 263,303 | 10,038 | 17,081 | 61,492 | 114 | 605 | 82 | 84,104 | 18,640 | 35,011 | 45 | 33 | 40 | 1,271 | 60,598 | 54,802 | 24,902 | — | 446 |
| 15. Haddington | 116,680 | 7,748 | 8,616 | 17,061 | 114 | 2,008 | 118 | 45,590 | 2,989 | 14,447 | 88 | 186 | 140 | 1,120 | 26,001 | 60,388 | 16,088 | — | 988 |
| 16. Inverness | 138,824 | 50 | 13,120 | 80,409 | 875 | 10 | 49 | 40,018 | 9,425 | 11,121 | 1 | 17 | — | 902 | 29,001 | 27,970 | 40,311 | 7 | 994 |
| 17. Kincardine | 130,681 | 877 | 13,130 | 31,480 | 45 | 591 | 40 | 44,808 | 3,698 | 13,304 | — | — | 8 | 168 | 18,719 | 37,853 | 40,311 | — | 594 |
| 18. Kinross | 31,459 | 113 | 1,840 | 5,601 | 8 | 36 | — | 7,198 | 987 | 2,568 | — | 17 | 11 | 450 | 22,478 | 48,645 | 6,622 | 1 | 194 |
| 19. Kirkcudbright | 179,287 | 148 | 939 | 31,061 | 80 | 187 | 43 | 32,349 | 7,193 | 7,968 | 91 | 4 | 11 | 63 | 3,698 | 11,849 | 9,100 | — | 17 |
| 20. Lanark | 247,777 | 3,790 | 863 | 44,989 | 71 | 1,408 | 43 | 60,075 | 3,847 | 14,096 | 89 | 88 | 403 | 117 | 18,081 | 71,001 | 57,471 | — | 236 |
| 21. Linlithgow | 59,274 | 1,450 | 4,874 | 10,948 | 18 | 666 | 9 | 17,847 | 9,427 | 6,652 | 39 | 88 | 181 | 1,391 | 18,081 | 68,861 | 118,407 | — | 431 |
| 22. Nairn | 36,369 | 1 | 3,046 | 6,897 | 980 | 8 | 16 | 9,283 | 8,053 | 8,861 | 21 | 8 | 8 | 819 | 19,678 | 12,960 | 21,289 | 5 | 387 |
| 23. Orkney | 108,769 | 1 | 6,910 | 32,078 | 10 | 1 | 38 | 88,533 | 698 | 4,109 | — | — | — | 40 | 7,264 | 10,047 | 9,149 | — | 79 |
| 24. Shetland | 58,437 | — | 2,665 | 6,100 | — | — | — | 10,774 | 8,187 | 13,952 | — | — | 44 | 849 | 17,439 | 21,148 | 20,946 | — | 991 |
| 25. Peebles | 49,117 | — | 1,286 | 9,141 | — | — | 21 | 10,447 | 294 | 768 | — | — | 263 | — | 4,140 | 787 | 41,909 | — | 947 |
| 26. Perth | 346,788 | 8,005 | 24,697 | 69,848 | 398 | 2,785 | 79 | 105,018 | 91,028 | 81,008 | 34 | 13 | 69 | 1,063 | 63,308 | 6,087 | 11,909 | — | 39 |
| 27. Renfrew | 94,589 | 2,748 | 283 | 14,764 | 30 | 492 | 11 | 17,713 | 6,042 | 3,079 | 52 | 18 | 88 | 922 | 8,494 | 100,461 | 84,829 | — | 2,198 |
| 28. Ross & Cromarty | 182,049 | 2,877 | 13,188 | 38,188 | 948 | 8 | 87 | 48,491 | 10,838 | 16,698 | 21 | — | 18 | 728 | 97,788 | 18,891 | 49,447 | — | 845 |
| 29. Roxburgh | 181,606 | 1,448 | 14,533 | 38,684 | 91 | 645 | 64 | 51,650 | 2,288 | 26,015 | 66 | 4 | 452 | 887 | 29,202 | 37,109 | 18,987 | — | 844 |
| 30. Selkirk | 98,328 | 697 | 697 | 4,691 | 4 | 8 | 9 | 5,182 | 294 | 2,855 | — | — | 189 | 49 | 3,974 | 56,408 | 43,730 | — | 697 |
| 31. Stirling | 114,151 | 2,611 | 4,965 | 18,840 | 110 | 8,176 | — | 80,922 | 4,778 | 4,658 | 14 | 11 | 81 | 887 | 9,765 | 7,765 | 7,025 | — | 80 |
| 32. Sutherland | 31,011 | 56 | 2,468 | 8,079 | 72 | — | 46 | 10,461 | 2,028 | 1,818 | — | — | 15 | 508 | 9,968 | 28,668 | 49,101 | 89 | 1,418 |
| 33. Wigtown | 146,440 | 2,209 | 8,065 | 33,271 | 105 | 417 | — | 89,067 | 3,897 | 16,395 | 448 | 208 | 79 | 178 | 19,655 | 61,393 | 25,975 | — | 886 |
| **Total** | **4,769,613** | **74,728** | **270,417** | **1,030,727** | **7,290** | **19,874** | **1,557** | **1,404,708** | **189,101** | **490,804** | **2,101** | **1,910** | **8,891** | **17,296** | **704,086** | **1,461,989** | **1,172,169** | **111** | **19,642** |

TABLE No. 2.—NUMBER OF HORSES, CATTLE, SHEEP, AND PIGS, IN EACH COUNTY OF SCOTLAND.

| Counties | Horses (including Ponies). | | | Cattle. | | | | Sheep. | | | Pigs. |
| | Used solely for Agriculture, &c. | Kept solely for Breeding. | Total. | Cows and Heifers in Milk or in Calf. | Other Cattle. | | Total. | 1 Year Old and above. | Under 1 Year. | Total. | |
| | | | | | 2 years of Age and above. | Under 2 Years of Age. | | | | | |
|---|---|---|---|---|---|---|---|---|---|---|---|
| 1. Aberdeen | 20,204 | 5,916 | 26,920 | 40,688 | 41,600 | 75,841 | 157,477 | 102,843 | 88,849 | 196,695 | 7,170 |
| 2. Argyle | 4,234 | 3,005 | 7,189 | 22,054 | 16,027 | 21,761 | 60,442 | 717,545 | 283,187 | 999,789 | 4,243 |
| 3. Ayr | 6,181 | 2,556 | 8,737 | 43,996 | 14,517 | 20,819 | 88,382 | 216,322 | 129,457 | 344,779 | 12,445 |
| 4. Banff | 6,889 | 1,692 | 8,074 | 12,807 | 7,114 | 22,281 | 41,853 | 32,727 | 18,000 | 60,733 | 2,064 |
| 5. Berwick | 4,139 | 1,296 | 5,425 | 8,266 | 4,476 | 6,921 | 14,042 | 152,080 | 111,881 | 288,961 | 8,383 |
| 6. Bute | 809 | 319 | 1,128 | 2,807 | 1,255 | 2,666 | 7,438 | 20,461 | 18,678 | 40,139 | 641 |
| 7. Caithness | 8,907 | 1,292 | 9,189 | 6,765 | 8,450 | 90,028 | 90,028 | 88,699 | 94,673 | 88,372 | 1,647 |
| 8. Clackmannan | 615 | 208 | 718 | 1,808 | 1,050 | 1,188 | 3,406 | 6,588 | 2,949 | 9,537 | 1,628 |
| 9. Dumbarton | 1,878 | 607 | 1,885 | 6,945 | 2,320 | 3,628 | 12,838 | 47,517 | 21,980 | 69,447 | 759 |
| 10. Dumfries | 5,280 | 2,189 | 7,469 | 16,423 | 14,218 | 21,439 | 52,078 | 309,087 | 158,764 | 468,731 | 10,861 |
| 11. Edinburgh | 3,424 | 736 | 4,160 | 10,626 | 8,768 | 8,865 | 18,250 | 94,897 | 60,689 | 154,966 | 5,890 |
| 12. Elgin | 4,081 | 1,063 | 5,124 | 6,869 | 4,848 | 13,029 | 24,241 | 33,567 | 16,080 | 48,487 | 2,664 |
| 13. Fife | 7,728 | 2,443 | 10,166 | 8,788 | 14,063 | 14,675 | 38,076 | 42,317 | 26,968 | 69,275 | 5,866 |
| 14. Forfar | 8,343 | 2,012 | 10,368 | 11,920 | 10,210 | 17,575 | 45,505 | 52,670 | 86,716 | 119,886 | 4,004 |
| 15. Haddington | 2,892 | 569 | 2,811 | 1,960 | 4,396 | 3,006 | 9,062 | 88,408 | 48,621 | 111,999 | 2,830 |
| 16. Inverness | 6,756 | 2,161 | 8,917 | 20,849 | 9,085 | 22,058 | 52,567 | 506,818 | 182,489 | 684,307 | 2,818 |
| 17. Kincardine | 3,898 | 906 | 4,708 | 6,668 | 9,090 | 19,265 | 26,018 | 19,747 | 8,819 | 34,966 | 1,967 |
| 18. Kinross | 699 | 840 | 1,039 | 984 | 1,097 | 3,874 | 5,405 | 17,084 | 9,446 | 26,530 | 601 |
| 19. Kirkcudbright | 3,789 | 1,606 | 5,395 | 12,071 | 14,009 | 14,684 | 40,737 | 247,661 | 114,628 | 362,289 | 5,667 |
| 20. Lanark | 5,611 | 2,144 | 7,705 | 38,780 | 10,080 | 16,557 | 64,276 | 184,296 | 74,886 | 208,692 | 5,796 |
| 21. Linlithgow | 1,644 | 650 | 2,104 | 8,694 | 4,219 | 8,296 | 10,078 | 6,087 | 6,087 | 17,605 | 1,443 |
| 22. Nairn | 987 | 304 | 1,291 | 1,784 | 924 | 3,261 | 6,059 | 12,002 | 8,978 | 16,980 | 716 |
| 23. Orkney | 4,950 | 1,291 | 6,181 | 9,841 | 4,324 | 12,488 | 26,108 | 16,332 | 13,913 | 29,044 | 8,769 |
| 24. Shetland | 991 | 4,123 | 5,244 | 8,613 | 5,457 | 5,047 | 19,117 | 47,426 | 24,730 | 72,160 | 3,789 |
| 25. Peebles | 908 | 254 | 1,162 | 1,646 | 1,222 | 2,789 | 5,837 | 116,972 | 78,170 | 189,442 | 768 |
| 26. Perth | 10,977 | 3,351 | 14,328 | 19,501 | 23,178 | 34,960 | 78,634 | 474,728 | 200,868 | 675,081 | 7,741 |
| 27. Renfrew | 2,200 | 1,094 | 3,834 | 15,883 | 3,615 | 6,101 | 25,049 | 20,179 | 11,068 | 81,237 | 1,810 |
| 28. Ross and Cromarty | 5,880 | 1,073 | 7,603 | 17,647 | 9,188 | 16,146 | 43,181 | 250,086 | 95,492 | 345,678 | 6,655 |
| 29. Roxburgh | 3,688 | 799 | 4,482 | 4,692 | 5,821 | 6,575 | 16,488 | 273,292 | 198,786 | 468,075 | 8,344 |
| 30. Selkirk | 481 | 75 | 556 | 949 | 763 | 632 | 2,950 | 94,541 | 63,696 | 158,086 | 826 |
| 31. Stirling | 3,993 | 1,655 | 4,778 | 10,070 | 9,048 | 9,779 | 28,897 | 70,589 | 88,901 | 109,528 | 1,632 |
| 32. Sutherland | 2,301 | 687 | 1,788 | 2,576 | 2,980 | 4,419 | 13,975 | 169,314 | 45,820 | 214,484 | 1,078 |
| 33. Wigtown | 4,051 | 1,619 | 5,670 | 18,618 | 7,307 | 14,028 | 40,603 | 76,190 | 43,026 | 119,221 | 8,461 |
| Total, | 142,699 | 60,459 | 198,066 | 386,586 | 269,667 | 498,100 | 1,090,213 | 4,558,086 | 2,178,180 | 6,731,232 | 193,018 |

TABLE No. 3.—QUANTITIES AND VALUES OF THE IMPORTS OF LIVE CATTLE, SHEEP, AND SWINE, 1876 TO 1880.

| | QUANTITIES. | | | | | VALUES. | | | | |
|---|---|---|---|---|---|---|---|---|---|---|
| | 1876. | 1877. | 1878. | 1879. | 1880. | 1876. | 1877. | 1878. | 1879. | 1880. |
| | No. | No. | No. | No. | No. | £ | £ | £ | £ | £ |
| Live Cattle, | 271,276 | 201,198 | 253,462 | 217,768 | 886,724 | 4,960,440 | 3,817,490 | 5,080,702 | 4,839,481 | 7,793,060 |
| Live Sheep, | 1,041,829 | 874,065 | 892,135 | 944,888 | 941,121 | 2,925,962 | 2,107,465 | 2,171,004 | 2,252,884 | 3,206,456 |
| Live Swine, including Smoking Pigs, | 43,568 | 20,047 | 55,011 | 52,360 | 61,191 | 172,727 | 87,699 | 200,708 | 188,151 | 178,809 |
| Total, | 1,356,403 | 1,096,285 | 1,201,408 | 1,245,022 | 1,889,030 | 7,260,119 | 6,012,564 | 7,458,809 | 7,075,886 | 10,289,295 |

TABLE No. 4.—QUANTITIES AND VALUES OF THE IMPORTS OF BEEF AND PORK (SALTED), BACON AND HAMS, &c., 1876 TO 1880.

| | QUANTITIES. | | | | | VALUES. | | | | |
|---|---|---|---|---|---|---|---|---|---|---|
| | 1876. | 1877. | 1878. | 1879. | 1880. | 1876. | 1877. | 1878. | 1879. | 1880. |
| | Cwts. | Cwts. | Cwts. | Cwts. | Cwts. | £ | £ | £ | £ | £ |
| Meat— | | | | | | | | | | |
| Beef, salted, | 241,083 | 209,018 | 290,616 | 242,077 | 290,504 | 470,020 | 410,251 | 490,077 | 418,884 | 535,218 |
| Beef, fresh or slightly salted, | 178,208 | 468,867 | 508,807 | 509,250 | 727,892 | 467,640 | 1,276,141 | 1,840,285 | 1,618,674 | 1,889,780 |
| Unenumerated, salted or fresh, | 99,866 | 160,178 | 145,881 | 158,384 | 140,010 | 251,880 | 888,988 | 625,064 | 440,729 | 439,078 |
|   preserved other than salted, | 288,008 | 469,008 | 438,900 | 567,877 | 935,800 | 867,085 | 1,434,284 | 1,515,701 | 1,660,099 | 1,906,717 |
| Pork, salted and fresh, | 376,807 | 263,784 | 889,489 | 441,209 | 408,257 | 810,789 | 608,240 | 669,462 | 691,962 | 634,192 |
| Bacon and Hams, | 3,181,509 | 2,830,482 | 4,206,161 | 4,917,681 | 5,834,048 | 8,611,829 | 6,889,364 | 8,509,510 | 8,880,325 | 10,985,942 |
| Total, | 4,849,149 | 4,401,909 | 5,999,594 | 6,892,298 | 7,506,631 | 11,584,518 | 11,007,168 | 13,888,899 | 13,689,888 | 16,429,067 |
| Fish, | 996,119 | 1,071,802 | 905,088 | 1,160,140 | 1,343,434 | 1,450,074 | 1,840,250 | 1,541,580 | 1,652,957 | 1,660,710 |
| Poultry and Game (see Value), | . | . | . | . | . | 297,018 | 819,994 | 408,024 | 428,298 | 421,045 |
| Butter, | 1,652,402 | 1,637,403 | 1,790,517 | 1,789,721 | 2,328,806 | 9,718,228 | 9,548,838 | 9,964,068 | 10,879,451 | 12,141,094 |
| Cheese, | 1,531,204 | 1,652,920 | 1,968,859 | 2,045,869 | 1,775,907 | 4,297,763 | 4,771,808 | 4,946,696 | 3,894,017 | 5,001,614 |
| Lard, | 562,174 | 592,364 | 908,606 | 840,519 | 927,612 | 1,570,721 | 1,471,829 | 1,787,874 | 1,480,381 | 1,852,160 |
| Eggs,   Number, | 768,028,040 | 761,185,000 | 788,714,720 | 708,707,840 | 747,408,000 | 2,020,896 | 2,478,377 | 2,511,046 | 2,296,720 | 2,235,461 |
| Total, | . | . | . | . | . | 19,013,038 | 20,220,184 | 21,144,568 | 20,005,515 | 23,403,514 |

TABLE No. 5.—QUANTITIES AND VALUES OF THE IMPORTS OF WHEAT AND WHEAT FLOUR, 1876 TO 1880.

| | QUANTITIES. | | | | | VALUES. | | | | |
|---|---|---|---|---|---|---|---|---|---|---|
| | 1876. | 1877. | 1878. | 1879. | 1880. | 1876. | 1877. | 1878. | 1879. | 1880. |
| | Cwts. | Cwts. | Cwts. | Cwts. | Cwts. | £ | £ | £ | £ | £ |
| Wheat, . . . | 44,454,657 | 54,269,800 | 40,906,484 | 60,591,795 | 55,201,024 | 23,178,011 | 33,885,487 | 27,433,444 | 31,403,171 | 30,621,711 |
| Wheat Flour, . | 5,959,821 | 7,377,303 | 7,825,079 | 10,728,252 | 10,558,318 | 4,741,515 | 6,808,983 | 6,784,197 | 3,501,349 | 8,700,109 |
| Total, | 50,414,478 | 61,647,103 | 57,734,563 | 70,820,047 | 65,820,246 | 27,919,526 | 40,694,419 | 34,217,011 | 39,070,120 | 39,827,820 |

TABLE No. 6.—QUANTITIES AND VALUES OF THE IMPORTS OF BARLEY, OATS, RYE, MEAL, AND MALT, 1876 TO 1880.

| | QUANTITIES. | | | | | VALUES. | | | | |
|---|---|---|---|---|---|---|---|---|---|---|
| | 1876. | 1877. | 1878. | 1879. | 1880. | 1876. | 1877. | 1878. | 1879. | 1880. |
| | Cwts. | Cwts. | Cwts. | Cwts. | Cwts. | £ | £ | £ | £ | £ |
| Barley, . . . | 9,772,945 | 12,069,620 | 14,156,919 | 11,540,314 | 11,705,290 | 8,747,686 | 5,898,019 | 5,542,503 | 4,804,409 | 5,011,159 |
| Oats, . . . | 11,911,019 | 13,910,035 | 12,774,420 | 13,471,000 | 13,830,782 | 4,620,450 | 4,992,879 | 4,587,005 | 4,490,927 | 4,984,468 |
| Indian Corn, . | 39,963,389 | 30,477,818 | 41,673,906 | 36,148,379 | 37,224,783 | 12,703,092 | 9,864,612 | 12,696,402 | 9,918,601 | 11,168,080 |
| Peas and Beans, | 6,518,806 | 6,110,985 | 8,666,300 | 4,248,057 | 4,728,364 | 2,561,352 | 2,351,189 | 1,408,140 | 1,642,277 | 1,922,498 |
| Rye, . . . | 182,366 | 241,299 | 343,895 | 207,263 | 120,112 | 45,658 | 96,983 | 125,291 | 91,858 | 51,768 |
| Buckwheat, . | 87,799 | 61,424 | 45,513 | 62,758 | 51,757 | 13,281 | 23,006 | 16,087 | 14,823 | 12,858 |
| Total, | 67,886,948 | 63,701,087 | 72,589,768 | 65,725,026 | 67,688,008 | 28,760,513 | 22,968,787 | 24,305,074 | 20,968,455 | 23,094,831 |
| Barley Meal, . | 521 | 511 | 496 | 2,417 | 1,011 | 928 | 281 | 106 | 511 | 844 |
| Oatmeal, . . | 100,681 | 168,418 | 703,088 | 646,028 | 626,415 | 100,847 | 108,880 | 458,888 | 891,002 | 878,870 |
| Indian Meal, . | 7,708 | 2,712 | 41,747 | 87,080 | 55,874 | 16,471 | 17,294 | 83,278 | 25,585 | 80,842 |
| Rye Meal, . | 17,116 | 47,468 | 50,822 | 8,945 | 6,250 | 6,820 | 17,024 | 20,986 | 8,132 | 4,820 |
| Pea Meal and Bean Meal, | 297 | 10 | 696 | 690 | 118 | 189 | 12 | 442 | 251 | 01 |
| Buckwheat Meal, | 88 | 10 | 16 | 92 | 68 | 60 | 23 | 18 | 92 | 69 |
| Meal unenumerated, | 98,255 | 8,806 | 5,711 | 4,112 | 22,450 | 12,744 | 4,088 | 3,384 | 1,999 | 12,106 |
| Total, | 224,875 | 818,088 | 807,884 | 608,670 | 714,280 | 149,390 | 149,110 | 512,100 | 492,503 | 482,618 |

## TABLE No. 7.—Average Prices of Various kinds of Animals, Dead Meat, and Provisions, 1876 to 1880.

| Kinds of Animals, Dead Meat, &c. | | 1876. | 1877. | 1878 | 1879. | 1880. |
|---|---|---|---|---|---|---|
| Animals—Oxen and Bulls from all countries, | each | £17 17 11 | £18 19 6 | £22 12 2 | £21 17 6 | £22 0 11 |
| " Sheep, including lambs, from all countries, | " | 2 2 9 | 2 8 8 | 2 8 8 | 2 7 8 | 2 8 2 |
| Bacon—From all countries, | per cwt. | 2 18 0 | 2 7 10 | 1 18 7 | 1 14 4 | 2 0 0 |
| Hams—From all countries, | " | 2 19 9 | 2 18 11 | 2 8 1 | 2 8 9 | 2 6 6 |
| Beef, salted—From all countries, | " | 1 19 6 | 1 19 2 | 1 18 1 | 1 14 6 | 1 16 10 |
| " Admiralty prices {American, | " | 2 6 0½ | 2 8 4 | — | — | 2 0 2¾ |
| " Admiralty prices {Deptford, " | " | 3 7 4½ | 3 10 4⅝ | — | — | 3 0 1¼ |
| Pork, salted—From all countries, | " | 2 2 0 | 1 19 7 | 1 18 1 | 1 19 11 | 1 12 7 |
| " Admiralty prices, | " | 3 7 10½ | 3 3 8¼ | 2 15 5½ | — | 2 18 1 |
| Butter—From all countries, | " | 5 17 1 | 5 16 7 | 5 10 10 | 5 1 6 | 5 4 5 |
| Cheese—From all countries, | " | 2 15 4 | 2 17 3 | 2 10 3 | 2 2 9 | 2 17 4 |
| Potatoes—From all countries, | " | 0 5 9 | 0 5 11 | 0 5 5 | 0 5 9 | 0 5 10 |
| Eggs—From all countries, | per 120 | 0 8 4 | 0 7 11 | 0 7 8 | 0 7 2 | 0 7 2 |
| Lard—From all countries, | per cwt. | 2 16 8 | 2 9 8 | 1 19 4 | 1 18 10 | 1 19 11 |
| Milk—Bethlehem Hospital prices, | per gallon | 0 1 3 | 0 1 3 | 0 1 8 | 0 1 3 | — |

## TABLE No. 8.—Return of the Average Prices of Wool in each of the Years from 1861 to 1880.

| Years. | Australian. | South African. | English Fleeces. | Years. | Australian. | South African. | English Fleeces. |
|---|---|---|---|---|---|---|---|
| | Per lb. s. d. | Per lb. s. d. | Per lb. s. d. s. d. | | Per lb. s. d. | Per lb. s. d. | Per lb. s. d. |
| 1861 | 1 7¾ | 1 1⅛ | — | 1871 | 1 2½ | 1 1 | 1 1 |
| 1862 | 1 7½ | 1 2¼ | — | 1872 | 1 8 | 1 4½ | — |
| 1863 | 1 6¾ | 1 2⅜ | — | 1873 | 1 8¼ | 1 4½ | 1 11 |
| 1864 | 1 9⅜ | 1 5¼ | — | 1874 | 1 2¾ | 1 4¾ | — |
| 1865 | 1 7½ | 1 3⅛ | 2 0 to 2 1 | 1875 | 1 4¼ | 1 4¼ | 1 6½ |
| 1866 | 1 8⅛ | 1 5½ | 1 9 " 1 10 | 1876 | 1 3¼ | 1 3¾ | 1 5¼ |
| 1867 | 1 7⅛ | 1 2⅜ | 1 7 | 1877 | 1 3 | 1 3¾ | 1 4¼ |
| 1868 | 1 3⅛ | 1 2⅛ | — | 1878 | 1 2¼ | 1 3½ | 1 3¼ |
| 1869 | 1 2⅛ | 1 2¼ | 1 8½ | 1879 | 1 2¼ | 1 2¼ | 1 0¼ |
| 1870 | 1 3½ | 1 3⅛ | — | 1880 | 1 2¼ | 1 3¼ | 1 2½ |

TABLE No. 9.—Average Prices (per Imperial Quarter) of Home-grown Wheat, Barley, and Oats in the Weekly Market of Edinburgh for the Years 1877, 1878, 1879, 1880, and 1881.

| Weekly Market day Wednesday | | WHEAT | | | | | BARLEY | | | | | OATS | | | | |
|---|---|---|---|---|---|---|---|---|---|---|---|---|---|---|---|---|
| | | 1877 | 1878 | 1879 | 1880 | 1881 | 1877 | 1878 | 1879 | 1880 | 1881 | 1877 | 1878 | 1879 | 1880 | 1881 |
| | | s. d. | s. d. | s. d. | s. d. | s. d. | s. d. | s. d. | s. d. | s. d. | s. d. | s. d. | s. d. | s. d. | s. d. | s. d. |
| January | 1 | 45 11 | 55 1 | 39 2 | 43 1 | 44 10 | 34 10 | 38 3 | 33 10 | 33 3 | 33 0 | 26 6 | 27 7 | 21 6 | 26 7 | 23 0 |
| | 2 | 48 2 | 55 0 | 38 0 | 46 11 | 44 4 | 35 0 | 33 11 | 33 3 | 38 0 | 34 4 | 27 2 | 28 4 | 21 8 | 26 5 | 23 0 |
| | 3 | 45 8 | 49 0 | 40 4 | 39 2 | 46 3 | 34 6 | 34 11 | 33 9 | 32 5 | 33 6 | 26 7 | 28 3 | 22 0 | 26 6 | 23 6 |
| | 4 | 45 6 | 44 10 | 38 3 | 38 0 | 44 4 | 34 8 | 33 8 | 34 2 | 31 6 | 34 0 | 26 9 | 28 7 | 22 1 | 26 10 | 23 4 |
| | 5 | 43 4 | 45 8 | . | . | | 35 0 | 32 7 | . | . | | 27 1 | 28 7 | . | | |
| February | 1 | 42 5 | 42 5 | 38 0 | 37 1 | 43 5 | 33 11 | 31 5 | 24 8 | 31 8 | 34 8 | 27 1 | 28 3 | 21 10 | 26 2 | 23 2 |
| | 2 | 42 2 | 43 4 | 37 8 | 38 1 | 41 9 | 34 4 | 32 4 | 34 8 | 33 10 | 33 4 | 26 0 | 28 10 | 21 8 | 25 11 | 23 1 |
| | 3 | 42 6 | 39 6 | 38 6 | 38 0 | 43 0 | 34 7 | 31 10 | 34 10 | 33 1 | 32 6 | 26 1 | 28 3 | 22 1 | 27 9 | 23 1 |
| | 4 | 43 5 | 42 7 | 38 0 | 41 7 | 42 3 | 34 2 | 32 8 | 35 8 | 30 6 | 33 4 | 27 3 | 29 4 | 22 1 | 27 8 | 23 6 |
| | 5 | 44 7 | 41 10 | 38 4 | 38 9 | 41 2 | 35 4 | 32 6 | 35 10 | 30 0 | 34 3 | 27 8 | 30 11 | 23 1 | 26 6 | 23 6 |
| March | 1 | 46 9 | 43 8 | 39 9 | 35 9 | 40 0 | 36 11 | 32 1 | 33 8 | 30 3 | 33 11 | 28 5 | 31 0 | 22 8 | 27 7 | 24 0 |
| | 2 | 46 11 | 43 6 | 40 0 | 41 1 | 47 1 | 33 1 | 31 4 | 37 5 | 29 11 | 36 1 | 27 7 | 31 2 | 22 11 | 27 8 | 23 6 |
| | 3 | 49 4 | 44 0 | 42 0 | 44 10 | 43 9 | 37 7 | 33 1 | 37 7 | 32 5 | 36 2 | 28 10 | 30 11 | 23 7 | 28 10 | 23 8 |
| | 4 | | | | 51 11 | 42 8 | | | | 31 6 | 36 4 | | | | 29 0 | 23 10 |
| | 5 | | | | | | | | | | | | | | | |
| April | 1 | 48 0 | 46 5 | 42 5 | 44 4 | 42 11 | 36 0 | 33 2 | 38 4 | 32 2 | 36 2 | 29 3 | 31 11 | 24 4 | 30 1 | 24 8 |
| | 2 | 51 4 | 46 3 | 40 0 | 44 11 | 43 3 | 37 9 | 31 8 | 36 8 | 31 11 | 35 0 | 28 6 | 32 9 | 23 5 | 28 10 | 24 10 |
| | 3 | 43 7 | 46 4 | 41 10 | 39 6 | 44 11 | 37 9 | 34 10 | 37 4 | 28 9 | 35 0 | 29 7 | 32 5 | 23 2 | 29 4 | 24 2 |
| | 4 | 60 5 | 46 6 | 42 2 | 42 6 | 40 0 | 38 6 | 32 9 | 38 5 | 30 8 | 33 7 | 29 3 | 32 0 | 23 8 | 29 6 | 25 0 |
| | 5 | | | 41 6 | | | | | 37 0 | | | | 24 6 | | | |
| May | 1 | 63 7 | 46 1 | 42 1 | 43 4 | 44 5 | 37 5 | 31 10 | 36 8 | 29 5 | 33 5 | 31 8 | 31 5 | 24 2 | 28 6 | 25 7 |
| | 2 | 63 4 | 43 9 | 42 11 | 44 0 | 49 1 | 37 3 | 30 5 | 34 4 | 31 8 | 34 5 | 30 10 | 31 7 | 24 8 | 29 3 | 25 2 |
| | 3 | 61 1 | 43 4 | 42 7 | 41 0 | 45 0 | 37 8 | 31 6 | 34 7 | 26 11 | 34 8 | 30 8 | 30 6 | 23 8 | 29 3 | 24 9 |
| | 4 | 57 0 | 41 11 | 42 10 | 43 0 | 44 2 | 36 8 | 30 9 | 36 0 | 29 5 | 32 0 | 30 1 | 31 5 | 24 3 | 29 7 | 24 0 |
| | 5 | 57 1 | 41 11 | . | . | | 30 4 | 28 5 | b | . | | 30 2 | 31 10 | . | | |
| June | 1 | 58 6 | 37 4 | 41 6 | 44 1 | 46 0 | 33 10 | 29 9 | 33 4 | 27 6 | 34 6 | 30 7 | 32 3 | 24 3 | 29 4 | 24 7 |
| | 2 | 58 9 | 42 6 | 41 11 | 43 6 | 47 7 | 34 7 | 29 5 | 37 3 | 27 11 | 34 0 | 30 5 | 30 11 | 24 2 | 29 7 | 24 7 |
| | 3 | 53 6 | 36 7 | 41 5 | 41 8 | 47 6 | 34 2 | 30 2 | 37 0 | 27 1 | 35 2 | 30 4 | 31 7 | 24 7 | 29 8 | 25 2 |
| | 4 | 55 0 | 39 2 | 41 2 | 39 4 | 48 1 | 33 8 | 29 8 | 36 10 | 28 8 | 34 1 | 30 0 | 30 11 | 25 0 | 29 3 | 24 2 |
| | 5 | | | | 38 6 | 47 11 | | | | 26 11 | | | | | 30 5 | 24 7 |
| July | 1 | 56 6 | 36 0 | 43 5 | 43 5 | 44 7 | 34 2 | 29 0 | 35 6 | 27 2 | 27 0 | 30 8 | 31 2 | 24 10 | 24 11 | 24 11 |
| | 2 | 58 1 | 35 11 | 43 9 | 43 7 | 46 8 | 33 1 | 25 6 | 36 9 | 24 6 | 33 2 | 30 3 | 31 2 | 25 5 | 23 11 | 24 2 |
| | 3 | 59 8 | 38 8 | 44 8 | 42 4 | 47 4 | 29 6 | 26 11 | 35 2 | 23 10 | 33 4 | 30 8 | 31 7 | 25 11 | 26 0 | 24 2 |
| | 4 | 62 4 | 37 11 | 47 5 | 42 0 | 43 8 | 34 5 | 27 6 | 34 4 | 27 10 | | 30 8 | 31 2 | 25 6 | 29 8 | 24 2 |
| August | 1 | 57 10 | 39 4 | 43 0 | 39 4 | 44 9 | 33 10 | 27 9 | 38 2 | 28 6 | 27 0 | 30 2 | 30 6 | 26 2 | 29 11 | 24 7 |
| | 2 | 59 0 | 39 4 | 40 11 | 33 10 | 44 9 | 33 3 | 26 7 | 31 8 | 25 2 | 30 0 | 31 4 | 30 8 | 23 9 | 30 0 | 24 9 |
| | 3 | 58 4 | 38 10 | 45 10 | 40 8 | 45 1 | 34 11 | 26 8 | | 24 6 | 31 3 | 31 4 | 30 3 | 25 2 | 29 1 | 25 1 |
| | 4 | 58 2 | 37 9 | 46 8 | 40 5 | 45 7 | 35 3 | 25 1 | 35 0 | 27 5 | 34 0 | 30 7 | 30 3 | 26 4 | 27 6 | 26 8 |
| | 5 | 59 8 | 38 11 | | 52 10 | | 34 8 | 32 6 | | | | 32 1 | 30 5 | | | 26 8 |
| September | 1 | 58 11 | 38 4 | 44 11 | 36 0 | 58 6 | 33 11 | 31 8 | 40 3 | 24 6 | 34 0 | 32 7 | 31 4 | 29 6 | 23 7 | 26 0 |
| | 2 | 60 8 | 58 11 | 45 11 | 32 3 | 54 8 | 31 7 | 35 7 | | 33 7 | 34 0 | 31 0 | 29 11 | 29 10 | 24 0 | 25 11 |
| | 3 | 60 0 | 37 10 | 46 9 | 32 3 | 57 0 | 30 2 | 36 11 | | 33 8 | 34 2 | 31 0 | 37 1 | 29 4 | 24 5 | 25 11 |
| | 4 | 60 0 | 38 4 | 50 8 | 38 5 | 57 3 | 36 1 | 35 7 | 36 4 | 34 7 | | 32 4 | 35 4 | 28 1 | 24 4 | 36 7 |
| | 5 | | | | 36 6 | | | | | 33 4 | | | | | 22 8 | |
| October | 1 | 60 10 | 44 4 | 52 9 | 39 8 | 58 6 | 34 7 | 34 7 | 34 1 | 34 2 | 35 6 | 32 9 | 25 5 | 25 8 | 23 8 | 25 1 |
| | 2 | 60 4 | 56 0 | 54 0 | 43 5 | 57 3 | 33 10 | 35 4 | 37 2 | 36 1 | 37 0 | 32 5 | 24 9 | 25 8 | 24 4 | 25 2 |
| | 3 | 62 7 | 56 5 | 55 9 | 42 4 | 47 5 | 34 8 | 35 3 | 34 10 | 35 10 | 35 0 | 31 2 | 25 5 | 25 8 | 24 11 | 25 0 |
| | 4 | 60 3 | 39 7 | 59 0 | 40 7 | 45 4 | 31 3 | 34 4 | 35 10 | 35 0 | 27 9 | 31 0 | 25 10 | 26 4 | 25 10 | |
| | 5 | 57 10 | 60 6 | 56 7 | | | | 34 1 | 35 0 | 32 5 | | 30 4 | 25 10 | 26 4 | | |
| November | 1 | 63 4 | 40 2 | 58 6 | 42 0 | 37 5 | 33 8 | 31 8 | 31 8 | 27 0 | 25 10 | 29 5 | 26 3 | 24 9 | 23 4 | 24 7 |
| | 2 | 59 4 | 40 5 | 43 11 | 50 9 | | 33 2 | 35 8 | 34 9 | 24 7 | | 29 4 | 26 6 | 25 8 | 22 2 | 23 2 |
| | 3 | 56 4 | 39 3 | 53 7 | 44 0 | | 33 6 | 34 9 | 33 8 | 24 7 | | 28 10 | 26 5 | 25 6 | 24 7 | 22 0 |
| | 4 | 51 7 | 39 6 | 47 6 | 46 2 | | 33 1 | 34 8 | 29 7 | 34 7 | | 29 3 | 26 8 | 23 6 | 24 9 | 21 1 |
| | 5 | | | | | | | | | 25 2 | | | | | | |
| December | 1 | 53 9 | 40 2 | 43 0 | 43 0 | 35 9 | 32 8 | 36 7 | 30 8 | 34 4 | 24 6 | 28 5 | 21 9 | 24 5 | 24 6 | 21 8 |
| | 2 | 53 2 | 40 8 | 42 0 | 44 12 | 33 2 | 32 10 | 34 4 | 33 2 | 33 2 | 24 9 | 27 7 | 22 8 | 22 11 | 23 8 | 22 2 |
| | 3 | 43 11 | 40 3 | 49 10 | 37 7 | 39 2 | 33 1 | 33 11 | 33 8 | 30 8 | 25 | 28 3 | 21 7 | 21 7 | 23 8 | 21 1 |
| | 4 | 52 0 | 40 0 | 47 5 | 42 10 | 30 11 | 33 8 | 32 5 | 32 8 | 33 7 | 24 5 | 28 1 | 21 5 | 25 8 | 23 5 | 21 6 |
| | 5 | | 40 2 | 49 8 | 40 0 | | | | 33 2 | 32 7 | | | 21 7 | 36 9 | 23 3 | |

# APPENDIX (A).

# PROCEEDINGS AT BOARD MEETINGS.

## MEETING OF DIRECTORS, 2ND FEBRUARY 1881.

*Present*—Lord Arthur Cecil, Sir Henry Seton Steuart of Touch, Bart.; Sir James R. Gibson-Maitland of Barnton, Bart.; Sir James H. Gibson-Craig of Riccarton, Bart.; Mr. Ainslie of Costerton; Mr. Balfour of Balbirnie; Professor Balfour; Mr. Dickson of Corstorphine; Mr. Scott Dudgeon, Longnewton; Mr. Elliot, Blackhaugh; Rev. John Gillespie, Mouswald Manse; Colonel Gillon of Wallhouse; Mr. Maxtone Graham of Cultoquhey; Colonel Hare of Calderhall; Mr. Hope, Duddingston; Mr. Irvine of Drum; Mr. Elliott Lockhart of Borthwickbrae; Mr. Mackenzie of Portmore; Mr. Mylne, Niddrie Mains; Mr. Pott of Dod; Mr. Ralston, Glamis House; Mr. Smith, Whittinghame; Mr. John Turnbull Smith, C.A.; Professor Wilson, and Dr. Aitken—Mr. Smith, Whittinghame, in the chair.

Mr. F. N. MENZIES reported apologies for the absence of the Earl of Mar and Kellie; Sir Windham Carmichael Anstruther, Bart.; Admiral Sir William Edmonstone, Bart; Mr. Cunningham, Tarbreoch; Mr. Scott, Glendronach; and Mr. Walker of Dowland, C.B.

Letters were submitted from the Marquis of Lothian, K.T., expressing his gratification at the terms of the resolutions passed at the last general meeting on his retiring from the office of President, and as to his services on the occasion of the Kelso Show; from the Duke of Richmond and Gordon, K.T., acknowledging receipt of the intimation of his election, and stating that he felt much flattered at being chosen President of the Society; from Lord Polwarth, acknowledging on behalf of the county of Roxburgh receipt of the resolution adopted on the 19th; and from Mr. Smith, chief magistrate, Kelso, expressing the sense of gratitude the Town Committee felt by the vote of thanks passed at the general meeting.

AGES OF SHORTHORN CATTLE.—The remit from the general meeting in regard to the appointment of a Committee to consider the question as to the age of shorthorn cattle was read, when, after some discussion, it was resolved to delay the selection till the Board meeting on the 2nd of March, it being considered impossible to have the matter carefully settled previous to issuing the prize lists for the Stirling Show, as well as to give the Directors time to consider who should form the committee.

AGRICULTURAL STALLION FOR STIRLING DISTRICT.—Sir James R. Gibson-Maitland, Bart.; Mr. Ballingall, Blair-Drummond; and Mr. Paterson, Plean, were appointed a committee to make arrangements for the service of the horse in the district.

LOUPING-ILL AND BRAXY.—The Committee appointed on the 5th of January to consider the nature of the course to be adopted in carrying out the investigation in regard to Louping-ill and Braxy, and to give an estimate of the cost the inquiry is likely to involve, met on the 26th of January, and recommended (1) that in the meantime a preliminary pathological and botanical investigation should be instituted; that Professor Williams, with such local assistance as can be obtained, should be employed to conduct the pathological part of the inquiry; and that Dr. Aitken, assisted by Mr. Brotherston and Mr. Geddes, should undertake the botanical; and (2) that a grant of £100 would be required to carry through this preliminary investigation.

The Board approved of the report, it being understood that the sum required should not exceed £100.

FOOT-AND-MOUTH DISEASE.—The Secretary was instructed to write to Mr. Peel, the clerk of the Council, calling attention to the Order of Council of 3rd January 1881, clause 9, c. iv.—"Movement into, from another district"—which is telling very much on the sale of fat cattle in Scotland. By this Order not only is a licence required to be got from a local authority in Scotland, but a licence must also be obtained from the district into which the animals are to be sent. This causes very considerable delay and expense, and has had the effect of reducing the price of fat stock. The Directors consider that this precaution is quite unnecessary, as the cattle are sent from a non-infected district into perhaps an infected one, but for slaughter. A large number of

*a*

cattle are purchased in Scotland every week for consumption in the midland towns in England, and before these can be moved it is necessary that a licence be procured from the town or district into which they are going. The Directors, considering this an unnecessary precaution, deemed it expedient to call the attention of the Privy Council to it.

OLEO MARGARINE.—A letter was read from Sir Herbert E. Maxwell, M.P., stating that he had given notice of a motion on the large quantity of oleo margarine which is now imported into this country and undersells our dairy butter, and stating that it would very much strengthen his hands if those interested would move in the matter.

The Directors considered that it would be most desirable that a different brand was put upon the casks containing this substance and those containing butter, so as to let the consumer know what he was getting. They thought, however, that at present they should not move in the matter till they saw what steps were taken in consequence of Sir Herbert's motion.

## MEETING OF DIRECTORS, 2ND MARCH 1881.

*Present*—Lord Arthur Cecil : Sir Windham Carmichael Anstruther of Anstruther, Bart. ; Admiral Sir William Edmonstone of Duntreath, Bart. ; Sir James Henry Gibson-Craig of Riccarton, Bart. ; Mr. Cunningham, Tarbreoch ; Mr. Dingwall, Ramornie ; Mr. Elliot, Blackhaugh ; Mr. Maxtone Graham of Cultoquhey ; Rev. John Gillespie, Mouswald Manse ; Colonel Hare of Calderhall, Philpston House ; Mr. Hope, Duddingston ; Mr. Irvine of Drum ; Mr. Kennedy of Sundaywell, Brandleys ; Mr. Mackenzie of Portmore ; Mr. Murray of Dollerie ; Mr. Mylne, Niddrie Mains ; Mr. Smith, Whittinghame ; Mr. John Turnbull Smith, C.A.; Mr Walker of Bowland, C.B.; Major Wauchope of Niddrie-Marischal, Professor Wilson, and Dr Aitken—Mr Smith, Whittinghame, in the chair.

Mr. F. N. MENZIES reported apologies for the absence of Lord Balfour of Burleigh ; Sir Henry J. Seton Steuart of Allanton, Bart.; Mr. Dickson of Corstorphine ; Colonel Gillon of Wallhouse ; Mr. Eliott Lockhart of Borthwickbrae ; Mr. Ralston, Glamis House ; Mr. Smith, chief magistrate, Kelso.

Before proceeding to the business on the programme, the following resolutions were unanimously passed :—

THE LATE EARL OF SEAFIELD.—" That the Directors of the Highland and Agricultural Society of Scotland desire to express the sincere regret with which they have received the information of the death of the Right Hon. John Charles, Earl of Seafield, K.T., and their sense of the obligations which the Society owed to him, both as a Vice-President and as Convener of local committees."

THE LATE MR. SMOLLETT OF BONHILL.—" That the Directors of the Highland and Agricultural Society of Scotland have to record the deep regret with which they regard the death of Mr. Alexander Smollett of Bonhill—one of their number—and their sense of the valuable assistance which the Society had on many occasions received from him as an Extraordinary Director and Convener of local committees."

FOOT-AND-MOUTH DISEASE.—A letter was read from Mr. Peel, in reply to a request from the Directors that the Privy Council would take into consideration the needless delay and trouble that were occasioned by compelling those trucking cattle from Scotland into England not only to have a licence from the uninfected district in Scotland, but also from the receiving district in England, which might or might not be infected. The letter drew attention to Order in Council (598) of 1851, Regulation U (W. A.), by which the licence from the clean district from which the cattle are sent was to be discontinued, but the licence from the receiving district still continued.

The Directors, considering that it would save much time if the licence from the sending district had been continued and the licence from the receiving district discontinued, and as fat cattle have deteriorated very considerably in form from this arrangement, instructed the Secretary to write again to Mr. Peel, in the hope that the Privy Council will reconsider the matter. He was also instructed to request Mr. Peel to lay before the Privy Council the necessity for great care being taken that trucks which go from Scotland into England to a diseased district are not loaded with hay, cake, or other food for stock, and returned to Scotland without being properly cleansed and disinfected.

KELSO SHOW, 1880.—A letter was read from Sir George H. Scott Douglas of Springwood Park, Bart., acknowledging, on the part of the local committee, the vote of thanks accorded to the committee by the general meeting in January last.

STIRLING SHOW, 1881.—The Secretary reported that the competition of stallions for agricultural purposes for the premium of £100 offered by the Society for the best stallion to serve this season in the Stirling district had taken place at Glasgow on the 22nd February, when the judges—Mr. M'Kean, Lumloch; Mr. Smith, Stevenson Mains; and Mr. Ure, Bogton—had selected "Topsman," belonging to Mr. James Johnston, Lochburnie—the charge for the service (£2) to be paid at the end of the season, and £3 extra for every foal. The horse will be shown at Stirling market on a day to be arranged by the sub-committee, and to commence then to travel the district, which comprises the counties of Stirling, Dumbarton, and Clackmannan, and the western division of Perthshire.

AGES OF SHORTHORN CATTLE.—In accordance with the resolution by the general meeting in January last, a committee was appointed to consider and report on the proposal to change the date of calculating the birth of shorthorned cattle exhibited at the Society's shows from the 1st of January to the 1st of December, with special instructions to take steps to ascertain the views on the proposed change of all persons who were breeders or exhibitors of shorthorns which have been entered at the Society's general shows during the last eight years, and to consult with the Royal Agricultural Society of England. The Secretary was instructed to communicate with the gentlemen selected before publishing their names.

## SPECIAL MEETING OF DIRECTORS, 23RD MARCH 1881.

*Present*—The Earl of Mar and Kellie; Lord Balfour of Burleigh; Sir James Ramsay Gibson Maitland of Barnton, Bart.; Sir James H. Gibson-Craig of Riccarton, Bart.; Mr. Balfour of Balbirnie; Mr. Dingwall, Ramornie; Mr. Scott Dudgeon, Longnewton; Mr. Elliot, Blackhaugh; Mr. Forman, Duncrahill; Colonel Gillon of Wallhouse; Mr. Maxtone Graham of Cultoquhey; Mr. Hope, Duddingston; Mr. Mackenzie of Portmore; Mr. Mylne, Niddrie Mains; Mr. John Turnbull Smith, C.A.; Major Wauchope of Niddrie-Marischal—Mr. Maxtone Graham in the chair.

Apologies were reported for the absence of Lord Arthur Cecil; Sir M. R. Shaw Stewart of Greenock and Blackhall, Bart.; Sir Hew Dalrymple of North Berwick, Bart.; Sir W. C. Anstruther of Carmichael, Bart.; Admiral Sir William Edmonstone of Duntreath, Bart.; Sir Henry J. Seton Steuart of Touch, Bart.; Mr. Ainslie of Costarton; Mr. Cunningham, Tarbreoch; Mr. Dickson of Corstorphine; Admiral Maitland Dougall of Scotscraig; Rev. John Gillespie, Mouswald Manse; Mr. Harris, Earnhill; Mr. Irvine of Drum; Mr. Murray of Dollerie; Mr. Scott, Glendronach; Mr. Smith, chief magistrate, Kelso; Mr. Smith, Whittinghame; Mr Smythe of Methven.

The business had reference principally to a letter from the Privy Council as to continuing Order of Council (617), prohibiting the movement of cattle into Scotland.

## MEETING OF DIRECTORS, 6TH APRIL 1881.

*Present*—Lord Arthur Cecil; Lord Balfour of Burleigh; Sir James R. Gibson Maitland of Barnton, Bart.; Sir James H. Gibson-Craig of Riccarton, Bart.; Mr. Balfour of Balbirnie; Mr. Dingwall, Ramornie; Mr. Scott Dudgeon, Longnewton; Rev. John Gillespie, Mouswald Manse; Colonel Gillon of Wallhouse; Mr. Maxtone Graham of Cultoquhey; Mr. Hope, Duddingston; Mr. Elliott Lockhart of Borthwickbrae; Mr. Mackenzie of Portmore; Mr. Pott of Dod; Mr. Ralston, Glamis House; Mr. Smith, Whittinghame; Mr. John Turnbull Smith, C.A.; Professor Wilson; Dr. Aitken—Mr. Maxtone Graham of Cultoquhey in the chair.

Mr F. N. MENZIES reported apologies for the absence of Sir W. C. Anstruther, Bart.; Admiral Sir William Edmonstone, Bart.; Sir Henry J. Seton Steuart, Bart.; Provost Anderson, Stirling; Mr. Cunningham, Tarbreoch; Mr. Irvine of Drum; Mr. Kennedy of Sundaywell; Mr. Mylne, Niddrie Mains; Mr. Scott, Glendronach; Mr. Murray of Dollerie; and Mr Walker of Bowland, C.B.

Letters were reported from the Earl of Seafield and Mr. P. B. Smollett of Bonhill, expressing their deep appreciation of the terms in which the Board recorded the services to the Society of the late Earl of Seafield and Mr Alex. Smollett of Bonhill.

LOUPING-ILL AND BRAXY.—It was reported that the special committee appointed to carry out the investigation in regard to louping ill and braxy had held a meeting on the 30th March, when it was agreed to have a condensed report drawn up from information received from every county in Scotland; and that Professor Williams should begin visiting the farms as soon as the disease appears, commencing his investigations in West Teviotdale, going on to Dumfriesshire and other districts.

FOOT-AND-MOUTH DISEASE.—In reference to the proceedings at last Board meeting the following letter was read :—

"Veterinary Department, Privy Council Office, 44 Parliament Street,
"Westminster, S.W., March 7, 1881.

"Sir,—I have submitted to the Lords of the Council your letter of the 2nd instant. I am directed by the Lords of the Council to state, in reply to the first paragraph, that the point to which you refer does not depend on any Order of Council, but that the Contagious Diseases (Animals) Act, 1878, requires the licence of the local authority of the infected area to be given before animals can be moved into it. In reply to the second paragraph, I am to inform you that the Lords of the Council are in communication with the railway companies, and hope that the anticipated danger may be averted.—I am, sir, your obedient servant,                "C. L. PEEL.
"The Secretary, Highland and Agricultural Society,
"3 George IV. Bridge."

The Lords of the Council having inquired what were the views of the Directors as to continuing Order of Council 617 after the 31st March, a special meeting of the Board was held on the 23rd March, when the following resolution was unanimously agreed to :—" That the Privy Council be requested to retain in force the existing Order as regards the transmission of cattle from England into Scotland; and that as regards sheep the existing Order be relaxed to the following extent, viz., that sheep which have been sent into Northumberland and Cumberland from Scotland for wintering or to turnips, and still belong to the same parties who despatched them, may during the the first ten days of April be moved back again to their original grazings in Scotland, but only under certificate of the local authority of the county out of which they are to be moved."

The new Order was submitted, from which it appeared that the resolution of the Directors was adopted by the Lords of the Council.

ROYAL COMMISSION ON AGRICULTURE.—The Secretary reported that application having been made for the use of the Society's chambers for the Royal Commission on Agriculture, from the 6th to the 14th of April, he, after consulting some of the Directors resident in Edinburgh, had considered it right to grant the request.

PRESENTATION OF BOOKS.—The third volume of the Clydesdale Stud Book, presented by the Clydesdale Horse Society; and Part I., Volume III., of the Galloway Herd Book, given by the Council of the Galloway Cattle Society, were submitted ; and the Secretary stated that he had, in name of the Directors, thanked the Councils of both Societies for the presentations.


## MEETING OF DIRECTORS, 4TH MAY 1881.

*Present*—Lord Balfour of Burleigh ; Mr. Ainslie of Costerston ; Mr. Dingwall, Ramornie ; Mr. Maxtone Grahame of Cultoquhey ; Colonel Hare of Calderhall ; Mr. Hope, Duddingston ; Mr. Mylne, Niddrie Mains ; Mr. Scott, Glendrounach ; Mr. Smith, Whittinghame ; Professor Wilson ; Dr. Aitken—Mr. Smith, Whittinghame, in the chair.

Mr. F. N. MENZIES reported apologies for the absence of Sir Michael R. Shaw Stewart, Bart. ; Sir Henry J. Seton Steuart, Bart. ; Mr. Cunningham, Tarbreoch ; Mr. Dickson of Corstorphine ; Mr. Elliot, Blackhaugh ; Colonel Gillon of Wallhouse ; Mr. Irvine of Drum ; Mr. Kennedy of Sundaywell, Brandleys ; Mr. Eliott Lockhart of Borthwickbrae ; Mr. Mackenzie of Portmore ; Mr. Murray of Dollerie ; Mr. Pott of Dod ; Mr. Ralston, Glamis ; Mr. Smith, chief magistrate, Kelso ; and Mr. John Turnbull Smith, C.A.

FOOT-AND-MOUTH DISEASE.—The Secretary stated that, after communicating with the Society, the Privy Council had renewed the Order prohibiting the movement of animals by land or by water from any place or port in England or Wales to any place or port in Scotland till the 31st day of May.

The other business had reference principally to the Veterinary Department and the Stirling Show.


## MEETING OF DIRECTORS, 1ST JUNE 1881.

*Present*—Sir Henry J. Seton Steuart of Allanton, Bart. ; Sir H. James H. Gibson-Craig of Riccarton, Bart. ; Mr. Cunningham, Tarbreoch ; Mr. Dingwall, Ramornie ; Mr. Elliot, Blackhall ; Mr. Forman, Duncrahill ; Rev. John Gillespie, Mouswald

Manse; Mr. Maxtone Graham of Coltoquhey; Mr. Hope, Duddingston; Mr. Irvine of Drum; Mr. Eliott Lockhart of Borthwickbrae; Mr. Pott of Dod; Mr. Smith, Whittinghame; Mr. John Turnbull Smith, C.A.; Colonel Williamson of Lawers: Professor Wilson; Dr. Aitken—Mr. Smith, Whittinghame, in the chair.

Mr. F. N. MENZIES reported apologies for the absence of Sir Michael Shaw Stewart, Bart.; Admiral Sir William Edmonstone, Bart.; Mr. Balfour of Balbirnie; Colonel Hare of Calder Hall; Mr. Harris, Earnhill; Mr. Kennedy of Sundaywell; Mr. Mackenzie of Portmore; Mr. Ralston, Glamis; Mr. Scott, Glendronach; Mr. Smith, chief magistrate, Kelso; and Mr. Campbell Swinton of Kimmerghame.

THE LATE RIGHT HON. W. P. ADAM.—Before proceeding to the business of the day, the Board directed the Secretary to record in the minutes the deep regret with which the Directors regard the death of the Right Hon. William P. Adam of Blairadam, and to express their sense of the assistance which the Society had received from him as a Member and Extraordinary Director.

COMMISSION ON AGRICULTURE.—The following letter from the Duke of Richmond and Gordon, K.G., addressed to the Secretary, was read:—

"8 Richmond Terrace, Whitehall,
"4th May 1881.

"Sir,—As President of the Royal Commission on Agriculture, I have to ask you to be so good as to convey the thanks of the Commissioners to the Directors of the Highland and Agricultural Society for their kindness in lending their rooms in Edinburgh for the meetings of the Commission, and also for the facilities they afforded for carrying on the business of the Commission. I trust that the Members of the Society were not inconvenienced by our temporary occupation of their rooms. I have also to thank you and the other officials of the Society for the assistance you rendered during the stay of the Commission in Edinburgh.—I am, Sir, your obedient servant,
(Signed)          "RICHMOND AND GORDON."

AGES OF SHORTHORN CATTLE.—The report by the committee appointed to consider whether the ages of shorthorn cattle to be exhibited at the Society's shows should be counted from 1st January or 1st December was before the meeting, from which it appeared that the committee, in accordance with the remit from the Directors, sent circulars with the view of ascertaining the opinions of all persons who were breeders or exhibitors of shorthorns at the Society's general shows during the last eight years, and also consulted the Royal Agricultural Society of England. The Society had received replies from ninety-eight. Of these eight were neutral, thirty-one were of opinion that the ages should be calculated from 1st December, and fifty-nine were in favour of adhering to the present mode of counting the ages from 1st January. The answer from Mr. Jenkins, the Secretary of the Royal Agricultural Society of England, was to the effect that for some years there had been a growing feeling in favour of altering their previous date of 1st July to the 1st of January, which is now the date adopted. The committee were of opinion that Mr. Mollison produced several strong reasons in favour of the ages of shorthorn and polled being calculated from the same date; but as the subject was not included in the remit, the committee felt that it could not be taken up. It was ultimately resolved that, in consequence of the majority of the answers being in favour of the 1st of January, to recommend the Directors to adhere to that date.

MEETING OF DIRECTORS, 15TH JUNE 1881.

Present—The Earl of Mar and Kellie; Lord Arthur Cecil; Lord Balfour of Burleigh; Sir George H. Scott Douglas of Springwood Park, Bart.; Sir Alexander Muir Mackenzie of Delvine, Bart.; Sir Henry J. Seton Stenart of Touch, Bart.; Sir James Ramsay Gibson-Maitland of Barnton, Bart.; Mr. Ainslie of Costerton; Professor Balfour; Mr. Dickson of Corstorphine; Mr. Dingwall of Ramornie; Colonel Gillon of Wallhouse; Mr. Maxtone Graham of Cultoquhey; Mr. Milne Home of Milne Graden; Mr. Hope, Duddingston; Mr. Irvine of Drum; Mr. Kennedy of Sundaywell; Mr. Pott of Dod; Mr. Scott, Glendronach; Mr. Smith, Whittinghame; Mr. John Turnbull Smith, C.A.; Mr. Walker of Bowland, C.B.; Colonel Williamson of Lawers—The Earl of Mar and Kellie in the chair.

Apologies were reported for the absence of Sir James H. Gibson-Craig of Riccarton, Bart.; Mr. Ralston, Glamis; and Professor Wilson.

The business had reference principally to the subjects to be brought before the general meeting of this date.

## SPECIAL MEETING OF DIRECTORS, 6TH JULY 1881.

*Present*—Sir James R. Gibson-Maitland of Barnton, Bart.; Sir James H. Gibson-Craig of Riccarton, Bart.; Mr. Dingwall, Ramornie; Mr. Elliot, Blackhall; Rev. John Gillespie; Colonel Gillon of Wallhouse; Mr. Milne Home of Milne Graden; Mr. Hope, Duddingston; Mr. Irvine of Drum; Mr. Mackenzie of Portmore; Mr. Mylne, Niddrie Mains; Mr. Walker of Bowland, C.B.; and Dr. Aitken—Mr. Dingwall, Ramornie, in the chair.

Mr. F. N. MENZIES reported apologies for the absence of Sir Michael R. Shaw Stewart, Bart.; Sir Henry J. Seton Steuart. Bart.; Mr. Dickson of Corstorphine; Mr. Kennedy of Sundaywell; Mr. Eliott Lockhart of Borthwickbrae; Mr. Murray of Dollerie; Mr. Pott of Dod; Mr. Ralston, Glamis House; Mr. Scott, Glendronach; Mr. Smith, Whittinghame; Mr. J. Turnbull Smith, C.A.; Mr. Smith, chief magistrate, Kelso; and Professor Wilson.

VETERINARY SURGEONS BILL.—The Secretary stated that, in accordance with the resolution at the last general meeting, the Earl of Mar and Kellie had presented the petition and given notice of the necessary amendment on the Veterinary Surgeons' Bill, which had since been agreed to by those introducing the Bill.

AGRICULTURAL EDUCATION.—The Secretary stated that, in conformity with the instructions at last meeting, he had communicated with Sir Francis R. Sandford, Education Department, London, on the subject of introducing the study of the principles of agriculture in the Board Schools in Scotland; and he submitted a letter from Sir Francis stating that the Lords of the Committee of Council on Education had under their special consideration arrangements by which encouragement will be given to the study of the principles of agriculture in the schools under inspection, and that they trust these arrangements, when finally settled, will be found to go far to meet the wishes of the Society.

ENGLISH STOCK ENTERED FOR STIRLING SHOW.—The Directors resolved that, as the Privy Council Order would prevent stock from England coming to Stirling, that the entry-money should be returned.

THE DARBY DIGGER.—A letter was submitted from Mr. George C. Phillips, London, stating by desire of Mr. Darby, that it would be quite impossible with their present engagements to put in an appearance this year; but that if the Society would be likely to offer a medal which would bring the digger into competition with any other system, they would guarantee to be in Scotland next year.

FISHERIES EXHIBITION.—The Secretary stated that at a recent meeting of the joint committees of the Edinburgh Town Council, the Highland and Agricultural Society, and the Scotch Fisheries Improvement Association, an executive committee, consisting of four members from each of the joint committees, with power to add to their number, had been appointed. Sir James Gibson-Maitland, Bart., Mr. Archibald Young (Commissioner of Scotch Salmon Fisheries), and himself (Mr. F. N. Menzies) had agreed to act as honorary secretaries.

## MEETING OF DIRECTORS, 2ND NOVEMBER 1881.

*Present*—Lord Polwarth; Sir Michael R. Shaw Stewart of Blackhall, Bart.; Sir G. Graham Montgomery of Stanhope, Bart.; Sir Alexander Muir Mackenzie of Delvine, Bart.; Sir Henry J. Seton Steuart of Allanton, Bart.; Mr. Cunningham, Tarbreoch; Mr. Dingwall, Ramornie; Mr. Scott-Dudgeon, Longnewton; Mr. Elliot, Blackhaugh; Rev. John Gillespie, Mouswald Manse; Mr. Hope, Duddingston; Mr. Irvine of Drum; Mr. Kennedy of Sundaywell; Mr. Eliott Lockhart of Borthwickbrae; Mr. Murray of Dollerie; Mr. Mylne, Niddrie Mains; Mr. Pott of Dod; Mr. Ross, Bachilton; Mr. Smith, Whittinghame; Mr. John Turnbull Smith, C.A.; Professor Wilson; and Dr. Aitken—Mr. Smith, Whittinghame, in the chair.

Mr. F. N. MENZIES reported apologies for the absence of Sir Windham Carmichael Anstruther, Bart.; Admiral Sir William Edmonstone, Bart.; Sir James H. Gibson-Craig, Bart.; Mr. Balfour of Balbirnie; Colonel Gillon of Wallhouse; Colonel Hare of Calder Hall; Mr. Milne Home of Milne Graden; Mr. Mackenzie of Portmore; Mr. Scott, Glendronach; and Mr. Walker of Bowland, C.B.

DECEASED MEMBERS.—Before proceeding with the business on the programme, it was agreed to record in the minutes an expression of the Directors' deep regret at the death of the Earl of Home and the Earl of Airlie, K.T., both of whom had at different periods filled with much acceptance the office of Vice-President; also, to enter on the minutes a resolution expressive of the loss sustained by the Society by the death of Mr. Gilchrist Clark of Speddoch, who had acted both as an Ordinary and an Extraordinary Director.

KELSO SHOW, 1880.—The premiums awarded for two-year-old shorthorn heifers, Highland cows, and for mares in foal (payment of which had been suspended till birth of produce was certified) were reported to have been finally decided as follow :—*Shorthorn Heifers*—1, The Duke of Northumberland, "Rose of Annandale ;" 2, Evan Baillie of Dochfour, Inverness, "Sweet Pea ;" 3, Clement Stevenson, Sandyford Villa, Newcastle-on-Tyne, "Alice Smeaton." *Highland Cows*—1, The Earl of Seafield, K.T., Castle Grant, "Dulnain ;" 2, John Stewart, Bochastle, Callander, "Mhaighdeann Bhudhe ;" 3, James Duncan, Benmore Home Farm, Greenock, "Riabhach Mholach." *Mares in Foal*—1, James Cunningham, Tarbreoch, Dalbeattie, "Evelyn ;" 2, David Riddell, Blackhall, Paisley, "Madaline ;" 3, the Earl of Ellesmare, Worsley Hall, Manchester, "Darling ;" 4, no award.

STIRLING SHOW, 1881.—*Awards*.—The Directors approved of the awards at the late Show at Stirling, and the Chairman was authorised to sign orders for the money premiums, which the Secretary was instructed to issue, along with the medals, as early as convenient.

SCIENTIFIC AGRICULTURE.—On the motion of Mr. Eliott Lockhart of Borthwickbrae, it was remitted to a committee—consisting of Lord Polwarth ; Mr. Maxtone Graham of Cultoquhey ; Mr. Eliott Lockhart of Borthwickbrae ; Sir James Gibson-Craig of Riccarton, Bart. ; Rev. John Gillespie, Mouswald ; Mr. Pott of Dod ; Sir A. Muir Mackenzie of Delvine, Bart. ; Mr. Dickson of Corstorphine ; Mr. Hope, Duddingston ; Mr. Mackenzie of Portmore ; Mr. Mylne, Niddrie Mains ; Mr. Dingwall, Ramornie ; Mr. Cunningham, Tarbreoch ; Mr. Scott-Dudgeon, Longnewton ; Mr. Elliot, Blackhaugh ; and Mr. Scott, Glendronach—to consider in what way scientific agriculture and education could best be promoted and stimulated, and the results of experiments in all branches more readily be brought within the view of all who are interested therein.

GENERAL SHOWS.—It was remitted to the Committee on General Shows to suggest the amount of prizes and adjust the regulations for the general show to be held at Glasgow in 1882 ; and to consider a resolution by the Polled Cattle Society regarding polled cattle at the Society's shows being entered in or eligible for the herd-book. It was also remitted to the same committee to prepare the classes of stock for the Inverness Show in 1883.

DIRECTORS AND OTHER OFFICE-BEARERS.—It was remitted to a committee—consisting of Lord Polwarth ; Lord Balfour of Burleigh ; Sir Michael R. Shaw Stewart, Bart. ; Sir A. Muir Mackenzie, Bart. ; Sir James Ramsay Gibson Maitland, Bart. ; Mr. Cunningham, Tarbreoch ; Mr. Dingwall, Ramornie ; Mr. Scott-Dudgeon, Longnewton ; Rev. John Gillespie ; Mr. Hope, Duddingston ; Mr. Pott of Dod ; Mr. Ralston, Glamis ; Mr. Smith, Whittinghame ; Mr. Eliott Lockhart of Borthwickbrae ; Mr. Mackenzie of Portmore —to suggest the list for 1882.

DISTRICT COMPETITIONS.—The premiums awarded for brood mares in the eastern district of Berwickshire, at the competition held there in 1880, were announced to have been finally adjudged as follow :—1, Robert White, Cairncross ; 2, Gavin Jack, Foulden Newton ; 3, Alexander Flint, Nether Mains.

THE LATE RIGHT HON. W. P. ADAM.—A letter was read from Mr. C. E. Adam of Blairadam, conveying to the Chairman and Board of Directors his mother's sincere thanks for their kind expression of appreciation of her late husband, as recorded in their resolution of 1st June ; and thanking the Secretary also for his kind expression of sympathy.

## MEETING OF DIRECTORS, 7TH DECEMBER 1881.

*Present*—Lord Polwarth ; Sir Michael R. Shaw Stewart of Blackhall, Bart. ; Sir James R. Gibson Maitland of Barnton, Bart. ; Sir James H. Gibson-Craig of Riccarton, Bart. ; Mr. Cunningham, Tarbreoch ; Mr. Dickson of Corstorphine ; Mr. Dingwall, Ramornie ; Mr. Scott Dudgeon, Longnewton ; Mr. Dundas of Arniston ; Mr. Forman, Duncrahill ; Rev. John Gillespie, Mouswald ; Mr. Maxtone Graham of Cultoquhey ; Colonel Hare of Calder Hall ; Mr. Hope, Duddingston ; Mr. Irvine of Drum ; Mr. Kennedy of Sundaywall ; Mr. Eliott Lockhart of Borthwickbrae ; Mr. Pott of Dod ; Mr. Ross, Bachilton ; Mr. Smith, Whittinghame ; Mr. John Turnbull Smith, C.A. ; Mr. Campbell Swinton of Kimmerghame ; Mr. Walker of Bowland, C.B. ; Professor Wilson ; and Dr. Aitken—Mr. Smith, Whittinghame, in the chair.

Mr. F. N. MENZIES reported apologies for the absence of Sir Windham C. Anstruther, Bart. ; Admiral Sir William Edmonstone, Bart. ; Sir Alexander Muir Mackenzie, Bart. ; Sir Henry Seton Steuart, Bart. ; Mr. Elliot, Blackhaugh ; Mr. Milne Holme of Milne Graden, Mr. Mackenzie of Portmore, Mr. Murray of Dollerie ; Mr. Ralston, Glamis House ; and Mr. Scott, Glendronach.

DECEASED MEMBERS.—Before taking up the business of the programme, the Directors entered on their minutes resolutions expressive of their sense of the services to the Society of the late Sir John Stewart Richardson of Pitfour, Bart., and the late Mr. Graham Somervell of Sorn, convener of the county of Ayr, and of the loss which the Society had sustained by their death, both gentlemen having on various occasions held the office of Ordinary and Extraordinary Director.

A letter was read from the Earl of Home, conveying to the Directors his sincere gratitude for their kind expressions and regret regarding his father's death, as recorded in their resolution of 2nd November.

INTERNATIONAL FISHERIES EXHIBITION, EDINBURGH, 1882.—The Board agreed to subscribe 100 guineas to the guarantee fund being raised in connection with the International Fisheries Exhibition to be held at Edinburgh in April next.

GENERAL SHOWS—Glasgow Show, 1882.—At the meeting of the Board in November, it was remitted to the Committee on General Shows to suggest the premiums and revise the regulations for the Show to be held at Glasgow next year. The Committee held its meeting on 16th November, and recommended premiums to the amount of £2783 ; and that the Show should be held at the usual period—namely, from the 25th to the 28th of July, both days inclusive.

The report was approved of, and the Secretary was instructed to submit the premium list and regulations to a meeting of members to be held in the George (late Queen's) Hotel, Glasgow, on Wednesday the 14th current, at one o'clock.

Inverness Show, 1883.—The classes for the proposed Show at Inverness in 1883, as suggested by the General Show Committee, were submitted to the Board, previous to being laid before a meeting of members to be held at Inverness on Friday the 16th current, at one o'clock.

AGRICULTURAL EXAMINATIONS.—The examinations for the Society's certificate and diploma in agriculture and for the Society's certificate in forestry were fixed to be held on the 17th, 18th, and 19th April 1882, candidates being required to lodge intimation on or before the 3rd of April with the Secretary, from whom further information may be obtained.

## MEETING OF DIRECTORS, 4TH JANUARY 1882.

*Present*—Lord Arthur Cecil ; Sir M. R. Shaw Stewart of Greenock and Blackhall, Bart. ; Sir J. H. Gibson-Craig of Riccarton, Bart. ; Dr. Balfour ; Mr. Cunningham, Tarbreoch ; Mr. Dingwall, Ramornie ; Mr. Scott Dudgeon, Longnewton ; Mr. Dundas of Arniston ; Mr. Elliot, Blackhaugh ; Rev. John Gillespie, Mouswald Manse ; Mr. Maxtone Graham of Cultoquhey ; Colonel Hare of Calder Hall ; Mr. Hendrie of Larbert ; Mr. Hope, Duddingston ; Mr. Eliott Lockhart of Borthwickbrae ; Mr. Murray of Dollerie ; Mr. Mylne, Niddrie Mains ; Mr. Pott of Dod ; Mr. J. Turnbull Smith, C.A. ; Mr. Smith, Whittinghame ; Mr. Campbell Swinton of Kimmerghame ; Mr. Walker of Bowland, C.B. ; Professor Wilson ; and Dr. Aitken—Mr. Smith, Whittinghame, in the chair.

Mr. F. N. MENZIES reported apologies for the absence of Sir W. Carmichael Anstruther, Bart. ; Admiral Sir William Edmonstone, Bart. ; Sir Henry J. Seton Steuart, Bart. ; Colonel Gillon of Wallhouse ; Mr. Milne Home of Milne Graden ; Mr. Irvine of Drum ; Mr. Kennedy of Sundaywell ; Mr. Mackenzie of Portmore ; Mr. Ralston, Glamis House ; and Mr. Scott, Glendronach.

Letters were read from Sir James T. Stewart Richardson of Pitfour, Bart., conveying to the Directors the thanks of his family for the resolution passed at the Board meeting on the 7th December regarding the death of his father ; and from Mrs. Graham Somervell of Sorn, expressing her sincere thanks for the manner in which the Directors recorded their regard and esteem for her late husband.

FOOT-AND-MOUTH DISEASE.—The Secretary reported that he had that morning learned that Foot-and-Mouth Disease had broken out on two farms near Millom, in Cumberland, and that he had immediately sent a telegram to the Privy Council Office to ask that Cumberland be shut out from Scotland at once. Professor Brown, of the Veterinary Department, had telegraphed back that the matter was under consideration, and that in the meantime Local Authorities in Scotland could protect themselves by declining to give the necessary licence for the movement of animals out of Cumberland under article 5 of the Order.

OFFICE-BEARERS.—The Secretary reported that the names of the noblemen and gentlemen to be proposed by the Directors at the General Meeting on the 18th current to fill the vacancies in the list of office-bearers for 1882 had been published in terms of the Charter.

DIRECTORATE.—The report by committee appointed to consider the business arrangements of the Society, and the present system of selecting Directors, was submitted, Mr. Scott Dudgeon giving notice of a motion at general meeting, of which see report.

GLASGOW SHOW, 1882.—The report of the meeting of members held at Glasgow on the 14th of December was submitted, from which it appeared that the premium list for the General Show to be held there in the last week of July was approved of, subject to the following suggestions for the consideration of the Board:—1st, That in the family prizes for Clydesdales the first premium should be increased from £10 to £20, and the others in proportion in both sections; 2nd, That the Glasgow Society should get £100 towards the premium for a horse to travel the district of the show, and a special grant of £50 for 1882; 3rd, That the date of entry for stock should be extended to Wednesday 14th June.

The Board agreed to all the suggestions, the family prizes for Clydesdales being fixed in both sections at £20, £15, £10.

INVERNESS SHOW, 1883.—The Secretary reported having attended a meeting at Inverness on the 16th of December, when the classes of stock as suggested by the Committee on General Shows had been approved of, subject to the following proposals:—1, That there should be a section for one-year-old Highland bulls; 2, that there should be a family prize in the Highland breed; 3, that in fat stock there should be two sections for polled oxen; 4, that the usual premium should be offered for a Clydesdale stallion to serve in the district of the Show; 5, that in swine the large breed should be omitted; 6, that handsome prizes should be offered for turnip-lifters.

The Board agreed to all the suggestions except the last, the Implements to be tried having already been fixed and advertised, and a very exhaustive trial of turnip-lifters having just taken place.

LOUPING-ILL AND BRAXY.—Mr. Eliott Lockhart of Borthwickbrae presented the first report of the Committee on Louping-ill and Braxy, and on his motion the Board agreed to recommend to the General Meeting to vote £200 to continue the investigation, on condition that the Committee on the subject endeavour to raise a like sum, or as near it as possible, in the districts where Louping-ill and Braxy prevail.

CHEMICAL DEPARTMENT.—Dr. Aitken reported that he had examined minutely the reports sent in by those local analytical associations who had applied for the Society's grant, and that he had prepared a digest of the analyses. He had classified them in various ways, and had brought out some important results, which he thought would be useful to farmers, and instructive to them in the use and purchase of manures. Mr. Scott Dudgeon suggested that, in view of the approach of the time when farmers would be buying their manures, it would be advantageous if Dr. Aitken could get ready a report upon this subject to be read at the General Meeting, to be held in a fortnight. This was agreed to.

---

## MEETING OF DIRECTORS, 18TH JANUARY 1882.

*Present*—The Earl of Mar and Kellie; Lord Arthur Cecil; Admiral Sir William Edmonstone of Duntreath, Bart.; Sir Windham C. Anstruther, Bart.; Sir Alexander Muir Mackenzie of Delvine, Bart.; Sir James Gibson-Craig of Riccarton, Bart.; Mr. Ainslie of Costerton; Mr. Balfour of Balbirnie; Professor Balfour; Mr. Graham Binny, W.S.; Mr. Cunningham, Tarbreoch; Mr. Dingwall, Ramornie; Admiral Maitland Dougall of Scotscraig; Mr. Scott Dudgeon, Longnewton; Mr. Dundas of Arniston; Mr. Elliot, Blackhaugh; Rev. John Gillespie, Mouswald Manse; Colonel Gillon of Wallhouse; Mr. Maxtone Graham of Cultoquhey; Lieutenant-Colonel Hare of Calder Hall; Mr. Hope, Duddingston; Mr. Irvine of Drum; Mr. Kennedy of Sundaywell; Mr. Eliott Lockhart of Borthwickbrae; Mr. Mackenzie of Portmore; Mr. Murray of Dollerie; Mr. Mylne, Niddrie Mains; Mr. Pott of Dod; Mr. Ross, Bachilton; Mr. Scott, Glendronach; Mr. Smith, Whittinghame; Mr. J. Turnbull Smith, C.A.; Dr. Aitken.

Mr. F. N. MENZIES reported apologies for the absence of the Duke of Richmond and Gordon, K.G.; the Earl of Glasgow; Lord Polwarth; Sir Michael R. Shaw Stewart Bart.; Sir Henry J. Seton Stewart, Bart.

The business had reference principally to the subjects to be brought before the General Meeting of this date.

## GENERAL MEETING, 15TH JUNE 1881.

The Right Hon. the EARL OF MAR AND KELLIE, Vice-President, in the Chair.

NEW MEMBERS.—118 New Members were elected.

The Hon. GEORGE WALDEGRAVE LESLIE asked the Secretary how many members were in the Society. The reason he asked this was that he was sorry to see the sister Society in England had diminished very much owing to the agricultural distress. He would be glad to see that confidence was maintained in this Society by the increase of its members.

Mr. F. N. MENZIES, Secretary, said that in the existing list there were 4812 members. They had added 118 to-day, which made the total number now 4930. From that had to be deducted any deaths that might have happened since the 1st January. On the whole, there was a decrease of about twenty in the two years.

STIRLING SHOW, 1881.—Colonel Gillon of Wallhouse reported that the Stirling Show would be held in the King's Park on the 26th of July, and three following days. The entries closed on the 10th inst., and the following is an abstract of the head of stock and implements contrasted with the previous Show at Stirling and the late Shows at Perth and Kelso :—

|              | Stirling. | | Perth. | Kelso. |
|              | 1881. | 1873. | 1870. | 1880. |
|--------------|-------|-------|-------|-------|
| Cattle,      | 336   | 406   | 383   | 275   |
| Horses,      | 215   | 297   | 253   | 226   |
| Sheep,       | 393   | 622   | 470   | 488   |
| Swine,       | 39    | 96    | 56    | 42    |
| Poultry,     | 365   | 534   | 200   | 244   |
| Collie Dogs, | 21    | —     | —     | —     |
| Implements,  | 2001  | 1400  | 2207  | 1578  |

The counties embraced in the district of the Show are Stirling, Dumbarton, and Clackmannan, and the western division of Perthshire. The following gentlemen have been named to act on the General Committee of Management :—

*Stirlingshire*—Hon. C. S. B. H. Kincaid Lennox, Lennox Castle, Lennoxtown ; C. H. H. Wilsone of Dalnair. Endrick Bank, Drymen ; Colonel John S. Stirling of Gargunnock. Stirling ; Sir Charles E. F. Stirling of Glorat, Bart., Campsie ; James Blackburn, Killearn House, Glasgow ; James Murray, Catter House, Drymen ; William Stirling of Tarduff, Linlithgow ; J. G. Urquhart of Vallore, Linlithgow ; W. A. Maclachlan of Auchentroig, Balfron ; J. T. S. Paterson, Plean, Stirling ; Alexander Buchanan, Whitehouse, Stirling ; James M'Laren, Sauchie, Stirling ; R. Stark, Camelon, Falkirk : James Tod, Binns, Denny ; James Jardine, Killman, Fintry. *Dunbartonshire*—H. E. Crum Ewing of Strathleven, Ardencaple Castle, Helensburgh ; A. C. Douglas of Mains, Milngavie ; A. J. D. Brown of Balloch, Alexandria ; Colonel James Colquhoun, Ben Cruach Lodge, Arrochar ; J. M. Martin, yr. of Auchendennan, Bloomhill, Cardross ; W. Burt Wright of Auchenvole, Kilsyth ; John Macfarlan, Faslane, Garelochhead ; William Fleming, Tilliechewan, Alexandria ; Robert Renwick, Dalmuir, Dumbartonshire ; John Duncan, jun., Auchenbee, Croy, Glasgow. *Clackmannanshire*—William Allan, Park, Clackmannan ; Donald Fisher, Jellyholm, Alloa ; James A. Farnie, Hilton, Alloa ; Alex. M'Nab, Middleton Kerse, Menstrie, Stirling ; James Orr of Harvieston, Dollar. *Western Division of Perthshire*—P. Sharp, Bardrill, Blackford ; D. Bollingall, Blairdrummond, Stirling ; P. M'Caull, Dykedale, Dunblane ; William Stirling Young, Keir Mains, Bridge of Allan ; J. M'Lachlan, Doune Lodge, Burn of Cambus, Stirling ; J. B. Baillie Hamilton, Cambusmore, Callander ; John Stewart, Bochastle, Callander ; Charles Carrick, Baad, Stirling ; Patrick Stirling, yr. of Kippendavie, Kippenross, Dunblane ; G. H. M. Binning Home of Argaty, Doune. *Town of Stirling*—Bailies Watt, Murray, Davie, and Lawson, Stirling ; William Simpson, Treasurer ; Robert S. Shearer, Dean of Guild ; George Christie, Southfield House, Stirling. There will also be a large deputation of Directors and other office-bearers, with Sir James R. Gibson-Maitland, Bart., as convener. At a meeting of the General Committee held at Stirling on the 10th, the following sub-committees were appointed:—Admission to Parade Gallery—Messrs. Blackburn, Killearn, convener; Murray, Catter House; Edmond, Gallamuir; and Nimmo, Foot o' Green. Forage Yard—Messrs. Paterson, Plean, convener; Stark, Summerford; and Buchanan, Whitehouse. Police—The Provost of Stirling, convener; Sir Henry J. Seton Steuart, Bart. Banquet and Ball—Duke of Montrose, convener; Earl of Mar and Kellie, Lord Balfour of Burleigh, Colonel Murray of Polmaise, deputy-convener; Sir James Gibson-Maitland, Bart.; the Provost of Stirling, Mr. Shearer, Stirling; Mr. Campbell Douglas of Mains; Colonel Stirling of Gargunnock, Colonel Drummond Moray, Messrs. Stirling, yr. of Kippendavie, Fernie, Hilton; Dewar, King's Park, and Ballingall, Blairdrummond. Accommodation of Strangers—The Town of Stirling Committee, the Provost convener.

The Hon. GEORGE WALDEGRAVE LESLIE asked what arrangements had been made with the railway companies?

Colonel GILLON said he believed that the railway companies' arrangements were intended to be very satisfactory. Of course he could not guarantee that they would be carried out.

The Hon. GEORGE WALDEGRAVE LESLIE asked if any remonstrance had been made with the directors of the North British Railway Company in regard to pulling down the bridge going into Stirling? It was better that it should be pulled down rather than that it should fall down. As it stood at present it would inconvenience a great many of the exhibitors. A remonstrance might be made with the directors to push forward the works so as to get the bridge up in time for the Show.

The CHAIRMAN said he was afraid that, considering the state in which the bridge was at present, there was not the slightest chance of its being completed in time. It was now too late to make any remonstrance.

The Hon. GEORGE WALDEGRAVE LESLIE further asked what was to be done about the trial of Implements at Stirling Show—for instance the steam-digger?

The CHAIRMAN stated that there had been no steam-digger entered, but the Secretary had been instructed to communicate with the Exhibitor of the steam-digger in England, to see if it could be brought to Stirling. Everything would be done that could be to have it brought there.

The Hon. GEORGE WALDEGRAVE LESLIE—What about the other Implements? Are they to be tried at the Show, or elsewhere?

Mr. MENZIES—They will be tried after the Show, at a time to be arranged. That is all stated in the regulations.

The report was approved of.

GLASGOW SHOW, 1882.—Colonel Gillon then said—It will be in the recollection of those who were present at the January meeting that the Society, with great cordiality, agreed to hold the Show at Glasgow in 1882. The list of classes which I then submitted have since been published. The Directors placed themselves in communication with the gentlemen in the district, by whom measures have been taken for putting the necessary arrangements in train. Some of the counties embraced in the district have come forward in a liberal and prompt manner. The Commissioners of Supply for Lanark, at their meeting of the 30th of April, adopted the recommendation of their Finance Committee that a voluntary assessment of one farthing in the pound should be levied for the purpose of helping to defray the expense of the Show. It was, however, resolved that in the event of more than £800 being realised, only that sum should be contributed, and that the surplus should be laid aside towards meeting the expenses of the next Show which the Society may hold in the county. The Commissioners of Supply for Bute have, as on former occasions, agreed to a similar assessment at the same rate. The Town Council of Glasgow have agreed to grant the use of a part of the Green for the Showyard, and also to give the Society a donation of £200 in connection therewith. (Applause.)

AGES OF SHORTHORN CATTLE.—Colonel Gillon next read the report by the Committee of the Highland and Agricultural Society appointed to report whether the ages of shorthorn cattle to be exhibited at the Society's Shows should be counted from 1st

January to

mately agreed that the question as to the age of shorthorn cattle only should be referred to a Committee to be appointed by the Directors. In accordance with this resolution, the Directors at their meeting on the 2nd of March, appointed a committee to consider and report on the proposed change, with special instructions to take steps to ascertain the views of all persons who were breeders or exhibitors of shorthorns which have been entered at the Society's General Shows during the last eight years, and to consult with the Royal Agricultural Society of England. The Committee held a preliminary meeting on the 11th May, when the terms of the letters to exhibitors and to the Secretary of the Royal Agricultural Society of England were submitted. A second meeting was held on the 25th May to consider the answers to the circular, and report thereon. In response to the circular, the Society received replies from 98 breeders or exhibitors. Of these 8 were neutral, 31 were of opinion that the ages should be calculated from 1st December, and 59 were in favour of adhering to the present mode of counting the ages from 1st January. The answer from Mr. Jenkins, the Secretary of the Royal Agricultural Society, was to there effect that for some years there had been a growing feeling in favour of altering their previous date of 1st July to the 1st January, or (as the Council preferred to put it) not to mention any date from which the age of animals was to be calculated; but this practically amounts to the first day of the year. The Committee were of opinion that Mr. Mollison produced several strong reasons in favour of the ages of shorthorn and polled being calculated from the same date; but as the subject was not included in the remit, the Committee felt that it could not be taken up. It was ultimately resolved, that in consequence of the majority of the answers being in favour of the 1st of January, to recommend the Directors to adhere to that date. Colonel Gillon concluded by stating that the Directors unanimously approved of the report, and directed it to be brought up at this meeting.

The report was approved of.

AGRICULTURAL EDUCATION.—Mr. Irvine of Drum reported that the examination of candidates for the diploma and certificate in agriculture took place on the 28th, 29th, and 30th March, when twenty gentlemen enrolled their names as candidates, and the following passed :—*For Diploma*—Lawford D. Govar, Findon, Worthing; William Henderson, East Elrington, Haydon Bridge; Marcus Sandison, Hemprigge, Wick; Frederick Herman Weber, 44 Green Street, Grosvenor Square, London. *For First Class Certificate*—A. S. Alexander, 4 Belhaven Terrace, Glasgow; Daniel Bain, Wick; Thomas A. Buttar, Corston, Coupar-Angus; Alfred Hardie, Oxford House, Stockport. *For Second Class Certificate*—Benjamin Hepburn, Preston Mains, Prestonkirk; John Martin Little, jun., Bonnington House, Blackheath, London; Samuel Naismith, 2 Tarvit Street, Edinburgh; James Rodger, Inchock, Arbroath; John S. Peter, 5 Ravelston Place, Edinburgh. The two prizes of £6 and £4, given by the Society to the class of agriculture in the University of Edinburgh, were this year awarded by special examination to—1, William Henderson, Northumberland; 2, Daniel Bain, Caithness, and James Craig, Fifeshire (equal).

TECHNICAL SCHOOLS OF AGRICULTURE.—The report by the Standing Acting Committee on Agricultural Education, to whom it was referred to consider and report on Colonel Innes's motion at the general meeting in January last, viz.:—"That there is urgent need of the establishment of central technical schools of agriculture, and that it is the duty of the Society to encourage the establishment of such schools," was then by Mr. Irvine of Drum, as follows:—"The Committee having given the matter remitted to them their best consideration, may observe that the Society has on various occasions beneficially employed its influence for encouraging the youth of the country connected with agriculture to devote greater attention than had hitherto been done to the study of the different branches of science which have a relation more or less direct to agriculture. In 1856 the Society established a special agricultural education department, when it received from Government a supplementary charter authorising the Society to take steps for directing and promoting the education of young agriculturists, by laying down a defined curriculum of study, and by granting diplomas to those who, on examination, should be found qualified in the science and practice of agriculture. Examinations are held annually in Edinburgh, at which diplomas and certificates are conferred on qualified candidates without reference to places or modes of education. There are now fifty-two holders of the Society's diploma located in various parts of the country fully qualified to give sound elementary instruction in agriculture. These diplomas are accepted by the Science and Art Department as qualifying the holders ' to earn payments by results' in the same way as the department teachers. There are also twenty holders of first-class and sixteen of second-class certificates. While the Society pays the fees and travelling expenses of the examiners, it exacts no fees from the candidates coming up for examination. Successful candidates for the diploma are, by a byelaw enacted in 1873, eligible to be elected free life members of the Society. In 1868, the Society supplemented the endowment of the Chair of Agriculture in the Edinburgh University by an annual grant of £150; and since 1865 it has annually voted £10 (given in two sums of £6 and £4) to the students who pass the best and second best examination in the agricultural class. In 1874, with the view of encouraging instruction in the elements of agriculture so as to qualify for the diploma or certificate, the Society established ten bursaries of £20 each and five of £10 each to be competed for by ____ in the ____

curriculum. The £20 bursaries are tenable for one year at the University of Edinburgh, for the purpose of enabling the holders to take the classes necessary to qualify for the Society's certificate or diploma; and the £10 bursaries are tenable for the same period, to enable the holders to receive another year's preparation at the schools. Advantage has been taken of these bursaries by pupils educated at the following schools :—High School, Edinburgh'; George Watson's College, Edinburgh ; Edinburgh Institution ; School of Arts, Edinburgh ; Dollar Academy, Dundee Institution, Dumfries Academy, Ayr Academy, Wick Science School, Ballantrae Parochial School ; Rattray's Academy, Aberdeen ; St. Mungo's Parish School, Glencairn Parish School, Hexham Public School, Brampton Academy, and Fyvie School. Amongst the colleges and schools at which candidates for the diploma and certificates have been educated are :—Trinity College, Cambridge ; Royal Agricultural College, Cirencester ; Dulwich College, Surrey ; Owens College, Manchester ; Clevedon College, Harrow School ; Winchester College ; Repton School, Derbyshire ; Hexham School, Edinburgh University, Aberdeen University, Fettes College, Glasgow Academy, Veterinary and Agricultural College, Glasgow ; Aberdeen School of Chemistry, Edinburgh High School, Pulteneytown School, East Linton School, Montrose Academy, Fyvie School ; Morison's Academy, Crieff ; Kells Parish School, New Cumnock Free Church School, Prestonkirk Free Church School, Greenloaning School, Kirkwall School, Wick Science School. The Committee conceive that by the steps above set forth, and more particularly by the institution of the fifteen bursaries of the total annual value of £250 specially offered to the pupils of schools in which the sciences connected with agriculture are taught, the Society has, in the absence of greater funds, done in the past what it could to encourage the establishment of such schools as those referred to by Colonel Innes. The Committee confidently hope that these bursaries, as they become better known, will be taken advantage of by the pupils of other schools where the sciences may be introduced, and they have only further to suggest that the Society memorialise the Government to engraft the teaching of agriculture into the board schools of the country. The Directors approved of the report, and directed it to be brought before this meeting."

Mr. IRVINE, after reading the report, moved its adoption.

Mr. MILNE HOME of Milne Graden said he did not know that the report was to come before the meeting. He should be very glad, however, to second the motion ; at the same time making this remark, that he understood that the motion of Colonel Innes, to which the report referred, recommended a wider distribution of the Society's influence than merely to confine it to Edinburgh. He had some idea, from old recollections —but Mr. Forbes Irvine would know—that there was a school in Aberdeen. He understood that there was a professorship or lectureship on the science of agriculture in Aberdeen, and he thought it would be for the good of the Society to offer prizes to the students in that class, if there were such a class, who underwent a particular examination. It would be for the Directors, or rather for the Committee on Agricultural Education, to consider what ought to be done, but at all events the more encouragement the Society gave in that way the better.

Mr. IRVINE of Drum said that amongst the other institutions mentioned in the report there was the Aberdeen School of Chemistry.

Mr. MILNE HOME said he understood that there were bursaries and prizes, but that they were all monopolised by Edinburgh, whereas none were given to any other school in the country.

The SECRETARY said that the £10 bursaries were open to the students of any school, but the £20 bursaries were tenable for one year at the University of Edinburgh.

The report was then adopted.

THE SOCIETY'S EXPERIMENTAL STATIONS.—Dr. Aitken, chemist to the Society, reported on the Society's experimental stations :—" In the volume of the *Transactions* just issued, there is contained a condensed report of the experiments carried on at the Society's stations during the past season. The last crop of the rotation—viz., oats—has been sown under the most favourable conditions, and the various manures have been applied with the utmost precision at both stations. The field at Harelaw, which has hitherto been in too high a state of fertility for our experiments, is now reduced to a condition which, I think, will be found very favourable for exhibiting the effects of the different kinds of manure which have been applied to it. I look forward with much interest to the appearances which will be presented on that field this summer, and am hopeful that, from its proximity to the railway station of Longniddry, it may attract the attention and receive the inspection of those for whose benefit the experiments have been instituted. As an additional inducement to those who may care to visit the stations, I may say that a new set of labels has been prepared, indicating not only the number of each plot, but also the precise nature and amount of the manures applied to it, so that any one going over the plots may be able to understand the experiments without a guide and without a plan. Besides the ordinary set of experiments on the large and small plots, I have this year made use of part of the spare ground at Harelaw to test the value of potash as a manure for the potato crop, both in the form of sulphate and of muriate. It is very gratifying to find that the value of agricultural experiments is year by year being better appreciated, and that the number of workers in the field is on the increase. In the first place, we have the Aberdeenshire Association, whose work is well known, and whose indefatigable chemist has been doing valiant battle all round in upholding the value of insoluble phosphates as a manure for the turnip crop, and also for other crops. In volume xiii. of the *Transactions* we have also a careful set of experiments by Mr. Lawson, Sandyford, who adduces quite extraordinary testimony in favour of the superior excellence of undissolved phosphates as a manure for turnips on the Braes of Angus. On the other hand, we have an equally careful set of experiments, carried out on the home farm of the Marquis of Tweeddale, showing in a far more extraordinary degree the superior value of dissolved phosphates as a turnip producer on that soil; and we have our own experiments with turnips on both our stations giving very decided evidence in the same direction. It is not unnatural that those who are engaged in such investigations, and strongly impressed with the accuracy of their own work, should be filled with a desire to have their results corroborated by others, and look with suspicion upon the work of those who find results that lead to different conclusions. That, however, is wrong. Let each one accord to others engaged in the same work the accuracy which he claims for himself, and welcome, for the truth's sake, well-earned results, however much they may run counter to those of his own finding. The experiments before us, similar as they are in almost all respects, differ very widely in one—namely, that they have been conducted in widely different localities, and on totally different soils; and granting, what cannot be doubted, that they have been carefully and accurately carried out, we are led to the conclusion that soils differ greatly in character and act very differently on manures. Those engaged in manurial investigations are too apt to regard the manure as everything, and to undervalue the great importance of the differences which exist in the characters of soils. Keeping that in view, we should conclude from the experiments which I have noticed, that on some of the soils of Aberdeenshire, if turnips are grown with soluble and insoluble phosphates, side by side, the former will yield a crop on an average about 7 per cent. heavier than the latter. If the experiment is tried in Forfarshire, the probability is that the *undissolved* phosphates will produce 10 per cent. more than the other. If the experiment is tried in the Lothians, then the *dissolved* phosphates will likely cause an increase of 20 per cent., or more, than the same phosphate undissolved, and in the neighbourhood of Yester the soil manured with dissolved phosphate may yield a crop 50 per cent. heavier than that manured with the other. I submit that this shows the need of being cautious and guarded in generalising from experiments conducted in one district. In my report I have described one method by which a farmer may begin the study of his soil; and I promise that he will be both a wiser and a richer man who tries it and applies it. I hope that the number of experimenters will go on increasing, until every farmer is in some measure an experimenter, and until an experimental station of some kind in co-operation with this Society is found in every county of Scotland."

FORESTRY DEPARTMENT.—Professor Balfour reported that the examinations for the Society's certificates in forestry took place on the 28th, 29th, and 30th March, when a second-class certificate was conferred on Mr. Alex. Inglis, Tyninghame, Prestonkirk.

VETERINARY DEPARTMENT.—Colonel Williamson of Lawers reported that the last examination which is to be held under the auspices of the Society took place on the 15th, 19th. and 20th April last, when thirty students presented themselves for examination, and out of that number twenty succeeded in obtaining certificates.

THE VETERINARY SURGEONS BILL.—Professor MacFadyean, in moving that the Society petition against clause 3 of this Bill, stated that, in order to explain the full force of the clause, he would read it with the preamble. The preamble began by stating—"Whereas it is expedient that provision be made to enable persons requiring the aid of a veterinary surgeon for the cure or prevention of diseases in or injuries to horses and other animals, to distinguish between qualified and unqualified practitioners, be it therefore enacted," &c. Then clause 3 of the Bill than thus—"On and after the first day of October, one thousand eight hundred and eighty-one, a person shall not be entitled to take or use the name or title of veterinary surgeon, or veterinary practitioner, or any other name, title, addition, or description, implying that he is a member of the Royal College of Veterinary Surgeons, or is otherwise qualified to practise, or is a practitioner of veterinary surgery, unless he is registered as a member of the said Royal College." The Bill thus sought to obtain exclusive privileges for the members of the Royal College of Veterinary Surgeons. It declared by implication that those who practised on the strength of the certificate granted by this Society were in no sense qualified practitioners. That was surely a most anomalous thing, as the Royal College was not called into existence until twenty years after this Society instituted its veterinary examinations. It might be supposed also that the graduates of this Society had received an inferior education and undergone an examination less rigorously conducted. That, however, was not the case; and the period of study required by this Society has always been the period required by the Royal College. One sought in vain for any reason or explanation why the clause stood as it was. There was one thing he could conceive some one advancing as an apology for the clause in its present form. It was true that a few years ago an agreement was entered into between this Society and the Royal College, under which graduates of the Society might be enrolled and registered as members of the Royal College of Veterinary Surgeons on immediate payment of a fee without any examination. But it seemed to him that that was a powerful argument against the clause, because by coming to that agreement the Royal College of Veterinary Surgeons accepted the degree of the Highland Society as sufficient proof of education equal to what it desired from its own graduates, and admitted that the holder was qualified for practising the veterinary art. But, further than that, the agreement was never intended to be anything else than permissive. By this measure it was sought to make it compulsory. It was true that a considerable number of graduates had thought it expedient to take advantage of that agreement, but a considerable number also—he thought a great number—maintained that no higher qualification was obtainable in this country than the veterinary certificate of this Society. They refused to be admitted to the Royal College by what some considered was a back-door entrance. If the Bill became law, it would be put into operation against those gentlemen, and should the Society not take any action on the matter these graduates would feel as if the Society had deserted them. The past history of the Society in its attitude towards the veterinary students had been one of unvaried beneficence, and to stand idly by and see this injustice done and indignity put upon its graduates, would be to a large extent to vitiate its own past conduct. He therefore begged to move—"That this meeting transmit a memorial, signed by its chairman, petitioning Parliament to amend the Veterinary Surgeons Bill as follows, viz., to insert after clause 8 the words ' or holds the veterinary certificate of the Highland and Agricultural Society of Scotland.'"

Professor BALFOUR seconded the motion. He thought this another instance of the desire there was in England for the centralising of affairs in London, and said that if this proposal was to take away the position of those holding the degrees of the Society they ought decidedly to set their faces against it.

The Hon. GEORGE WALDEGRAVE LESLIE asked who brought the bill into Parliament —was it in connection with the Privy Council, or was it a matter of the Royal College only?

Mr. MENZIES stated that it was brought in by Lord Aberdare.

Sir GRAHAM MONTGOMERY suggested that the Society, in petitioning against the clause, should make Scotch members aware of the state of the case, and that the Secretary should get some member to put a notice on the paper to move the rejection of the clause when the Bill went into committee, otherwise the Bill might slip through at some early hour in the morning, and they would lose the opportunity of getting the clause amended.

The motion was agreed to.

HIGHLAND INDUSTRIES AND FISHERIES.—Sir JAMES RAMSAY GIBSON-MAITLAND of Barnton, Bart., in the absence of Sir James R. Gibson-Craig of Riccarton, Bart., convener of the committee recently appointed by the Directors in charge of this department, said—The attention of the Directors having been some time ago called to the present position of the fisheries of Scotland and other Highland industries, the subject was remitted to a committee, consisting of Sir Michael Shaw Stewart, Bart.; Sir James R. Gibson-Maitland, Bart.; Sir James Gibson-Craig, Bart.; General Burroughs of Rousay, C.B.; Mr. Irvine of Drum; Professor Wilson; and Mr. Archibald Young, one of the Commissioners of Scotch Salmon Fisheries. At their first meeting the committee requested the Secretary to prepare a statement showing what the original objects of the Society were, and what the Society did formerly in promoting the fisheries and other industries in the Highlands of Scotland. From the statement submitted to the committee at their second meeting, it appeared that among the original objects it was proposed to examine into the Highlands and Islands; to establish towns, villages, and harbours therein; to open communication by roads and bridges; to extend and promote fisheries; to encourage agriculture; and to introduce manufactures—that the first advertisement of premiums by the Society was published in March 1785, when various gold medals were offered for essays relative to the fisheries and on the state of manufactures in the Highlands, particularly woollen and linen. The statement also showed that the premiums were continued for several years, and that numerous awards were made for reports, more particularly on subjects connected with the fisheries; and that other sources of industry peculiar to the Highlands were subjects of competition and reward. It was found that to the exertions of the Society are due among other things the establishment of the British Fisheries Society, founded for the express object of establishing towns and villages on the coasts of the Highlands and Islands, particularly on such parts as were best adapted for fishing stations; the Scottish Board of Fisheries; relief from the duty of coal carried coastwise; and the relaxation of the salt laws. The Society was also the means of directing attention to the practicability of opening a navigable communication between Lochgilp and Loch Crinan. It furnished Mr. Telford, the Government engineer, with a report on the communication from the eastern to the western seas, called the Caledonian Canal. The information acquired and communicated to Mr. Telford was acknowledged by him in the fullest manner. At the request of Mr. Telford, the Society reported on the importance of opening communication by roads and bridges in the Highlands ; and in consequence of the information and suggestions communicated, Government voted large sums for the purpose of enabling proprietors of estates in the Highlands to carry roads through districts where without such aid they could not possibly have been accomplished. In short, it was believed the Society had been productive of so much good in the past that the committee, anxious that the original objects should not be lost sight of, had no hesitation in recommending the Directors to re-establish a department on Highland industries and fisheries. To this the Board readily agreed. Since then the Secretary and other members of the Committee have had an opportunity of attending the National Fisheries Exhibition held at Norwich in April last. They considered it most interesting, and that much of it could be introduced into the Society's general shows. Recently the Council of the Scottish Fisheries Improvement Association have memorialised the Lord Provost, Magistrates, and Town Council of Edinburgh in favour of holding a national fisheries exhibition in Edinburgh in April 1882, and the matter has been remitted to the Lord Provost's Committee. At a subsequent meeting of the Society's Committee, a letter was read from the Secretary of the Scottish Fisheries Improvement Association, requesting the Directors to appoint a Committee to co-operate with the Lord Provost's Committee, the Council of the Scotch Fisheries Improvement Association, and the Fishery Board. The Directors acceded to the request, and appointed the Committee on Highland Industries and Fisheries to represent the Society. It has been also suggested that the exhibition proposed to be held in Edinburgh in April next should be made international.

Mr. MILNE HOME said that what was much wanted in this country was what existed in other countries for the protection of the fresh-water fish—namely, Government inspectors, who should perambulate the country and see that the law was carried out. In England and Ireland there were inspectors who had these powers, and who reported when they considered necessary. In Scotland they were so badly off as to have no inspectors and no boards. Application had been made to the Government to have this state of matters remedied, but nothing had yet been done. The Fisheries Improvement Association, of which he had the honour of being a member, was formed in the hope of inducing the Government to take up the matter, and establishing greater protection for the fresh-water fisheries. He trusted the Highland and Agricultural Society, which was the most influential Society in Scotland, would take up this matter in earnest. It was not for a young society such as the one to which he had referred to deal with the question so much as for this Society with its 5000 members to do so. It would no doubt be listened to by the Government if it made some application to have better protection for the fisheries. Several applications had been made to the Government on the subject, but they had been received only with courteous terms and empty promises. He hoped that the Directors would see their way to encourage the fisheries, and endeavour to obtain some improvement in the executive protection of these fisheries. He was reminded of a discussion that took place in the House of Lords the other night with reference to many subjects of public importance in Scotland which did not receive that attention from Government which they out to receive. This was one subject which ought to receive their attention, and he might mention that the Convention of Royal Burghs had sent up remonstrances on the subject. He thought that it would not be out of the way to sent up petitions to both the House of Lords and the House of Commons, asking that more attention should be given to Scotch affairs. This subject of the fisheries was a good illustration of how much had been promised and how little had been done.

Sir JAMES GIBSON-MAITLAND said he thought that the whole history of this Society was a sufficient guarantee that they would get something from Government if they made the necessary representations. They had been successful hitherto, and he had no doubt they would be successful again.

The motion was unanimously adopted.

Mr. IRVINE of Drum laid on the table the *Transactions* of the Society ; and the proceedings terminated with a vote of thanks to the chairman.


## GENERAL MEETING AT STIRLING, 27TH JULY 1881.

The Right Hon. the EARL OF MAR AND KELLIE, Vice-President, in the chair.

The CHAIRMAN, in opening the proceedings, said—My Lords and gentlemen, the only business before the meeting is a series of resolutions to be proposed by the Hon. Mr. Waldegrave Leslie. I hope that Mr. Leslie and the gentlemen who speak on these resolutions will be as brief as they possibly can, and confine themselves to the matter before us, because these meetings considerably interfere with the business of the Show. Before calling on Mr. Waldegrave Leslie, I should say the Duke of Richmond, the President of the Society, has sent a letter regretting very much his inability to attend here to-day. He is entertaining the Prince and Princess of Wales at Goodwood, and cannot be here.

The Hon. G. WALDEGRAVE LESLIE then said—My Lord, I promise to obey your Lordship's instructions, and to occupy as little time as possible on the present occasion. I will begin by asking *seriatim*, according to your directions, what the Directors have done with regard to the resolution carried at the last meeting of the Council regarding the finances of the Society?

Mr. MURRAY of Dollerie, Convener of the Finance Committee, said—My Lord, I wish to state, in the first place, in answer to my friend, Mr. Waldegrave Leslie, if he will allow me to call him so, that the Directors have been obeying his resolution throughout all their proceedings, and we have nothing more to do in obedience to that resolution than follow the course we have been following for many years. But in respect to two particulars to which Mr. Leslie has called our attention—namely, the accumulation of the funds and the application of the capital fund of the Society—I wish to give two particular answers. In the first place, with respect to accumulation, we have no accumulation whatever from the ordinary funds of the Society since the Directors ceased to act upon the authority given to them by the charter to use up the life subscriptions. The charter ordered these life subscriptions to be applied in general terms to capital; but some years ago, finding capital was sufficient for the ordinary purposes of this Society, they ceased to apply these life subscriptions to the capital fund. That has not been done to the ordinary fund; but on two separate occasions—the Shows at Glasgow and Edinburgh—the sums received were so very large that the Directors found themselves obliged to consider how they should apply this surplus. They applied it to the addition of capital, and we had no orders to do otherwise. We added to the capital considerably from these large shows, but we have not used any of the ordinary funds of the Society for that purpose. That is the answer to the question as to whether we have or have not added to the capital. With respect to the other question, whether we have spent the capital, I have, in answer to that question, simply to make a quotation from the charter. I am anxious that this quotation should be distinctly understood and expressed in any report of this meeting, so that there may be no misapprehension with respect to future proceedings. The quotation is :—" No part of the capital, either already acquired or to be so formed, shall be afterwards applied, except by authority of a General Meeting, and upon intimation of the intended application being made at two meetings of the Board of Directors, previous to such General Meeting." These are the words, so that you see if any honourable gentleman, a member of this Society, wishes the capital to be used he has to give notice twice to the Directors of his intention, so that it may be reported at the meeting of the Society what his intention is. It must be a special application for some special purpose.

Mr. WALDEGRAVE LESLIE—After that explanation, I give notice that I will bring forward my resolution at the January meeting.

The Marquis of LOTHIAN—But I should like Mr. Waldegrave Leslie to move his resolutions. A great number of gentlemen have come here to-day, solely for the purpose of giving their opinion regarding them. He may bring the resolutions forward at the January meeting, but after he has given intimation to all the members of the Society that he was to lay them before the meeting to-day, it is not fair that he should bring them here to this meeting for no purpose whatever.

Mr. WALDEGRAVE LESLIE—But I could not do it until I got the answer to my first question.

The Marquis of LOTHIAN—I understand that Mr. Waldegrave Leslie now proposes to bring up this subject at the January meeting.

Mr. WALDEGRAVE LESLIE—Having heard the report of the Convener of the Finance Committee, I am unable to answer that, because the information is certainly new.

The Marquis of LOTHIAN—Then I do not think Mr. Waldegrave Leslie is acting with respect to the Society. If he gives notice of a motion for discussion without having proper information, and having information which he has not verified, and on which he insists on moving a series of resolutions—not knowing anything about the subject—then he does not treat the Society with proper respect.

Mr. WALDEGRAVE LESLIE—I asked the information, and I have only this moment received it.

The CHAIRMAN—I may say that Mr. Waldegrave Leslie might have had the information he has now got by asking for it from the Directors. Perhaps Mr. Waldegrave Leslie will now proceed with the next resolution.

Mr. WALDEGRAVE LESLIE—I want to state preliminarily in regard to the notice of motion I have given that I have no wish whatever to attack any person, because I am certain any one in this tent will bear me witness that on calling at the office of the Society he will receive nothing but civility and attention alike from the Secretary and his efficient staff. But what I wish to make a few remarks upon is a system by which the whole time of the Secretary is not devoted to the interests of the Society.

The CHAIRMAN—I think that is the third resolution. Will you confine yourself to the first, if you please ?

Mr. WALDEGRAVE LESLIE—In the resolutions I put in a proviso as to the grave times of agricultural depression of the present and last year, and I wish to draw the attention of the members of this Society to what has been done in the English Society, where, out of a directorate of fifty members, there are no fewer than twenty-one gentlemen connected with it who farm themselves principally, and also there are twenty-one having farms, and four implement makers, and one seed merchant. That has worked exceedingly well in the ancient Society of England, and I do not see why the same experiment should not be tried here. I am led to understand, since I came into the yard this morning, that this matter has been occupying the attention of the Directors, and that they propose to receive a report in the month of November, and to lay it before the General Meeting in January, and such being the information I have received, I do not wish to press this in the shape of a resolution, but will leave this matter also till the January meeting, when we shall receive this report. I do so because I do not wish now to occupy time or to forestall what the Directors may be able to do in their greater wisdom. I wish also to say, with regard to these committees, that I think ——

The CHAIRMAN—That is the second resolution, I think ?

Mr. WALDEGRAVE LESLIE—Yes.

The CHAIRMAN—Then have you done with the first ?

Mr. WALDEGRAVE LESLIE—I have done with the first.

Mr. CAMPBELL SWINTON of Kimmerghame—Since Mr. Waldegrave Leslie, although he has not intimated his intention of pressing his motion at present, has expressed an opinion with regard to it, I think it may not be amiss to say a single word in addition to what has been mentioned, that this subject is at present under the consideration of the Directors. The matter was discussed to some extent at the Kelso meeting, and following that by a Committee of Directors, which has been appointed under the presidency of Mr. Scott Dudgeon, and during his absence from the country of my Lord Polwarth, maturely to consider the matter of electing the office-bearers of this Society, or rather the suggesting to the general meeting of persons to be appointed to the various offices to the Society. But I do not think it would do to allow this large and important meeting to separate without putting Mr. Leslie right with regard to the composition of the Board of Ordinary Directors. I will not anticipate—for I do not know what it may be—the report of the committee now sitting on the subject, but yet I may say that it will be very difficult for them to suggest in regard to the composition of the Board anything that would more entirely meet the views of my honourable friend who suggested this motion with regard to the composition of the Directorate. The motion points out that the Directorate should be composed of proprietors or tenants interested in agricultural pursuits—I forget the exact words—and not occupied chiefly with other professional duties. There could not be, as it happens, a more inopportune or inappropriate period for bringing this motion forward than the present, because, with the exception of one gentleman—a rev. gentleman—who is, I believe, the first minister of the Church who ever sat on the Board of Direction [*]—one of whom I may say, in a parenthesis, that I believe he is as good a farmer as he is a minister. With the exception of that rev. gentleman, there is not on the present list of Ordinary Directors a single man who is not either a proprietor, and thereby interested in agricultural pursuits, or a tenant-farmer, known for his skill in these matters. I have sat often—I do not sit at present—on the Board of Ordinary Directors, and I am free to acknowledge that I have seen benefit accruing from representatives of other professions being occasionally members of the Board. I have seen very useful advocates, very useful Writers to the Signet, and very useful accountants members of the Board of Directors ; but at this moment the Board of Direction does not contain one single man who is concerned in any of these professions. It consists entirely either of landed proprietors or of tenant-farmers, who have been selected for their special knowledge of the subject. As to how the experience of landed proprietors is to be decided when they are appointed to the Directorate, I do not know whether my honourable friend would suggest a competitive examination for that purpose, but I think you may consider that a man has an interest in land from the fact that he possesses it, and has a great stake in it. I would also remind my honourable friend, what he seems to have forgotten, that there is a rule of this Society by which every member of the Society has an individual voice in the selection of Directors, because it is a rule that every member is not only empowered, but is requested, to suggest, previous to the annual general meeting, the names of gentlemen whom he would wish placed on the Board of Direction. There is such a rule, and the Directors have often lamented that it is not more generally acted on, and if I am not

---

[*] The late Principal Baird, who was for many years chaplain to the Society, acted as an Ordinary Director of the Society during the years 1827, 1828, 1829, and 1830.

mistaken my honourable friend never on one occasion suggested the name of a single gentleman whom he wished placed on the Board of Direction. I think it scarcely consistent—excellent as my friend and energetic as he is in these matters—to sit silent all the year, at the very time when he is asked to suggest members for the Direction, and afterwards to come here and find fault with those who have been selected, and who, as I have shown you, are men who exactly meet his requirements, because none of them are interested in other professions.

Mr. WALDEGRAVE LESLIE—May I explain one word? I do not think that the great bulk of the members were aware of the power of suggesting gentlemen for the Board. I certainly was not aware of it, and we must say we are indebted to Mr. Swinton for his kindness in apprising us, and now that we know we have the power we may exercise it.

The CHAIRMAN said that it was advertised every year, and if Mr. Waldegrave Leslie did not read the advertisements it was his own fault.

Lord POLWARTH, in the absence of the convener of the committee which was appointed to deal with this particular subject, said that the fact that a committee had been appointed to deal with this subject was a tacit acknowledgment that the arrangement at present was not satisfactory to the general membership. Although he was not able to put before the meeting the proposals of that committee, because they had not yet been submitted to the Directorate, he assured them that the members of the committee were most anxious that the responsibility of the choice of Directors should, so far as consistent with the charter, rest upon the general membership of the Society. He was of opinion that, in order that the Society should maintain a real vitality throughout, there should be a feeling of responsibility as to the choice of those who were to hold office in the Society. They might be satisfied that the report would be satisfactory to the general membership.

Mr WALDEGRAVE LESLIE—Now, in regard to the second resolution—that the lists of members of the various committees should be revised and reduced—I wish to draw attention to the fact that in the books of the Society there are no less than twelve committees, and that one is amissing—that is, the Steam Committee. I believe I was the member of the Society who first brought forward the matter, that it was desirable to have a committee to consider the question of steam cultivation. As far as I can remember, that committee met only once. The then convener was the pioneer of subsoil cultivation—the late Marquis of Tweeddale—and it was long after his death that that committee went on under the presidency of the Marquis of Lothian; but somehow or other this committee had never met, and it has been purged out of the list, I don't know why. It appears to me that the matter of steam cultivation in the Society in these days cannot be ignored; and I think that one of the greatest cultivators of the day, the Master of Blantyre, is one who should be on the Directorate of the Society. I think it is very hard that year after year should pass away without having him placed on the Directorate. There is another committee—that of machinery—of which I am a member, and I do not remember that we have ever been called together; and I am told by members of other committees that some do meet and some do not meet, but that there are so many members of some committees that the work is not thrown upon three or four working members, and the consequence is that the committees never meet and never do anything. I beg to suggest that the lists of members of the various committees should be revised and reduced, and I hope that this subject will be undertaken by the Directors, and considered themselves, before January.

Mr. MACKENZIE of Portmore—In reference to what has been said, I have to inform this meeting—and probably many present must know the fact already—that every year the Directors of the Society revise the lists of the committees, and make such alterations as they think will be most beneficial for carrying on the work most efficiently. This is the answer to the question of the revision, but Mr. Leslie goes on to say that the members of the committees should be reduced in number. Well, I have myself the honour to be the convener of one of these committees, and I serve upon some of the others, and I know from practical experience that, although the committee I preside over is one composed of a large number of members, we often have considerable difficulty in getting together a sufficient number of gentlemen to fairly take into consideration matters brought before us, and if you reduce the numbers further you will simply increase that difficulty. People cannot always attend; and unless you have a large number on the committee you will frequently find the attendance is too small to entrust to it the important work which devolves upon these committees.

Mr. WALDEGRAVE LESLIE—What has become of the Steam Committee?

The CHAIRMAN—That is not a question of reducing the number of committees. I am informed that committee was amalgamated with another, so that it has been reduced to a certain extent. It has been amalgamated with the Machinery Committee.

Mr. WALDEGRAVE LESLIE—Then why is it the Machinery Committee were never called together?

Mr. MYLNE, Niddrie Hains—I can assure Mr. Leslie that the Machinery Committee is regularly called together.

Mr. WALDEGRAVE LESLIE—I have never had a summons to attend the meetings.

Mr. MENZIES, Secretary—If you did not receive the notices, I am perfectly certain they were sent.

Mr. WALDEGRAVE LESLIE—I will take your word for it  With regard to the third resolution—that the whole business time of the secretarial staff of the Society should be given exclusively to the work of the Society—I wish to say from my heart that nothing in my mind has occurred to make this at all a personal question, which, I am informed by some people it is considered to be.  I shall not press the motion, because it would be painful to an individual.  I may be permitted to say that my opinion, and the opinion of a large number of the members of the Society, are strongly in favour of having the whole time of our able Secretary, who is a man of most undoubted ability and great energy, devoted to the work of the Society.  We think it would be better to get his whole time, as in the case of the secretary of the Royal Society of England.  I am informed, however, that at the time of his appointment by the Directors this question was carefully gone into, and that the agreement come to was that he should be at liberty to a certain extent not to give his whole business time to the work of the Society.  That compact was made, and I should be sorry to break that honourable compact by anything that might be offensive, disagreeable, or painful, or likely to act as a breach of compact with a gentleman in the position of our Secretary.  I was not aware of this, and I hope that what I have brought forward will be taken in good part and acted upon as far as possible.

Mr MARTIN, yr. of Auchendennan, as one of the gentlemen who was in favour of the showyard meetings being held annually, begged most seriously to protest against a meeting such as the present.

Mr. WALKER of Bowland asked if the hon. gentleman was speaking to Mr Waldegrave Leslie's motion.

Mr. MARTIN said he protested most sincerely against the use to which the meetings had been put.  Many gentlemen believed that the showyard meetings would be both useful and desirable in the interests of the Society, if for nothing else than to let the members get a good wholesome grumble every year, and tell what they had to complain of.  But if the meetings were to be brought together to consider proposed resolutions, some of which, notwithstanding the explanations that had been made, were of the most offensive kind, he protested against such proceedings.  Those resolutions had been circulated throughout the country, and not only in Scotland but in England the papers had been writing about things they knew absolutely nothing about, owing to the printed notices of motions.  It was putting the meeting to a disgraceful use to bring forward resolutions of the kind, and then for the proposer of them to say, "If I had known what I know now, I would never have brought the resolution forward," while the information was at the disposal of every member of the Society.  Not only the honour of the Society but the feelings of their officials who served them as well were concerned.  If the hon. gentleman who had brought forward the resolution was so impressed with the services of those officials to the Society, a more graceful way of showing his appreciation might have been found than by presenting the notices of motion.  He had a suggestion to make with a view of rendering the meetings useful and pleasant, and for the good of the Society.  There was, perhaps, a little tendency on the part of those promoting the meetings to put forward resolutions by way of having some business to take up.  His suggestion was that the Directors might see their way to bring up the formal resolutions and votes of thanks which were passed at the January meeting at the summer Show, where they would be more in place.  It would be more natural to have those votes of thanks passed at the summer Show, where the gentlemen interested were present, than at the January meeting, for many members of the Society did not attend that meeting, and heard nothing of the votes of thanks, whilst the gentlemen to whom the votes of thanks were tendered were frequently absent.

Mr WALKER of Bowland concurred in the remarks of Mr Martin, and inquired whether or not Mr Waldegrave Leslie withdrew his motion.

Mr. WALDEGRAVE LESLIE—I don't press it.  (Cries of "Withdraw.")  I withdraw it.

Mr. VILLIERS, Closeburn Hall, said, with regard to the notices of motion by Mr Waldegrave Leslie, he could not help thinking that the meeting would not allow such resolutions simply to be passed over to one side by the proposer saying, "I withdraw them."  On reading the last resolution, which had been printed and circulated amongst members of the Society, it struck him as of a very ambiguous nature.  The wording of it might have reference to one whose name, he honestly believed, required only to be mentioned to be received with applause by all the meeting—viz., the secretary of the Society, Mr. F. N. Menzies  The motion might also refer to the gentlemen employed on Mr. Menzies' staff.  To any of those persons the resolution would be an unpleasant one to have brought forward, and would be especially unpleasant if carried. He could not help thinking it would have been more candid on the part of the hon. gentleman who had intimated the resolutions when bringing them forward to have said *bona fide* that he had some matter of complaint against the Secretary of the Society. The members could then have had an opportunity of voting "Yes" or "No" as to their appreciation of his services; the question would have been perfectly understood and all ambiguity removed. Abstract resolutions hardly ever produced much effect, and the resolution before the meeting was an abstract one. He had endeavoured to speak temperately, but he could not sit still and hear a gentleman whom he respected immensely—not from personal friendship, though he hoped he had that also—dealt with as the resolution proposed. He respected Mr. Menzies immensely for the intense energy and zeal with which he applied himself to the work of the Society. The motion should not only be cordially and heartily withdrawn, but something more should be done. He ventured to say, from all he had seen of the duties of the secretarial office, and the manner in which those duties were discharged by the Secretary and those employed with him, and having witnessed the energy of Mr. Menzies in the showyards for many years, he ventured to move that, instead of putting aside the resolution of Mr. Waldegrave Leslie, that the following be passed :—"That this Society has perfect confidence in its Secretary, and desires to express approval of the manner in which his duties as Secretary are performed."

The Earl of AIRLIE asked if this proposal was meant as an amendment to the motion of Mr. Waldegrave Leslie.

Mr. Harris, Earnhill, said he was one of those supposed not to be represented in the Society. He was simply a tenant-farmer from the North. He had, perhaps, never exchanged a hundred words with Mr. Menzies on anything but official business for the last two or three years, during which he had had the honour of a seat at the Board. He must say that on every occasion he had found Mr. Menzies a most excellent official; urbanity, punctuality, and all good points which should distinguish an official he certainly possessed. Mr. Menzies addressed him in the same way as he would address a nobleman. Mr. Menzies was not a party man; everything seemed to be right about him. As a tenant-farmer, he (the speaker) would simply say to his friends that the management of the Society could not be in better hands than at present.

The Marquis of LOTHIAN, as the late President of the Society, cordially endorsed every word that had fallen from Mr. Villiers and Mr. Harris. During the four years of his presidency he had a great deal of communication with the Secretary, whom he saw both at general meetings and at the Board of Directors' meetings, and nothing could possibly exceed the efficiency with which he conducted the business of the Society in every respect which it fell to him to do. He (Lord Lothian) had come to the meeting at considerable inconvenience to himself, not intending to take any part in the proceedings unless it was absolutely necessary to do so; but when he saw a series of resolutions before them which, whether carried or not, if spoken to, appeared of the most serious description, and seeing that those resolutions had been printed in the newspapers and disseminated over the country, he thought it his duty to come to the meeting, and, if necessary, say something in defence of the Society which did him the honour to make him President for four years. The meeting had been called together to consider these resolutions, and the hon. gentleman who had given notice of them now admitted that he did not know what he was talking about, and that if he had formerly had the information he now possessed he would not have tabled the resolutions. The hon. gentleman had further said he had no resolutions to propose, that he was going to think over the matter, and bring them forward subsequently. His Lordship, proceeding, said—I object entirely to that mode of doing business. It is a matter of astonishment that Mr. Leslie, of all people in the world, should have tabled such resolutions. He was once a member of the House of Commons, and a gentleman who has been in that position, and who has been secretary to the Speaker, ought, at any rate, to know what business is. Anybody knowing Mr. Leslie's antecedents would think he had some knowledge of what he was talking about. The first resolution has been withdrawn. The second resolution refers to the Directors, and Mr. Leslie might have known before this that there is a committee on the subject to report before the January meeting. Is it respectful to the Society that we should be called together to take up such subjects when the gentleman who brings forward the motions has never taken the trouble to find out what he is talking about? The third resolution on the list is to the effect that the various committees should be revised and reduced, but in what he said he has been proved to be altogether wrong. Why did he not find out what the facts were? He complained that the Steam Committee had been abolished without being aware of the fact that it had been amalgamated with the Machinery Committee, of which he is himself a member. He should surely have seen about that before he brought his motion forward. He says he did so in order to obtain information, but this is not the place for any one to get information of the character he desired. What he should have done would have been to go to the Directors, and find out the state of matters from them, and then, if they would not give it, to complain to the meeting. But every member is bound to find out the exact position of any matter regarding which he brings any complaint, and not trust merely to what turns up. Then, Mr. Leslie, in what I call his fourth resolution, makes certain statements from which the public would infer that our secretarial staff carried on the work carelessly, and that the Directors were somewhat indifferent as to the way in which it was carried on. That is, no doubt, the impression that will go out, and Mr. Leslie must have been aware of it. Now, however, Mr. Leslie, finding that the feeling is not with him, is to walk out of the room without doing anything further, and leave the whole country to infer that we are not caring about our work, and quite indifferent as to the way in which it shall be carried out. I am exceedingly glad that Mr. Villiers has brought his motion before the meeting, so that we are now in a position to give a distinct negative to Mr. Leslie's proposal. Before I sit down I would, in a word, express the extreme inconvenience to which the bringing forward of these proposals has put us. They have been the means of bringing many members from a distance, and they are now occupying our time and preventing us from visiting the implements and the cattle in the yard, the special purpose for which these shows were constituted; and this has been done in order that motions may be brought forward which would be much better, if not more legally, discussed at the January meeting, and this, too, when the gentleman who takes this step confesses that he has no information on the subject.

Ex-Provost Duncan, Rothesay, bore testimony to the great care with which Mr. Menzies had acted in the awarding of the prizes in an agricultural essay competition in the west of Scotland. Mr. Menzies had impressed him very favourably by the manner in which he had discharged his work on that occasion, and he had great pleasure in giving his testimony to that effect.

The Chairman—Will Mr. Leslie say whether he withdraws his motion, or is his position that he does not wish to press it?

Mr. Waldegrave Leslie—I thought I had made it clear, but if you wish it I will make it still more clear. I have not pressed my motion for the reasons I have stated.

The Chairman—But do you withdraw it?

The Earl of Airlie—A motion once put cannot be withdrawn unless by leave of the meeting.

Mr. Waldegrave Leslie—I did not move the resolution.

Mr. J. M. Martin of Auchendennan—Mr. Leslie found no seconder, and therefore his motion is not before us.

The Chairman—That is so; and therefore Mr. Villiers' amendment becomes the substantive motion which you are to vote upon.

The motion being put thus to the meeting was carried practically unanimously, quite a forest of hands being held up in its support. The result was received with loud cheering.

The Chairman—I think there can be no doubt about it. I need not ask for a show of hands on the other side, because I think the motion is carried.

Mr. Waldegrave Leslie, amid much laughter, proposed a vote of thanks to the Chairman, and the proceedings terminated.


## GENERAL MEETING, 18TH JANUARY 1882.

The Right Hon. the Earl of Mar and Kellie, Vice-President, in the Chair.

The Secretary (Mr. F. N. Menzies) read a letter of apology from the Duke of Richmond and Gordon, President, stating his inability to be present; also letters from Lord Polwarth, the Earl of Glasgow, Sir Michael Shaw Stewart, and Sir Henry Seton-Steuart.

New Members.—The Secretary then read the list of 115 gentlemen who had been proposed as members of the Society, and who were elected by ballot.

Office-Bearers.—The following nobleman and gentlemen were elected to fill the vacancies in the list of Directors for 1882:—*Vice-Presidents.*—The Duke of Argyll, K.T.; the Earl of Glasgow, the Earl of Stair, Lord Polwarth. *Ordinary Directors.*—Andrew Allan, Munnoch; Arthur H. Johnstone Douglas, of Lockerbie; Alex. Dudgeon, Easter Dalmeny; Thomas Gordon Duff, Park House; James Mollison, Dochgarroch Lodge; Thomas Munro Nicoll, Littleton; George J. Walker, Portlethen. *Extraordinary Directors.*—The Hon. Greville R. Vernon, Auchans House; the Hon. the Lord Provost of Glasgow, Sir Robert J. Milliken Napier of Milliken, Bart.; Sir

Thomas Edward Colebrooke of Crawford, Bart., M.P.; Sir Simon Macdonald Lockhart of Lee and Carnwath, Bart.; Sir Archibald C. Campbell of Blythswood, Bart.; Captain David Boyle of Shewalton, R.N.; Colin G. Campbell of Stonefield; Charles Dalrymple of Newhailes, M.P.; Colonel W. W. Hozier of Newlands; Frederick Ernest Villiers, Closeburn Hall.

ACCOUNTS FOR 1880–81.—Mr Murray of Dollerie submitted the accounts for the past year, which were approved of.

ARGYLL NAVAL FUND.—Admiral Maitland Dougall of Scotscraig submitted the accounts for the past year, which were approved of.

STIRLING SHOW, 1881.—Colonel Gillon of Wallhouse said he had to report on the General Show which took place at Stirling in July last. Full details having been published at the time, it was unnecessary for him to detain the meeting long. He need only say that the stock was of a superior character, and that the exhibits generally were in no respects inferior to any at the Shows held under the auspices of the Society, although he regretted the meeting had resulted in a loss, as would be observed from the accounts which have just been submitted. The Earl of Mar and Kellie took a warm interest in the success of the Show, and, in the absence of the President, filled the chair at the General Meeting in the showyard, and presided at the public banquet. In Sir James Gibson-Maitland the Society had the advantage of a most zealous Chairman of the Local Committee. The counties embraced in the district of the Show had all contributed to the auxiliary fund, while the Provost and Magistrates afforded every facility in their power. He had therefore to move—1. That the thanks of the Society be given to the Right Hon. the Earl of Mar and Kellie, Vice-President, with the expression of the high sense entertained by the Society of his ability in presiding at the General Meeting in the showyard, and discharging the duties of Chairman at the public banquet, in the unavoidable absence of the Duke of Richmond and Gordon, K.G., President. 2. That the thanks of the Society be given to Sir James Ramsay Gibson-Maitland of Barnton, Bart., Convener of the Local Committee elected by the counties of Stirling, Dumbarton, Clackmannan, and Perth, for his energy and zeal in furthering the success of the Show, and to the individual members of that Committee for their very efficient co-operation in carrying into effect the various arrangements of the meeting. 3. That the thanks of the Society be given to the Commissioners of Supply for the counties of Stirling, Dumbarton, Clackmannan, and Perth, for the liberality with which the auxiliary fund was provided. 4. That the thanks of the Society be given to Robert Anderson, Esq., Provost, and to the other members of Town Council of Stirling, for their active and ready assistance in everything connected with the proceedings.

GLASGOW SHOW, 1882.—Colonel Gillon said he had next to submit the premium list and regulations for the Glasgow Show, as finally arranged. The list had been submitted to a meeting of members held at Glasgow last month, and the suggestions then made had since been considered, and fully given effect to by the Directors. It had been arranged that the Show should be held from the 25th to the 28th of July, both days inclusive. The last day for the entry of implements had been fixed for the 1st of June, and for stock 14th June. The premiums amount to £2818, being the largest sum ever offered at any show of the Society. The counties of Lanark, Renfrew, and Bute had, as on former occasions, agreed to liberal voluntary assessments to assist in defraying the expenses of the meeting; while the Lord Provost and Magistrates of Glasgow have voted £200, besides placing a part of the public green of the city at the disposal of the Society for the purpose of the showyard. Sir Michael Shaw Stewart of Blackhall, Bart., had been named chairman of the Local Committee of Superintendance, an appointment which, he doubted not, would meet the hearty approval of the meeting.

INVERNESS SHOW, 1883.—Colonel Gillon reported that the General Show for 1883 would be held at Inverness, and he submitted the list of the classes of stock for which premiums would afterwards be offered.

These reports were adopted.

DIRECTORATE.—The following report by committee appointed to consider the business arrangements of the Society, and the present system of selecting Directors, was held as read :—

I. *Remit to and Appointment of Committee.*—At the meeting of the Board held on the 5th January 1881, the following resolution was adopted :—"That a committee be appointed to consider the business arrangements of the Society, and the present system of selecting members to act as Directors, and report to a subsequent meeting what alterations, if any, may be required in the by-laws or other procedure to ensure the best representation of the whole membership of the Society on its Board of Management." The following members were then appointed a committee in terms of the resolution :—Lord Polwarth; Lord Reay; Rev. John Gillespie, Mouswald; Mr Dingwall, Ramornie; Mr. Scott Dudgeon, Longnewton; Mr. Mackenzie of Portmore;

Mr. Walker of Bowland, C.B.; Mr. Mylne, Niddrie Mains; Sir Alexander Muir Mackenzie of Delvine, Bart.—Mr. Scott Dudgeon to be convener.

II. *Report by Committee.*—In terms of the above remit, your committee met on the 6th of April, 25th May, and 12th October, and having given the whole subject their most careful consideration, have to suggest that Nos. 5, 6, 7, 8, and 9 of the by-laws should be cancelled. These are as follow :—

5. The Secretary shall, thirty days before the meeting of Directors, at which the list of Ordinary and Extraordinary Directors for the ensuing year is to be made up, intimate, by advertisement in any two or more of the Edinburgh newspapers, that the Directors are prepared to receive from members of the Society, within eight days from the date of such intimation, the names of such members as they may desire to suggest for the consideration of the Directors, in making up the list to be recommended for the adoption of the Society at the general meeting in January.

6. The Society shall annually, at the general meeting in January, choose out of the ordinary members a Board of thirty Directors, special regard being had to the convenience of one-third of that number for attending meetings of the Board held in Edinburgh.

7. The Society shall also at same meeting choose twenty Extraordinary Directors, of whom at least ten out of the whole number to be resident in the district in which the Show of the year is to be held.

8. The President shall not continue in office for more than four consecutive years. The four Vice-Presidents, the seven senior Ordinary Directors, and the ten senior Extraordinary Directors shall retire annually; and the President, Vice-Presidents, and Directors (ordinary and extraordinary), who so vacate office, shall not be eligible to be re-elected in the same capacity for at least one year. Any Ordinary Director who shall not have attended a meeting of the Board of Directors for one year, unless prevented by bad health, shall be held to have vacated his seat in the Direction. The list of office-bearers to be proposed by the Directors for election at the general meeting shall be published in any two or more of the Edinburgh newspapers fourteen days preceding.

9. The Board of Directors shall meet on the first Wednesday of each month during the sittings of the Court of Session, and occasionally, as business may require, on a requisition by three Directors to the Secretary, or an intimation by him. Committees shall be appointed by the Directors, and shall in all cases report procedure to them for their consideration and approval. The Directors shall keep a record of their proceedings, to be laid before the general meetings for their consideration and direction. All members of the Society, though not in the Direction, may attend the meetings of the Directors and deliver their opinion, but they shall have no vote. The President, Vice-Presidents, Directors (ordinary and extraordinary), Treasurer, and Honorary Secretary shall be entitled to vote at meetings of the Board.

And that the following should be adopted :—

5. The Society shall annually, at the general meeting in January, choose out of the ordinary members a Board of thirty-two Directors, at least one-half of whom shall be tenant-farmers or others paying the lower subscription. At the same meeting it shall also choose twenty Extraordinary Directors, ten of whom shall be resident in the district in which the Show of the year is to be held; the other ten shall be selected because of their known interest in, and experience of, the business of the Society, and of these at least three shall be tenant-farmers.

6. A list of Office-bearers and Directors shall be annually submitted by the Board of Directors for election by the Society at the general meeting in January. The Board, at its June meeting each year, shall appoint a committee of its members to prepare such list, and to submit it for its consideration at its November meeting, that the same may be finally adjusted. The list shall be published in two Edinburgh and two Glasgow newspapers at least fourteen days preceding the general meeting.

7. The members of the Society resident in each of the eight Show districts shall, every year, before the 10th October, send to the Secretary the name of a member to act as an Ordinary Director, and their recommendation shall have due weight given to it by the Board of Directors in the preparation of the list which it submits to the Society for election at the general meeting. Regulations for this purpose shall be framed by the Board.

8. The President shall not continue in office for more than four consecutive years. The Vice-Presidents, the ten Extraordinary Directors chosen because of their connection with the Show district, and at least eight of the senior Ordinary Directors (one from each of the Show districts), shall not be eligible to be re-elected in the same capacity for at least one year. Any Director who shall not have attended a meeting of the Board for one year, unless prevented by bad health, shall be held to have vacated his seat at the Board.

9. The Board of Directors shall meet on the first Wednesday of the months of November, December, April, and June, when all the important business of the Society shall

be transacted, and occasionally as business may require, on a requisition by three Directors to the Secretary, or on intimation by him. The Board shall keep a record of its proceedings, to be laid before the general meetings of the Society for its consideration. The President, the Vice-Presidents, the Directors (ordinary and extraordinary), the Treasurer, and the Honorary Secretary shall be entitled to a vote at meetings of the Board. Members of the Society, though not in the Direction, may attend the meetings of the Board and deliver their opinion, but they shall have no vote. Committees shall be appointed by the Board of Directors, and they shall in all cases report procedure to the Board for its consideration. For the transaction of the routine business of the Society, the Board of Directors shall appoint a general committee of its members to meet on intimation by the Secretary. These meetings, as well as the meetings of other important committees, shall be grouped so as to suit the convenience of members residing at a distance from Edinburgh.

The foregoing report was under the consideration of the Directors at their meetings on the 2d November and 7th December, when, after discussion, the proposed new by-laws were agreed to in the following terms:—

5. The Secretary shall, in the first week of November, intimate by advertisement in two of the Edinburgh and two of the Glasgow newspapers that the Directors are prepared to receive from members of the Society, within eight days from the date of such intimation, the names of such members as they may desire to suggest for the consideration of the Directors, in making up the list to be recommended for the adoption of the Society at the general meeting in January.

6. The Society shall annually, at the general meeting in January, choose out of the ordinary members a Board of thirty-two Directors, at least one-half of whom shall be tenant-farmers or others paying the lower subscription. At the same meeting it shall also choose twenty Extraordinary Directors, ten of whom shall be resident in the district in which the Show of the year is to be held; the other ten shall be selected because of their known interest in, and experience of, the business of the Society, and of these at least three shall be tenant-farmers.

7. A list of Office-bearers and Directors shall be annually submitted by the Board of Directors for election by the Society at the general meeting in January. The Board, at its November meeting each year shall appoint a committee of its members to prepare such list, and to submit it for consideration at its December meeting, that the same may be finally adjusted. The list shall be published in two Edinburgh and two Glasgow newspapers at least fourteen days preceding the general meeting.

8. The President shall not continue in office for more than four consecutive years. The Vice-Presidents, the ten Extraordinary Directors chosen because of their connection with the Show district, and the eight senior Ordinary Directors, shall not be eligible to be re-elected in the same capacity for at least one year. Any Director who shall not have attended a meeting of the Board for one year, unless prevented by bad health, shall be held to have vacated his seat at the Board.

9. The Board of Directors shall meet on the first Wednesday of each month from November till June inclusive, and occasionally as business may require, on a requisition by three Directors to the Secretary, or on intimation by him. The Board shall keep a record of its proceedings, to be laid before the general meetings of the Society for its consideration. The President, Vice-Presidents, the Directors (ordinary and extraordinary), the Treasurer, and the Honorary Secretary shall be entitled to vote at meetings of the Board. Members of the Society, though not in the Direction, may attend the meetings of the Board and deliver their opinion, but they shall have no vote. Committees shall be attended by the Board of Directors, and they shall in all cases report procedure to the Board for its consideration.

Mr. SMITH, Whittinghame, said it had fallen to him to bring up the report, and move it approval. He thought that the committee to whom it was delegated to look into this matter were entitled to credit and thanks, as through their efforts it was now made clear that one-half of the ordinary Directors should be tenant-farmers. He thought that of itself was a most desirable change to be made. It brought out a good representation of the Society apart from anything else. Besides that, there must be at least three tenant-farmers Extraordinary Directors, and it had been observed that ten of these Extraordinary Directors were to be selected from the district in which the annual Show was held. He thought they were all agreed that that was satisfactory. The only point of difference was one that he considered to be more a practical question than one of principle, and that was the nomination of the Directors. What was submitted in the Report was:—"The Secretary shall, in the first week of November, intimate by advertisement in two of the Edinburgh and two of the Glasgow newspapers that the Directors are prepared to receive from members of the Society, within eight days from the date of such intimation, the names of such members as they may desire to suggest for the consideration of the Directors, in making up the list to be recommended for the adoption of the Society at the general meeting in January." The counter-motion was:—"The members of the Society resident in each of the eight Show districts shall every year, before the 10th of October, send to the Secretary the name of a member to act as an Ordinary Director, and their recommendation shall have due weight given to it by the Board of Directors in the preparation of the list which it submits to the Society for election at the general meeting. Regulations for the purpose shall be framed by the Board." He should have liked very much, and he thought it would have thrown light on the subject, if they had had these regulations now before them. It would, perhaps, have given them to understand—if this motion was to be adopted—how it was to be carried out. It was a very simple proposal, leaving it open to each individual member of the Society to select from the whole body of the Society and nominate any one he pleased, and afterwards giving due intimation in the newspapers. But if they were to restrict this and confine the selection to districts, he did not know how the mind of the districts was to be ascertained. If it were done by voting-papers, it would cause a considerable amount of trouble and expense; if by representatives, then in each of these districts there were several local societies, some large and some small. Would these representatives be on an equal footing? or would it practically come to this, that the nomination would fall into the hands of a few gentlemen who took an interest in the matter; and probably these gentlemen might be altogether members of the same local society? Then if they had a nomination from each of these local societies, how was the matter to be dealt with? Not differently from what it was at present. They had at present nominations in the wide-spread area of all the districts; these came before the Directors, who at present exercised their opinion in the same way as it was asked in this motion, and selected members from the various districts. But from experience he could say that, considering the number of meetings the Directors had to attend in Edinburgh— eight of them annually, besides a great number of committee meetings—he had found that on many occasions it was difficult to go on with business, from the circumstance that there was not a quorum present. The spirit and true intention of Mr. Scott Dudgeon's motion, as he understood it, was that in four years the Board of Directors would consist of four members from each of these districts arbitrarily. But if at present, with a preponderance of members living in the neighbourhood of Edinburgh, and within easy access of Edinburgh, it was difficult to find a quorum, it would be impossible a quorum could be got if the members were more widely spread. They had representatives from the northern districts of the Society's operations, highly worthy men; but if they multiplied them and the preponderance of the area went beyond Edinburgh, then he said they should reduce the quorum from seven to two or three, or the business would come to a dead-lock. If that were done, it would come to this, that the business of the Society, make any election they liked of Directors, would be carried on necessarily by those within easy access of Edinburgh. The hour of meeting was one or half-past one, to suit the farmers going to the market; but in about an hour after gentlemen began to drop away, and before the business of the meeting was ended, there was, perhaps, a bare quorum present. Mr. Scott Dudgeon's motion might have a popular sound about it; but he thought it was still more popular to leave the selection to be made from the whole Society, rather than by the dividing of it into districts. If there was anything that would popularise and benefit the Society, he for one was sure every one would heartily go in with it; but what was proposed by the amendment was only what was so in appearance, and not in reality or practical working.

Mr. MAXTONE GRAHAM of Cultoquhey seconded the motion.

Mr. SCOTT DUDGEON, Longnewton, who was received with applause, said that as a Director of the Society he felt himself in rather a peculiar position in having to move an amendment to a recommendation coming from the Board of Directors. As convener of the committee to which this question was referred, naturally his duty would have been to move the adoption of the report. But, unfortunately, the Board had, by a narrow majority, rejected a most important part of the alteration which that committee recommended—one which he considered by far the most important, and which very much nullified all the others, because it was the one upon which all the others were based. Such being the case, he felt himself obliged to take the course he now did, and by bringing the matter before this general meeting give the members of the Society an opportunity of expressing their opinion upon it. As they were all aware, considerable dissatisfaction had for many years been expressed—and with much justice he thought—that the management of the Society had been of too exclusive a nature; that a certain proportion of the members of the Society, for the most part in and near Edinburgh, had almost entirely monopolised the conduct of the Society. No imputation did he mean to cast on these gentlemen. He believed they had acted in the most attentive and energetic manner to promote the best interests of the Society, but members in other parts of the country had naturally felt dissatisfied with this arrangement. In a national Society, visiting as it did every district in Scotland, and having for its object the interests of agriculture throughout the whole country, and being supported by the subscriptions of individuals connected with land in every part of Scotland, it was with much justice urged as only right that its Board of Management should embrace representatives from all the districts of Scotland. The proposals of the Committee, in so far as regarded the giving those members of the Society who paid the lower subscription that share in the management which from their numbers they had a right to demand they should have, the Board, he was glad to say, had agreed to recommend for their adoption. The tenant-farming element, it would be found on examination of the list of membership, was more than double in numerical importance, and quite equal in subscribing importance, to the landed proprietor element of the whole Society. A reform, therefore, which proposed that tenant-farmers and those paying the lower subscription should in future have a largely increased representation on the Society's Board of Management was in the right direction: that they, in place of having, as had been the custom hitherto, only some seven or eight representatives out of a total of fifty-seven, should in future have at least nineteen representatives on the Board out of a total of fifty-nine. This, he said, was well, but this alone would not suffice. More was needed, and it was to ensure the wider distribution of representatives over the different districts of Scotland, as well as that these should be the choice of the members themselves in these districts, that he had to propose that the by-law as drawn up by the committee should be substituted for the existing by-law No. 5, which the Directors had again asked the meeting to agree to. Unless some such regulation as that which the committee recommended were adopted, there was no guarantee that there should not be a continuance of the evil which had been so generally and loudly complained of. The Directorate of the Society might still continue to be the same exclusive body, electing as it did now its own successors, independent altogether of what might be the wishes of its members. And they should have the Society managed, as heretofore, by a certain definite number of gentlemen in the near neighbourhood of Edinburgh. The method hitherto in operation for the selection of the Directorate had been apparently devised for the purpose of keeping the Board as exclusive and as closely guarded from without as it was possible to imagine, and one which he thought would take more eloquence and persuasiveness to defend than even the gentlemen who opposed his motion could bring to bear upon the understandings of all who were possessed of ordinary intelligence. The practice had been for the Directors, who were responsible for the list of new Office-bearers for the ensuing year to be laid before the general meeting, to delegate the preparation thereof to a committee composed as follows:—Of the Honorary Secretary and Honorary Treasurer, the Conveners of the different committees (twelve in number), and those tenant-farmers on the Board who retired for the year (usually two in number.) Now, the selection being entrusted to a committee constituted as that was, really amounted to placing the choice of the Directorate in the hands of almost the same individuals year after year, because, as any one could satisfy himself by examining the lists of committee published in the *Transactions*, it would be found that the conveners of the different committees were seldom changed, very properly holding these offices for a long series of years. For instance, out of the twelve conveners who were at present presiding over the committees, six had served for at least twelve years, the other six for periods varying from ten to two years. He asked them if a more effective device could be hit upon for making the Directorate a close and exclusive body, and of preventing outsiders gaining admission to its sacred precincts? For, be it remembered, though the election of all Office-bearers rested by the charter in the hands of this general meeting each year; yet, as they all knew, it really rested with those who were entrusted with the preparation of the list to be submitted thereat. Seeing that had been the method of procedure, it was not to be wondered at that the Board of Management of the Society had failed to secure the confidence of its members generally. It was true that from outside pressure an apparent consulting of the wishes of members had been granted of late years—viz., that provided for in the by-law No. 5, which they were asked to re-enact, whereby members had the privilege of suggesting names of individuals to serve on the Board; but, for several reasons, as those acquainted with the matter knew, this regulation had practically resulted in nothing. And some, he knew, urged its failure as a reason against this new scheme he was advocating. But the provisions in this by-law were widely different from the provisions in the other, and he was hopeful, if adopted, would lead to very different results. Here the assurance was given that the nominations made by the several districts should have proper respect paid to them; and again, there was the provision with which the by-law concluded, that regulations should be framed to ensure that the by-law should be carried out in each district, and that efficient means should be taken to ascertain whom the members resident therein desire to nominate as their representatives on the Board. The committee did not consider it their duty to frame these regulations, believing it better to leave these for future consideration, as a matter of detail which could without difficulty be arranged, provided the scheme was accepted by the Society. It is urged by Mr. Smith and other opponents of the by-law that, if carried out, they would have representatives chosen who resided so far from Edinburgh that they would not take the trouble or be at the expense of attending the meetings of the Board. But he had yet to learn that Directors at the greatest distance from Edinburgh had hitherto attended to the duties of their office less efficiently than those residing in or very near to it. Distances were now very different from what they were when this ancient Society was instituted and its charter obtained. Besides, out of the eight districts into which the Society divides itself for Show purposes, five of these are—none of them more than—two hours' ride by rail from Edinburgh—viz., Kelso, Edinburgh, Stirling, Glasgow, and Perth; while portions of the districts of other two—viz., Dumfries and Aberdeen—were not a great deal further removed; so that there was really only one district—viz., that of Inverness—which was not at any very inconvenient distance. But there was nothing in the by-law to prevent the members in the Inverness district, if so minded, to nominate as their representatives individuals residing within an accessible distance from Edinburgh, gentlemen in whom they had confidence, and whom they knew would look after their interests. Another objection taken to the by-law, and this he considered much the most weighty one, was that by it members had no guarantee that even if they made nominations these should be approved by the Board, and should be recommended for election at the general meeting. This was, doubtless, true; but he thought there could be no doubt that if members in the different districts showed a real interest in the matter, and with any unanimity nominate representatives, neither would the Board itself dare to ignore their choice, nor would the general meeting fail to confirm it. By the adoption of the by-law he confidently believed that, to all intents and purposes, the election of all Ordinary Directors would be found to have fallen absolutely into the hands of the members themselves. In conclusion, he would merely say that the whole question was given the utmost attention to by the committee, which carefully considered it in all its aspects, and with great unanimity agreed to the terms of the by-law, as that which, without violating the spirit or the words of the charter, would "ensure the best representation of the whole membership of the Society on its Board of Management." Perhaps he should say that some members of the committee were disposed to have thrown the election out and out into the hands of members in the different districts; not only asking them to nominate, but asking them to elect, without the possibility of reversal by the Board or by the general meeting. Lord Reay, who gave great attention to the subject and lent valuable assistance in drawing up the new by-laws, was among these. His Lordship, he regretted, was unable to be present that day, but he had written to him stating that he endorsed his (Mr. Scott Dudgeon's) view, and was prepared for greater changes, which his Lordship believed were not only allowed, but required by the observance of the terms of the charter. He left the matter with the utmost confidence in the hands of that large meeting, feeling that he at any rate had done his duty as a Director and as Convener of the Committee which considered the question, in giving the members of the Society an opportunity of expressing their views on this important question.

Mr. BALLINGALL, Dunbog, seconded the amendment, and while admitting that in the past the Directors had animated by a desire to do their duty, maintained that hitherto the most numerous body of the membership—tenant-farmers—had not had anything like adequate representation at the Board.

Commander STEWART said that, as they were aware, the next Show of the Society was to be held in Glasgow, and in Argyllshire for some time they had been anxious to get a member on the Board of Directors. The name of the president of one of their local societies was sent in, but no notice was taken of it. He wished them to notice that there was not a Director from the county of Argyll, although the Show was to be held in Glasgow.

The Rev. JOHN GILLESPIE, Mouswald, said that, as he cordially concurred in the particular by-law which the Directors rejected by a narrow majority, he would give one or two reasons why he supported the amendment of Mr Scott Dudgeon. He had analysed the list of Directors for the last year, and he had done so with the greatest possible care. He had taken the eight Show districts as the basis, and he found that Edinburgh last year had 9 of the Directors; Kelso, 6; Dumfries, 3; Glasgow, 2½; Stirling, 1½; Aberdeen, 1; and Inverness, 1. Three Show districts—Edinburgh, Kelso, and Perth—last year had 21 out of 30 Directors, and if they added the three members from the district of Dumfries, that made 24 for four districts. Glasgow, Stirling, Aberdeen, and Inverness were thus left with the miserable representation of 6. He had also made an analysis for the last ten years, from which it appeared that Edinburgh had 11·3, and thus it had nearly an average of 38 per cent. on the whole. One year there were as few as 8, but in another 15, or one-half of the whole. Kelso had 4·2; Perth, 3·9; Glasgow, 3·1½; Stirling, 2·7½; Aberdeen, 2·4; Dumfries, 1·7; and Inverness, 0·6. That satisfied him as a member of the committee that some change was necessary—that something ought to be done to give the different districts of the Society something like a more equal, if not an absolutely equal, representation on the Board of Directors. He did not think that there was any ground for the expense that Mr Smith supposed would be incurred through the proposed change.

Mr WALKER of Bowland said that, as a member of the committee which considered this subject, and as he differed from them, he thought it his duty to state the ground on which he came to that conclusion. His objections were very much of a practical nature, and not grounded on principle, although he thought to a certain extent there was principle involved. He would state two objections conclusive against their making this change at present. One was that the proposed mode of selecting members in each district would be a very different thing from the present system, whereby every member was entitled to send up a name for the consideration of the directors. He believed if they carried out this proposal, and if the Directors did not accept the nominations that might be made, the result would be a collision between the Directors and the members of the Society. He thought that was a thing that would be extremely deplorable. He did not think they would desire to force the Directors to select as one of the Board a gentleman whom they thought would make a bad Director. Mr Dudgeon and Mr Gillespie very strongly advocated the proposed change on the ground of its being representative. Now, he thought it was impossible that it could be representative, as they had no machinery for calling a meeting together. They had no machinery to compel gentlemen to send in answers to voting papers in a district. He did not think that representation was at all intended by the charter, or that it was at all desirable that there should be a strict representation of each district. His second objection was that it would be impracticable in the working, and his advice was to rest content with those changes which the Directors agreed to in the meantime. He thought that Mr. Scott Dudgeon had thrown out a rather unworthy taunt against the committee which had been the standing committee for the selection of names. Now, these gentlemen were all old members of the Society and office-bearers, and surely when they delegated to any body to select persons for the purpose, they preferred those with some experience—men who had some previous connection with the Society in preference to those who had come into the Society knowing nothing about the business.

Mr. HADDON, Honeyburn, said he had no doubt that the tenant-farmers would do justice to the Society by sending men who would perform their duties in a satisfactory manner.

Mr. COWE, Balhousie, said that the difficulty he felt in supporting Mr Scott Dudgeon's motion was that he did not go far enough, although he felt that it was better to take half a loaf than nothing at all.

The motion and amendment were then put to the meeting, when Mr Scott Dudgeon's amendment was carried by a large majority.

## CHEMICAL DEPARTMENT.

Dr. AITKEN read the following reports on Experimental Stations, and Analyses of Analytical Association :—

EXPERIMENTAL STATIONS.—At a recent meeting of the Chemical Committee, it was resolved, as the experiments at the Society's stations are now entering on the second rotation, to try the effect of autumn-manuring as compared with spring manuring. Accordingly each plot has been divided into two, one-half for autumn and one-half for spring-manuring. The manures have already been spread on one of the stations, and they will be put upon the other as soon as it is in a condition to receive them. Considerable improvements have taken place in the laboratory, a large part of which has now been fitted up expressly for agricultural work, and this much-needed change will greatly facilitate the analytical work in connection with the Society's stations, and other experimental inquiries now being carried on by the chemical department.

ANALYSES OF ANALYTICAL ASSOCIATION.—At the general meeting of the Society held a year ago, it was resolved that, with the view of encouraging as well as regulating the conduct of Analytical Associations, the Society should contribute from its fund a sum not exceeding £250 annually towards defraying the expense incurred by them in the analysis of manures and feeding stuffs. The amount of the contribution was fixed at 5s. for each full analysis, and 2s. 6d. for each partial analysis, and certain conditions were arranged under which these grants were obtainable.

Most of the analytical associations in the country entered into communication with the Society, and thirteen of them were able so to arrange their rules as to bring them into conformity with the conditions required for the obtaining of the grant. Others were unable to modify their modes of procedure in time to obtain the grant for the past year, but most, if not all of them, will be in a position to obtain the grant this year.

The following are the names of the Associations who have made accurate returns of their analyses, the number and kind of analyses, and the amount of the grants they have obtained :—

| | | Arbroath. | Buchan. | Caithness. | Carse of Gowrie. | Inverness. | Kelso. | Kincardine. | Lanarkshire. | Menteith. | Orkney. | Easter Ross. | Wester Ross. | Strathdun. | Total. |
|---|---|---|---|---|---|---|---|---|---|---|---|---|---|---|---|
| Standard Manures. | Bones | 3 | 7 | 2 | 1 | 2 | 2 | ... | 4 | ... | 3 | 4 | 6 | 3 | 33 |
| | Dissolved Bones | 3 | 5 | 8 | 1 | 16 | 3 | 4 | 5 | ... | 3 | 4 | 4 | 7 | 65 |
| | Superphosphates | ... | 7 | 2 | ... | 3 | 5 | 1 | 1 | ... | ... | 3 | 6 | 2 | 30 |
| | Peruvian Guano | ... | ... | 1 | 1 | ... | 3 | 4 | 2 | ... | ... | ... | 1 | 2 | 14 |
| | Fish Guano | ... | ... | 1 | ... | ... | 1 | ... | 1 | ... | ... | ... | ... | ... | 3 |
| | Ichaboe Guano | ... | ... | ... | ... | ... | 1 | ... | 1 | ... | ... | ... | ... | ... | 2 |
| | Ground Phosphates | ... | ... | ... | ... | ... | 1 | ... | ... | 1 | ... | ... | ... | ... | 2 |
| Special Manures. | Turnip Manures | 1 | ... | ... | ... | 1 | 1 | ... | 6 | ... | ... | ... | 1 | 4 | 14 |
| | Potato Manures | 1 | ... | ... | 2 | ... | ... | ... | 2 | ... | ... | ... | 1 | 4 | 10 |
| | Dissolved Guanos | ... | ... | ... | ... | ... | ... | ... | 1 | ... | ... | ... | 3 | 1 | 5 |
| | Miscellaneous | ... | ... | ... | 2 | ... | 2 | ... | 3 | 1 | ... | ... | 1 | 1 | 9 |
| Salts, Feeding Stuffs. | Linseed Cake | 3 | 1 | 3 | 1 | ... | 3 | ... | 1 | ... | ... | 5 | ... | 2 | 19 |
| | Cotton Cake | 1 | ... | ... | ... | 1 | 2 | ... | ... | ... | ... | ... | ... | ... | 4 |
| | Hemp Cake | ... | ... | ... | ... | ... | 1 | ... | ... | ... | ... | ... | ... | ... | 1 |
| | Compound Cakes | ... | 1 | ... | ... | ... | ... | ... | ... | ... | ... | 1 | ... | ... | 3 |
| | Nitrate of Soda | 1 | ... | ... | ... | ... | ... | ... | ... | ... | ... | ... | ... | 1 | 3 |
| | Potash Manures | 3 | ... | ... | ... | 1 | 2 | ... | 1 | ... | ... | ... | ... | 1 | 7 |
| | Total | 15 | 21 | 17 | 8 | 24 | 27 | 0 | 24 | 2 | 8 | 17 | 22 | 27 | 221 |

The chief disqualification was found to be the want of a proper guarantee for each manure and feeding-stuff purchased. Without such a guarantee it is needless to say that no efficient control can be exercised over the quality of these substances, and little or nothing can be done to prevent loss from unfortunate speculations; for to buy a manure without a guarantee is to make a speculation. I would strongly impress upon farmers the importance of obtaining a written guarantee for all the manures and feeding stuffs which they purchase. Manure manufacturers and merchants of standing are always willing to give a guarantee with their wares. They buy their materials in that way, and that is the way in which they prefer to sell, so that however much and however deservedly a farmer may trust to his manure merchant for supplying him with really good materials, he should never neglect to obtain a written guarantee denoting the percentage of each valuable constituent, and thus he will not only know it, but be able to refer to it at any time. Without that it is difficult to see how there can be an intelligent and accurate use of manures and feeding stuffs.

Besides the 221 analyses contained in the above table, there were 14 others which were disqualified for the want of a proper guarantee. There are 195 analyses of manures and 26 of feeding stuffs. Among the manures the most popular is dissolved bones, of which there are 65 analyses, or exactly one-third of the whole. Next comes bones, of which there are 33 analyses, so that half of the manure samples analysed were bones either dissolved or undissolved. Superphosphates come next with 30 samples, and next Peruvian guano 14 samples; then come various special manures, amounting to 38 samples in the aggregate, and small numbers of other kinds of manure.

With so many analyses before us of manures used during one season by farmers in various parts of the country, and supplied by manure manufacturers and merchants of all kinds, an excellent opportunity is afforded of making a general survey of the character of the manure supply. Accordingly, at considerable cost of time and labour, I have carefully examined all the analyses, and have arranged and classified them in various ways, with the view of eliciting some information that may be of use to farmers in the purchase of manures.

The use of artificial manures is now so general, and the money expended on their purchase so enormous, that it has become a matter of vital importance to farmers to exercise great economy in their purchase. To do this, he must know what are the important constituents of a manure, what are the characteristics of a good manure, and be able to judge from the results of analysis what is the nature of the manure, no matter by what name it may be called, and to estimate approximately its value as a fertiliser. In the remarks which follow, I cannot do more than refer to some of these things, and must leave the still more important subject of the economical and intelligent application of manures quite untouched. To enter fully into such matters would require a course of lectures, and I purpose delivering in this hall a course of lectures on the subject of "Manures and their Application," beginning next Wednesday. In the meantime, I shall confine myself strictly to some statistics of the analyses sent in by the associations.

First in the classification of manures comes bones. I am glad to see that there are very few samples of rough bones, crushed bones, or bone-dust, but that nearly all are samples of bone meal. The finer that bones are ground the more valuable are they as a manure, and money spent in grinding is well spent. The average composition of the bone samples is 51 per cent. of phosphates and nearly 4½ of ammonia. This is a high average, and it shows that the bones supplied have been of good quality. A few of the samples analysed have evidently not been pure bones. Some contain less phosphates and more ammonia than can occur in genuine bones. Others contain more of both than genuine bones can contain. These have evidently been mixtures; but as I have not seen the samples, I have no means of knowing of what they were composed. They are able to be sold cheaper than genuine bones. The average price of bone meal, I find, is £8, 2s. per ton, while that of the mixtures is £7, 9s. It would be better if such mixtures were not sold as bone meal, but rather under some name indicating their character. There is no name in common use indicating a mixture of nitrogenous matter and insoluble phosphate, which need not be bone. Perhaps the term "nitrophosphate" would describe them better than any other; and when bones enter largely into their composition, they might be called "bone nitrophosphate." Very few of the bone manures seem to have been overcharged. One sample from the Wester Ross Association has been bought at about £1 per ton above the average value, and a few others have been bought by other associations at from 10s. to 15s. per ton over the average value; but perhaps these have been ground to a very fine flour, and may have been well worth the extra cost.

I come next to dissolved bones, which is the favourite manure. A careful examination of the analyses shows plainly that much that is sold under the name of "dissolved bones" has no claim to such a title. Probably all the samples had some bone material in them, but there has been a great deal of mixing. The peculiarity of dissolved bones is that it is a manure containing nitrogenous matter along with soluble phosphate. And here again we are in want of a name to indicate such a manure when it does not consist of bone. A manure consisting of some nitrogenous material such as shoddy, blood, horn dust, &c., along with superphosphate, is naturally sold as "dissolved bones" for want of some more accurate name. Perhaps "nitrosuperphosphate" would be a good name for such manures. They may be very good manures—quite as good as dissolved bones, or perhaps better—but it is a pity to give them a name which is misleading. The word "bone" has a charm for a farmer, and dissolved bones have a value which might almost be called sentimental.

In the practical business of life, however, when we are carrying on an industry for the sake of profit, the indulgence of sentiment is frequently found to be very disadvantageous, and I think the analyses before us show that farmers may pay too dearly for the sentiment surrounding the term "dissolved bones."

From an examination of the ordinary analyses of dissolved bones, it is not always possible for a chemist to say whether they are analyses of genuine dissolved bones or not. They may have all the characters of analyses of pure bones, and yet may have been obtained from mixtures into whose composition bones did not enter. A very critical examination and minute analysis may show that an imitation manure is in whole or in part not a bone manure; but in the ordinary practice of manure analyses a well-made mixture passes easily for a sample of pure dissolved bones, so that no chemist is entitled to say, from the results of his analysis, that any sample consists of pure dissolved bones or genuine dissolved bones. When a mixture is made unskilfully, then a chemist is able to affirm quite positively, from the results of his analysis, that it is not a sample of genuine or pure dissolved bones.

From the 65 analyses of dissolved bones sent in, I have selected 16 which cannot possibly have been derived from genuine bones dissolved in sulphuric acid. I have no means of knowing what they are or how they were made, but their analyses show that they have a composition inferior to dissolved bones, and they amount to one-fourth of the whole number of samples. It may be fairly presumed that they are composed, in part at least, of materials cheaper than bones, and we should therefore expect that their price would be proportionately small.

The average price of the 49 samples whose analyses more or less resemble that of genuine dissolved bones, is £7, 5s. per ton. And by selecting units based upon that valuation—viz., 3s. 6d. per unit of soluble phosphate, 2s. per unit of insoluble phosphate, and 16s. per unit of ammonia—I find that the average value of these manures, as calculated from their analyses, is also £7, 5s. These are units to which no objection can be taken, for they are fixed by the prices themselves.

By applying these units to the 14 samples which are not real dissolved bones, I find that their average value is £5, 8s. per ton. Their average selling price, however, is £6, 17s. per ton, so that they have been sold at an average of £1, 9s. per ton dearer than genuine dissolved bones. But that is taking a very charitable view of the matter, for had we chosen units of lower value corresponding to the lower value of the materials of which the imitations were made, we should have found that there was an average overcharge of more than £2 per ton on these spurious dissolved bones. Even at the higher valuation, I find that the Caithness Association has paid £7 per ton for a manure called vitriolated bones whose value is £5 per ton, Strathearn has paid £7, 8s. for a manure whose value is £5, 2s., and the Lanarkshire Association has actually paid £8, 10s. for a manure whose value reckoned at the highest is only £5, 6s. per ton.

In this last manure the practice is adopted of guaranteeing the nitrogenous part, not as ammonia, but as sulphate of ammonia, because the number is about four times as large as the number expressing the percentage of ammonia. This is a practice frequently adopted in guaranteeing low-class and spurious manures, and one can scarcely avoid the inference that it is done with the view of making the manure appear to be richer in ammonia than it really is, and unfortunately farmers are not all so well acquainted with chemical nomenclature as to know the difference between ammonia and sulphate of ammonia. If they were to adopt the method of dividing the amount of sulphate of ammonia by four, and calling that the amount of ammonia, this objectionable practice would soon cease.

Among the other samples of dissolved bones which have been analysed, there are a few for which prices have been paid that are much in excess of their value, notably one supplied to the Carse of Gowrie Association at the very high price of £9, 5s. per ton, its proper value being £7, 2s.

From what has been said it will be seen that in buying dissolved bones farmers cannot be sure that they get them, and that they are to a considerable extent being supplied with various mixtures under the name of dissolved bones, and that they are paying for these, in many cases, prices far in excess of their value. Dissolved bones are no doubt an excellent manure, but farmers are apt to have too exalted an opinion of them, and to pay for a poor manure a higher price than it is worth, simply because it is called dissolved bones. So far as my experience goes, I think that if a farmer gets a manure with 20 per cent. or upwards of soluble phosphate and 2½ per cent. or upwards of ammonia, he need not trouble himself to inquire whether it was derived from bones or not, and the less bone he is able to see in it the better. Visible fragments of bone in such a manure may seem a satisfactory thing to a farmer who has a respect for bones, but they are really an indication that the bones have been imperfectly dissolved, or perhaps added to some other dissolved phosphate of different origin.

The dissolved phosphate in bone is no better than any other dissolved phosphate, and the ammonia is rather slower than most forms of ammonia. A little magnesia and a very little potash are contained in bone, but the amount in dissolved bones is so slight as scarcely to affect the value of that manure.

The next manure is superphosphate, of which the average quality is very high, viz., about 30 per cent. soluble phosphate; the average price is £4, 15s. per ton, and most of the samples agree well with their guarantees. There are three or four exceptions which are much overcharged. One sample from the Buchan Association falls far below its guarantee, and is priced at £4, 5s., while its value is only £2, 13s., being an overcharge £1, 12s. per ton. Another from Easter Ross is overcharged to the extent of £1, 15s. per ton. But these are exceptional cases, and upon the whole the superphosphates are high-class manures well up to their guarantees, and with values closely agreeing with their prices.

The Peruvian guanos contain mostly about 30 per cent. phosphates, of which about 11 to 12 per cent. is soluble, and are guaranteed to contain 10 per cent. of ammonia, but few come within 1 per cent. of the guarantee. Some fall far below it. One from the Kincardine Association is nearly 3 per cent. low in ammonia, and is £2 above its value. Another from the Lanarkshire Association contains not much more than half the guaranteed amount of ammonia, and is priced at £3, 8s. 6d. per ton over its value. I suppose, however, that in such cases where the manures fall short of the guarantee a corresponding reduction of price will be accepted.

Among the guanos are five which have had sulphuric acid added to them, and they therefore show a high percentage of soluble phosphate. They have all been sold at prices much over their value. The average overcharge is upwards of 50s. per ton, taking the most liberal view of the matter. One sample from the Strathearn Association is priced at £11, 8s., while its value is certainly not more than six guineas including a good profit, that is to say five guineas lost upon a six guinea manure. To invest money in that manner means simply rapid ruin, but the most lamentable thing about it is, that this extra price is paid for the spoiling of good Peruvian guano by dosing it with sulphuric acid.

I next come to the thirty-eight special manures. Fourteen of these are called turnip manures, and ten are called potato manures. These are manures containing soluble and insoluble phosphates and ammonia with or without potash, and may be valued in the same way as dissolved bones, which they more or less resemble. Adopting that method of valuation, I find that on an average about £1 per ton is paid for turnip manure over that which is paid for an equal value of dissolved bones. A few are sold at a cheaper rate, but the majority are sold at prices ranging from 15s. to £2 per ton over their equivalent in dissolved bones.

The prices paid for potato manures are still more extravagant. Their average price is £9, 7s., and their average value reckoned by the units applicable to dissolved bones is £7, 1s., showing an average excess of price over value of £2, 6s. per ton. One potato manure from Carse of Gowrie is charged at £3, 8s. over its value, and another from Strathearn is priced at £11 per ton, while its value is £6, 15s. at most, showing a difference of £4, 5s. per ton, which has simply been given away.

In a purchase of barley manure Strathearn has been still more unfortunate, having paid £9 per ton for what was worth at most £4, 17s., thereby losing £4, 3s. per ton. The other special manures are variously named and variously priced. One called a "universal manure," another called a "top-dressing manure," and another called a "compound manure," have values equal to or better than their price ; and one called a "special manure," bought by the Kelso Association, is 21s. per ton better than its price ; but the remaining manures are greatly over-priced, the average overcharge being upwards of £3 per ton.

As an example of the great disproportion which exists between the profits derived from the sale of standard and special manures, we may take the returns of the Strathearn Analytical Association.

That association has bought fourteen standard manures and ten special manures, and the following are the prices paid per ton for them, and the values calculated from the results of analysis :—

STRATHEARN ANALYTICAL ASSOCIATION.

*Standard Manures.*

| | | Price. | Value. | Overcharge. |
|---|---|---|---|---|
| 1. | Dissolved Bones, | £8 0 0 | £7 6 0 | £0 14 0 |
| 2. | | 7 5 0 | 7 14 0 | . |
| 3. | | 6 15 0 | 7 0 0 | ... |
| 4. | | 7 5 0 | 7 0 0 | . |
| 5. | | 7 5 0 | 7 14 0 | ... |
| 6. | | 7 8 0 | 5 2 0 | 2 6 0 |
| 7. | | 7 0 0 | 5 13 0 | 1 7 0 |
| 8. | Bone Meal, | 8 2 0 | 8 6 0 | . . |
| 9. | | 8 5 0 | 8 10 0 | . . |
| 10. | | 8 5 0 | 8 8 0 | . . |
| 11. | Superphosphate, | 4 0 0 | 4 15 0 | . . |
| 12. | ,, | 4 5 0 | 4 11 0 | ... |
| 13. | Peruvian Guano, | 13 0 0 | 13 7 0 | . . |
| 14. | ,, | 11 10 0 | 10 10 0 | 1 0 0 |
| | Average, | £7 14 6 | £7 11 0 | £0 3 6 |

*Special Manures.*

| | | Price. | Value. | Overcharge. |
|---|---|---|---|---|
| 1. | Turnip Manure, | £8 7 6 | £7 0 0 | £1 7 6 |
| 2. | | 9 10 0 | 7 17 0 | 1 13 0 |
| 3. | | 8 7 6 | 7 0 0 | 1 7 6 |
| 4. | | 6 2 6 | 6 4 0 | ... |
| 5. | Potato Manure, | 11 0 0 | 6 15 0 | 4 5 0 |
| 6. | | 9 7 6 | 6 7 6 | 3 0 0 |
| 7. | | 9 7 6 | 6 8 0 | 2 19 6 |
| 8. | | 9 7 6 | 6 8 0 | 2 19 6 |
| 9. | Barley Manure, | 9 0 0 | 4 17 0 | 4 3 0 |
| 10. | Dissolved Guano, | 11 8 0 | 6 7 0 | 5 1 0 |
| | Average, | £9 3 9 | £6 10 4 | £2 13 5 |

It will be seen that the majority of the standard manures have been bought at prices somewhat under their value. Nos. 6 and 7 are exceptions, and not genuine dissolved bones, but come under that category which I have already described as nitrosuperphosphates. But for these two spurious manures the average price of the standard manures would have been below their average calculated value, that is to say, their selling value, including the sellers' profit.

A glance at the special manures shows a very different state of matters ; all but one have been sold at prices above their proper selling value, and some of them have been sold at truly scandalous prices.

It is to be hoped, for the sake of the prosperity of our farmers, who are struggling manfully up against hard times, that not many have made such unfortunate purchases as some of the farmers of Strathearn.

It is somewhat comforting to turn from this statement to another of a very different kind. Here is a statement of the manures bought by the Kelso Association, which I understand, is the oldest Analytical Association in Scotland :—

| | Price. | Value. |
|---|---|---|
| Bone Meal, . . . . | £7 7 6 | £8 19 0 |
| " . . . . | 7 10 0 | 8 10 0 |
| Dissolved Bones, . . . | 6 15 0 | 6 6 0 |
| " . . . . | 6 10 0 | 7 3 0 |
| " . . . . | 6 10 0 | 7 10 0 |
| Superphosphate, . . . | 5 15 0 | 6 2 0 |
| " . . . . | 4 0 0 | 4 12 0 |
| " . . . . | 4 0 0 | 4 12 0 |
| " . . . . | 4 0 0 | 4 15 0 |
| Peruvian Guano, . . . | 7 12 6 | 9 5 0 |
| " . . . . | 7 12 6 | 8 13 0 |
| Ichaboe Guano, . . . | 11 7 6 | 10 5 0 |
| Fish Guano, . . . | 11 0 0 | 11 5 0 |
| Turnip Manure, . . . | 6 5 0 | 6 17 0 |
| Special Manure, . . . | 5 10 0 | 5 14 0 |
| " . . . . | 5 10 0 | 6 11 0 |
| . . . . | £6 14 0 | £7 6 0 |

In almost every case the manures have been bought at less than their value, the average increase of value over price being 12s. per ton.

The members of this association, from long experience, seem to know well both what to buy and how to buy, and the excellence of their purchases shows that such associations are capable of doing a great deal of good, and the progress they have made in the art of buying manures should be an encouragement to all younger associations.

It will naturally be asked, why it is that special manures are frequently sold at such exorbitant prices? I have examined their analyses, but have looked in vain for anything in them to explain their dearness. Their composition is very various, and even among manures sold under the same name the greatest diversity is found to exist.

When merchants advertise manures as specially adapted for certain crops, one is naturally led to look for some special characteristics entitling them to their name. In the case of turnip manures, for instance, I find that they may contain upwards of 20 per cent. soluble phosphates, or they may contain less than 2 per cent.; of insoluble phosphate they may contain a little over 3 per cent. or a little over 30 per cent.; of ammonia, the amount may be anywhere between 1 and 6 per cent.; and as regards potash, opinions seem equally divided as to whether there should be any at all ;—those that contain potash have it in amounts ranging from ½ per cent. up to about 7¼ per cent.

Potato manures have from 12 to 24 per cent. soluble phosphate, and as regards their other constituents, they show even greater variations than turnip manures ; while the other special manures variously named have various compositions, but very similar to what may be found among turnip and potato manures. One is apt to conclude, from a consideration of these analyses, that if manure is made to contain a little of everything, you may call it what you like. If it is called "dissolved bones," you may get it for £7 per ton ; if it is called "turnip manure," you may pay £8 per ton for it ; while if it is called "potato manure," you will probably require to pay £9 per ton for it, or perhaps a little more. The chief difference seems to lie in the name, and the name commands the price.

I have compared the turnip manures supplied to various districts, to see whether the differences in their composition could be explained by the different soil requirements of one district from those of another, but I find that the turnip manures supplied to one district differ as widely among themselves as they do from those supplied to districts far remote from it. It is possible that such differences may be no greater than the differences of soil requirement in the same district, and from the small number of analyses before us this year, one is not entitled to make any general statement on that subject.

If I found one district preferring one kind of turnip manure, and another preferring another, and if I were assured that these preferences were directed by the results of accurate manurial experiments conducted in each district, it would be an exceedingly gratifying circumstance, for it would be a proof of high intelligence and great progress among our farmers. Undoubtedly turnip manures ought to differ considerably according to the soil and climate of the district where they are applied. To make a general formula of a manure for the turnip crop or for any other crop, such as we find in books upon artificial manures, and to recommend it for universal application, shows a great want of rudimentary education in the science of manuring. But the great differences which exist among special manures of the same name supplied to the Analytical Association are, I fear, not to be explained upon the ground of scientific selection on the part of farmers. I know that there is a great want of accurate knowledge in such matters, and that an immense amount of money is annually spent in the purchase of manures which are applied in a very haphazard manner.

Farmers are apt to buy a turnip manure because it is called a turnip manure, and they know too little about what ought to be the composition of the manures they *should* buy, and still less about the composition of the manures they *do* buy. They take the advice of the manure merchant, and I should think that a manure merchant with a large practice and a knowledge of farming is, from his many-sided experience, exceptionally well qualified to give advice regarding manures ; but what is most to be desired, and what we should now earnestly endeavour to attain, is that farmers should come to know for themselves better than any one can tell them what is the manurial treatment their soils require for the production of the various crops they grow. That is a measure of knowledge which can only be attained by careful and accurate experiment.

Analytical associations have been doing good work, and some have a great deal of good work to begin to, in learning how to buy manures skilfully and having them analysed on the co-operative principle ; but there is a far greater work before them in the way of agricultural experiment, in order to determine what are the best kinds of manure to use for various purposes, and the best way to use them. The money that is able to be saved by a judicious purchase of manure is considerable, but it sinks into insignificance in comparison with that which may be saved by the wise application of the manures they buy. In the organisations which the associations possess, there is an excellent opportunity for the formation of experimental clubs such as have been formed in Ross-shire, and I hope that ere long the example set by them will be followed by all the analytical associations in Scotland.

It would take up too much of our time if I were to enter into any further details regarding the analytical reports sent in, accordingly I must delay all consideration of the analysis of feeding stuffs and other substances until another occasion.

I have drawn your attention to a somewhat unpleasant subject, but I hope it will have the effect of making farmers more careful in the purchase of their manures. My remarks may occasion some dissatisfaction to certain manure merchants, but not to that large class to whom farmers are so much indebted, and whom we all wish to see succeeding, the better class of our manure manufacturers who carry on a legitimate trade, and are content with reasonable profits.

## SCIENTIFIC AGRICULTURE.

Mr. Eliott Lockhart, of Borthwickbrae, submitted the following report by the Special Committee on Scientific Agriculture, which was read and approved of :—

The committee have given their best attention to the important questions remitted to them, viz., "To consider in what way scientific agriculture and education could best be promoted and stimulated, and the results of experiments in all branches more readily be brought within the view of all who are interested therein," but before submitting their suggestions for the improvement of agricultural education, they think it expedient to take a glance at what is being done in other countries.

In all the European countries agricultural education would seem to be more or less under State management, notably in Germany, where there are a very large number of schools, academies, and colleges, with farms and gardens attached to them.

In America there are agricultural colleges in most, if not all, the States, in which, however, with few exceptions, agriculture and general education are combined ; but it is pointed out by Mr Johnston, in his evidence before the Ontario Agricultural Commission, 1880, that "those institutions alone have been successful which have been purely agricultural colleges, notably Michigan and Massachussetts, in so far as they adhered closely to agricultural subjects and science relating thereto, and exacted a fair share of daily labour, thus making the theoretical and practical go hand in hand."

In speaking of the Ontario Agricultural College, of which Mr. Johnston is an ex-president, he says, "It excels in its basis any other in America or Europe, except Germany, in these five cardinal points :—1. It does not attempt anything but strictly agricultural education. 2. It is not a mechanical or generally industrial college. 3. It is not in any sense a literary institution, with a leaning to agricultural subjects. 4. It places as much importance on a course of apprenticeship as it does on a course of study. 5. It makes manual labour a stern reality as well as a name, causing its students to perform the work of a farm of 500 acres." The ordinary courses of study extends over two years. The whole expense is borne by the Provincial Legislature, small tuition fees being charged, but the students being paid for their labour.

Turning to our own country, there is no State control, properly so called, although aid is given in the following ways by the Science and Art Department :—(a) Classes have been established at the Normal School of Science, South Kensington, at which teachers and others can qualify themselves to conduct agricultural classes; (b) grants are given to such qualified teachers; (c) scholarships are offered to students; (d) a full agricultural course is about to be established at the Royal School of Mines.

In England there are the Royal Agricultural College at Cirencester, and the College of Agriculture, Downton, near Salisbury, both of which have farms attached to the colleges, and impart practical instruction. There are also several schools. The Royal Agricultural Society gives scholarships, and grants certificates and diplomas.

In Scotland, the report of the Standing Committee of Council to the general meeting of members in June last, shows clearly what is done by the Highland and Agricultural Society, the disappointing feature in the report being the very small number of diploma and certificate holders—fifty-two and sixteen respectively. In Glasgow, an Agricultural College in connection with the Veterinary College has been started, and is now in its second winter session; but as yet the classes are not well attended. There is a farm in connection with this college about six miles off, but within easy access by train every half hour, on which the practical work is explained to the students. The ordinary course extends over two years; but there is also a shorter course in connection with the Science and Art Department. In Aberdeen a Central Technical School of Agriculture was established some five or six years ago, and for the first three years it appeared to be progressing satisfactorily under the able superintendence of Mr. A. T. Jamieson. This school was last year brought under the notice of the members of our Society by Colonel Innes. Arrangements had been made for a higher course of instruction, and funds would have been forthcoming, but as a sufficient number of students did not come forward, it was decided in August last to suspend operations—a very discouraging state of matters, and very much to be regretted.

In Ireland there appears to be a much more systematic gradation of agricultural education, and much more control and assistance given by Government. The first principles of agriculture are taught in the national schools. A considerable number of these have small farms attached. There are a certain number of model schools with farms attached; while for higher education there is the college at Glasnevin, entirely supported by the State, at which the farm plays an important part, and last year yielded a very good return. Admissions to the college are of three classes—1. Free resident students, 25 are admitted each year by competitive examination; 2. Paying resident students, 25 in number, who pay £7, 10s. per half year; 3. Extern students, who board and lodge themselves, paying a tuition fee of £2 per quarter. The practical instruction embraces gardening, small and large farm cultivation and management, and the students take part in every farm operation.

The committee have had the benefit of Professor Wilson's opinion, who thinks greater publicity should be given to the scholarships and bursaries offered by the Highland and Agricultural Society, as he thinks that if more widely known, and more fully taken advantage of, the present University course meets, in the meantime, existing wants. He is strongly opposed to the idea of a college farm.

At the request of the committee, Dr Aitken also submitted his views in writing, of which the following are extracts:—". . . . . No scheme for the propagation of scientific knowledge among our farmers can be satisfactory that does not especially provide for the better education of the rising generation of farmers. Agriculture is now a science, or rather the application of a number of sciences, and requires for its proper comprehension as wide a range of scientific knowledge as any learned profession. . . . . Nothing but a college specially organised and equipped for the training of agriculturists, is capable of affording young farmers, or intending farmers, the means of acquiring, in a direct and thorough-going manner, the knowledge which is now necessary to the proper understanding of the scientific principles upon which the varied practice of agriculture rests. . . . . And if such an institution could be founded, whether by private beneficence, public subscription, or Government endowment, or all three combined, it would be the greatest boon that could be bestowed on the farmers and landed proprietors of this country."

In the opinion of the committee, the system of agricultural education in Scotland fails at both ends. The first principles should be taught in elementary schools, at any rate in rural districts, which would form the first grade. Scholars would thus be prepared to take advantage of the Science and Art Department classes, forming the second grade. But the weakest part of our system seems to be in the higher education in colleges. The charges at the English colleges are so high as to be beyond the means of the ordinary farmer class in Scotland, for whom such instruction is most needed. The course at the Edinburgh University does not appear to meet the difficulty, it only embraces the principles of agriculture, and without either practical instruction, or teaching of the kindred subjects which students are required to pass for our Society's certificates or diploma. This may possibly answer as regards normal teaching, but it seems of little use as regards higher agricultural education, in which theory and practice should be combined. So that, while fully admitting that the classes under the Science and Art Department, and the course at the Edinburgh University, may be doing good up to a certain point, it appears to the committee that little or nothing is being done towards the higher education of those who really intend to make agriculture their business, and that there is therefore an urgent need for the establishment in Scotland of one or more agricultural colleges, with farms attached, at which practical instruction and manual labour would play an important part, and at which the charges would be so moderate as to be within the means of farmers' sons, or those who really wish to obtain a thorough practical education, and who are prepared to put their shoulders to the wheel.

The committee are of opinion that the Government should be approached, and strongly urged to extend the aid already given by the Science and Art Department, and to assist in the establishment of agricultural colleges.

It is no doubt a very discouraging feature of the whole question, that there appears to be such a disinclination to take advantage even of the imperfect opportunities already afforded ; but it would be fatal on that account to discontinue making every effort to awaken those interested in agriculture to the vital importance of training up the coming agriculturists to a thorough knowledge of the science of their business, without which they cannot expect to meet the increased competition, coupled with the uncertainties of climate, to which they will be exposed. In regard, then, to agricultural education, the committee recommend—1. That the Education Department be again memorialised to recognise the elements of agriculture as a specific subject, and for which a grant may be earned, in elementary schools. 2. That the aid afforded by the Science and Art Department should be made more widely known. 3. That as far as possible the scholarships and bursaries offered by the Highland and Agricultural Society should be more fully advertised and made known. 4. That there is an urgent need for the establishment in Scotland of one or more agricultural colleges, in which higher scientific teaching would be combined with practice, but at which the charges would be within the means of those who intended to make agriculture their business. 5. That these resolutions be laid before the Royal Agricultural Commission, and the importance of the subject of higher agricultural education be very strongly urged upon them.

In regard to scientific agriculture, it must be apparent to every one that real progress can only be made by means of experiments. These are no doubt continually being made by individuals, but the benefits thus obtained are in most cases entirely local, showing that there is a need for organisation, by means of which the number of experiments might be very much increased, and the beneficial results brought within the reach of a very much larger number. The advantages of experimental stations have been thoroughly recognised in Germany, where there are a large number, and they would seem to be extending in France, Italy, and other countries. In England, experiments are carried on under the auspices of the Royal Agricultural Society at Woburn, by Mr. Lawes at Rothamstead, and at both the Agricultural Colleges. In Scotland there are the two stations conducted by the Society's chemist, and there is an Agricultural Association in the county of Aberdeen, which was established in 1875. There are five stations, the first established in Scotland at which, under the guidance of Mr. Jamieson, a series of very important experiments have been carried on, and the association has annually published most interesting and valuable reports. Under the auspices of this association and Mr Jamieson, two stations have also been established in England, at Huntingdon and in Kent. Dr Aitken, at the request of the committee, submitted a report, of which the following is an extract :—

"The first thing that ought to be done is to make the best possible use of the organisation that exists in the form of local analytical associations and other farmers' clubs throughout the country. Now that the analytical associations, or most of them, are coming into correspondence with the Highland and Agricultural Society, and making the Society a bond of union in promoting the work which they have been organised to do, I think it behoves the Society to take the initiative in diverting the energies of these associations in a new and practical direction. I would invite them all to co-operate in the carrying out of a few simple, practical, and practicable field experiments on a small scale, and easy of comprehension, in order to prove for themselves and see for themselves—1. What are the most effective and economical manures to apply for each district, and the most economical way to apply them. 2. The most economical method of producing a pound of beef or mutton under the conditions of each particular district. Let each association be asked to choose from among its members one or more farmers able and willing to experiment, and personally superintend the whole experiment. Let them be asked to write a report of the experiment, and have it read and discussed before their association. Let these reports and the chief points of interest in the discussion be published, and a copy be sent to the Highland and Agricultural Society. Let the Society prepare a combined report of all the experiments for publication, either in the *Transactions* or in a separate form, for distribution among the associations, &c. Let each association subscribe or find an annual sum to defray the expense of these experiments, and let the encouragement of local effort, and the employment of local resources be the basis of the experiments (for anything that would tend to pauperise the associations or take from them the responsibility and control of the experiments would directly impair their usefulness). Let a list of experiments be also prepared, including any recent improvements in agriculture practice, and let each association choose from among the number one or more which its members would be willing to try, and let it be asked that the experiment be done under the direction of the Highland and Agricultural Society, and that the results be reported to it."

Seeing the important work that was being carried on in Aberdeen through the energetic co-operation of proprietors and tenants, and considering that it would be of immense value that the number of such associations should be very much increased, the committee issued the following queries :—

1. Would it be possible to organise a series of lectures on scientific and practical agriculture in your district? Would they be likely to be well attended? And what chance would there be of meeting expenses?

2. Could not a series of experiments suitable to the district be organised under the guidance of a qualified chemist assisted by local committees? Also trials of implements?

3. Offer any suggestions.

(1) Their views being that what had been done in one county might surely be undertaken in many more, either by the formation of new associations, or expanding the sphere of existing farmers' clubs or analytical associations. (2) That experiments likely to prove suitable to the district would be of great local value, and would enable those in the district to realise the great advantage to be derived from such experiments. (3) That by means of these associations a series of experiments throughout the country might possibly be suggested and organised by the Society's chemist, whereby comparisons could be made with a number of centres or stations, instead of, as at present, with only two. (4) That experiments should not be restricted to the application of manures, but should include varieties of cropping, rearing and fattening stock, dairy farming, trials of implements, and in every direction that would add to our knowledge in all branches of agriculture. (5) That occasional lectures might be given, either in illustration of experiments, or on any subject bearing on agricultural science, that would be likely to prove interesting or instructive to those in the locality. (6) That by collating and publishing annually the reports of experiments from the various districts, careful comparisons could be made, and a mass of useful information would be obtained. But beyond giving advice, if called upon ; suggesting such a series of experiments as would prove generally important for comparisons ; or forming a general centre of communication,—it was not in view of the committee that the Society, from the very limited means at its disposal, either could or should assist pecuniarily in the work of such associations.

The committee regret to state that the answers to their queries are very disappointing. In only a few districts does there appear to be any real appreciation of the value of experiments, or any chance of associations being formed, or of the expenses being met locally. In many districts, while admitting that experiments and lectures might be useful, it seems to be thought that such should be undertaken by the Highland and Agricultural Society, or by any one else than those who would be primarily benefited ; while from some districts the reply is that they do not consider either experiments or lectures would be of any use.

In spite of discouraging replies, the committee feel confident that the formation of agricultural associations, on the Aberdeenshire model, would prove of incalculable value, and that their establishment should be encouraged by the Highland and Agricultural Society in every possible way ; and to this end, though their establishment and maintenance should be through local effort and enterprise, the committee recommend that in the meantime the fees of the Society's chemist should be paid to any association asking his services to deliver an introductory lecture, and agreeing to pay his expenses.

Since the above was written, the committee have heard with great satisfaction of the intention of associations to commence a series of experiments in Ross, and by the Galashiels Farmers' Club.

Sir A. MUIR MACKENZIE suggested that steps should be taken to publish in a cheap form the accounts of their experiments connected with agriculture, as he thought they would be of great advantage.

The Rev. Mr. GILLESPIE, Mouswald, said that one of the recommendations of the report was that the results should be laid before the Agricultural Commission, and he suggested that that should be done by means of a deputation, and he moved accordingly.

Mr VILLIERS seconded the motion.

Colonel INNES of Learney said they had had the experience of several years in carrying on a technical school in the north, but they had at present found it desirable to suspend their operation; but he thought an effort should be made by the Society to have something done throughout the country in connection with this matter. It would be a very desirable thing no doubt to place the services of Dr Aitken at the command of local associations to give lectures. But he would suggest that the Society, which no doubt could not apply large funds to this purpose, might do something more than it proposed. It was a little discouraging to say that the expenses of the lecture must be paid for by the local society obtaining the benefit of his services. The expenses might not be very much. He was sure that if Dr Aitken went down to Aberdeen he would meet with great hospitality, and not be put to much expense.

Mr. SCOTT-DUDGEON—I thought the chemist's expenses were to be paid.

Mr. ELLIOT LOCKHART—The fees; not the expenses.

After some further discussion, it was agreed that the results be sent to the Commission, and the matter generally remitted to the Directors, and with the suggestion as to the deputation.

## LOUPING-ILL AND BRAXY.

Mr. ELLIOT LOCKHART submitted the First Report of Committee on Louping-ill and Braxy.

*Geography.*—In reply to circulars, your committee have received information that "louping-ill" or "trembling" prevails more or less over the pastoral districts of the following counties:—

| | |
|---|---|
| Caithness, | Little known. |
| Sutherland, | Slightly. |
| Ross-shire, | Slightly. |
| Nairn, | Very slightly. |
| Inverness-shire—Inverness District, | Uncommon. |
| Fort-William District, | Generally prevalent. |
| Isle of Skye, | Do. |
| Argyllshire, | General throughout. |
| Dumbarton, | Not very prevalent. |
| Stirling—Western Division, | Occasionally. |
| Perthshire—South-west, | Common. |
| West, | Not very prevalent. |
| Bute, | Pretty general. |
| Arran, | Slightly. |
| Lanarkshire—Upper Ward, | Slightly. |
| Ayrshire—South, | In several parishes. |
| Wigtownshire, | { Prevails throughout muirland in Kirkcowan and Penninghame parishes. |
| Kirkcudbright, | Slightly. |
| Dumfriesshire, | { Prevalent in Upper Nithsdale, Annandale, and Eskdale. |
| Peebles, | Prevails in parts of county. |
| Selkirk, | { Prevails more or less over all pastoral districts. |
| Roxburgh, | Prevails westward of Jed Water. |

Between the middle of April and the end of June, the following districts were carefully examined by Mr. Andrew Brotherston, accompanied either by Dr. Aitken, Dr Hamilton, Professor Williams, or Mr. P. Geddes; and through the kind assistance of Mr. Peach, of the Geological Survey, Mr. Brotherston has been able to give the geological formation:—

| | |
|---|---|
| Roxburghshire—Upper Teviot, Allan Water, Borthwick Water, | { Upper and Lower Silurian and boulder clay, with occasional trap hills and dykes. |
| Minto Hills, | { Rocks—Upper Old Red Sandstone, with boulder clay and Lower Silurian; hills volcanic. |
| Jed Water—Upper part, | { Carboniferous and Upper Silurian, with trap hills. |
| Lower part, | Old Red Sandstone. |
| Liddesdale—Whithaugh, | { Lower Carboniferous blue clays and impure limestones, alternating with massive sandstones (Cement stone series). |
| Selkirkshire—Borthwickhead and Rankleburn, | { Upper and Lower Silurian boulder clay occasional trap hills and dykes. |

| | |
|---|---|
| Dumfrieshire—Upper Eskdale, | Upper and Lower Silurian boulder clay; occasional trap hills and dykes. |
| Lower to Langholm, | Upper Silurian. |
| Upper Ewes Water, | Do. |
| Do., from Arkleton to Langholm, | Upper Old Red and Carboniferous Sandstones, with broad platform of trap. |
| Wauchope—North side, | Upper Silurian. |
| South, | Carboniferous Sandstones. |
| Upper Tarras Water, | Upper Old Red Sandstone hill tops; platforms of trap from Arkleton Shiel downwards; Carboniferous rocks. |
| Nithsdale—Euchan Water, Upper part, | Lower Silurian. |
| Lower do., | Coal measures. |
| Mennick, | Lower Silurian. |
| Peeblesshire—Bonnington, | Lower Silurian, with a few trap dykes. |
| Skye—Farms of Drynoch, Corrybreck, and Culishadder, | Tertiary basalt. |

Of the above, the upper part of Eskdale Muir and Mennick Water are almost entirely free from the disease; but it is clear that it is not confined to any particular soil or geological formation, and prevails over a wide series, from the Lower Silurian through the Upper Silurian, Old Red and Carboniferous Sandstones, to the basalt of the Tertiary period.

*Botany.*—On the other hand, the noticeable characteristic of those places liable to the disease, as pointed out by Mr. Brotherston last year in his report to the Teviotdale Farmers' Club, was fully confirmed, viz., the large amount of withered herbage of preceding years, especially *Nardus stricta* (mat grass or wire bent) and *Aira cæspitosa* (tufted hair grass or bull-snouts), which on examination were invariably found covered with minute fungi, chiefly *Cladosporium herbarum.*

Part of Mr. Brotherston's report of last year is appended, in which he suggests ergot as the cause, and gives a list of grasses which were also found very much ergotised.

In Upper Eskdale Muir (already mentioned as free from the disease), while the formation is the same as Borthwick and Rankleburn, there was very much less *Nardus stricta* or *Aira cæspitosa*, there being a large amount of heather and floe moss, with extensive beds of peat, the heather being intermixed with *Juncus squarrosus* (stool bent), *Scirpus cæspitosus* (deer's hair), *Eriophorum vaginatum* (harestail cotton grass), and *Aira flexuosa* (waved hair grass); lower down, where this disease prevails extensively on the steep grassy slopes, there was an abundance of withered grasses, *Nardus stricta*, &c., and much less wet or other spretty lands. Again, in Mennick Water (also free), the hills are steep, dry, and bare.

*Pathology.*—Professor Williams found that the disease in question was confounded with several other ailments prevailing at the same time of year, all being described under the one name, "Louping-ill."

In a majority of cases he considers the cause to have been neither more nor less than poverty or starvation.

The following diseases were also confounded under the common term:—

1. "Joint-ill, or rheumatic and suppurative inflammation of the joints in lambs. The symptoms are briefly as follows:—Swellings of one or several joints, lameness, pains, loss of flesh; sometimes the inflamed joints suppurate and burst, the fever now increases in intensity, and the lamb generally succumbs; but if the swellings do not burst, the lamb may not die; as a rule, however, it continues lame, unthrifty, and has its limb deformed. This disease has been described as being associated with an unhealthy condition of the navel. I found that it was so in a few instances only, and that disease, originating perhaps in the navel, was not uncommon without any affection of the joint.

2. Many lambs were examined *post-mortem*, which were said to have died of 'louping-ill,' when the cause of death was found to be impaction of the fourth stomach with wool, in many cases this organ was quite filled with wool, the bowels empty of food; and if any milk was present at all, it was found in the other, and at this age imperfectly developed compartment of the stomach, where it could give no nourishment to the body, but rather act as an irritant by undergoing the process of putrefaction.

"The practice of 'udder locking,' that is, of pulling off the hairy wool surrounding and in the neighbourhood of the udder, is now not practised, although I am told that at one time it extensively prevailed. I consider it ought again to be carried out, as it would be the means of saving many lambs which annually die from this form of impaction of the true digestive stomach.

3. Navel-ill, without disease of the joint, is also confounded with 'louping-ill.' The symptoms are those of great prostration, even to inability to stand, when the disease has existed for some time; convulsions absent; the umbilical cord is enlarged,

soft, flabby, and its vessels filled with an unhealthy dark-coloured blood. In the healthy young animal that portion of the umbilical cord contained within the animal's body, and consisting of blood-vessels, becomes after birth rapidly converted from hollow tubes into ligaments extending to the liver and bladder; but in these unhealthy lambs I found it to consist of a hollow, containing a turbid fluid, and even pus, whilst abscesses were found in the liver, kidneys, spleen, and around the spine, involving both the spinal column externally, and extending into the spinal canal.

"I may here state that one half-bred lamb, fed on cultivated grasses, the only one so fed and bred that I found affected with disease during the spring investigation, was said to have marked symptoms of 'louping-ill'; but on examination I found it had partial paralysis of the hind quarters, owing to the pressure of an abscess on the spinal cord, and arising from this disease primarily established in the navel.

"Of the above described maladies, confounded with the true 'louping-ill' or 'trembling,' the first is due to vicissitudes of climate, on some farms prevailing during easterly winds, but at one place I was told it was most common during west winds. I found, however, that a sudden change of weather, especially if too cold, and if the aspect faced the wind, this as well as 'louping-ill' prevailed to a greater extent, and the mortality was much increased.

"Of the second disease, viz., impaction of the stomach with wool, it may be stated that the remedy is apparent, and that the last, or secondary abscesses, prevails more or less amongst all young animals, foals, calves, as well as lambs, and seems to arise sometimes from local injuries to the navel string at the time of birth; from some constitutional predisposition or taint, perhaps derived from the mother, and sometimes from episootic influences beyond our control."

But apart from, and in addition to these maladies, Professor Williams satisfied himself that a disease of the nervous system really has an existence, and prevails extensively amongst lambs, and still more so amongst full-grown sheep, occasionally attacking cattle, and said also to attack pigs. The symptoms being "fits of convulsions, automatic movements of the limbs, spasms across the loins, elevation of the head, jerky breathing, unnatural brightness of the eyes in some, but increased dulness, approaching to blindness, in others. In some cases the animals retained their consciousness and desire for food. In those cases where ability to stand and move about remained, I found that the sight of a dog, or any other source of excitement, caused them to fall prostrate, some on their belly and chest, others on their sides, in which position they would remain, breathing heavily, with nose extended, trembling violently for a short period. If raised on to their legs, they would walk away trembling violently."

"Early in May I had an opportunity of witnessing during life, and of dissecting after death, a well-marked case of the disease, in a stage during which the symptoms were not marked or overcome by those of the prostration of strength which succeeds in those cases where life is prolonged for some time.

"The symptoms were briefly as follows, viz., gnashing of the teeth, frothing at the mouth, head drawn back, with nose poked out by the contraction of the muscles of the neck; convulsions, lying prostrate, inability to stand when lifted on its feet.

"This sheep (ewe) was killed and immediately examined. The internal organs contained in the abdominal and thoracic cavities were found quite healthy; the lungs contained a few round worms (strongles), but their number was quite insignificant, and could have had no influence over the health of the sheep. The contents of the stomachs and intestines were quite natural and sufficiently abundant, consisting, of course, of such herbage and leaves as we could see on the land, very much withered, and but little green grasses. This sheep was in good condition and well nourished. The blood was carefully examined with a microscope magnifying 600°, but nothing abnormal could be detected.

"The spinal cord, however, presented an appearance, which, in the majority of cases examined afterwards, was a leading and distinguishing characteristic, the appearance referred to being due to the pressure of an exudate, or formation of a gelatinous appearance and nature, lying within the spinal canal, and surrounding the spinal cord, more particularly around the roots of the great nerves. This exudate is of a pale sherry colour, of the consistence of cold jelly, appearing almost bloodless or non-vascular to the naked eye; but when subjected to microscopic examination, it is seen to consist of cells and tubes, the nature of which are not exactly yet determined, and will require further examination and experience.'

Further on in the season, when the disease was in full operation, many more cases were seen and examined; and in regard to the "exudation," Professor Williams remarks, "that it was not equally manifest in all cases; in some it was very abundant, but in others it was scarcely observable; and in all cases where it could be seen, it was found to be in patches here and there, generally most abundant in the regions of the loins, but in a minority of cases at the junction of the spinal cord with the medulla oblongata, or the continuation of the cord contained within the head,—in other words, just outside the head, in the neck, within the spinal canal.

"I have stated that this exudate was scarcely observable in a few cases, in a few others it could not be seen at all; and this, I think, explains the discrepancy on this head found in the writings of others who have studied this disease, some stating there is an increase of the spinal fluid, meaning the exudate, I suppose, whilst others state they have never seen this condition."

From his examination of a large number of cases, Professor Williams was led to form the opinion that the disease was due "to the injection of grasses in a diseased condition from the invasion of various fungi."

The exudate was also observed by Dr. Aitken, who was led early in the inquiry to think that the cause of disease would be found due to either the direct or indirect action of a germ poison, and that its locus was probably in the tissue of the cord, and most probably in the cerebro-spinal fluid, and he determined to work upon this theory. He made preparations of the exudate and other tissues of the spine, and these are now being examined. He has also been so fortunate as to secure the co-operation of Dr. D. J. Hamilton, and they "determined to work upon the theory of a special germ in the cerebro-spinal fluid," should any cases be found in Skye.

The expedition to Skye in September was undertaken because your committee were informed there was generally an autumn outbreak of "trembling" on certain farms, and it was important to identify "louping-ill" and "trembling" beyond a doubt, and also to compare the vegetation with the districts already visited.

The results were not altogether satisfactory; only one case, a lamb, was obtained, and in Professor Williams' opinion the *post-mortem* examination only gave negative evidence as to the true nature of the case. As, however, it appeared to Dr. Aitken and Dr. Hamilton to have all the distinctive appearances of "louping-ill," they made a careful diagnosis of the case.

"The hind legs were paralysed to some extent, the pulse was 104°, and the temperature 106° F. The respirations were 30 per minute, and somewhat irregular.

"Having the means of testing the germ theory all provided, the animal was killed and cultivations were attempted with the blood, aqueous humor, and cerebro-spinal fluid. After twelve hours in the warm chamber, the blood and aqueous humor remained inactive, but the cerebro-spinal fluid was found to be cultivating vigorously. Specimens were taken of the germs, and drawings made of the culture. They resembled closely the germs found in chicken cholera.

"A second cultivation was immediately set agoing, but owing to the difficulty of maintaining a proper temperature in the chamber, during the changes of external temperature, the cultures were for two hours subjected to a temperature of 110° to 116° Fahr., and the growth came to an end. The results obtained were very encouraging, and pointed to the correctness of the germ theory."

Dr. Aitken is therefore still strongly in favour of this theory; "and as experience and dexterity and a proper knowledge of the best conditions for culture are necessary to ensure success in that kind of investigation, I have determined," he writes, "to practise cultivation of various secretions and discharges during the winter, so as to be able to apply the process more successfully next spring."

*Ixodes* (ticks.)—In addition to the two species identified in the Teviotdale report as *I. marginata* and *I. erinaceus*, a smaller species was seen on several farms visited, chiefly about the noses of the sheep. A still smaller species of Arachnoid, closely resembling Ixodes, was also found in large numbers early in the season amongst specimens of withered *Nardus stricta*, but neither of these have as yet been identified.

It is clear that the large quantities of rank and withered grass afford cover for ticks; and as they are only found, as far as experience goes, in those places liable to the disease, those farms in Upper Eskdale Muir, for instance, which are free from the disease, are also free from ticks, the natural inference is, that there must be some connection, though on the other hand many sheep may be covered with them without having the disease. Possibly they may be mere concomitants, but it is also quite possible that they may be the carriers of some virus.

Professor Williams is quite of this opinion, bearing out also that expressed by Professor Robertson in the Teviotdale report—"That it seems to be more in accordance with our present knowledge of morbid processes in animal bodies, that it (the tick) should be regarded rather as the carrier of a specific blood poison than as the active agent in a general or special spinal disturbance from peripheral nerve irritation."

The work already done by those intrusted with the investigation has necessarily been hitherto of a preliminary kind, the very diverse and conflicting views entertained by farmers regarding the nature and cause of the disease has required that their observations should extend over a wide area; and this has entailed an amount of expense which will not require to be repeated.

The result of their inquiries has been to bring the investigation within certain narrow limits, so that they will now be able to proceed with the thorough examination of the nature and cause of the disease when it makes its appearance next spring. It would be premature at this stage, or until the real causes have been ascertained beyond doubt, to enter on the subject of remedial or preventative measures, beyond stating that it has been brought to the notice of the committee that at Minto Kaimes the disease has at any rate been very much mitigated, since the tenant has taken to cutting over the coarser grasses with a reaper; beneficial results are also said to have been obtained on other farms by burning, and also partial grazing with cattle.

*Report on the Flora of Upper Teviotdale, in Connection with its Relation to "Louping-ill" in Sheep.*

Gentlemen,—Acting upon the instructions received from your Secretary, I proceeded to the localities indicated to make an exhaustive examination of the vegetation existing upon certain hill pastures in the district of Upper Teviotdale, for the purpose of discovering, if possible, the cause of the disease in sheep known by the name of "louping-ill," which is prevalent on some spots in that district.

The first farm visited was Broadhaugh, on June 17, 1879. On the following day I made an examination of the uncultivated part of the farm and also some of the cultivated land, noting every phanerogamic plant seen and the predominating cryptogams, without detecting anything in the vegetation at that time capable of producing the symptoms of louping-ill, as there were no plants noted but what are found on healthy places. I was then forced to the conclusion that the disease was not caused by the vegetation in a normal state. Neither did the geological formation differ from that of many places that are free from that disease. Some other cause had to be looked for. Knowing something of the nature and properties of ergot, it struck me forcibly at the time that it was the most probable cause, as from the appearance of the pastures at that time I had good reasons to believe that ergot would be prevalent in the autumn. The manner in which they were treated—leaving them very rough for winter and spring feeding—being the most suitable way to encourage its growth. Besides, the symptoms of louping-ill are similar to what would be produced by poisonous doses of that parasite.

Part of Harwood was next visited, and found to be somewhat similar to Broadhaugh, but with more "heather" (*Calluna vulgaris, Erica Tetralix*, and *E. cinerea*), "stool bent" (*Juncus squarrosus*), and other heath-loving plants.

Skelfhill was next examined, and the altitude being greater—from 847 feet at the house to 1745 on the top of Skelfhill pen, and about 2000 feet on Cauldcleuch—some of the lower level plants were missed, and a number of sub-alpine species noted, in addition to those seen on the lower farms (the parts formerly examined were from above 500 to 900 feet above sea-level), but still nothing likely to induce the disease. The same may be said of Howpasley, where the altitudes of the parts examined ranged from 700 to 1561 feet. There also a few additional species were observed, and, like Skelfhill, wanting some of the plants that grow at lower levels.

Owing to the weather and other causes, which put a stop to the investigation, I did not get back to the district until July 28th, when Howcleuch, Borthwickbrae, and Harden were gone over with a like result, viz., without discovering any plants that would be injurious to sheep, when in their normal state, or any different species, with one exception—*Meum athamanticum* at Howpasley—from those found on the Cheviot range, and other healthy places on the Borders. It must not be understood that no poisonous plants whatever were seen. For instance, *Digitalis purpurea*, which is poisonous, occurred on some spots, but the same plant grows in very much greater profusion on many of the healthiest places.

To make the investigation as complete as possible, I shortly afterwards examined several similarly situated places, which are said to be free from louping-ill, viz., one of the Cheviots, Bowden Moor, and several hills in Peeblesshire, and, according to altitude, found no material difference in the species of plants from those seen in Upper Teviotdale, but the pastures were eaten closer and very much barer naturally, with the exception of Bowden Moor, which was rougher, and more resembled the infected places.

A second visit was found to be necessary in the autumn, to see if the condition of the vegetation was in any way altered. Accordingly, Howpasley was revisited on the 24th of September, and, as I suspected, ergot was then found in great abundance. There I gathered "spurs" of ergot from sixteen different species of grasses. All the other farms, formerly examined, were afterwards gone over, and ergot found plentifully on them all except Howcleuch, where it was very local and in small quantity, not nearly so much in proportion to the extent of the ground, a large portion of the drier parts producing very few flowering stems of the grasses. On the different places ergot was found on twenty-three species in all, viz.:—

1. *Anthoxanthum odoratum* (sweet vernal grass).
2. *Digraphis arundinacea* (red canary grass).
3. *Alopecurus pratensis* (meadow fox-tail grass).
4. *Phleum pratense* (cat's-tail grass, Timothy grass).

5. *Agrostis vulgaris* (fine bent grass).
6. *Aira cæspitosa* (tufted hair grass, "bull-snouts).
7. *Aira flexuosa* (waved hair grass).
8. *Avena pratensis* (narrow-leaved oat grass).
9. *Avena elatior* (oat-like soft grass).
10. *Holcus mollis* (creeping soft grass).
11. *Holcus lanatus* (meadow short grass, Yorkshire fog).
12. *Glyceria fluitans* (floating meadow grass).
13. *Poa annua* (annual meadow grass).
14. *Poa pratensis* (smooth-stalked grass).
15. *Poa trivialis* (rough-stalked grass).
16. *Briza media* (common quaking grass).
17. *Dactylis glomerata* (cock's foot grass).
18. *Festuca duriuscula* (hard fescue grass).
19. *Festuca elatior* (tall fescue grass).
20. *Festuca pratensis* (meadow fescue grass).
21. *Triticum repens* (couch grass).
22. *Lolium perenne* (rye grass).
23. *Nardus stricta* (mat-grass, "wire bent").

The following grasses were noted, but no ergot observed on them, although it is probable that most of them are liable to be ergotised at some part of the season or in some years :—

*Alopecurus geniculatus* (floating fox-tail grass).
*Agrostis alba* (marsh bent grass).
*Agrostis canina* (brown bent grass).
*Aira caryophyllea* (silvery hair grass).
*Aira præcox* (early hair grass).
*Avena flavescens* (yellowish oat grass).
*Avena pubescens* (downy oat grass).
*Triodia decumbens* (decumbent heath grass).
*Molinia cærulea* (purple melic grass, "broad or flying bent.")
*Cynosurus cristatus* (crested dog's-tail grass).
*Festuca ovina* (sheep's fescue grass).
*Festuca ovina* var. *vivipara* (viviparous grass).
*Bromus mollis* (soft brome grass).

The *Juncaceæ* and *Cyperaceæ*, which form a large portion of the pasturage in some parts of the district, were all, so far as I saw, free from ergot; but some of the *Cyperaceæ*—e.g., *Carex panicea, C. glauca*, and some others—were very subject to smut (*Ustilago urceolarum*). I am not aware whether the eating of the plants affected with this fungus has any bad effect, but it is possible that it may, as another species of the genus (*U. grandis*), which affects reeds (*Arundo Phragmites*), "has the remarkable property of greatly affecting the health of the labourers employed in cutting and sorting them, producing not only a sense of oppression, but swelling of the head, the formation of vesicles, besides other symptoms, such as are produced by cantharides."

It may here be necessary to explain what ergot is, its appearance and life history. Ergot is the first, or rather second stage (*sclerotium*) of *Claviceps purpurea*, Tul. It is easily noticed when it projects, as it generally does when fully grown, beyond the *palæ* (chaff-scales) of the plant on which it is growing. The "spurs" are horn-shaped, sometimes straight, but usually curved; irregularly cylindrical and grooved. The colour externally is generally purple-black; internally it is white, sometimes purplish. The spurs vary greatly in size, according to the species of the host plant (the largest seeded grasses producing large ergot and *vice versa*), and also on the same plant. I gathered them in Upper Teviotdale, varying from less than ⅛ of an inch to over 1 inch in length from the same species. The ergot, when full grown, drops out of the chaff scales or falls along with the stems of the grasses, amongst which it lies dormant throughout the winter and spring. During the summer the perfect fungus (*Claviceps purpurea*) is produced. The fungi, which grows out from all sides of the sclerotium, are indefinite in number, varying from one to upwards of twenty; and the least bit of an ergot, according to Mr A. S. Wilson, will produce a fungus. It (the fungus) has a slender flexuous stem (*stipe*), varying in length, with a small globular head (*humentium*). When these are ripe the conceptacles containing the spores shoot them out into the air, where they float about till some of them find a suitable habitat on the germen of any grass florets that are open at the time. Those ergotised soon become covered with mycelium, from which the ergot is developed, again to fall and lie till the following summer, when the perfect fungus is produced, once more ready to disseminate its spores. Such is the annual course run by this fungus. Ergot, like many other fungi, besides being reproduced from the spores of the perfect fungus, is propagated by the sparmatia or conidia, which form its outer covering while in the young and growing state. Much difference of opinion exists as to the kind of season most conducive to the growth of ergot. Some say a dry season is most productive, others that a wet one suits it best. It appears that moist warm weather, when the *claviceps* is growing, and dry when it is disseminating its spores, will be most apt to produce a large crop. It does not appear to be particular as to altitude, soil, or exposure. On the Borders I have seen it on the sea coast, extending all through the low cultivated parts of the district up to about 1500 feet on Howpasley. Grasses on wet and dry, rich and poor, soils are alike subject to it. *Glyceria fluitans* (growing in water) and *Nardus stricta* (whether it is growing on the drier parts of the hills and moors or in wet ground) are both very often attacked, especially the latter, which is abundant in Upper Teviotdale. *Lolium perenne* in rich cultivated alluvial soils, or on dry bare roadsides, is equally affected. In shady woods or on open moors ergot thrives equally well. It will thus be seen that wherever grasses that are subject to this parasite are allowed to flower and perfect their seeds at the time that the spores of *Claviceps purpurea* are floating about, there it will grow. Some seasons one part of a farm may be bad with it while another is clear, according to the time and also to the weather when the grasses are in flower on that particular part. As a rule, the later flowering specimens are most subject. Crops of ryegrass that are grown for hay do not suffer, as they are too early in flower ; but late-flowering heads of the same are very liable to be ergotised. . . . .

As requested by you, I went to Dykeraw on September 20th, where I met Mr. Elliot. Owing to the earliness of the season, most of the ergot and also the seeds of the grasses had already fallen ; but on the part where the disease was worst there was abundance of *Nardus stricta*, one the most liable to be ergotised ; while on the healthier and improved parts of the farm there were very few grasses that are subject to ergot to any great extent.

I went to Skelfhill and Broadhaugh on September 17th and 18th, and found (as I had noticed last year) numerous minute fungi both on the young and *withered* leaves, and brought a quantity of each with me. As the annual conference of the Cryptogamic Society of Scotland was being held at Glasgow at that time, I went there, taking samples of each to try and identify them as far as possible. Dr. Buchanan White, F.L.S., editor of the *Scottish Naturalist*, kindly undertook to examine them, and took them home with him for that purpose. He found the greater number of them immature, and therefore unnameable, and said they might possibly be in a better state in early spring. Both *Scirpus cæspitosus* (deer's-hair), and *Eriophorum vaginatum* (hare's-tail cotton grass), two of the earliest "grasses," were very much infested with the immature state of some fungus. *Cladosporium herbarum* was abundant on the decaying leaves of most of the grasses, especially *Nardus stricta*. The *uredo* state of *Puccinia graminis* (*Trichobasis rubigo vera* or *red rust*) was also common. See *North British Agriculturist*, September 2, 1880, page 609, for a note regarding the last (*Trichobasis*), in which it is stated that Dr. J. E. Taylor, of the Ipswich Museum, writing with reference to an epidemic among lambs, has no doubt that lambs have suffered from blood-poisoning by eating too much of this unnutritious grass (*i.e.*, infested with *Trichobasis*). The stomach filled with millions of the fungus spores, which are probably strongly alkaline, would, he thinks, produce the blood-poisoning. Referring to the above, Dr. White says—"It seems to me, however, that the spores of some allied species are really more or less poisonous."

The most difficult thing with these minute fungi will be the difficulty of testing their effect ; but if it can be proven that they are in any degree poisonous, doubtless they will assist in developing any spring disease in sheep, as they are very plentiful. I was sorry that I could not collect ergot in quantity, as at the time that I was there it was mostly fallen ; but the ergot of rye is the same species, and so will have the same effect. It is a pity that last year's experiments with it were a failure—indeed, they were of no use whatever in testing the effects of ergot on sheep, as the ergot used appears to have lost its strength. . . . .

ANDREW BROTHERSTON.

*Oct. 19th, 1880.*

BRAXY.—Information received by the committee shows that it prevails in the following localities :—

| | |
|---|---|
| Shetland—Unst, | Uncommon. |
| Fetlar, | Common. |
| Caithness, | Slight. |
| Sutherland, | Slight. |
| Skye and other Islands, | Prevalent. |
| Inverness—Inverness District, | Slight. |
| Fort-William, | Prevalent. |
| Nairn, | Prevalent. |

| | | | | |
|---|---|---|---|---|
| Kincardine, | . | . | . | Slight. |
| Perth—S.W., | | | | Prevalent. |
| Other Districts. | | | | Slight. |
| Argyll, | . | . | . | Prevalent. |
| Bute, | . | . | . | Prevalent. |
| Arran, | . | . | . | Prevalent. |
| Dumbarton, | | | | Prevalent in parts of County. |
| Stirling—West, | . | . | . | Prevalent in Buchanan district. |
| Ayr, | . | . | . | { Prevalent in Carrick district, especially about Barr. |
| Lanark—Upper Ward, | | | | Prevalent. |
| Haddington, | | | | Prevalent on certain farms. |
| Roxburgh, | | | | Prevalent. |
| Peebles, | | | | Prevalent in parts of County. |
| Selkirk, | | | | Prevalent. |
| Dumfries—Upper and Middle Nithsdale, | | | | Prevalent. |
| Upper Annandale, | | | | Prevalent. |
| Eskdale, and Ewes Water, | | | | Prevalent. |
| Wigtown, | . | . | . | Prevalent. |
| Kirkcudbright, | . | . | . | Slightly. |

The amount of mortality and pecuniary loss sustained by proprietors and farmers from this disease is enormous, and the discovery of a means of preventing or mitigating its ravages would be one of the greatest boons that could be bestowed on the very large number who suffer by it.

The chief difficulty attending the investigation into the nature of the disease is its sudden and rapidly fatal character, so that animals are frequently found dead before they have been noticed to be ailing. This is the season of the year when it is most prevalent, and Professor Williams, Dr. Aitken, and Dr. Hamilton have been giving the disease their best attentions. Professor Williams' researches so far support his former opinion that it is analogous to, if not identical with, anthrax; while through the hearty co-operation and assistance, however, of Mr. Sanderson, Bonnington, near Peebles, on whose farm the disease is very prevalent, Dr. Aitken and Dr. Hamilton have been successful in getting a case of "sickness," "inflammation," or "braxy," during the progress of the disease, as well as others very soon after death. The result of their investigations, so far as they have gone, leave no doubt on their minds that this also is a "germ disease," and they are sanguine that further investigations will enable them to provide a preventative. This is a line of investigation which, in the hands of Pasteur and other French chemists and physiologists, has been attended with marvellous results, and on which the French Government are annually spending several thousand pounds.

In this country, on the other hand, such matters are left to private enterprise, and it seems only right that the Highland and Agricultural Society should, as far as possible, lead the van in this as well as in other inquiries in which the interests of agriculture are so deeply concerned; and to the committee it seems hardly possible that a portion of the funds of the Society could be better applied than in the thorough working out of this present inquiry into the nature and causes of those fell diseases affecting so largely the health and mortality of the sheep stock over the greater part of the pastoral districts of Scotland. The committee, therefore, hope the Directors will see their way to make such a grant as will ensure such an important end.

The report was adopted.

AGRICULTURAL BURSARIES.—Mr. Mylne, Niddrie Mains, reported that the examination for the Society's bursaries was held on the 26th of October, when Daniel Finlayson, Wick; Peter Reid, Waulkmill, Linlithgow; James Walker, 24 St. Andrew Square, Edinburgh; Henry Angus Watson, U.P. Manse, Forres; and R. P. Wright, Downam, Ballantrae, passed for bursaries of £20 each; and Robert J. Campbell, Slaguaw, Castle Douglas; George Cormack, Humster, Wick; James Grant, Wick; and Robert Seton, East Watton, Wick, for bursaries of £10 each.

DISTRICT COMPETITIONS.—Mr. Campbell Swinton of Kimmerghame reported the premiums awarded in 1881, and those offered in 1882.

COTTAGE COMPETITIONS.—Mr. Campbell Swinton, in the absence of Mr. Maxwell Inglis of Loganbank, reported the premiums awarded in 1881, and those offered in 1882.

PREMIUMS AWARDED FOR REPORTS IN 1881 AND OFFERED IN 1882—"TRANSACTIONS" FOR 1882.—The Secretary, in the absence of Mr. Irvine of Drum, reported the premiums awarded for reports in 1881, and those offered in 1882; and the contents of the forthcoming volume of Transactions.

On the motion of Mr. Eliott Lockhart, a vote of thanks was accorded to the Earl of Mar and Kellie for presiding, and the proceedings terminated.

## REPORT OF THE SOCIETY'S VETERINARY EXAMINATIONS.

### FIFTY-EIGHTH SESSION, 1880–81.

The examinations for this session were held on Monday, Tuesday, and Wednesday, 18th, 19th, and 20th April, the practical part of the examinations taking place on Monday in Messrs. Swan's New Auction Mart, Haymarket, kindly put at the disposal of the Society by those gentlemen, and at the abattoirs. This is the last examination which will take place under the auspices of the Highland and Agricultural Society. In future the place of the Society will be taken by the Royal College of Veterinary Surgeons, London.

The presentation of the certificates took place on Wednesday in the chambers of the Highland and Agricultural Society, when an apology for absence was intimated from Colonel Gillon of Wallhouse.

Professor BALFOUR, who presided, stated that thirty candidates had entered for examination, of whom twenty had passed.

Certificates were then presented to the following:—James W. H. Ashe, Cork; John A. Bull, Tysoe; William Watt Dollar, London; Joseph Doyle, Enniscorthy; James Gibson, Rousay, Orkney; William Graham, Cummertrees; Thomas Green, Manchester; John F. Healy, Cork; Lionel L. Leach, Boston, Lincolnshire; Isaiah Leather, Liverpool; Charles James Martin, Chesterfield; F. H. Osgood, Boston, U.S.; F. C. Rice, Springfield, Mass., U.S.; John H. Riches, Norwich; John Roberts, Wrexham; John A. Thomson, Co. Down; Frederick Whittaker, Bury; W. O. Williams, Edinburgh; Robert Willmot, William Woods, Wigan. Best Practical Examination—1 (gold medal), William Woods; 2 (silver medal), John A. Thomson. Best General Examination—1 (gold medal), W. W. Dollar; 2 (silver medal), William Woods.

Board of Examiners.—Botany—Professor Balfour, Dr. Cloghorn of Stravithie, St. Andrews. Chemistry—Dr. W. Craig, A. Inglis M'Callum. Anatomy—Dr. Dycer, C. Cunningham, Slateford; A. Spreull, Dundee. Practical and Clinical Examinations—Thomas A. Dollar, London; Finlay Dun, 2 Portland Place, London, W.; Tom Taylor, Manchester; John Lawson, Manchester; John Borthwick, Kirkliston; C. Cunningham, Slateford; Andrew Spreull, Dundee; Alex. Pottie, Paisley; W. D. Connochie, Selkirk. Physiology and Histology—Dr. Dycer, C. Cunningham, Slateford; Andrew Spreull, Dundee. Materia Medica—Professor Balfour, Finlay Dun, Dr. Craig, A. I. M'Callum. Diseases of Horses—John Borthwick, Kirkliston; John Lawson, Manchester; Tom Taylor, Manchester. Diseases of Cattle, Sheep, Swine, and Dogs—Thomas A. Dollar, London; Alex. Pottie, Paisley; W. D. Connochie, Selkirk.

Dr. DYCER said the examiners had all been very well satisfied with those who had been successful in obtaining certificates. He was sorry to say that they would not have the pleasure of meeting in this place again, but they wished them all success in life; and he was sure they would all do credit to the college they had come from, and honour to the certificates and diplomas they had obtained. He proposed a vote of thanks to Professor Balfour for presiding.

Mr. DOLLAR, London, had much pleasure in proposing a vote of thanks to Mr. Menzies, of the Highland and Agricultural Society. No one except those who came to those examinations, or were in close contact with Mr. Menzies, could have the slightest idea of the interest he took in veterinary matters. In some places just now it was fashionable to sneer at the Highland and Agricultural Society, and at everything connected with it; but no one could dispassionately look over the history of the Highland and Agricultural Society, and what it had done in connection with the veterinary profession, without coming to the conclusion that it had done more for the profession than any other body in the United Kingdom. He should be remiss in proposing this vote of thanks if he did not mention the founder of the veterinary profession in this country. In 1818 a gentleman of the name of William Dick returned from London, and commenced lecturing in Edinburgh; but it was nine years after that time before the Highland and Agricultural Society began to grant certificates to those who had received the benefit of his lectures and of his education generally in connection with the horse. He had also to mention the name of Dr. Balfour, through whom those attending the college in Clyde Street had the entrée of all the different courses of lectures at the University. At one time six of these classes were so open, and he believed that to a great extent the men who had made the greatest mark in the profession owed a deep debt of gratitude to the medical profession in Edinburgh for their great liberality in allowing them to attend their classes free of charge, and in giving support to Professor Dick when he was struggling to found a veterinary college. Although they were now attending what might be called a funeral service, still, if their examination was dead, the people who had assisted in carrying it through were not dead; and he must again refer to a section of their profession, and say that the amount of ingratitude in some of them to the Highland and Agricultural Society was something that he detested. One ought always to speak well of the bridge that carried them over, and of the ladder upon whose rungs they had risen to distinction. Unfortunately, that had not been the feeling towards the Highland and Agricultural Society. That was a thing that he was very sorry for, because, having a great interest in the veterinary profession and in its best welfare, he considered that their profession could not have too much of external influence to assist it; and as regarded a public body that had taken so much interest in the profession, they ought not, immediately they could go without it, try to kick it down. He wished it to be on record that the Highland and Agricultural Society had done more to raise the veterinary profession than any other public body. For nineteen years he had had the pleasure of acting as an examiner, and he must tender his thanks, and the thanks of the other gentlemen on the Board, to the worthy Secretary, Mr. Menzies, for his uniform courtesy and kindness, and for the great interest he had taken in the veterinary profession.

Professor BALFOUR, in seconding the motion, said that a more diligent, active, and pleasant man than Mr. Menzies he did not know.

Mr. MENZIES, in returning thanks, said that Mr. Dollar was quite right in saying that he had taken the greatest interest in the veterinary profession, and he was very sorry that in a kind of way the Highland Society was now going to be severed from it, at least so far as regarded examination. He was glad to say, however, that the Directors had determined to keep up the veterinary department; and if the veterinary profession required any aid of the Society at any time, he had not the least doubt they would find the Directors willing to give it. He proposed a vote of thanks to Messrs. Swan & Sons, for having granted the free use of their excellent market for the practical examinations.

Professor WILLIAMS said that all connected with the schools felt much indebted to the examiners for the way in which they had performed their duties. He endorsed all that had been said of the Highland Society. It had done more than any other body in Great Britain to advance veterinary science.

The proceedings then terminated.

# PREMIUMS AWARDED BY THE SOCIETY IN 1881-82.

## I.—REPORTS, 1882.

### AGRICULTURAL.

1. John Ainslie, jun., Hillend, Lothian Burn, for a Report on Manure made with and without Cover, . . . . . . . £15 0 0
2. William Cochran, Overdale House, Dunblane, for a Report on Tea and Silk Farming in New Zealand, . . . . . . 15 0 0
3. James Tait, 26 Windsor Street, Edinburgh, for a Report on the Physiological Distinction of the Scottish Peasantry, . . . . . 15 0 0
4. Russell Swanwick, M.R.A.C., Royal Agricultural College Farm, Cirencester, and E. W. Prevost, Ph.D., F.R.S.E., 1 Cecily Hill, Cirencester, for a Report of Experiments on Potatoes with different Manures, 2 Medium Gold Medals, 12 4 0
5. Peter Kilpatrick, Durley Manor, Bishops Waltham, Hants, for a Report on the Cultivation of Cabbage, . . . . . . 10 0 0
6. James Shields, Byers, Bathgate, for a Report on the Reclamation of Moss Land, . . . . . . . . . 10 0 0
7. Alexander Lovie, Towie, Auchmedden, Fraserburgh, for a Report on the Reclamation of Waste Land, . . . . . . 10 0 0
8. A. Septimus Alexander, 4 Belhaven Terrace, Glasgow, for a Report on the Treatment of Border Leicester Ewes and Lambs. Medium Gold Medal, 6 2 0
9. George Armatage, M.R.C.V.S., Clarence Villa, 65 Hayter Road, Brixton Rise, S.W., for a Report on Sturdy in Sheep, . . . . 5 0 0
10. William Hay, Tillydesk, Ellon, for a Report on the Composition of Crops in average Produce, . . . . . . . 5 0 0
11. John Milne, Mains of Lauthers, Turriff, for a Report of Experiments in Cattle Feeding, . . . . . . . . 5 0 0
12. William Thomson, Auchenraith, High Blantyre, for a Report on the best System of Bee Culture, . . . . . . 5 0 0
13. David W. Wemyss of Newton Bank, St Andrews, for a Report on the Cultivation of Prickly Comfrey, . . . . . . 5 0 0
14. R. M. Malloch, Balhaldie, Braco, Perthshire, for a Model of Cattle Truck, Minor Gold Medal, 3 15 0

### FORESTRY.

15. Robert Hutchison of Carlowrie, Kirkliston, for a Report on Old and Remarkable Elms in Scotland, . . . . . . 10 0 0
16. Robert Hutchison of Carlowrie, Kirkliston, for a Report on Old and Remarkable Lime Trees in Scotland, . . . . . 10 0 0
17. Robert Hutchison of Carlowrie, Kirkliston, for a Report on the *Picea grandis*, 5 0 0
18. Robert Hutchison of Carlowrie, Kirkliston, for a Report on the Severe Winter of 1880-81 on Trees and Shrubs, . . . . 5 0 0
19. Donald Stalker, Kilmun, for a Report on Plantations, &c., on the Estates of Benmore and Kilmun, . . . . Minor Gold Medal, 3 15 0

£155 16 0

## II.— STIRLING SHOW, 1881.

### CLASS I.—CATTLE.

#### SHORTHORN.

TWEEDDALE GOLD MEDAL—Best SHORTHORN BULL in the Yard.

James Bruce, Burnside, Fochabers, " Knickerbocker " (38,150) . . . 20 0 0

SECTION 1. BULLS calved before 1st January 1879.

1. James Bruce, Burnside, Fochabers, " Knickerbocker " (38,150) . . . 25 0 0
2. James A. Gordon, Udale, Invergordon, " Rosario 2d " (42,309) . . . 12 0 0
3. A. & A. Mitchell, Alloa, " Colonel " (42,948) . . . . 6 0 0

Breeder of Best Bull—The Duke of Buccleuch and Queensberry, K.G., Dalkeith, . . . . . . . Silver Medal, 0 16 0

V. H. C., Walter Scott, Glendronach, Huntly, " Cossack " (39,633). H. C., Sir Thomas Buchan Hepburn of Smeaton Hepburn, Bart., Prestonkirk, " Smeaton Hero " (42,419).

Carry forward. £88 16 0

Brought forward,   £63 10 0

### Section 2. BULLS calved on or after 1st January 1879.

1. Walter Scott, Glendronach, Huntly, "Good Hope,"    .    .    25 0 0
2. Robert Drysdale, Old Mills, Craigforth, Stirling, "Royal Hero,"   .   12 0 0
3. Charles H. Dundas, Garriehrew, Dunira, Crieff, "Young Bywell,"   .   6 0 0
C., Adam Sharp, Rothes, "Earl of Rothes."

### Section 3. BULLS calved on or after 1st January 1880.

1. James Bruce, Burnside, Fochabers, "Claymore,"    .    .    12 0 0
2. Adam L. Cochrane, Kingsknowes, Galashiels, "Sunnyside Carlos,"   .   6 0 0
3. John Law, New Keig, Whitehouse, Aberdeen, "May Day,"    .    3 0 0
C., Lord Polwarth, Broomhall, St Boswells, "Victor Regalia."

### Section 4. COWS of any age.

1. Lord Polwarth, Broomhall, St. Boswells, "Wave of the Ocean,"    .    20 0 0
2. The Duke of Buccleuch and Queensberry, K.G., Dalkeith Park, Dalkeith, "Cherry Maid,"    10 0 0
3. William A. Mitchell, Auchnagathle, Whitehouse, Aberdeen, "Almond,"   .   5 0 0
H. C., John Law, New Keig, Whitehouse, Aberdeen, "Volinda."   C., Alexander Buchanan, Whitehouse, Stirling, "Rose of Tralee."

### Section 5. HEIFERS calved on or after 1st January 1879.

1. Charles H. Dundas, Garriehrew, Dunira, Crieff, "Rose Alpine,"   .   12 0 0
2. James Watt, Garbity, Fochabers, "Emily Hope,"    .    6 0 0
3. Lieutenant-Colonel John Murray of Polmaise, Stirling, "Second Duchess of Connaught,"    .    .    .    3 0 0

### Section 6. HEIFERS calved on or after 1st January 1880.

1. James Watt, Garbity, Fochabers, "Dorothy,"    .    .    10 0 0
2. Lord Polwarth, Broomhall, St. Boswells, "Wave of the Pacific,"   .   5 0 0
3. James Shaw, Tillyching, Lumphanan, Aberdeen, "Emma 2d,"    .    3 0 0
V. H. C., John Law, New Keig, Whitehouse, Aberdeen, "Velina."   H. C., James Bruce, Burnside, Fochabers, "Spicy 4th."   C., James Watt, Garbity, Fochabers, "Marchioness 9th."

## AYRSHIRE.

### Section 7. BULLS calved before 1st January 1879.

1. William Bartlemore, Netherhouses, Lochwinnoch, Paisley, "The Baron of Buchlyvie,"    20 0 0
2. James Sands, Greenfoot, Gargunnock, "Pretender,"    .    .    10 0 0
3. The Duke of Buccleuch and Queensberry, K.G., Drumlanrig, Thornhill, "Scottish Chief" (200),    5 0 0
Breeder of Best Bull—Duncan Keir, Hardieston, Port of Monteith,   Silver Medal,   0 16 0
V. H. C., Thomas Tennant of Priestgill, Strathaven, "Kilbirnie."   H. C., T. D. C. Graham, Dunlop House, Stewarton, "Fenwick Laddie" (142).   C., Robert Wardrop, Garlaff, Cumnock, "Wattieston Prince."

### Section 8. BULLS calved on or after 1st January 1879.

1. Sir Michael R. Shaw Stewart, Bart., Ardgowan, Greenock, "Lord Raglan,"   .   20 0 0
2. D. C. Willison, Dalpeddar, Sanquhar, "Lord Raglan,"    .    10 0 0
3. Andrew Hoggan, jun., Busby Farms, Busby, Lanarkshire, "Herd Laddie,"   .   5 0 0
V. H. C., Alex. Craig, Over Milton, East Kilbride, "Duncan."   H. C., Thomas Martin, Muiryhill, Thornhill, "Pride of the Glen."   C., John M. Martin, Auchendennan Farm, Balloch, "Endymion" (297).

### Section 9. BULLS calved on or after 1st January 1880.

1. Robert Wardrop, Garlaff, Cumnock, "King Coil,"    .    10 0 0
2. The Duke of Buccleuch and Queensberry, K.G., Drumlanrig, Thornhill, "The Star of Drumlanrig" (247),    5 0 0
3. The Duke of Buccleuch and Queensberry, K.G., "Marquis 2d of Drumlanrig" (249),    3 0 0
V. H. C., Andrew M'Dowall, Auchtralure, Stranraer, "Royal Sovereign."   H. C., James A. Hamilton of Whiteshawgate, Strathaven, "Lord Douglas."   C., James Craig, Robroyston, Bishopbriggs, "Roderick Dhu."

Carry forward,   £200 12 0

|  | Brought forward, | £290 | 12 | 0 |

#### Section 10.  COWS in Milk, calved before 1st January 1878.

1. The Duke of Buccleuch and Queensberry, K.G., Drumlanrig Castle, Thornhill, "Heroine 2d of Drumlanrig," . . . . 15 0 0
2. T. D. C. Graham, Dunlop House, Stewarton, "Darby" (918), . . 8 0 0

#### Section 11.  COWS in Milk, calved on and after 1st January 1878.

1. Andrew Hoggan, jun., Busby Farms, Busby, "Busby," . . . 15 0 0
2. John Lang, Baild, Gargunnock, "Rosa," . . . . 8 0 0
3. Duncan Keir, Buchlyvie, "Monarch" (988), . . . . 4 0 0
V. H. C., The Duke of Buccleuch and Queensberry, K.G., "Minnie of Drumlanrig."
H. C., The Duke of Buccleuch and Queensberry, K.G., "Delight of Drumlanrig."

#### Section 12.  COWS in Calf, of any age, or HEIFERS in Calf, calved before 1st January 1879.

1. The Duke of Buccleuch and Queensberry, K.G., "Dainty 2d of Drumlanrig," . 15 0 0
2. The Duke of Buccleuch and Queensberry, K.G., "Adela of Drumlanrig," . 8 0 0
3. James Scott, Nowlands, Bothwell, "Pride of Bothwell." . . 4 0 0
V. H. C., John Meikle, Seafield, Bathgate, "White Lady."  H. C., Sir Michael R. Shaw Stewart, Bart., Ardgowan, Greenock.  C., Duncan Keir, Buchlyvie, "Beauty 2d of Buchlyvie" (453).  C., Thomas Lloyd, Minard Castle, Minard, "Cherry."

#### Section 13.  HEIFERS calved on or after 1st January 1879.

1. John Meikle, Seafield, Bathgate, "The Princess," . . . 10 0 0
2. The Duke of Buccleuch and Queensberry, K.G., "Alice of Drumlanrig," . 5 0 0
3. Charles Kay, Mill Farm, Gargunnock, "Rosalee," . . . 3 0 0
V. H. C., Duncan Keir, Buchlyvie, "Beauty 3d of Buchlyvie."  H. C., Sir Michael R. Shaw Stewart, Bart., Ardgowan, Greenock, "Princess."  C., Andrew M'Dowall, Auchtralure, Stranraer, "First Love."

#### Section 14.  HEIFERS calved on or after 1st January 1880.

1. Robert Wardrop, Garlaff, Cumnock, "Snowflake," . . . 8 0 0
2. Andrew Hoggan, jun., Busby Farms, Busby, "Just in Time," . . 4 0 0
3. James Wilson, Boghall, Houston, "Frisky," . . . 2 0 0
H. C., Robert Wardrop, Garlaff, Cumnock, "Ayrshire Lassie."  C., Robert Cadzow, Borland, Biggar, "Missie 3d."

#### Section 15.  COWS of any age, and three or more of their Descendants, Male or Female.—No Entry.

### POLLED ANGUS OR ABERDEEN.

#### Section 16.  BULLS calved before 1st December 1878.

1. Sir George Macpherson Grant, Bart., M.P., Ballindalloch, "Justice" (1462), . 20 0 0
2. Thomas Ferguson, Kinnochtry, Coupar-Angus, "Prince of the Realm" (1695), . 10 0 0
3. William James Tayler, Rothiemay House, Huntly, "Sir Maurice" (1319), . 5 0 0
Breeder of Best Bull—Sir George Macpherson Grant, Bart., M.P., Ballindalloch, Silver Medal, . 0 16 0
H. C., Alexander Mann, Ballintomb, Grantown, "Kaiser" (1253).  C., "John M'Dougall, Goodyburn, Perth, "Norman of Powrie" (1257).

#### Section 17.  BULLS calved on or after 1st December 1878.

1. R. C. Auld, Bridgend, Whitehouse, Aberdeen, "Knight of the Shire" (1609), . 20 0 0
2. Representative of the late Robert Walker, Montbletton, Banff, "Young Hero," . 10 0 0
3. Lieut.-Col. George Arthur Ferguson of Pitfour, Mintlaw, "Marischal Keith" (1627), . . . . . . . 5 0 0
H. C., Thomas Dawson Brodie of Gairdoch, Powfoulis Home Farm, Falkirk, "Zulu Chief" (1704).

#### Section 18.  BULLS calved on or after 1st December 1879.

1. William M'Combie of Easter Skene, Skene, Aberdeen, "Paris the Third," . 10 0 0
2. The Earl of Strathmore, Glamis Castle, Forfar, "Bismarck 2d," . . 5 0 0
3. William James Tayler, Rothiemay House, Huntly, "Royal Victor" (1780), . 3 0 0
H. C., William M. Skinner, Drumin, Glenlivet, "Express."

|  | Carry forward, | £488 | 8 | 0 |

Brought forward,   £438   8   0

### Section 19. COWS of any age.

1. Sir George Macpherson Grant, Bart., M.P., Ballindalloch, "Maid of Avon" (2995),     15 0 0
2. William James Tayler, Rothiemay House, Huntly, "Kate Darling" (3573),     8 0 0
3. Sir Dudley C. Marjoribanks, Bart., M.P., Guisachan Home Farm, Beauly, "Pride of Aberdeen 18th" (4321),     4 0 0
 V. H. C., William M. Skinner, Drumin, Glenlivet, "Sweetheart 4th" (3985). H. C., The Earl of Southesk, K.T., Kinnaird Castle, Brechin, "Vine 2d of Skene" (3329). C., The Earl of Strathmore, Glamis Castle, Glamis, Forfar, "Bar Bell."

### Section 20. HEIFERS calved on or after 1st December 1878.

1. The Earl of Airlie, K.T., Cortachy Castle, Kirriemuir, "Miranda" (4204),     10 0 0
2. James Reid, Greystone, Alford, Aberdeen, "Bella 2d of Greystone,"     5 0 0
3. George Reid, Baads, Peterculter, Aberdeen, "Isla 3d" (4376),     3 0 0
 V. H. C., Sir George Macpherson Grant, Bart., M.P., "Rose Blossom" (4173). H. C., William M'Combie of Easter Skene, Skene, Aberdeen, "Peggy."

### Section 21. HEIFERS calved on or after 1st December 1879.

1. The Earl of Strathmore, Glamis Castle, Glamis, "Sibyl 4th" (4326),     8 0 0
2. The Earl of Southesk, K.T., Kinnaird Castle, Brechin, "Essence" (4547),     4 0 0
3. William James Tayler, Rothiemay House, Huntly, "Lily o' the Nile" (4576),     2 0 0
 V. H. C., William M'Combie of Easter Skene, Skene, Aberdeen, "Highland Mary." H. C., William M. Skinner, Drumin, Glenlivet, "Sweetheart 5th." C., The Earl of Strathmore, "Fairy 8th."

## GALLOWAY.

### Section 22. BULLS calved before 1st January 1878.

1. The Duke of Buccleuch and Queensberry, K.G., "Stanley" (1348),     20 0 0
2. James Cunningham, Tarbreoch, Dalbeattie, "Knowsley" (1279),     10 0 0
3. Robert Jardine of Castlemilk, M.P., Lockerbie, "Beaconsfield" (1344),     5 0 0
Breeder of Best Bull—The Duke of Buccleuch and Queensberry, K.G. Silver Medal,     0 15 0
 V. H. C., J. Jardine Paterson of Balgray, Lockerbie, "Olden Times" (1369).

### Section 23. BULLS calved on or after 1st January 1879.

1. John Graham of Shaw, Lockerbie, "John Highlandman" (1531),     20 0 0
2. The Duke of Buccleuch and Queensberry, K.G., "Harden 2d" (1458),     10 0 0
3. Frederick E. Villiers, Closeburn Hall, Thornhill, "Prince Victor" (1569),     5 0 0
 V. H. C., James Richardson, Mossburn, Lockerbie, "Diamond" (1584). H. C., W. & J. Shennan, Balig, Kirkcudbright, "Normandy" (1533).

### Section 24. BULLS calved on or after 1st January 1880.

1. Robert Jardine of Castlemilk, M.P., Lockerbie, "Premier of Castlemilk" (1642),     10 0 0
2. W. & J. Shennan, Balig, Kirkcudbright, "Chelmsford" (1568),     5 0 0
3. J. S. & A. Nivison, Lairdlaw, Dalbeattie, "Premier" (1620),     3 0 0
 V. H. C., John Irving & Sons, Isle of Dalton, Lockerbie, "The Banker" (1575).

### Section 25. COWS of any age.

1. The Duke of Buccleuch and Queensberry, K.G., Drumlanrig, Thornhill, "Hannah 4th of Drumlanrig" (2638),     15 0 0
2. The Duke of Buccleuch and Queensberry, K.G., Drumlanrig, Thornhill, "Alice 3d of Drumlanrig" (2986),     8 0 0
3. Robert Jardine of Castlemilk, M.P., Lockerbie, "Jenny Duke" (3842),     4 0 0
 V. H. C., The Duke of Buccleuch and Queensberry, K.G., "Lady Stanley of Drumlanrig" (2858). H. C., Robert Jardine of Castlemilk, M.P., "Miss Rain of Castlemilk" (2896).

### Section 26. HEIFERS calved on or after 1st January 1879.

1. Robert Jardine of Castlemilk, M.P., Lockerbie, "Susan of Balig 8th,"     10 0 0
2. Frederick E. Villiers, Closeburn Hall, Thornhill, "Lady Stanley of Closeburn" (3803),     5 0 0
3. J. Jardine Paterson of Balgray, Lockerbie, "Rosebud" (3971),     3 0 0
 V. H. C., The Duke of Buccleuch and Queensberry, K.G., "Nightingale 2d of Drumlanrig" (3653). H. C., The Duke of Buccleuch and Queensberry, K.G., "Lady Florence of Drumlanrig" (3651). C., The Duke of Buccleuch and Queensberry, K.G., "Fanny 7th of Drumlanrig" (3658). C., Frederick E. Villiers, Closeburn Hall, Thornhill, "Mary of Closeburn" (3804).

|  | Brought forward, | £681 | 4 | 0 |

**SECTION 27. HEIFERS calved on or after 1st January 1880.**

| 1. Robert Jardine of Castlemilk, M.P., Lockerbie, "Lady Nancy 2d " (3981), | 8 | 0 | 0 |
| 2. Frederick E. Villiers, Closeburn Hall, Thornhill, "Sally of Closeburn " (3806), | 4 | 0 | 0 |
| 3. James Cunningham, Tarbreoch, Dalbeattie, "Ranee 2d " (3965), | 2 | 0 | 0 |

V. H. C., The Duke of Buccleuch and Queensberry, "Nundina 3d of Drumlanrig" (3892). H. C., The Duke of Buccleuch and Queensberry, "Hannah 6th of Drumlanrig " (3621). C., Robert Jardine of Castlemilk, M.P., "Lady Marion 3d " (3979).

## HIGHLAND.

**SECTION 28. BULLS calved before 1st January 1878.**

| 1. Duncan M'Diarmid, Camuserricht, Rannoch, "Ailpean," | 20 | 0 | 0 |
| 2. The Duke of Sutherland, K.G., Dunrobin, Golspie, "Gille Dubh," | 10 | 0 | 0 |
| 3. The Duke of Athole, K.T., Blair Castle, Blair Athole, " Oscar 3d," | 5 | 0 | 0 |
| Breeder of Best Bull—The Duke of Athole, K.T., Blair Castle, Blair Athole, Silver Medal, | 0 | 15 | 0 |

V. H. C., The Earl of Seafield, Castle Grant, Grantown, "Rory," H. C., John M'Naughton, Braes of Balquhidder, Lochearnhead, "Gille Ruadh." C., James Duncan, Home Farm, Benmore, Kilmun, "Roderick Dhu."

**SECTION 29. BULLS calved on or after 1st January 1878.**

| 1. John Stewart, Duntulm, Portree, "Fear-a-Bhalla," | 20 | 0 | 0 |
| 2. Peter M'Martin, Leingaustein, Luib, Stirling, "Rob Roy," | 10 | 0 | 0 |
| 3. The Earl of Breadalbane, Taymouth Castle, Aberfeldy, "Fingal," | 5 | 0 | 0 |

V. H. C., John Stewart, Bochastle, Callander, "Cuilean Campbeul." H. C., The Earl of Seafield, Castle Grant, Grantown, "Wallace." C., Alexander M'Donald, Nether Largie, Lochgilphead, "Maroagh O'Brian."

**SECTION 30. BULLS calved on or after 1st January 1879.**

| 1. Duncan Stewart, Monachyle, Lochearnhead, "Gille Dubh," | 10 | 0 | 0 |
| 2. Alexander Macdonald, Balranald, Lochmaddy, "Raahl," | 5 | 0 | 0 |
| 3. The Duke of Athole, K.T., Blair Castle, Blair-Athole, "Tormaid Og," | 3 | 0 | 0 |

V. H. C., Hector Arch. Campbell, Ardfenaig, Bunessan, "Gille Buidhe." H. C., George A. Cox of Invertrossachs, Callander, "Rob Ruadh."

**SECTION 31. COWS of any age.**

| 1. The Duke of Athole, K.T., Blair Castle, Blair-Athole, "Rosie 3d," | 15 | 0 | 0 |
| 2. John Stewart, Bochastle, Callander, "Chaisin Dhuide," | 8 | 0 | 0 |
| 3. John Stewart, Bochastle, Callander, "Froiseag Dhubh," | 4 | 0 | 0 |

V. H. C., The Earl of Seafield, Castle Grant, Grantown, "Bynach." H. C., The Earl of Breadalbane, Taymouth Castle, Aberfeldy, "Mally." C., John Stewart, Bochastle, Callander, " Mairi Og."

**SECTION 32. HEIFERS calved on or after 1st January 1878.**

| 1. John Stewart, Duntulm, Portree, "Guanach," | 10 | 0 | 0 |
| 2. John Stewart, Duntulm, Portree, "Targheal," | 5 | 0 | 0 |
| 3. The Duke of Athole, K.T., Blair Castle, Blair-Athole, "Ribhinn," | 3 | 0 | 0 |

V. H. C., James Duncan, Home Farm, Benmore, Kilmun, "Highland Mary." H. C., The Earl of Breadalbane, Taymouth Castle, Aberfeldy, "Stac Bhuidhe." C., The Duke of Athole, K.T., Blair Castle, Blair-Athole, "Donnag Og."

**SECTION 33. HEIFERS calved on or after 1st January 1879.**

| 1. John Stewart, Bochastle, Callander, "Annag Bhuidhe," | 8 | 0 | 0 |
| 2. The Earl of Breadalbane, Taymouth Castle, Aberfeldy, "Maggie 3d," | 4 | 0 | 0 |
| 3. John Stewart, Duntulm, Portree, "Targheal Riabhach," | 2 | 0 | 0 |

V. H. C., James Duncan, Home Farm, Benmore, Kilmun, "May Queen." H. C., Hector A. Campbell, Ardfenaig, Bunessan, "Kilfinndine Ruach." C., Lord Kinnaird, Rossie Priory, Inchture, "Mairi Malamhin "

## FAT STOCK.

**SECTION 34. HIGHLAND OXEN calved before 1st January 1878.**

| 1. C. S. Home Drummond Moray of Blair-Drummond, Stirling, | 5 | 0 | 0 |
| 2. The Earl of Seafield, Castle Grant, Grantown, "Geordie," | 3 | 0 | 0 |

H. C., The Duke of Sutherland, Dunrobin Mains, Golspie. C., C. S. Home Drummond Moray of Blair Drummond, Stirling.

|  | Carry forward, | £851 | 0 | 0 |

|  |  |  |  |
|---|---|---|---|
| Brought forward, | £851 | 0 | 0 |

SECTION 35. HIGHLAND OXEN calved on or after 1st January 1878.

| 1. C. S. Home Drummond Moray of Blair Drummond, Stirling, | 4 | 0 | 0 |
|---|---|---|---|
| 2. C. S. Home Drummond Moray of Blair Drummond, Stirling, | 2 | 0 | 0 |
| C., The Earl of Seafield, Castle Grant, Grantown, "Donald." | | | |

SECTION 36. POLLED OXEN calved before 1st January 1879.

| 1. William M'Combie, of Easter Skene, Skene, Aberdeen (Polled Aberdeen), | 5 | 0 | 0 |
|---|---|---|---|
| 2. Commander G. D. Clayhills Henderson, R.N., Invergowrie, Dundee (Polled Angus), | 3 | 0 | 0 |
| C., Commander G. D. Clayhills Henderson, R.N., Invergowrie, Dundee (Polled Angus). | | | |

SECTION 37. POLLED OXEN calved on or after 1st January 1879.

| 1. The Earl of Mansfield, K.T., Scone Palace, Perth (Polled Angus), | 4 | 0 | 0 |
|---|---|---|---|
| 2. William M'Combie, of Easter Skene, Skene, Aberdeen (Polled Aberdeen), | 2 | 0 | 0 |

SECTION 38. OXEN of any other Pure or Cross Breed calved before 1st January 1879.

| 1. Lord Balfour of Burleigh, Kennet, Alloa (cross between Ayrshire and Shorthorn), | 5 | 0 | 0 |
|---|---|---|---|

SECTION 39. OXEN of any other Pure or Cross Breed calved on or after 1st January 1879.

| 1. John Law, New Keig, Whitehouse, Aberdeen (cross between Shorthorn and Cross) | 4 | 0 | 0 |
|---|---|---|---|

SECTION 40. CROSS-BRED HEIFERS calved before 1st January 1879.

| 1. James Reid, Greystone, Alford, Aberdeen (cross between Shorthorn and Cross), | 5 | 0 | 0 |
|---|---|---|---|
| 2. Lord Balfour of Burleigh, Kennet, Alloa (cross between Ayrshire and Shorthorn), | 3 | 0 | 0 |

SECTION 41. CROSS-BRED HEIFER, calved on or after 1st January 1879.

| 1. James Bruce, Burnside, Fochabers (cross between Shorthorn and Cross), | 4 | 0 | 0 |
|---|---|---|---|

EXTRA CATTLE.

Very Highly Commended.

| Highland Bull, "Calum Riabhach," Lord Kinnaird, Rossie Priory, Inchture, Medium Gold Medal, | 6 | 2 | 0 |
|---|---|---|---|

Highly Commended.

| Polled Cow, "Princess" (914), Thomas Ferguson, Kinnochtry, Coupar Angus, | 3 | 0 | 0 |
|---|---|---|---|
| Highland Heifer, The Duke of Sutherland, Dunrobin Mains, Golspie, | | | |
| Minor Gold Medal, | 3 | 15 | 0 |

|  |  |  |  |
|---|---|---|---|
| | £904 | 17 | 0 |

CLASS II.—HORSES

FOR AGRICULTURAL PURPOSES.

STALLION TO TRAVEL THE DISTRICT OF THE STIRLING SHOW IN SEASON 1881.

| James Johnston, Lochburnie, Maryhill, "Topsman," | 100 | 0 | 0 |
|---|---|---|---|

SECTION 1. STALLIONS foaled before 1st January 1878.

| 1. David Riddell, Blackhall, Paisley, "Sanquhar," | 35 | 0 | 0 |
|---|---|---|---|
| 2. Allan M'Kay, Crossarthurlie, Barrhead, "Hawkhead," | 25 | 0 | 0 |
| 3. Peter Crawford, Dumgoyack, Strathblane, "The Master," | 15 | 0 | 0 |
| 4. James Houldsworth of Coltness, Wishaw, "Baron Renfrew" (37), | 5 | 0 | 0 |
| Breeder of Best Stallion—D. C. Willson, Dalpoddar, Sanquhar, Silver Medal, | 0 | 16 | 0 |
| V. H. C., Sir Michael R. Shaw Stewart, Bart., Ardgowan, Greenock, "Top-Gallant." H. C., David Riddell, Blackhall, Paisley, "Blantyre." C., Simon Beattie, Preston Hall, Annan, "The Lord Harry." | | | |

SECTION 2. ENTIRE COLTS foaled on or after 1st January 1878.

| 1. Andrew Montgomery, Boreland, Castle Douglas, "Cornwall" (1420) | 25 | 0 | 0 |
|---|---|---|---|
| 2. Andrew M'Dowall, Auchtralure, Stranraer, "Belted Knight" (1305), | 15 | 0 | 0 |

|  |  |  |  |
|---|---|---|---|
| Carry forward, | £220 | 16 | 0 |

| | | | |
|---|---|---|---|
| Brought forward, | £220 | 16 | 0 |
| 3. James Johnston, Lochburnie, Maryhill, "Lord Douglas," | 8 | 0 | 0 |
| 4. Peter Ferguson, Rock Cottage, Renfrew, "Strathleven," | 4 | 0 | 0 |

V. H. C., Peter Crawford, Dumgoyack, Strathblane, "Good Hope." H. C., Alexander Brackenridge, Stevenston Mains, Holytown, "Sir Michael," (1530). C., David Riddell, Blackhall, Paisley, "Royal Stamp."

### SECTION 3. ENTIRE COLTS foaled on or after 1st January 1879.

| | | | |
|---|---|---|---|
| 1. James Park, Dechmont, Cambuslang, "Never Behind." | 15 | 0 | 0 |
| 2. David Riddell, Blackhall, Paisley, "Jacob Wilson," | 10 | 0 | 0 |
| 3. Peter Crawford, Dumgoyack, Strathblane, "Charmer," | 5 | 0 | 0 |
| 4. John M'Master, Culholm Mains, Stranraer, "Victor Chief," | 3 | 0 | 0 |

V. H. C., William Wylie, 33 Princes Street, Perth, "Star o' Gowrie." H. C., Matthew Gilmour, Town of Inchinnan, Paisley, "Sunbeam." C., Peter Crawford, Dumgoyack, Strathblane, "Sir William."

### SECTION 4. ENTIRE COLTS foaled on or after 1st January 1880.

| | | | |
|---|---|---|---|
| 1. Lawrence Drew, Merryton, Hamilton, | 12 | 0 | 0 |
| 2. William Stevenson, Lochgrog, Bishopbriggs, "Lanarkshire Lad," | 8 | 0 | 0 |
| 3. R. & J. Findlay, Springhill, Baillieston, Glasgow, "Springhill Tom," | 4 | 0 | 0 |
| 4. James Johnston, Lochburnie, Maryhill, "Marquis," | 2 | 0 | 0 |

V. H. C., David Riddell, Blackhall, Paisley. H. C., James Gourlie, West Farm, Tollcross, "Look Here." C., James Beattie, Newbie House, Annan, "Blood Royal."

### SECTION 5. MARES (with Foal at foot) foaled before 1st January 1878.

| | | | |
|---|---|---|---|
| 1. John Waddell of Inch, Bathgate, "Evelyn," | 25 | 0 | 0 |
| 2. Lawrence Drew, Merryton, Hamilton, "Queen," | 15 | 0 | 0 |
| 3. Thomas Muirhead, Townhill, Dunfermline, "Jessie," | 8 | 0 | 0 |
| 4. James M'Nab, Glencshil House, Menstrie, "Nelly," | 4 | 0 | 0 |

H. C., The Earl of Mansfield, K.T., Scone Palace, Perth, "Countess."

### SECTION 6. MARES (in Foal) foaled before 1st January 1878.

| | | | |
|---|---|---|---|
| 1. John Waddell of Inch, Bathgate, "Mary Gray," | 20 | 0 | 0 |
| 2. David Riddell, Blackhall, Paisley, "Emma," | 10 | 0 | 0 |
| 3. Andrew M'Dowall, Auchtralure, Stranraer, "May Belle," | 5 | 0 | 0 |
| 4. Sir Michael R. Shaw Stewart, Bart., Ardgowan, Greenock, "Pansy," | 3 | 0 | 0 |

V. H. C., Simon Beattie, Preston Hall, Annan, "Looline." H. C., John Macdonald, Porterfield, Renfrew, "Porterfield Maid." C., William Edmond, Hillhead of Catter, Drymen, "Maggie."

### SECTION 7. FILLIES foaled on or after 1st January 1878.

| | | | |
|---|---|---|---|
| 1. David Cross of Knockdon, Maybole, "Young Hawkie," | 15 | 0 | 0 |
| 2. Alexander Baird of Urie, Stonehaven, "Bonnie Jean," | 8 | 0 | 0 |
| 3. Allan Kirkwood, Killermont, Maryhill, "Flora," | 4 | 0 | 0 |
| 4. Sir Michael R. Shaw Stewart, Bart., Ardgowan, Greenock, "Annot Lyle." | 2 | 0 | 0 |

V. H. C., John Waddell of Inch, Bathgate, "Cherry." H. C., John Howatson, Fullwood, Stewarton, "Young Maggie." C., John Galbraith, Croy Cunningham, Killearn, "Maggie Lauder."

### SECTION 8. FILLIES foaled on or after 1st January 1879.

| | | | |
|---|---|---|---|
| 1. James Picken, Leigh Langside, Craigie, Kilmarnock, "Nancy Lee," | 10 | 0 | 0 |
| 2. Robert Wilson, Mansewran, Kilbarchan, "Jess," | 5 | 0 | 0 |
| 3. Lawrence Drew, Merryton, Hamilton, | 3 | 0 | 0 |
| 4. Thomas Kerr, Whitehill, Sanquhar, "Myrie," | 2 | 0 | 0 |

V. H. C., Robert Hay, 146 Barrack Street, Glasgow, "Susie." H. C., The Earl of Strathmore, Glamis Castle, Glamis, "Eva of Glamis." C., Sir Michael R. Shaw Stewart, Bart., Ardgowan, Greenock, "Leonora." C., William Vivers, Dornoch Town, Annan, "Nancy."

### SECTION 9. FILLIES foaled on or after 1st January 1880.

| | | | |
|---|---|---|---|
| 1 James Brownlee, East Whitburn Farm, Whitburn, | 8 | 0 | 0 |
| 2. John Waddell of Inch, Bathgate, | 4 | 0 | 0 |
| 3. John Waddell of Inch, Bathgate, | 2 | 0 | 0 |

| | | | |
|---|---|---|---|
| Carry forward, | £444 | 16 | 0 |

|  | Brought forward, | £444 | 16 | 0 |

4  James M'Nab, Glenochil House, Menstrie, "Mary," . . . . 1 0 0

V. H. C., Alexander Baird of Urie, Stonehaven, "Nazli." H. C., Walter Park, Hatton, Bishopton, "Bessie." H. C., Sir Michael R. Shaw Stewart, Bart., Ardgowan, Greenock. C., Archibald Russell, Wishaw House, Wishaw, "The Lady of Lyons." C., John Hendry Chapel, Ringford, "Nancy."

SECTION 10.   DRAUGHT GELDINGS foaled before 1st January 1878.

1.  R. Sinclair Scott, Craigievar, Wemyss Bay, "Colin Oig," . . . 8 0 0
2.  Graham Brothers, North Broomage House, Larbert, "Conqueror," . 4 0 0

SECTION 11.   DRAUGHT GELDINGS foaled on or after 1st January 1878.

1.  Robert Wilson, Manswraes, Kilbarchan, "Smiler," . . . 6 0 0
2.  Thomas A. Carrick, East Cambusdrenny, Stirling, "Jamie," . . 3 0 0

## HUNTERS AND ROADSTERS.

SECTION 12.   BROOD MARES (with Foal at foot), suitable for field.

1.  Allan Kirkwood, Carbrans Farm, Cumbernauld, "Jessie," . . . 20 0 0
2.  J. P. M'Bride, M'Alpine Street, Glasgow, "Daisy," . . . . 10 0 0
C.  Robert Smith of Brentham Park, Stirling, "Dolly Varden."

SECTION 13.   MARES or GELDINGS suitable for field, foaled before 1st January 1877.

1.  James Jamieson, 22 Douglas Crescent, Edinburgh, Gelding, "Indian Warrior," . 20 0 0
2.  James Tod, Easter Cash, Strathmiglo, Gelding, "Zulu," . . . 10 0 0
H. C., William Roberts, Auctioneer, Bathgate, Gelding, "The Baron."

SECTION 14.   MARES or GELDINGS suitable for field, foaled on or after 1st January 1877.

1.  Peter Curror, Lenchats Beath, Cowdenbeath, Gelding, "Shamrock," . 20 0 0
2.  James Thom, Leden Urquhart, Strathmiglo, Gelding, "Sunbeam," . 10 0 0
C., R. H. Cowper, Viewfield, Busby, Glasgow, Mare, "Lady Durham."

SECTION 15.   MARES or GELDINGS suitable as hackneys or roadsters, between 14 and 15 hands high.

1.  William Walker, Torbrex Farm, Stirling, Gelding, "Dandy," . . 10 0 0
2.  Patrick Kynoch, M.D., Greenlaw, Berwickshire, Mare, "Hero," . . 5 0 0
C., James Sharp, Viewfield, Blackford, Perthshire, Mare, "Speel."

SECTION 16.   STALLIONS, MARES, or GELDINGS for Leaping.

1.  James Macqueen, Princes Street, Perth, Mare, "May Morn," . . 15 0 0
2.  James Drummond, Blacklaw, Dunfermline, Gelding, "Rutherford," . 10 0 0
3.  James Tod, Easter Cash, Strathmiglo, Gelding, "Zulu," . . . 5 0 0

## EXTRA HORSES.

### Very Highly Commended.

John M. Martin, Auchendennan Farm, Balloch, Cob Pony Stallion, "Mars," . 5 0 0

### Commended.

Alexander Baird of Urie, Stonehaven, Arab Stallion, "Vizier," Silver Medal, . 0 16 0
William Catton Branford, 86 George Street, Edinburgh, Arab and Basuto Stallion, "Moscow Masupha," . . . . . Silver Medal, 0 16 0

## PONIES.

SECTION 17.   HIGHLAND STALLIONS, 14½ hands high and under. No Entry.

SECTION 18.   HIGHLAND MARES or GELDINGS between 13 and 14½ hands high. No Entry.

SECTION 19.   MARES or GELDINGS between 12½ and 14 hands high.

1.  Alexander Crombie, Thornton Castle, Laurencekirk, Gelding, "Sultan," . 4 0 0
2.  John Bowie, Coldoch, Blair Drummond, Stirling, Gelding, "Young Dandy," . 2 0 0
C., G. H. Binning Home of Argaty, Doune, Mare.

|  | Carry forward, | £614 | 8 | 0 |

Brought forward, £614 8 9

#### Section 20. MARES or GELDINGS under 12½ hands high.

1. Alexander Crombie, Thornton Castle, Laurencekirk, Mare, "Midge," . . 4 0 0
2. John Christie of Cowden, Cowden Castle, Dollar, Mare, "May," . . 2 0 0
C., James Stewart, Denovan House, Denny Mare, "Joey."

£620 8 0

## CLASS III.—SHEEP.
### BLACKFACED.

#### Section 1. TUPS, above 1 Shear.

1. David Foyer, Knowehead, Campsie, . . . . . 12 0 0
2. James M'Nab, Glenochil House, Menstrie, . . . 8 0 0
3. John Fleming, Ploughland, Strathaven, . . . . 4 0 0
V. H. C., David Foyer, Knowehead, Campsie.  H. C., The Earl of Stair, K.T., Loch-inch, Stranraer.  C., John Sloan, Barnhill, Patna.

#### Section 2. SHEARLING TUPS.

1. Charles Howatson of Glenbuck, Lanark, . . . . 12 0 0
2. David Foyer, Knowehead, Campsie, . . . . . 8 0 0
3. John Fleming, Ploughland, Strathaven, . . . . 4 0 0
V. H. C., Charles Howatson of Glenbuck, Lanark.  H. C., David Foyer, Knowe-head, Campsie.  C., James Duncan, Home Farm, Benmore, Kilmun.

#### Section 3. Pens of 3 EWES, above 1 Shear, with LAMBS.

1. Charles Howatson of Glenbuck, Lanark, . . . 10 0 0
2. Archibald Orr Ewing of Ballikinrain, M.P., . . . 5 0 0
3. James Duncan, Home Farm, Benmore, Kilmun, . . 2 0 0
V. H. C., Patrick Melrose, West Loch, Eddlestone.  H. C., David Foyer, Knowe-head, Campsie.

#### LAMBS.

1. James Duncan, Home Farm, Benmore, Kilmun, . . 2 0 0
2. Charles Howatson of Glenbuck, Lanark, . . . . 1 0 0
H. C., James Duncan, Blairmore Farm, Greenock.  C., David Foyer, Knowehead, Campsie.

#### Section 4. Pens of 3 SHEARLING EWES or GIMMERS.

1. James Duncan, Home Farm, Benmore, Kilmun, . . 10 0 0
2. Charles Howatson of Glenbuck, Lanark, . . . . 5 0 0
3. The Earl of Stair, K.T., Lochinch, Stranraer, . . 2 0 0
V. H. C., James Duncan, Blairmore Farm, Greenock.  H. C., The Earl of Stair, K.T., Lochinch, Stranraer.  C., David Foyer, Knowehead, Campsie.

#### Section 5. Pens of 1 Aged TUP, 2 EWES, 2 SHEARLINGS, and 2 LAMBS. The Ewes to have Lambs in Season 1881, and all bred by Exhibitor, except Aged Tup.

1. Charles Howatson of Glenbuck, Lanark, . . . 8 0 0
2. David Foyer, Knowehead, Campsie, . . . . . 4 0 0
3. Patrick Melrose, West Loch, Eddlestone, . . . 2 0 0
H. C., Archibald Orr Ewing of Ballikinrain, M.P., Killearn.  C., James Duncan, Blairmore Farm, Greenock.

### CHEVIOT.
#### Section 6. TUPS, above 1 Shear.

1. John A. Johnstone, Archbank, Moffat, . . . . 12 0 0
2. John A. Johnstone, Archbank, Moffat, . . . . 8 0 0
3. John A. Johnstone, Archbank, Moffat, . . . . 4 0 0
H. C., James Brydon, jun., Holm of Dalquhairn, Carsphairn, Galloway.

#### Section 7. SHEARLING TUPS.

1. John A. Johnstone, Archbank, Moffat, . . . . 12 0 0
2. James Brydon, Kinnelhead, Moffat, . . . . . 8 0 0
3. John A. Johnstone, Archbank, Moffat, . . . . 4 0 0
H. C., John A. Johnstone, Archbank, Moffat.

Carry forward, £147 0 0

Brought forward, £147 0 0

### Section 8.　Pens of 3 EWES, above 1 Shear, with LAMBS.

1. James Brydon, Kinnelhead, Moffat, . . . . . 10 0 0

### LAMBS.

1. James Brydon, Kinnelhead, Moffat, . . . . 2 0 0

### Section 9.　Pens of 3 SHEARLING EWES or GIMMERS.

1. Sir G. Graham Montgomery of Stanhope, Bart., Stobo Castle, Stobo, 10 0 0
2. The Duke of Sutherland, K.G., Dunrobin Mains, Golspie, . 5 0 0

### BORDER LEICESTER.

### Section 10.　TUPS, above 1 Shear.

1. Samuel Jack, Mersington, Coldstream, . . . . 12 0 0
2. Arthur J. Balfour of Whittinghame, M.P., Prestonkirk, . 8 0 0
3. Robert Fender, Northfield, Coldingham, . . . 4 0 0
C., James Nisbet of Lambden, Greenlaw.

### Section 11.　SHEARLING TUPS.

1. James Melvin, Bonnington, Wilkieston, . . . . 12 0 0
2. Thomas Clark, Oldhamstocks Mains, Cockburnspath, . . 8 0 0
3. Thomas Clark, Oldhamstocks Mains, Cockburnspath, . . 4 0 0
V.H.C., Andrew Smith, Castlemains, Gifford.　H. C., Arthur James Balfour of
Whittinghame, M.P., Prestonkirk.　H. C., The Earl of Dalhousie, Panmure,
Carnoustie.

### Section 12.　Pens of 3 EWES above 1 Shear.

1. George Simson, Courthill, Kelso, . . . . 10 0 0
2. James Nisbet of Lambden, Greenlaw, . . . . 5 0 0
3. George Simson, Courthill, Kelso, . . . . 2 0 0

### Section 13.　Pens of 3 SHEARLING EWES or GIMMERS.

1. James Melvin, Bonnington, Wilkieston, . . . . 10 0 0
2. Thomas Clark, Oldhamstocks Mains, Cockburnspath, . . 5 0 0
3. Robert Kay, Linton Bankhead, Kelso, . . . . 2 0 0
C., The Earl of Dalhousie, Panmure, Carnoustie.　C., George Simson, Courthill,
Kelso.

### LEICESTER.

### Section 14.　TUPS above 1 Shear.
No Entry.

### Section 15.　SHEARLING TUPS.
No Entry.

### Section 16.　Pens of 3 EWES above 1 Shear.
No Entry.

### Section 17.　Pens of 3 SHEARLING EWES or GIMMERS.
No Entry.

### COTSWOLD AND LINCOLN.

### Section 18.　TUPS above 1 Shear.

1. Francis Gibson, Woolmet, Dalkeith, (Cotswold), . . 3 0 0

### Section 19.　SHEARLING TUPS.

1. Francis Gibson, Woolmet, Dalkeith (Cotswold), . . 3 0 0
2. Francis Gibson, Woolmet, Dalkeith (Cotswold), . . 2 0 0
3. Francis Gibson, Woolmet, Dalkeith (Cotswold), . . 1 0 0

### Section 20.　Pens of 3 EWES above 1 Shear.

1. Francis Gibson, Woolmet, Dalkeith (Cotswold), . . 3 0 0

### Section 21.　Pen of 3 SHEARLING EWES or GIMMERS—Not forward.

Carry forward, £368 0 0

Brought forward,   £268   0   0

## SHORT WOOLLED.

### Section 22.  TUPS above 1 Shear.

1. The Earl of Strathmore, Glamis Castle, Glamis (Shropshire),   .   .   .   3   0   0
2. The Earl of Mansfield, K.T., Scone Palace, Perth (Shropshire),   .   .   .   2   0   0
3. Francis Gibson, Woolmet, Dalkeith (Shropshire)   .   .   .   1   0   0
H. C., Lord Polwarth, Humbie, Upper Keith, (Shropshire),

### Section 23.  SHEARLING TUPS.

1. The Earl of Strathmore, Glamis Castle, Glamis (Shropshire),   .   .   .   3   0   0
2. Francis Gibson, Woolmet, Dalkeith (Shropshire),   .   .   .   2   0   0
3. Francis Gibson, Woolmet, Dalkeith (Shropshire),   .   .   .   1   0   0
V. H. C, The Earl of Strathmore, Glamis Castle, Glamis (Shropshire).  H. C.,
Francis Gibson, Woolmet, Dalkeith (Shropshire).  C., David Buttar, Corston,
Coupar Angus (Shropshire).

### Section 24.  Pens of 3 EWES above 1 Shear.

1. Francis Gibson, Woolmet, Dalkeith (Shropshire),   .   .   .   3   0   0
2. Francis Gibson, Woolmet, Dalkeith (Shropshire),   .   .   .   2   0   0
3. The Earl of Mansfield, K.T., Scone Palace, Perth (Shropshire),   .   .   .   1   0   0

### Section 25.  Pens of 3 SHEARLING EWES or GIMMERS.

1. Francis Gibson, Woolmet, Dalkeith (Shropshire),   .   .   .   3   0   0
2. Francis Gibson, Woolmet, Dalkeith (Shropshire)   .   .   .   2   0   0
3. David Buttar, Corston, Coupar Angus (Shropshire),   .   .   .   1   0   0

### EXTRA SECTIONS.

### Section 26.  Pen of 5 BLACKFACED WETHERS, not above 4 Shear.

1. The Earl of Mansfield, K.T., Scone Palace, Perth,   .   .   .   4   0   0

### Section 27.  Pen of 5 CHEVIOT Wethers, not above 3 Shear.

1. The Duke of Sutherland, K.G., Dunrobin Mains, Golspie,   .   .   4   0   0

### Section 28.  Pen of 5 HALF-BRED WETHERS not above 1 Shear.
No Entry.

### Section 29.  Pens of 5 CROSS-BRED WETHERS, not above 1 Shear.

1. John M'Dougall, Goodlyburn, Perth,   .   .   .   .   4   0   0
2. John M'Dougall, Goodlyburn, Perth,   .   .   .   .   2   0   0

£306   0   0

## CLASS IV.—WOOL.

### Section 1  Best WOOLED TUP, Blackfaced Breed.

1. Charles Howatson of Glenbuck, Lanark,   .   .   .   3   0   0
2. David Foyer, Knowehead, Campsie,   .   .   .   2   0   0
H. C., James M'Nab, Glonochil House, Menstrie.  C., John Fleming, Ploughland,
Strathaven.

### Section 2.  Best WOOLED TUP, Cheviot Breed.

1. James Brydon, Kinnelhead, Moffat,   .   .   .   .   3   0   0
2. John A. Johnstone, Archbank, Moffat,   .   .   .   2   0   0

### Section 3.  Best WOOLED TUP, Leicester Breed.

1. James Melvin, Bonnington, Wilkieston,   .   .   .   3   0   0
2. William Wilson, Wolfstar, Ormiston,   .   .   .   2   0   0

£15   0   0

## CLASS V.—SWINE.

### LARGE BREED.

### Section 1  BOARS.—No Entry.

Section 2.  SOWS.

1.  The Earl of Mansfield, K.T., Scone Palace, Perth, . . . 5 0 0
2.  John M. Martin, Auchendennan Farm, Balloch, . . . 3 0 0

Section 3.  Pen of 3 PIGS, not above 8 months old.—No Entry.

### BLACK or BERKSHIRE.

Section 4.  BOARS.

1.  R. T. N. Spier of Culdees, Muthill, . . . . 5 0 0
2.  Sir William Forbes, Bart., Fintray House, Aberdeen, . . 3 0 0
3.  James Duncan, Home Farm, Benmore, Kilmun, . . 1 0 0
H. C., F. G. Forsyth Grant of Ecclesgreig, Montrose.

Section 5.  SOWS.

1.  James Duncan, Home Farm, Benmore, Kilmun, . . . 5 0 0
2.  Lord Clermont, Ravensdale Park, Newry, Ireland, . . 3 0 0
3.  Archibald Campbell Douglas of Mains, Milngavie, . . 1 0 0
H. C., Lord Clermont, Ravensdale Park, Newry, Ireland.

Section 6.  Pen of 3 PIGS, not above 8 months old.

1.  Archibald Campbell Douglas of Mains, Milngavie, . . 4 0 0

### SMALL BREED.

Section 7.  BOARS.—Not forward.

Section 8.  SOWS.

1.  Robert Philp, Royal Hotel, Bridge of Allan, . . . 5 0 0
2.  James Duncan, Home Farm, Benmore, Kilmun, . . 3 0 0
3.  James Duncan, Home Farm, Benmore, Kilmun, . . 1 0 0

Section 9.  Pen of 3 PIGS, not above 8 months old.—Not forward.

£30 0 0

### CLASS VI.—COLLIE DOGS.

Section 1.  Long-haired DOG, not above 6 Years old.

1.  Colin D. Nairn, 37 Earl Grey Street, Edinburgh, "Halla," . 3 0 0
2.  Thomas Pearson, Falkirk, "Rab," . . . . 2 0 0
3.  William Edmond, Fillhead of Cattor, Drymen, "Clyde," . 1 0 0
V. H. C., John Fleming, Ploughland, Strathaven, "Clyde." C., James Cullens,
    Cambusbarron, Stirling, "Rover"

Section 2.  Long-haired BITCH, not above 6 Years old.

1.  Colin D. Nairn, 37 Earl Grey Street, Edinburgh, "Flash," . 3 0 0
2.  James Chalmers, Rough Crook, Carnwath, "Tib," . . 2 0 0
3.  John Stewart, Home Farm, Ballindalloch, "Jip," . . 1 0 0
C., John Warner, Station Hotel, Forres, "Glen."

Section 3.  Short haired DOG, not above 6 Years old.—No Entry.

Section 4.  Short haired BITCH, not above 6 Years old.

1  John Drysdale, Aitkenhead, Clackmannan, "Colley," . . 3 0 0

£15 0 0

### CLASS VII.—POULTRY.

DORKING, Silver Grey.  Cock.—1. James Cranston, Holestane, Thornhill, . £1 0 0
                              2. James Cranston, Holestane, Thornhill, . 0 10 0
DORKING, Silver Grey.  2 Hens.—1. James Cranston, Holestane, Thornhill, 1 0 0
                              2. Alex. M'Ara, Culdees, Muthill, . 0 10 0
DORKING, Silver Grey.  Cockerel.—1. Alexander M'Ara, Culdees, Muthill, . 1 0 0
                              2. Captain J. W. M'Dougall, Orchill, Braco, Perthshire, 0 10 0

Carry forward,   £4 10 0

|  |  | £ | s | d |
|---|---|---|---|---|
| Brought forward, |  | £4 | 10 | 0 |

**DORKING, Silver Grey. 2 Pullets.**—1. Admiral Maitland Dougall of Scotscraig,
Tayport, · · · · · · 1 0 0
2. Alexander M'Ara, Culdoes, Muthill, · · · 0 10 0

**DORKING, Cold. Cock.**—1. James Cranston, Holestane, Thornhill, · · 1 0 0
2. Thomas Raines, Bridge Haugh, Stirling, · · 0 10 0

**DORKING, Cold. 2 Hens.**—1. James Cranston, Holestane, Thornhill, · · 1 0 0
2. David Ballingall, Blair Drummond, Stirling, · 0 10 0

**DORKING, Cold. Cockerel.**—1. Thomas Raines, Bridge Haugh, Stirling, · 1 0 0
2. Captain J. W. M'Dougall, Orchill, Braco, Perth-
shire, · · · · · · · 0 10 0

**DORKING, Cold. 2 Pullets.**—1. Sir George Macpherson Grant, Bart., M.P., The
Castle, Ballindalloch, · · · · 1 0 0
2. Captain J. W. M'Dougall, Orchill, Braco, Perthshire, · · · · · · 0 10 0

**COCHIN-CHINA. Cock.**—1. Fred. G. Forsyth Grant of Ecclesgreig, Montrose, 1 0 0
2. Fred. G. Forsyth Grant of Ecclesgreig, Montrose, · 0 10 0

**COCHIN-CHINA. 2 Hens.**—1. James Stout, 68 North Church Street, Dundee, · 1 0 0
2. Fred. G. Forsyth Grant of Ecclesgreig, Montrose, · 0 10 0

**COCHIN-CHINA. Cockerel.**—1. William Street, Burgh Muir, Stirling, · · 1 0 0
2. G. B. MacLeod, Polquhirter Cottage, New Cum-
nock, · · · · · · 0 10 0

**COCHIN-CHINA. 2 Pullets.**—1. Fred. G. Forsyth Grant of Ecclesgreig, Montrose, 1 0 0
2. William Street, Burgh Muir, Stirling, · · 0 10 0

**BRAHMAPOOTRA. Cock.**—1. William Nicoll, 148 Scotringburn, Dundee, · 1 0 0
2. Thomas Raines, Bridge Haugh, Stirling, · · 0 10 0

**BRAHMAPOOTRA. 2 Hens.**—1. Thomas Raines, Bridge Haugh, Stirling, · 1 0 0
2. Andrew Warwick, Outer Woodhead, Canonbie, · 0 10 0

**BRAHMAPOOTRA. Cockerel.**—1. William H. Benvie, 21 King Street, Dundee, · 1 0 0
2. Thomas Raines, Bridge Haugh, Stirling, · · 0 10 0

**BRAHMAPOOTRA. 2 Pullets.**—1. William Nicoll, 148 Scouringburn, Dundee, · 1 0 0
2. T. & J. M'Arthur, 64 Stirling Street, Alva, · 0 10 0

**SPANISH. Cock.**—1. G. B. MacLeod, Polquhirter Cottage, New Cumnock, · 1 0 0
2. Thomas Martin, Muiryhill, Thornhill, · · 0 10 0

**SPANISH. 2 Hens.**—1. William Street, Burgh Muir, Stirling, · · 1 0 0
2. James Norval, Hawkhill, Alloa, · · · 0 10 0

**SPANISH. Cockerel.**—1. William Street, Burgh Muir, Stirling, · · 1 0 0

**SPANISH. 2 Pullets.**—No award.

**SCOTCH GREY. Cock.**—1. William Pettigrew, jun., Blackhall, Shotts, · 1 0 0
2. William Pettigrew, jun., Blackhall, Shotts, · 0 10 0

**SCOTCH GREY. 2 Hens.**—1. James Chalmers, Rough Crook, Carnwath, · 1 0 0
2. William Pettigrew, jun., Blackhall, Shotts, · 0 10 0

**SCOTCH GREY. Cockerel.**—1. James Chalmers, Rough Crook, Carnwath, · 1 0 0
2. Robert Meiklejohn, Craigmill, Stirling, · · 0 10 0

**SCOTCH GREY. 2 Pullets.**—1. James Chalmers, Rough Crook, Carnwath, · 1 0 0
2. William G. M'Dougall, George Street, Stirling, · 0 10 0

**HAMBURG, Pencilled Cock.**—1. James Inglis, Kettle Bridge, Kettle, · 1 0 0
2. Andrew Mitchell, East Kerse Mains, Bo'ness, · 0 10 0

**HAMBURG, Pencilled. 2 Hens.**—1. Andrew Mitchell, East Kerse Mains, Bo'ness, 1 0 0
2. Andrew Warwick, Outer Woodhead, Canonbie, · 0 10 0

**HAMBURG, Pencilled. Cockerel.**—1. No award.
2. Andrew Warwick, Outerwoodhead, Canonbie, · 0 10 0

**HAMBURG, Pencilled. 2 Pullets.**—No award.

**HAMBURG, Spangled Cock.**—1. Andrew Warwick, Outer Woodhead, Canonbie, · 1 0 0
2. Miss Mary Mitchell, East Kerse Mains, Bo'ness, · 0 10 0

|  |  | £ | s | d |
|---|---|---|---|---|
| Carry forward, |  | £19 | 0 | 0 |

|  |  | £ | s | d |
|---|---|---|---|---|
| | Brought forward, | 39 | 0 | 0 |
| HAMBURG, Spangled. 2 Hens.—1. Mrs M. Keddie, Cowdenbeath, | | 1 | 0 | 0 |
| 2. Andrew Warwick, Outer Woodhead, Canonbie, | | 0 | 10 | 0 |
| HAMBURG, Spangled. Cockerel.—1. Captain J. W. M'Dougall, Orchill, Braco, Perthshire, | | 1 | 0 | 0 |
| 2. Andrew Warwick, Outer Woodhead, Canonbie, | | 0 | 10 | 0 |
| HAMBURG, Spangled. 2 Pullets.—1. John Morrison, Ochil Vale Cottage, Ochil Street, Alloa, | | 1 | 0 | 0 |
| 2. Captain J.W. M'Dougall, Orchill, Braco, Perthshire, | | 0 | 10 | 0 |
| POULTRY—Any other Pure Breed. Cock.—1. Robert Christie, 53 Cowane Street, Stirling (Creve Cœur), | | 1 | 0 | 0 |
| 2. Thomas Thomson, James Street, Cellardyke, (Polish), | | 0 | 10 | 0 |
| POULTRY—Any other Pure Breed. 2 Hens.—1. Andrew Warwick, Outer Woodhead, Canonbie (Black Hamburg), | | 1 | 0 | 0 |
| 2. The Earl of Mansfield, K.T., Scone Palace, Perth (White Dorking), | | 0 | 10 | 0 |
| POULTRY—Any other Pure Breed. Cockerel.—1. Thomas Fullarton, Loans, Troon (Creve), | | 1 | 0 | 0 |
| 2. The Earl of Mansfield, K.T., Scone Palace, Perth (White Dorking), | | 0 | 10 | 0 |
| POULTRY—Any other Pure Breed. 2 Pullets.—1. Thomas Fullarton, Loans, Troon (Creve), | | 1 | 0 | 0 |
| 2. The Earl of Mansfield, K.T., Scone Palace, Perth (White Dorking), | | 0 | 10 | 0 |
| GAME—Black or Brown Reds. Cock.—1. James Falconer, St. Ann's, Lasswade, | | 1 | 0 | 0 |
| 2. Thomas Raines, Bridge Haugh, Stirling, | | 0 | 10 | 0 |
| GAME—Black or Brown Reds. 1 Hen.—1. D. Harley, Hillwood, Ratho, | | 1 | 0 | 0 |
| 2. James Falconer, St Ann's, Lasswade, | | 0 | 10 | 0 |
| GAME—Black or Brown Reds. Cockerel.—1. T. & J. M'Arthur, 64 Stirling Street, Alva, | | 1 | 0 | 0 |
| 2. J. & C. Sneddon, Hillwood Cottages, Ratho, | | 0 | 10 | 0 |
| GAME—Black or Brown Reds. 1 Pullet.—1. James Falconer, St. Ann's, Lasswade, | | 1 | 0 | 0 |
| 2. D. Harley, Hillwood, Ratho, | | 0 | 10 | 0 |
| GAME—Any other Pure Breed. Cock.—1. James Falconer, St Ann's, Lasswade (Duckwing), | | 1 | 0 | 0 |
| 2. D. Harley, Hillwood, Ratho (Duckwing), | | 0 | 10 | 0 |
| GAME—Any other Pure Breed. 1 Hen.—1. D. Harley, Hillwood, Ratho (Duckwing), | | 1 | 0 | 0 |
| 2. James Falconer, St. Ann's, Lasswade (Pile), | | 0 | 10 | 0 |
| GAME—Any other Pure Breed. Cockerel.—1. D. Harley, Hillwood, Ratho (Duckwing), | | 1 | 0 | 0 |
| 2. James Falconer, St Ann's, Lasswade (Pile), | | 0 | 10 | 0 |
| GAME—Any other Pure Breed. 1 Pullet.—1. James Hall, Back Street, Leslie, Fife (Pile), | | 1 | 0 | 0 |
| 2. James Falconer, St. Ann's, Lasswade (Pile), | | 0 | 10 | 0 |
| BANTAMS—Game. Cock.—1. James Falconer, St. Ann's, Lasswade, | | 1 | 0 | 0 |
| 2. Miss Jane M. Frew, Kirkcaldy. | | 0 | 10 | 0 |
| BANTAMS—Game. 1 Hen.—1. James Falconer, St. Ann's, Lasswade, | | 1 | 0 | 0 |
| 2. Donald N. Taylor, 25 Strong Street, Forfar, | | 0 | 10 | 0 |
| BANTAMS—Game. Cockerel.—1. T. & J. M'Arthur, 64 Stirling Street, Alva, | | 1 | 0 | 0 |
| 2. D. Harley, Hillwood, Ratho, | | 0 | 10 | 0 |
| BANTAMS—Game. 1 Pullet.—1. D. Harley, Hillwood, Ratho, | | 1 | 0 | 0 |
| 2. T. & J. M'Arthur, 64 Stirling Street, Alva, | | 0 | 10 | 0 |
| BANTAMS—Sebright. Cock.—1. J. A. Dempster, 6 Albert Place, Stirling, | | 1 | 0 | 0 |
| 2. Miss Robina Frew, Kirkcaldy, | | 0 | 10 | 0 |
| BANTAMS—Sebright. 2 Hens.—1. J. A. Dempster, 6 Albert Place, Stirling, | | 1 | 0 | 0 |
| 2. Mrs Frew, Kirkcaldy, | | 0 | 10 | 0 |
| | Carry forward, | 70 | 10 | 0 |

Brought forward,    £70 10 0

BANTAMS—Sebright. Cockerel.—No Entry.

BANTAMS—Sebright. 2 Pullets.—No Entry.

BANTAMS—Any other Pure Breed. Cock.—1. Fred. G. Forsyth Grant of Ecclesgreig, Montrose (Black),    1 0 0
2. J. D. Donald, 48 King Street, Montrose,    0 10 0

BANTAMS—Any other Pure Breed. 2 Hens.—1. Miss Bessie P. Frew, Kirkcaldy (Booted),    1 0 0
2. J. D. Donald, 48 King Street, Montrose (Black),    0 10 0

BANTAMS—Any other Pure Breed. Cockerel.—1.—No Award.
2. Miss Robina Frew, Kirkcaldy (Booted),    0 10 0

BANTAMS—Any other Pure Breed. 2 Pullets.—No Entry.

DUCKS—White Aylesbury. Drake.—1. John Grierson, Edgerston Smithy, Jedburgh,    1 0 0
2. D. Harley, Hillwood, Ratho,    0 10 0

DUCKS—White Aylesbury. 1 Duck.—1. William H. Glass, St. John's Lane, Hamilton,    1 0 0
2. John Grierson, Edgerston Smithy, Jedburgh,    0 10 0

DUCKS—White Aylesbury. Drake (Young).—1. D. Harley, Hillwood, Ratho,    1 0 0
2. Hon. George Waldegrave Leslie, Leslie House, Leslie,    0 10 0

DUCKS—White Aylesbury. 1 Duckling.—1. D. Harley, Hillwood, Ratho,    1 0 0
2. Hon. George Waldegrave Leslie, Leslie House, Leslie,    0 10 0

DUCKS—Rouen. Drake.—1. Admiral Maitland Dougall of Scotscraig, Tayport,    1 0 0
2. Alexander M'Ara, Culdees, Muthill,    0 10 0

DUCKS—Rouen. 1 Duck.—1. Admiral Maitland Dougall of Scotscraig, Tayport,    1 0 0
2. William H. Glass, St John's Lane, Hamilton,    0 10 0

DUCKS—Rouen. Drake (Young).—1. Admiral Maitland Dougall of Scotscraig, Tayport,    1 0 0
2. William Hart, Pothill, Auchterarder,    0 10 0

DUCKS—Rouen. 1 Duckling.—1. Admiral Maitland Dougall of Scotscraig, Tayport,    1 0 0
2. The Earl of Mansfield, K.T., Scone Palace, Perth,    0 10 0

DUCKS—Any other Pure Breed. Drake.—1. Thomas Martin, Muiryhill, Thornhill (Pekin),    1 0 0
2. Andrew Warwick, Outer Woodhead, Canonbie (Pekin),    0 10 0

DUCKS—Any other Pure Breed. 1 Duck.—1. Thomas Martin, Muiryhill, Thornhill (Pekin),    1 0 0
2. Andrew Warwick, Outer Woodhead, Canonbie (Pekin),    0 10 0

DUCKS—Any other Pure Breed. Drake (Young).—No Entry.

DUCKS—Any other Pure Breed. 1 Duckling.—No Entry.

TURKEYS—Any Pure Breed. Cock.—1. David Wilson, Riccarton, Linlithgow (Norfolk),    1 0 0
2. Admiral Maitland Dougall of Scotscraig, Tayport, Fife, (Black Norfolk),    0 10 0

TURKEYS—Any Pure Breed. 1 Hen.—1. Admiral Maitland Dougall of Scotscraig, Tayport, Fife (Black Norfolk),    1 0 0
2. Simon Beattie, Preston Hall, Annan (Bronze),    0 10 0

TURKEYS—Any Pure Breed. Cock (Poult).—No Entry.

TURKEYS—Any Pure Breed. 1 Hen (Poult).—No Entry.

GEESE—Any Pure Breed. Gander.—1. The Earl of Mansfield, K.T., Scone Palace, Perth (Toulouse),    1 0 0
2. Fred. G. Forsyth Grant of Ecclesgreig, Montrose (Toulouse),    0 10 0

Carry forward,    £98 10 0

| | | |
|---|---|---|
| Brought forward, | £93 10 0 |

GEESE—Any Pure Breed. 1 Goose.—1. Andrew Warwick, Outer Woodhead,
Canonbie (Toulouse), . . . . . 1 0 0
 2. Fred. G. Forsyth Grant of Ecclesgreig, Montrose
(Toulouse), . . . . 0 10 0

GEESE—Any Pure Breed. Gander (Young).—1. James Duncan of Benmore,
Kilmun (Toulouse), . . . . 1 0 0
 2. Andrew Warwick, Outer Woodhead, Canonbie (Embden), 0 10 0

GEESE—Any Pure Breed. 1 Gosling.—1. Andrew Warwick, Outer Woodhead,
Canonbie (Embden), . . . 1 0 0
 2. James Duncan of Benmore, Kilmun (Toulouse), . 0 10 0

£94 0 0

### VIII.—IMPLEMENTS.

J. D. Allan & Sons, Culthill, Dunkeld, for Potato Digger, . . . . 15 0 0
William Dewar, Strathmartin, Dundee, for Potato Digger, . . . 10 0 0
John Wallace & Sons, 7 Graham Square, Glasgow, for Potato Digger, . 5 0 0
Benjamin Reid & Co., Aberdeen, for Manure Distributor, . . . 10 0 0
Shaw & Williamson, 130 Pleasance, Edinburgh, for Manure Distributor, . 5 0 0
Thomas Hunter, Maybole, for Turnip Lifter, . . . . 12 10 0
G. W. Murray & Co., Banff, for Turnip Lifter, . . . 12 10 0

£70 0 0

### CALEDONIAN APIARIAN SOCIETY.

Grant to, for 1881, . . . . . . . £20 0 0
David Wood, Benmore—Observatory Hive, . . . Silver Medal, 0 10 0
W. W. Young, Perth, Bee-Driving, . . . . Silver Medal, 0 10 0

£21 12 0

### ABSTRACT OF PREMIUMS.

Cattle, . . . . . . . . £904 17 0
Horses, . . . . . . . . 620 8 0
Sheep, . . . . . . . . 308 0 0
Wool, . . . . . . . . 15 0 0
Swine, . . . . . . . . 30 0 0
Collie Dogs, . . . . . . . 15 0 0
Poultry, . . . . . . . . 98 0 0
Implements, . . . . . . . 70 0 0
Caledonian Apiarian Society, . . . . . 21 12 0

£2089 17 0

### LIST OF JUDGES.

SHORTHORN.—John Cran, Kirkton, Inverness; H. Chandos Pole Gell, Hopton Hall, Wirksworth; John Wood, 8 The Crescent, Ripon.

AYRSHIRE.—Andrew Allan, Munnoch, Dalry, Ayr; George Crawford, High Knoweglass, East Kilbride; James Hamilton, Woolfords, Carnwath.

POLLED ANGUS OR ABERDEEN.—John Grant, Advie Mains, Strathspey; William Smith, Stone O'Morphie, Montrose; William Whyte, Spott, Kirriemuir.

GALLOWAY.—Maxwell Clark of Culmain, Crocketford, Dumfries; James Little, Fauld, Longtown.

HIGHLAND.—James J. Robertson, Kinloch, Morven, Oban; Peter Robertson, Achlity, Dingwall.

FAT STOCK.—Andrew Ralston, Glamis House, Glamis; Charles Smith, Whittinghame, Prestonkirk; Peter Eden, Cross Lane, Salford.

DRAUGHT STALLIONS AND ENTIRE COLTS.—Peter Anderson, Back Fey, Sorbie, Wigtownshire; James Weir, Sandilands, Lanark; Archibald Yuill, Netherside, Strathaven.

DRAUGHT MARES, FILLIES, AND GELDINGS.—William Brock, Barns of Clyde, Yoker; James Cunningham, Tarbreoch, Dalbeattie; John Thomson, Baillieknowe, Kelso.

HUNTERS, ROADSTERS, PONIES, AND EXTRA HORSES.—James Forrest, Port-Dundas, Glasgow; James Hope, Duddingstone, Edinburgh.

BLACKFACED.—P. M. Conacher, Gallin Cottage, Aberfeldy; Duncan M'Diarmid, Camuserioht, Rannoch; John Willison, junior, Acharn, Killin.

CHEVIOT.—David Hardie, Priesthaugh, Hawick; John Miller, Downreay, Thurso; John Robson, Newton, Bellingham, Northumberland.

BORDER LEICESTER.—William Ford, Fenton Barns, Drem; William Purves, Thurdistoft, Thurso; John Usher, Stodrig, Kelso.

LEICESTER, COTSWOLD, AND LINCOLN.—George Torrance, Sisterpath, Dunse; Robert C. Yeoman, Marsk Hall, Marske-by-the-Sea.

SHORT-WOOLLED.—John R. Evans, Uffington, Shrewsbury; T. J. Mansell, Dudmaston Lodge, Bridgnorth, Salop.

WOOL.—The Judges of the various Classes of Sheep.

SWINE.—Peter Eden, Crow Lane, Salford, and the Judges of Fat Stock.

COLLIE DOGS.—David Hardie, Priesthaugh, Hawick.

POULTRY.—Richard Teebay, Fulwood, Preston.

## LIST OF ATTENDING MEMBERS.

SHORTHORN.—Earl of Mar and Kellie, Alloa Park, Alloa; Alexander Young, Keir Mains, Dunblane.

AYRSHIRE.—Capt. Patrick Stirling, yr. of Kippendavie, Dunblane; Peter Sharp, Bardrill, Blackford.

POLLED ANGUS OR ABERDEEN.—J. M. Martin, yr. of Auchendennan, Bloomhill, Cardross; Charles Carrick, Baad, Stirling.

GALLOWAY.—Archd. Campbell Douglas of Mains, Milngavie; Bailie Watt, Stirling.

HIGHLAND.—J. B. B. Baillie Hamilton of Arnprior, Cambusmore, Callander; James Maclachlan, Doune Lodge, Stirling.

FAT STOCK AND SWINE.—A. J. Dennistoun Brown of Balloch, Balloch Castle, Dumbarton; Donald Fisher, Jellyholm, Alloa.

DRAUGHT STALLIONS AND ENTIRE COLTS.—William Forbes of Callendar, Falkirk; James A. Fernie, Hilton, Alloa.

DRAUGHT MARES, FILLIES, AND GELDINGS.—Colonel D. R. Williamson of Lawers, Crieff; James Kennedy of Sundaywell, Brandleys, Sanquhar.

HUNTERS, ROADSTERS, PONIES, AND EXTRA HORSES.—James Blackburn, Killearn House, Glasgow; William Stirling Young, Keir Mains, Dunblane.

BLACKFACED.—C. H. H. Wilsone, of Dalnair, Endrick Bank, Drymen; Peter M'Caull, Dykedale, Dunblane.

CHEVIOT SHEEP AND COLLIE DOGS.—J. G. Urquhart of Vallore, Linlithgow; James Jardine, Kilmun, Fintry.

BORDER LEICESTER.—Sir James H. Gibson Craig of Riccarton, Bart., Currie; William Allan, Park, Clackmannan.

LEICESTER, COTSWOLD, AND LINCOLN.—William Stirling of Tarduf, Linlithgow; James Murray, Catter House, Drymen.

SHORT-WOOLLED.—Colonel John S. Stirling of Gargunnock, Stirling; D. Ballingall, Blairdrummond, Stirling.

POULTRY.—W. Burt-Wright of Auchenvole, Croy; Bailie Davis, Stirling.

---

## III.—DISTRICT COMPETITIONS.

### CATTLE

| NAME OF DIST. | PREMIUM AWARDED TO | FOR | | AMOUNT. |
|---|---|---|---|---|
| *Turriff* | Walter Scott, Glendronach | Shorthorn Bull | Silver Medal | 0 15 0 |
| | Walter Scott, Glendronach | do. | Class I.* £4 & Med. Sil. Med. | 4 10 6 |
| | A. F. Nares, Brucktor | do. | do. | 3 0 0 |
| | John Milne, Mains of Leithers | do. | do. | 1 0 0 |
| | Alexr. Scott, Towie Barclay | do. | Class II.† £3 & Med. Sil. Med. | 3 10 6 |
| | Walter Scott, Glendronach | do. | do. | 2 0 0 |
| | Mrs Milne of Ardmiddle | do. | do. | 1 0 0 |
| | Miss Cruickshank, Monthlettom | Polled Heifer | £3 & Med. Sil. Med. | 3 10 6 |
| | John Craighead, Thomaston | do. | | 2 0 0 |
| | Garden Duff of Hatton | do. | | 1 0 0 |

Carry forward, £22 9 0

\* Aged Bulls.     † Two-year-old Bulls.

c

| NAME OF DIST. | PREMIUM AWARDED TO | FOR | | AMOUNT. | | |
|---|---|---|---|---|---|---|
| | | | Brought forward, | £29 | 9 | 0 |
| *Avondale* | Thomas Tennant, Strathaven | Ayrshire Bull | Silver Medal | 0 | 10 | 0 |
| | Thomas Tennant, Strathaven | do. | Class I. £2 & Med. Sil. Med. | 2 | 10 | 6* |
| | J. A. Hamilton, Whitehawgate | do. | do. | 1 | 10 | 0* |
| | John M'Millan, Bent | do. | do. | 0 | 10 | 0* |
| | A. Hoggan, jun., Busby | do. | Class II.‡ £3 & Med. Sil. Med. | 3 | 10 | 6 |
| | J. A. Hamilton, Whitehawgate | do. | do. | 2 | 0 | 0 |
| | Robert Allan, Whitehill | do. | do. | 1 | 0 | 0 |
| | John Steel, Waterhead | Ayrshire Heifer | £3 & Med. Sil. Med. | 3 | 10 | 6 |
| | A. Hoggan, jun., Busby | do. | | 2 | 0 | 0 |
| | Alex. Taylor, Netherholm | do. | | 1 | 0 | 0 |
| *Weem* | W. G. Steuart Menzies of Cul- dares | Ayrshire Bull | Silver Medal | 0 | 16 | 0 |
| *Deeside* | Lewis Strachan, Cluny | Shorthorn Bull Class II. £3 & Med. Sil. Med. | | 3 | 10 | 6 |
| | John Davidson, North Leys | do. | do. | 2 | 0 | 0 |
| | John Shepherd, Tersetts | do. | do. | 1 | 0 | 0 |
| | George Reid, Badds | Polled Heifer | £3 & Med. Sil. Med. | 3 | 10 | 6 |
| | J. W. Barclay, M.P., Auchlossan | do. | | 2 | 0 | 0 |
| | J. W. Barclay, M.P., Auchlossan | do. | | 1 | 0 | 0 |
| *Lorn* | D. & J. MacGregor, Ardconnel | Highland Bull Class I. £4 & Med. Sil. Med. | | 4 | 10 | 6 |
| | John M'Innes, Achnaba | do. | do. | 3 | 0 | 0 |
| | John Brown, Dalnacabaig | do. | do. | 1 | 0 | 0 |
| | Duncan M'Callum, Clenmackrie | do. | Class II. £3 & Med. Sil. Med. | 3 | 10 | 6 |
| | Chas. M'Lean, Pennyfuir | do. | do. | 2 | 0 | 0 |
| | Duncan M'Callum, Clenmackrie | do. | do. | 1 | 0 | 0 |
| | Duncan M'Callum, Clenmackrie | Highland Heifer | £3 & Med. Sil. Med. | 3 | 10 | 6 |
| | John Brown, Dalnacabaig | do. | | 2 | 0 | 0 |
| | Duncan M'Callum, Clenmackrie | do. | | 1 | 0 | 0 |
| *Inveraray* | John M'Arthur of Barbreck | Highland Bull Class I. £4 & Med. Sil. Med. | | 4 | 10 | 6 |
| | J. C. Kay of Cladich | do. | do. | 3 | 0 | 0 |
| | D. & P. M'Callum, Keppochan | do. | do. | 1 | 0 | 0 |
| | John M'Arthur of Barbreck | do. | Class II. £1 10s. & Med. Sil. Med. | 2 | 0 | 6* |
| | Colin M'Arthur, Tullich | do. | do. | 1 | 0 | 0* |
| | J. C. Kay of Cladich | do. | do. | 0 | 10 | 0* |
| | John M'Arthur of Barbreck | Highland Heifer | £1 10s. & Med. Sil. Med. | 2 | 0 | 6* |
| | John M'Arthur of Barbreck | do | | 1 | 0 | 0* |
| | Colin M'Arthur, Tullich | do. | | 0 | 10 | 0* |
| *Formartine* | William Duthie, Collynie | Shorthorn Bull | Silver Medal | 0 | 16 | 0 |
| | Alex. Davidson, Mains of Cairnbrogie | do. | Class I. Med. Sil. Med. | 0 | 10 | 6 |
| | James Black, Bartholchapel | do. | Class II. Med. Sil. Med. | 0 | 10 | 6 |
| | James Argo, Cairdseat | Polled Heifer | Med. Sil. Med. | 0 | 10 | 6 |
| *Kinglassie* | R. S. Aytoun of Inchdairnie | Shorthorn Bull | Class I. Med. Sil. Med. | 0 | 10 | 6 |
| | Arthur Bennet, Boggside | do. | Class II. Med. Sil. Med. | 0 | 10 | 6 |
| | John Armour, Goatmilk | Shorthorn Heifer | Med. Sil. Med. | 0 | 10 | 6 |
| *County of Ayr* | Duke of Buccleuch and Queens- berry, K.G. | Ayrshire Bull | Silver Medal | 0 | 16 | 0 |
| | Duke of Buccleuch and Queens- berry, K.G. | do. | Class I. Med. Sil. Med. | 0 | 10 | 6 |
| | Sir M. R. Shaw Stewart, Bart. | do. | Class II. Med. Sil. Med. | 0 | 10 | 6 |
| | Duke of Buccleuch and Queens- berry, K.G. | Ayrshire Heifer | Med. Sil. Med. | 0 | 10 | 6 |
| *Central Banffshire* | William Robertson, Aberdour Mains | Polled Bull | Class II. Med. Sil. Med. | 0 | 10 | 6 |
| | Duke of Richmond and Gordon | Shorthorn Heifer | Med. Sil. Med. | 0 | 10 | 6 |
| | | | Carry forward, | £96 | 13 | 0 |

\* Half Premiums awarded, the number of Lots being under five.
‡ One year old Bulls.

| NAME OF DIST. | PREMIUM AWARDED TO | FOR | | AMOUNT. |
|---|---|---|---|---|
| | | Brought forward, | | £98 13 0 |
| Stirling-shire | William M'Keich, Woodend | Ayrshire Bull | Silver Medal | 0 16 0 |
| | James Sands, Greenfoot | do. Class I. | Med. Sil. Med. | 0 10 0 |
| | Chas. Stewart, Gateside | do. Class II. | Med. Sil. Med. | 0 10 0 |
| | Colonel Murray of Polmaise | Shorthorn Heifer | Med. Sil. Med. | 0 10 0 |
| Islands of Mull, Coll, and Tiree | H. H. Pitcairn of Tiroran | Highland Bull | Silver Medal | 0 16 0 |
| | J. M'Niven, Fiddon | do | Class I. Med. Sil. Med. | 0 10 6 |
| | H. A. Campbell, Ardfenaig | do. | Class II. Med. Sil. Med. | 0 10 6 |
| | Robert Lang, Aros | Highland Heifer | Med. Sil. Med. | 0 10 6 |
| Renfrew-shire | Wm. Bartlemore, Netherhouses | Ayrshire Bull | Silver Medal | 0 16 0 |
| | Wm. Bartlemore, Netherhouses | do. | Class I. Med. Sil. Med. | 0 10 6 |
| | Sir M. R. Shaw-Stewart, Bart. | do. | Class II. Med. Sil. Med. | 0 10 6 |
| | Robert Gillespie, Boylestone | Ayrshire Heifer | Med. Sil. Med. | 0 10 6 |

## HORSES FOR AGRICULTURAL PURPOSES.

| | | | | | |
|---|---|---|---|---|---|
| Cupar and St Andrews | William Stevenson, Lochgrog | Stallion | . . . . | 25 0 0 |
| Dumfries Horse Association | David Riddell, Blackhall | Stallion | . . . . | 25 0 0 |
| Nairnshire | P. M'Robbie, Sunnyside | Stallion | . . . . | 25 0 0 |
| Earl of Selkirk's Tenantry and District | Peter Crawford, Dumgoyack | Stallion | . . . . | 25 0 0 |
| Central Strath-earn | David Alston, Hyndford | Stallion | . . . . | 25 0 0 |
| Eskdale and Liddesdale | Jas. Crawford, Brydekirk Mains | Stallion | . . . . | 25 0 0 |
| Morayshire | Joseph Tait, Waukmill | Stallion | . . . | 25 0 0 |
| East Dist. of Ber-wickshire | Gavin Jack, Foulden Newton | Brood Mare | . . £1 & Med. Sil. Med. | 4 10 6 |
| | Alex. Flint, Nether Mains | do. | . . . | 3 0 0 |
| | Henry Craw, Foulden West Mains | do. | . . . | 1 0 0 |
| Lauderdale | John W. Lawrie, Mitchelston | Brood Mare | . . £4 & Med. Sil. Med. | 4 10 6 |
| | John Bertram, Hartside | do | . . . | 3 0 0 |
| | John W. Lawrie, Mitchelston | do. | . . . | 1 0 0 |
| Machars | Robt. M'Dowall, Auchengallie | Brood Mare | . . £4 & Med. Sil. Med. | 4 10 6 |
| | Wm. Routledge, Elrig | do. | . . . | 3 0 0 |
| | T. & J. Picken, Barsalloch | do. | . . . | 1 0 0 |
| County of Peebles | W. A. Woddrop, Garvald House | Brood Mare | . . £4 & Med. Sil. Med. | 4 10 6 |
| | Lord Arthur Cecil, Orchard Mains | do. | . . . | 3 0 0 |
| | W. A. Woddrop, Garvald House | do. | . . . | 1 0 0 |
| East Dist. of Stir-lingshire | John Best, Inveravon | Brood Mare | . . £4 & Med. Sil. Med. | 4 10 6 |
| | John Gilchrist, Todhill | do. | . . . | 3 0 0 |
| | Robert Calder, Mumrills | do. | . . . | 1 0 0 |
| | | Carry forward, | | £323 8 0 |

| NAME OF DIST. | PREMIUM AWARDED TO | FOR | | AMOUNT. |
|---|---|---|---|---|
| | | | Brought forward, | £323 8 0 |
| *Lesmahagow* | James Vallance, Greathill | Brood Mare | £4 & Med. Sil. Mod. | 4 10 6 |
| | Andrew Leiper, Yardbent | do. | | 3 0 0 |
| | Gavin Hamilton of Auldtown | do. | | 1 0 0 |
| *Carrick* | Robert Harper, Myremill | Brood Mare | £4 & Med. Sil. Mod. | 4 10 6 |
| | Thomas Crawford, Drumbeg | do. | | 3 0 0 |
| | David Cross of Knockdon | do. | | 1 0 0 |
| *Dalbeattie* | Andrew Montgomery, Boreland | Two-year old Colt | £1 10. & Med. Sil. Mod. | 2 0 6* |
| | Wm. Montgomery, Banks | do. | | 1 0 0 |
| | Andrew M'Dowall, Drumglass | do. | | 0 10 0* |
| | Andrew Montgomery, Boreland | One-year old Colt | £2 & Med. Sil. Mod. | 2 10 6 |
| | R.D. Barrè Cunninghame, Duchrae | do. | | 1 0 0 |
| | James Cunningham, Tarbreoch | do. | | 0 10 0 |
| | William Gray, Muncraig | Two-year old Filly | £3 & Med. Sil. Mod. | 3 10 6 |
| | James M'Queen of Crofts | do. | | 2 0 0 |
| | David A. Hood, Balgreddan | do. | | 1 0 0 |
| | Andrew Montgomery, Boreland | One-year old Filly | £2 & Med. Sil. Mod. | 2 10 6 |
| | R D. Barrè Cunninghame, Duchrae | do. | | 1 0 0 |
| | James Cunningham, Tarbreoch | do. | | 0 10 0 |
| *Bhas Dist. of Wig-townshire* | John M'Master, Culhorn Mains | Two-year old Colt | £3 & Med. Sil. Mod. | 3 10 6 |
| | John M'Kissock, Glaik | do. | | 2 0 0 |
| | William Gibson, Beoch | do. | | 1 0 0 |
| | John M'Master, Culhorn Mains | One-year old Colt | £2 & Med. Sil. Mod. | 2 10 6 |
| | John M'Master, Culhorn Mains | do. | | 1 0 0 |
| | James Milroy, Galdenoch | do. | | 0 10 0 |
| | Robert Frederick, Drumflower | Two-year old Filly | £3 & Med. Sil. Mod. | 3 10 6 |
| | Stephen Hunter, Whiteleys | do. | | 2 0 0 |
| | Alexander Rankin, Aird | do. | | 1 0 0 |
| | Stephen Hunter, Whiteleys | One-year old Filly | £2 & Med. Sil. Mod. | 2 10 6 |
| | James Milroy, Galdenoch | do. | | 1 0 0 |
| | John M'Kissock, Glaik | do | | 0 10 0 |
| *Auchter-muchty* | James Blyth, Leckiebank | Two-year old Filly | £3 & Med. Sil. Mod. | 3 10 6 |
| | Ebenezer Bird, Glenduckie | do. | | 2 0 0 |
| | William Thom, Demperston | do. | | 1 0 0 |
| | James Blyth, Leckiebank | One year old Filly | £2 & Med. Sil. Mod. | 2 10 6 |
| | William Blyth, Colzie | do. | | 1 0 0 |
| | James Blyth, Leckiebank | do. | | 0 10 0 |
| *East of Fife* | James Blyth, Leckiebank | Two-year old Filly | £1 10s. & Med. Sil. Mod. | 2 0 6* |
| | James Blyth, Leckiebank | do. | | 1 0 0* |
| | James Blyth, Leckiebank | One-year old Filly | £2 & Med. Sil. Mod. | 2 10 6 |
| | T. Carstairs, Newbigging of Cares | do. | | 1 0 0 |
| *County of Clack-mannan* | James M'Nab, Glenochil | Two-year old Colt | £1 10s. & Med. Sil Mod. | 2 0 6* |
| | James M'Nab, Glenochil | do. | | 1 0 0* |
| | D. & T. Fisher, Jellyholm | do. | | 0 10 0* |
| | James M'Nab, Glenochil | One-year old Colt | £1 & Med. Sil. Mod. | 1 10 6* |
| | Arthur Robson, Carnlepow | do. | | 0 10 0* |
| | John Coubro, Hawkhill | do. | | 0 5 0* |
| | James M'Nab, Glenochil | Two-year old Filly | £3 & Med. Sil. Mod. | 3 10 6 |
| | James M'Nab, Glenochil | do. | | 2 0 0 |
| | James Morgan, Gogar | do. | | 1 0 0 |
| | James M'Nab, Glenochil | One-year old Filly | £2 & Med. Sil. Mod. | 2 10 6 |
| | A. M'Nab, Middleton Kerse | do. | | 1 0 0 |
| | James Orr, Harviestoun | do. | | 0 10 0 |
| *Lockerbie* | Robt. Jardine of Castlemilk, M.P. | Two-year old Filly | £3 & Med. Sil. Mod. | 3 10 6 |
| | A. Wells, Templand | do. | | 2 0 0 |
| | Andrew Dobie, Beston | do. | | 1 0 0 |
| | John Richardson, Purdonston | One-year old Filly | £2 & Med. Sil. Mod. | 2 10 6 |
| | John Common, South Corrielaw | do. | | 1 0 0 |
| | Mrs White, Nethercleugh | do. | | 0 10 0 |
| | | | Carry forward, | £423 13 0 |

\* Half Premiums awarded, the number of Lots being under five

SHEEP.

| NAME OF DIST. | PREMIUM AWARDED TO | FOR | | AMOUNT. |
|---|---|---|---|---|
| | | | Brought forward, | £423 18 0 |
| Northern | A. Cameron, Artafallie | Leicester Tup | Silver Medal | 0 15 0 |
| Pastoral | A. Cameron, Artafallie | do. | £1 10s. & Med. Sil. Mod. | 2 0 6* |
| Club | A. Cameron, Artafallie | do. | . . . . | 0 10 0* |
| | J. A. Gordon of Arabella | do. | . . . . | 0 5 0* |
| | A. Cameron, Artafallie | Leicester Shear. Tup | £3 & Med. Sil. Med. | 3 10 6 |
| | R. H. Harris, Earnhill | do. | . . . . | 1 0 0 |
| | John Hunter, Dipple | do. | . . . . | 0 10 0 |
| | A. Cameron, Artafallie | Leicester Ewes | £1,10s. & Med. Sil. Med. | 2 0 6* |
| | A. Cameron, Artafallie | do. | . . . . | 0 10 0* |
| | J. A. Gordon of Arabella | do. | . . . . | 0 5 0* |
| | A. Cameron, Artafallie | Leicester Gimmers | £1, 10s. & Med. Sil. Med. | 2 0 6* |
| | J. A. Gordon of Arabella | do. | . . . . | 0 10 0* |
| | A. Cameron, Artafallie | do. | . . . . | 0 5 0* |
| Nithsdale | James Brydon, jun., Holm of Dalquhairn | Cheviot Tup | . £3 & Med. Sil. Med. | 3 10 6 |
| | John Borland, Auchencairn | do. | . . . . | 1 0 0 |
| | James Brydon, jun., Holm of Dalquhairn | do. | . . . . | 0 10 0 |
| | James Brydon, jun., Holm of Dalquhairn | Cheviot Shear. Tup | £3 & Med. Sil. Med. | 3 10 6 |
| | James Brydon, jun., Holm of Dalquhairn | do. | . . . . | 1 0 0 |
| | D. C. Willison, Dalpeddar | do. | . . . . | 0 10 0 |
| | James Brydon, jun., Holm of Dalquhairn | Cheviot Ewes | £3 & Med. Sil. Med. | 3 10 6 |
| | John Borland, Auchencairn | do. | . . . . | 1 0 0 |
| | James Brydon, Kinnelhead | do. | . . . . | 0 10 0 |
| | James Brydon, Kinnelhead | Cheviot Gimmers | £1 10s. & Med. Sil. Med. | 2 0 6* |
| | James Brydon, Kinnelhead | do. | . . . . | 0 10 0* |
| | James Brydon, jun., Holm of Dalquhairn | do. | . . . . | 0 5 0* |
| Border | Thomas Elliot, Hindhope | Cheviot Tup | £3 & Med. Sil. Med. | 3 10 6 |
| Union | Robert Laidlaw, Rodono | do. | . . . . | 1 0 0 |
| | Thomas Elliot, Hindhope | do. | . . . . | 0 10 0 |
| | Thomas Clark, Oldhamstocks Mains | Border Leicester S. Tup | £3 & Med. Sil. Med. | 3 10 6 |
| | Thomas Clark, Oldhamstocks Mains | do. | . . . . | 1 0 0 |
| | Samuel Jack, Morsington | do. | . . . . | 0 10 0 |
| | Thomas Clark, Oldhamstocks Mains | Border Leicester Gmrs. | £3 & Med. Sil. Med. | 3 10 6 |
| | Robert Kay, Linton Bankhead | do. | . . . . | 1 0 0 |
| | Thomas Clark, Oldhamstocks Mains | do. | . . . . | 0 10 0 |
| Athole and | Alexander M'Laren, Balnacree | Leicester Tup | £1, 10s. & Med. Sil. Med. | 2 0 6* |
| Weem | A. B. Brooke, Cardney | do. | . . . . | 0 10 0* |
| | Alexander M'Laren, Balnacree | do. | . . . . | 0 5 0* |
| | Alexander M'Laren, Balnacree | Leicester S. Tup | £1 10s. & Med. Sil. Med. | 2 0 6* |
| | A. Conacher, Aldour | do. | . . . . | 0 10 0* |
| | James Robertson, Milton of Pitgur | do. | . . . . | 0 5 0* |
| | P. & D. Ferguson, Dalcapon | Leicester Ewes | . £3 & Med. Sil. Med. | 3 10 6 |
| | P. & D. Ferguson, Dalcapon | do. | . . . . | 1 0 0 |
| | A. Conacher, Aldour | do. | . . . . | 0 10 0 |
| | P. & D. Ferguson, Dalcapon | Leicester Gimmers | £1 10s. & Med. Sil. Med. | 2 0 6* |
| | P. & D. Ferguson, Dalcapon | do. | . . . . | 0 10 0* |
| | A. Conacher, Aldour | do. | . . . . | 0 5 0* |
| | | | Carry forward, | £484 1 6 |

* Half Premiums awarded, the number of Lots being under five.

| NAME OF DIST. | PREMIUM AWARDED TO | FOR | | AMOUNT. |
|---|---|---|---|---|
| | | Brought forward, | £444 | 1 6 |
| *Nether Lorn* | Mrs Gillies, Dunmore | Blackfaced Tup | . Silver Medal | 0 16 0 |
| | Robert Allan, Glenmore | do. | . £3 & Med. Sil. Mod. | 3 10 6 |
| | Robert Allan, Glenmore | do. | . . . . | 1 0 0 |
| | Mrs Gillies, Dunmore | do. | . . . . | 0 10 0 |
| | Robert Allan, Glenmore | Blackfaced Shear. Tup | £3 & Med. Sil. Med. | 3 10 6 |
| | Allan Hall, Dagnish | do. | . . . . | 1 0 0 |
| | Allan Hall, Dagnish | do. | . . . . | 0 10 0 |
| | Allan Hall, Dagnish | Blackfaced Ewes | . £3 & Med. Sil. Med. | 3 10 6 |
| | Mrs Gillies, Dunmore | do. | . . . . | 1 0 0 |
| | Robert Allan, Glenmore | do. | . . . . | 0 10 0 |
| | Robert Allan, Glenmore | Blackfaced Gimmers | £3 & Med. Sil. Med. | 3 10 6 |
| | Allan Hall, Dagnish | do. | . . . . | 1 0 0 |
| | Robert Allan, Glenmore | do. | . . . . | 0 10 0 |
| *Argyll* | R. Allan, Glenmore | Blackfaced Tup | . Silver Medal | 0 10 0 |
| | R. Allan, Glenmore | do. | . £3 & Med. Sil. Med. | 3 10 6 |
| | George Campbell, Ardifuir | do. | . . . . | 1 0 0 |
| | R. Allan, Glenmore | do. | . . . . | 0 10 0 |
| | James M'Kechnie, Askinsh | Blackfaced Shear. Tup | £3 & Med. Sil. Med. | 3 10 6 |
| | A. Sinclair, Upper Largie | do. | . . . . | 1 0 0 |
| | James M'Kechnie, Askinsh | do. | . . . . | 0 10 0 |
| | R. Allan, Glenmore | Blackfaced Ewes | . £3 & Med. Sil. Med. | 3 10 6 |
| | A. Sinclair, Upper Largie | do. | . . . . | 1 0 0 |
| | A. Sinclair, Upper Largie | do. | . . . . | 0 10 0 |
| | A. Sinclair, Upper Largie | Blackfaced Gimmers | . £3 & Med. Sil. Med. | 3 10 6 |
| | R. Allan, Glenmore | do. | . . . . | 1 0 0 |
| | A. Sinclair, Upper Largie | do. | . . . . | 0 10 0 |
| *United East Lothian* | A. J. Balfour of Whittinghame, M.P. | Leicester Tup | £1 10s. & Med. Sil. Med | 2 0 6* |
| | A. J. Balfour of Whittinghame, M.P. | do. | . . . . | 0 10 0* |
| | Andrew Smith, Castle Mains | Leicester Shear. Tup | £3 & Med. Sil. Med. | 3 10 6 |
| | Andrew Smith, Castle Mains | do. | . . . . | 1 0 0 |
| | A. J. Balfour of Whittinghame, M.P. | do. | . . . . | 0 10 0 |
| | Andrew Smith, Castle Mains | Leicester Gimmers | £1 10s. & Med. Sil. Med. | 2 0 6* |
| | Andrew Smith, Castle Mains | do. | . . . . | 0 10 0* |
| *Islay, Jura, and Colonsay* | Samuel Mitchell, Neraby | Blackfaced Tup | . Med. Silver Medal | 0 10 6 |
| | A. & J. W. Greenlees, Finlaggan | Blackfaced Shear. Tup | Med. Silver Medal | 0 10 6 |
| | Alexander M'Conechy, Daill | Blackfaced Ewes | . Med. Silver Medal | 0 10 6 |
| | Alexander M'Conechy, Daill | Blackfaced Gimmers | . Med. Silver Medal | 0 10 6 |
| *Dunoon* | John Macdonald of Garrachoran | Blackfaced Tup | . Med. Silver Medal | 0 10 |
| | James Duncan of Ballimore | Blackfaced Shear. Tup | Med. Silver Medal | 0 10 |
| | James Duncan of Benmore | Blackfaced Gimmers | . Med. Silver Medal | 0 10 |
| *Dalkeith* | Duke of Buccleuch and Queensberry, K.G. | Leicester Tup | . Silver Medal | 0 10 0 |
| | John Ainslie, jr., Illland | do. | . Med. Silver Medal | 0 10 6 |
| | William Wilson, Wolfstar | Leicester Shear. Tup | Med. Silver Medal | 0 10 0 |
| | R. Paterson, Langside | Leicester Ewes | . Med. Silver Medal | 0 10 6 |
| | R. Paterson, Langside | Leicester Gimmers | . Med. Silver Medal | 0 10 6 |
| *Upper Ward of Lanarkshire* | James J. Gillespie, Parkhall | Blackfaced Tup | . Med. Silver Medal | 0 10 6 |
| | James Greenshields, West Town | Blackfaced Shear. Tup | Med. Silver Medal | 0 10 6 |
| | George Warnock, Todlaw | Blackfaced Ewes | . Med. Silver Medal | 0 10 6 |
| | Alex. Williamson, Strancleugh | Blackfaced Gimmers | Med. Silver Medal | 0 10 6 |
| | | Carry forward, | £544 | 19 0 |

\* Half-Premiums awarded, the number of lots being under five.

| NAME OF DIST. | PREMIUM AWARDED TO | FOR | | AMOUNT. |
|---|---|---|---|---|
| | | | Brought forward, | £544 12 0 |
| Lochaber | D. P. M'Donald, Claggan | Blackfaced Tup | Silver Medal | 0 15 0 |
| | D. P. M'Donald, Claggan | do. | Med. Silver Medal | 0 10 6 |
| | H. K. Cameron, Clunes | Blackfaced Shear. Tup | Med. Silver Medal | 0 10 6 |
| | Alex. Craig, Glenfintaig | Blackfaced Ewes | Med. Silver Medal | 0 10 6 |
| | D. P. M'Donald, Claggan | Blackfaced Gimmers | Med. Silver Medal | 0 10 6 |
| Lower Annandale | Simon Beattie, Prestonhall | Draught Mare | Silver Medal | 0 15 0 |
| | James Beattie, Newbie House | Shorthorn Heifer | Med. Silver Medal | 0 10 6 |
| | R. Jardine of Castlemilk, M.P. | Galloway Heifer | Med. Silver Medal | 0 10 6 |
| | Andrew Mackie, Aitchison's Bank | Ayrshire Cow | Med. Silver Medal | 0 10 6 |
| | | | | £549 17 6 |

## SPECIAL GRANTS.

| | | | | |
|---|---|---|---|---|
| Glasgow Agricultural Society | Vote in aid of Premiums, | . | . | £50 0 0 |
| Ayrshire Association | Vote to Dairy Produce Show at Kilmarnock, | . | | 20 0 0 |
| Edinburgh Christmas Poultry Club | Vote in aid of Premiums, | . | . | 15 0 0 |
| Egilshay Society | Vote in aid of Premiums, | . | . | 3 0 0 |
| Unst Society | Vote in aid of Premiums, | . | . | 3 0 0 |
| | | | | £91 0 0 |

# MEDALS IN AID OF PREMIUMS GIVEN BY LOCAL SOCIETIES.

Medium Silver Medals were awarded to the following —

## ABERDEENSHIRE.

| NAME OF DISTRICT. | MEDAL AWARDED TO | FOR |
|---|---|---|
| Auchindoir, Kildrummie, and Forvie | William Walker, Ardhuncart | Polled Bull |
| | P. Cran, Brae Morlich | Polled Cow |
| | James Walker, Westside | Polled Heifer |
| | David Lumsden, Bacharn | Shorthorn Bull |
| Cluny, Monymusk, and Midmar | Alexander Dewar, Bethlen | Shorthorn Bull |
| | James Adam, Upper Todlochie | Leicester Ewes |
| Cromar, Upper Dee, and Donsids | Robert Anderson, Daugh | Polled Bull |
| | Robert Anderson, Daugh | Polled Cow |
| | Peter Thomson, Old Mill | Polled Calf |
| | Robert Dingwall, Blackmill | Shorthorn Bull |
| Donside | Sir William Forbes, Bart. | Swedish Turnips |
| | George Thompson, Jun. | Yellow Turnips |
| Ebrieside | John Littlejohn, Ebriehead | Polled Bull |
| | James Kirton, Denmore | Shorthorn Cow |
| | Alexander Knox, Little Annochie | Brood Mare |
| | John M. Anderson, Burngrains | Leicester Tup |
| | Mrs Mulvin, Drumwhindle | Cured Butter |
| Formartine | J. M. Pirie, Haddo | Turnips |
| | John Tough, Pitmedden | Potatoes |
| Fyvie | James Durno, Jackston | Shorthorn Bull |
| | James Durno, Jackston | Draught Mare |
| Inverurie | A. F. Nares, Bracktor | Shorthorn Heifer |
| | Geo Bean, Mains of Balquhain | Polled Heifer |
| Keithhall | James Mitchell, Caisomill | Pen of Poultry |
| Kinethmont | George Wilson, Auchmensie | Shorthorn Bull |
| | James Moir, Mains of Wardhouse | Shorthorn Cow |
| | William Milne, Mains of Drumminnor | Polled Bull |
| | John Stewart, Auchindollan | Draught Mare |
| | Mrs Moir, Mains of Wardhouse | Butter |
| Leochel Cushnie | R. C. Auld, Bridgend | Polled Bull |
| | C. Strachan, Tillyorn | Shorthorn Heifer |
| | James Strachan, Wester Fowlis | Turnips |

| NAME OF DISTRICT. | MEDAL AWARDED TO | FOR |
|---|---|---|
| | ABERDEENSHIRE—*continued.* | |
| *New Aberdour* | William Watson, Skelmanae | Brood Mare |
| | James Beedie, Ardlaw Mains | Polled Bull |
| | James Beedie, Ardlaw Mains | Polled Cow |
| | William Cardno, Tillinamoult | Collection of Seeds |
| | Robert Chapman, Foukburn | Collection of Roots |
| *North East Aberdeenshire* | George Cruickshank, Nether Cortes | Polled Bull |
| | James Dawson, Mill Farm | Shorthorn Cow |
| | Alexander Whyte, South Whitewell | Draught Mare |
| | Mrs Conits, Hatton | Dairy Produce |
| | James Whyte, Cardno Mains | Seeds |
| | James Whyte, Cardno Mains | Collection of Roots |
| *North of Scotland* | James Murray, Fauchfaulds | Turnips |
| | William Copland, Woodend | Potatoes |
| | ARGYLLSHIRE. | |
| *Lismore* | Dugald M'Gregor, Auchnaran | Highland Bull |
| | Dugald M'Gregor, Auchnaran | Draught Gelding |
| *Mull, Coll, and Tiree* | H. A. Campbell, Ardfenaig | Highland Heifer |
| | H. A. Campbell, Ardfenaig | Draught Mare |
| | John M'Niven, Fidden | Blackfaced Gimmers |
| | H. A. Campbell, Ardfenaig | Cheviot Gimmers |
| | AYRSHIRE. | |
| *Ardrossan* | Andrew Allan, Munnoch | Cheese |
| | William Smith, Corsankell | Cured Butter |
| *Beith* | William Bartlemore, Netherhouses | Ayrshire Bull |
| | William Love, Scoup | Ayrshire Cow |
| *Craigie* | William Hunter, Foulton | Ayrshire Bull |
| | Thomas Lindsay, Townend | Ayrshire Cow |
| | James Kilpatrick, Craigie Mains | Draught Mare |
| *Cumnock* | R. & P. Wardrop, Garlaff | Ayrshire Bull |
| | Andrew Wilson, Auchengilsie | Ayrshire Cow |
| *Dalry* | W. & D. Paton, Hourat | Brood Mare |
| | Robert Wotherspoon, Kersland | Ayrshire Bull |
| | James Craig, Holms of Caaf | Ayrshire Cow |
| | Gilbert Ferguson, Thirdpart | Ayrshire Heifer |
| *Dundonald* | John Caldwell, Bogside | Ayrshire Bull |
| | Ronald Bruce, Langholm | Ayrshire Cow |
| | John Barr, Harperland | Draught Mare |
| *Galston* | Hugh Drummond, Craighead | Ayrshire Bull |
| | William Lindsay, Killoch | Ayrshire Cow |
| | Arch. W. Taylor, Belisle | Draught Mare |
| *Galston (Horticultural)* | William Wilson, West Heads | Sweet Milk Cheese |
| | David Rankin, Crawlaw | Cured Butter |
| | Alexander Maxwell, Sparnelbank | Collection of Roots |
| *Kilmarnock* | T. D. C. Graham of Dunlop | Ayrshire Bull |
| | Mrs Lindsay, Killoch | Ayrshire Cow |
| *Loudoun & Lawjlee* | Thomas Donald, Crosstree | Ayrshire Bull |
| | Alexander Steel, Burnhead | Ayrshire Cow |
| | A. W. Taylor, Bullhill | Draught Mare |
| | James Mitchell, Cairnhill | Leicester Tup |
| *Muirkirk* | R. & P. Wardrop, Garlaff | Ayrshire Bull |
| | John Semple, Mid-Wellwood | Ayrshire Cow |
| | James Baird, Blindburn | Brood Mare |
| | Daniel Hyslop, Belston | Clydesdale Mare |
| | James Craig, Middlefield | Blackfaced Tup |
| | Daniel Craig, Netherwood | Blackfaced Tup |
| *New Cumnock* | R. & P. Wardrop, Garlaff | Ayrshire Bull |
| | James Wilson, Old Mill | Ayrshire Cow |
| | William Howat, Burnfoot | Brood Mare |
| | William Howat, Burnfoot | Blackfaced Tup |
| *Sorn and Dalgain* | James Baird, Blindburn | Ayrshire Bull |
| | J. & A. M'Crae, Holehousemill | Ayrshire Cow |
| | John Morton, Dykeneuk | Draught Mare |
| | Gavin Hamilton, Nethershields | Sweet Milk Cheese |
| | John Watson, Daldorch | Fences |

| NAME OF DISTRICT. | MEDAL AWARDED TO | FOR |
|---|---|---|

**AYRSHIRE—*continued*.**

| | | |
|---|---|---|
| *Stewarton* | T. D. C. Graham of Dunlop | Ayrshire Bull |
| | A. R. Foulds of Clerkland | Ayrshire Cow |
| *Tarbolton* | Hugh Wilson, Carngillan | Ayrshire Cow |
| | William Spiers, Lochlea | Draught Mare |
| *West Kilbride* | Arch. Wilson, Drumfilling | Ayrshire Bull |
| | John Hendry, Mains | Ayrshire Cow |
| | George Harvey, Gill | Sweet Milk Cheese |
| | William Kean, Overton | Cured Butter |
| | Mrs Harvey, Gill | Oat Cakes |

**BANFFSHIRE.**

| | | |
|---|---|---|
| *Spey, Avon, and* | James M'William, Stoneytown | Shorthorn Bull |
| *Fiddochside* | W. M. Skinner, Drumin | Polled Cow |
| | George Smith Grant, Achorachan | Blackfaced Tup |
| | James Sutor, Collie | Leicester Tup |

**BUTESHIRE.**

| | | |
|---|---|---|
| *Bute* | Robert M'Alister, Ascog | Ayrshire Cow |
| | William Barr, Kerrylamont | Ayrshire Heifer |
| | James Duncan, Kilmichael | Blackfaced Tup |

**DUMBARTONSHIRE.**

| | | |
|---|---|---|
| *Cumbernauld* | William Cullen, Barbegs | Ayrshire Cow |
| | James Mather, Bulloch | Ayrshire Bull |
| | Thomas Chalmers, Walton | Clydesdale Mare |
| *Western District of* | Donald M'Nab, Duchlage | Draught Mare |
| *Dumbartonshire* | Matthew Snodgrass, Milligs | Draught Gelding |

**DUMFRIESSHIRE.**

| | | |
|---|---|---|
| *Moffat and Upper* | James Johnstone, Hunterbeck | Ayrshire Cow |
| *Annandale* | John A. Johnstone, Archbank | Draught Mare |
| | John A. Johnstone, Archbank | Cheviot Tup |
| | George Kerss, Craigielands | Dorking Fowls |
| *Sanquhar* | Duke of Buccleuch and Queensberry, K.G. | Ayrshire Bull |
| | Duke of Buccleuch and Queensberry, K.G. | Ayrshire Cow |
| | Samuel Irving, Carco | Draught Mare |
| | D. C. Willison, Dalpeddar | Cheviot Tup |
| | J. & J. Moffat, Gateside | Blackfaced Tup |

**EDINBURGHSHIRE.**

| | | |
|---|---|---|
| *Western District of* | John Meikle, Groupfoot | Ayrshire Bull |
| *Mid-Lothian* | James Hamilton, Woolfords | Ayrshire Heifer |
| | David Alston, Hyndfordwalls | Clydesdale Stallion |
| | John Waddell of Inch | Clydesdale Mare |

**ELGINSHIRE.**

| | | |
|---|---|---|
| *Forres and Northern* | Lord Lovat, Beaufort Castle | Cross Ox |
| *Fat Cattle Club* | Lord Lovat, Beaufort Castle | Cross Heifer |
| | Earl of Seafield, Balnacaan | Wethers |
| | George Russell, Middlefield | Pig |
| | Simon Anton, Seafield | Collection of Roots |
| | Thomas Ross, Hillhead | Collection of Grain |

**INVERNESS-SHIRE.**

| | | |
|---|---|---|
| *Glen Urquhart* | James Shaw, Clunemore | Sandy Oats |
| | Major Grant, Drumbine | Champion Potatoes |
| | James Simpson, Drumnadrochit | Yellow Turnips |
| *Northern Counties* | Lord Lovat | Cross Ox |
| *Fat Show Club* | Lord Lovat | Cross Heifer |
| | Earl of Seafield | Wether Hoggs |
| | Sir K. S. Mackenzie of Gairloch, Bart. | Pig |
| | James A. Gordon of Arabella | Regent Potatoes |
| | Lord Lovat | Swedish Turnips |
| | Lord Lovat | Yellow Turnips |
| | John Oran, Keith | Poultry |

| NAME OF DISTRICT | MEDAL AWARDED TO | FOR |
|---|---|---|
| | INVERNESS-SHIRE—*continued.* | |
| *Strathspey* | John Grant, Mains of Advie | Polled Bull |
| | John Grant, Mains of Advie | Polled Cow |
| | William Allan, Clury | Draught Mare |
| | Donald Lawson, Auchnagallin | Sandy Oats |
| | Earl of Seafield | Turnips |
| | KINCARDINESHIRE. | |
| *Fettercairn* | James Kinross, Coldstream | Shorthorn Bull |
| | James Smith, Pittengardner | Brood Mare |
| | John Smith, Balmain | Collection of Roots |
| | LANARKSHIRE. | |
| *Cadder* | James Johnstone, Lochburnie | Clydesdale Mare |
| *Calderwaterhead* | James Williamson, Greenhead | Ayrshire Bull |
| | Thomas Smith, Hassockridge | Entire Colt |
| *Carmichael* | Robert Thorburn, Stonehill | Blackfaced Tup |
| | William Muir, Easter Sills | Leicester Tup |
| *Stonehouse* | Robert Allan, Whitehill | Ayrshire Bull |
| | John Hamilton, Bogside | Ayrshire Cow |
| | ORKNEY. | |
| *Rousay* | General Burroughs of Rousay C.B. | Shorthorn Bull |
| | General Burroughs of Rousay C.B. | Shorthorn Cow |
| | PERTHSHIRE. | |
| *Culross* | David Pearson, Blair Farm | Green Crop |
| | James Thomson, Middle Grange | Hay Crop |
| | James Thomson, Middle Grange | Farm Management |
| *M. Dist. of Athole and Tullymet* } | Mrs Duff, Logierait Mill | Green Crop |
| *Moulin.* | Adam Conacher, Aldour | Turnips |
| *Stormont Union* | William M'Laren, Pittendreich | Draught Gelding |
| | Thomas Ferguson, Kinnochtry | Polled Cow |
| | Thomas Ferguson, Kinnochtry | Leicester Tup |
| | Mrs Grant, The Pleasance | Dairy Produce |
| | David Buttar, Corston | Turnips |
| *Strathearn (Ornithological)* | John Gardiner, East Mill | Dorking Fowls |
| | Alexander M'Ara, Culdees | Scotch Grey Fowls |
| | RENFREWSHIRE. | |
| *Eaglesham* | James Allan, Inches | Draught Mare |
| *Lochwinnoch* | William Bartlemore, Netherhouses | Ayrshire Bull |
| | Hugh Jack, Auchengown | Ayrshire Cow |
| | ROSS-SHIRE. | |
| *Black Isle* | Arch. Cameron, Artafallie | Shorthorn Bull |
| | Colin Munro, Weston | Clydesdale Stallion |
| | Arch. Cameron, Artafallie | Leicester Tup |
| | W. G. C. Archer, Belmaduthy | Chevalier Barley |
| | James Fletcher of Rosehaugh | Finefellow Oats |
| | James Fletcher of Rosehaugh | Ryegrass Seed |
| *Wester Ross* | D. G. Ross, The Park | Shorthorn Bull |
| | M. Bethune, Brae | Draught Mare |
| | D. G. Fleming, Ardullie | Barley |
| | STIRLINGSHIRE. | |
| *Campsie, Strath-blane, and Bal-dernock* } | James Weir, Hole | Ayrshire Bull |
| | Peter Crawford, Dumgoyack | Clydesdale Mare |
| *Gargunnock* | James Sands, Greenfoot | Ayrshire Bull |
| | James Gray, Birkenwood | Clydesdale Mare |
| *Kilsyth* | Henry Young, Woodend | Ayrshire Cow |
| | James Graham, Auchencloch | Clydesdale Mare |

192 Medium Silver Medals, £100, 16s.

## PLOUGHING COMPETITIONS.

In 1880–81 the Society's Silver Medal was awarded at 111 Ploughing
Competitions as follows :—

### ABERDEENSHIRE.

| NO. | NAME OF SOCIETY. | PLACE OF COMPETITION. | SILVER MEDAL AWARDED TO |
|---|---|---|---|
| 1 | Aberdour. | Tyrie Mains. | Forbes Murray, Merryhillock. |
| 2. | Aboyne. | Mains of Aboyne | Alex. Anderson, Aboyne. |
| 3. | Corgarf. | Garchory. | Alex. M'Hardy, Burnside. |
| 4. | Crathie. | Mains of Abergeldie. | John Mackie, The Manse. |
| 5. | Echt, Skene, and Midmar. | Myrlewell. | James Simpson, Inverord. |
| 6. | Leochel Cushnie. | Wester Fowlis. | William Gilbert, Shiel. |
| 7. | Mar. | Mains of Tertowie. | Alex. Leiper, Littlemill. |
| 8. | Millbrex. | Blackpool. | William Malcolm, Badochell. |
| 9. | North-East Aberdeenshire. | Westertown. | Alex. Penny, Mid-Ardlaw. |
| 10. | Strichen. | Auchtygills. | William Lawrence, Hillfoot. |

### ARGYLESHIRE.

| 11. | Ardnamurchan. | Achateny. | Malcolm M'Millan, Achosaich. |
|---|---|---|---|
| 12. | Duror and Ballachullish. | South Ballachulish. | Duncan M'Callum, Ardshiel. |
| 13. | Inveraray. | Napier's Park. | Duncan M'Lullich, Inveraray. |
| 14. | Islay, Jura, and Colonsay. | Octavulin. | James M'Fadyen, Gruinart. |
| 15. | Kilfinan. | Auchgoyle. | John M'Alpine, Auchgoyle. |
| 16. | Killean and Kilcalmonell. | Tayinloanc. | Samuel Thomson, Dalmore. |
| 17. | Kintyre. | Dalrioch. | Duncan M'Phee, Darlochan. |
| 18. | Lismore. | Ballievoolan. | Duncan M'Gregor, Achnaran. |
| 19. | Lorn. | Foriochan. | Thomas Colthart, Lochnell. |
| 20. | Netherlorn. | Camuslaich. | Donald M'Lachlan, Ballycastle. |
| 21. | Salen. | Callachaly. | Duncan M'Nab, Ardnacross. |
| 22. | Strath of Appin. | Kinlochlauch. | Donald Black, North Shean. |

### AYRSHIRE.

| 23. | Ayr and Alloway. | Carcluie. | Hugh White, Carcluie. |
|---|---|---|---|
| 24. | Coylton. | Byres. | James M'Ilwraith, Knockahoggle. |
| 25. | Dalry. | Ryesholm. | James Blair, Holmes. |
| 26. | Dalrymple. | Burnton. | John Hannah, Broomberry. |
| 27. | Fenwick. | Gairdrum. | William Young, Mosside. |
| 28. | Galston. | Little Sorn. | Andrew Cameron, Molemountend. |
| 29. | Kilmarnock. | Onthank. | James Mackie, Drongan Mains. |
| 30. | Kirkmichael. | Guiltreehill. | Anthony M'Dowall, Barlangh. |
| 31. | Minnishant. | Midton. | James Blair, Holmes. |
| 32. | Monkton. | Muirhouse. | James Andrew, Muirhouse. |
| 33. | New Cumnock. | Castle Mains. | James Craig, House o' Water. |
| 34. | Sorn and Dalgain. | Daldorch. | George M'Kerrow, Daldillan. |
| 35. | Tarbolton. | Langlands. | Thomas M'Kay, Springbank. |
| 36. | West Kilbryde. | West Kilbride. | Thomas Bell, Carlung. |

### BANFFSHIRE.

| 37. | Boharm. | Balnagarrow. | Alex. Moggach, Balnagarrow. |
|---|---|---|---|
| 38. | Keith. | Auchindachig. | Peter Mitchell, Claypotts. |

### BERWICKSHIRE.

| 39. | Cockburnspath. | Neuk. | James Johnston, Fulfordlees. |
|---|---|---|---|

### BUTESHIRE.

| 40. | Arran. | Balnacoole. | Charles Cook, Torlin. |
|---|---|---|---|

### DUMBARTONSHIRE.

| 41. | Kilmaronock and Bonhill. | Ladrishbeg. | Walter Bilsland, Mains. |
|---|---|---|---|
| 42. | Kirkintilloch. | Bedcow. | Matthew Barrie, Haystone. |

### DUMFRIESSHIRE.

| 43. | Holywood. | Bearcroft. | Robert Irving, Heathfield. |
|---|---|---|---|
| 44. | Lochmaber. | Broomhill. | John Boyes, Halleaths. |

## EDINBURGHSHIRE.

| NO. | NAME OF SOCIETY. | PLACE OF COMPETITION | SILVER MEDAL AWARDED TO |
|---|---|---|---|
| 45. | Glencross. | New Milton. | Robert Wilson, Glencross Mains. |
| 46. | Lasswade. | Burghlee. | Thomas Leadbetter, Paradykes. |

### ELGINSHIRE.

| 47. | Urquhart. | Maft. | Walter Grant, Lochs. |

### FIFESHIRE.

| 48. | Crossgates. | Pitcorthie. | Andrew Leitch, Dunfermline. |
| 49. | Howe of Fife. | Arns Muir. | David Pottie, Cultmill. |
| 50. | Leslie. | Balsillie. | Robert Farmer, Findaty. |

### FORFARSHIRE.

| 51. | Tannadice and Oathlaw. | Milton of Finavon. | William Haggart, Barnyards. |
| 52. | Logie Pert. | Ardoch of Gallory. | William Mackie, Mill of Pert. |

### INVERNESS-SHIRE.

| 53. | Badenoch and Rothiemurchus. | Blargie. | Robert Russel, Gaskbeg. |
| 54. | Inverness. | Parks of Inshes. | James Souter, Parks of Inshes. |
| 55. | Laggan. | Cluny Mains. | Robert Russell, Gaskbeg. |
| 56. | Lochaber. | Inverlochy. | Alex. Cameron, Torlundy. |
| 57. | Strathspey. | Lynchurn. | James Young, Tullochgorm. |

### KINCARDINESHIRE.

| 58. | Durris. | Brigton. | Robert King, Spyhill. |
| 59. | Nigg. | Altens. | Adam Walker, Altens. |
| 60. | Portlethen. | Causeyport. | Alex. Yule, Causeyport. |
| 61. | Fickerton, Uris and Fetteresso. | Cowton. | William Moir, Backburn. |

### STEWARTRY OF KIRKCUDBRIGHT.

| 62. | Kirkcudbright. | Camee. | Edward Loan, Lowbanks. |
| 63. | Kirkpatrick-Durham. | Tarbreoch. | Robert Nish, Minnydew. |
| 64. | New Abbey. | Overton. | Samuel Young, Airds. |
| 65. | Berrick. | Berrick Park. | John Shennan, Baltg. |
| 66. | Troqueer. | Rotchell. | David Young, Airds. |

### LANARKSHIRE.

| 67. | Cadder. | Milton. | Walter Stewart, Buckley. |
| 68. | Calderwaterhead. | Backmuir. | James Barr, Townhead. |
| 69. | East Kilbride. | Netherton. | William Warnock, Craigend. |
| 70. | New Monkland. | Rochsolloch. | John Hunter, Dykehead. |
| 71. | Old Monkland. | Easterhouse. | John Sandilands, Woodhead. |

### LINLITHGOWSHIRE.

| 72. | Kinnell. | Woodhead. | Robert Maildo, Kinnell Kerse. |

### NAIRNSHIRE.

| 73. | Ardclach. | Mains. | Alexander Murdoch, Lynemoic. |

### ORKNEY.

| 74. | Egilshay. | Onziebust. | Wm. M. Mainland, Onziebust. |
| 75. | Orkney. | Saverock. | William Muir, Birstane. |
| 76. | Orphir. | Hobbister. | John Wards, Gear. |
| 77. | Rousay and Veira. | Trumland. | John Harrold, Trumland. |
| 78. | St Ola. | Seatter. | James Bichan, Mayfield. |
| 79. | Shapansay. | Balfour Mains. | John Scott, jun., Odinston. |
| 80. | South Ronaldshay. | Widewall. | William Sinclair, Berriedale. |
| 81. | Stronsay. | Housebay. | William Sinclair, Airy. |

### PEEBLESSHIRE.

| 82. | Peebles. | Howford. | Thomas Hughes, Cardrona. |

## PERTHSHIRE.

| NO. | NAME OF SOCIETY. | PLACE OF COMPETITION | SILVER MEDAL AWARDED TO |
|---|---|---|---|
| 83. | Ardoch. | Townhead. | James Stirling, Tamano. |
| 84. | Blairdrummond, &c. | West Drip. | Alexander Aitken, Baad. |
| 85. | Breadalbane (Eastern Dist.) | Farrochil. | James Scott, Comrie. |
| 86. | Breadalbane (Western Dist ) | Fulldrig. | John M'Pherson, Balnahanaid. |
| 87. | Comrie and Upper Strathearn. | Fairnca. | Duncan Kay, Tulybanocher. |
| 88. | Culross. | Balgonia. | George Spittal, Culross. |
| 89. | Dunblane. | Clayhills. | M. Murray, Hungryhill. |
| 90. | Foss and Strathtummel. | Foss Home Farm. | Donald M'Donald, Chamberbane. |
| 91. | Glenlyon. | Rordmore. | Peter Dewar, Balnahanaid. |
| 92. | Mid. District of Athole, &c. | Gudy. | John M'Donald, Balnaguard. |
| 93. | Monzievaird and Strowan. | Lochlane. | Wm. M'Rostia, Carse of Lennoch. |
| 94. | Moulin. | Pitfurie. | Duncan Fraser, Drumoharrie. |
| 95. | Rannoch. | Ardlarich. | Duncan M'Gregor, Lassintullich. |
| 96. | Strathbraan. | Borlick. | Wm. M'Intyre, Kennacoil. |
| 97. | Strathearn (Central). | Cairnie. | Robert Ewing, Chapel Bank. |
| 98. | Strathord. | Balmacolly. | John Cameron, Ardgaith. |
| 99. | Struan. | Calvine. | Alex. M'Intosh, Tomnacraig. |
| 100. | Weem. | Castle Menzies. | John M'Intosh, Tomintsold. |

## RENFREWSHIRE.

| | | | |
|---|---|---|---|
| 101. | Cathcart and Eastwood. | Eastwood Park. | William Jackson, Carrolside |
| 102. | Erskine and Inchinnan. | East Fulwood. | John Munn, Commonside. |
| 103. | Greenock, Gourock, &c. | Divert. | James Lang, Brachead. |
| 104. | Renfrewshire. | Knock. | John White, Fulwood. |

## ROSS-SHIRE.

| | | | |
|---|---|---|---|
| 105. | Tarbat. | Arboll. | Robert Douglas, Glamis Mains. |
| 106. | Craigforth and Touch. | Fallennich. | George Stewart, Kildean. |

## WIGTOWNSHIRE.

| | | | |
|---|---|---|---|
| 107. | Kirkmaiden. | Carrochtree. | Alex. M'Colm, Castle Clanyard. |
| 108. | Machars. | Airies. | Robert Ferguson, Baldoon. |
| 109. | Old Luce. | Back of Wall. | William Davidson, Dunragit. |
| 110. | Penningham, Minnygaff, &c. | Park. | James M'Dowall, Balterson. |
| 111. | Whithorn and Glasserton. | Longhill. | George Paterson, Craigdhu. |

111 Minor Silver Medals, £33, 6s.

---

## IV. COTTAGES AND GARDENS.

### 1. BEST KEPT COTTAGES AND GARDENS.

#### ABERDEENSHIRE.

| | | | | | | |
|---|---|---|---|---|---|---|
| Methlick ................. | Andrew Davidson | Cottage | £1 and Minor Silver Medal | £1 | 6 | 0 |
| | George Moir | do. | | 0 | 10 | 0 |
| | Alex. Mowat | do. | Minor Silver Medal | 0 | 6 | 0 |
| | Alex. Cheyne | Garden | £1 and Minor Silver Medal | 1 | 6 | 0 |
| | William Hutcheon | do. | | 0 | 10 | 0 |
| | William Ligertwood | do. | Minor Silver Medal | 0 | 6 | 0 |

#### DUMBARTONSHIRE.

| | | | | | | |
|---|---|---|---|---|---|---|
| Cardross ............... | David Smith | Cottage | £1 and Minor Silver Medal | 1 | 6 | 0 |
| | Alex. Gibson | do. | | 0 | 10 | 0 |
| | James Cassels | do. | Minor Silver Medal | 0 | 6 | 0 |
| | Alex Gibson | Garden | £1 and Minor Silver Medal | 1 | 6 | 0 |
| | John Keogh | do. | | 0 | 10 | 0 |
| | John M'Nab | do. | Minor Silver Medal | 0 | 6 | 0 |

Carry forward, £8 8 0

|  |  |  |  | Brought forward, | £8 | 8 | 0 |
|---|---|---|---|---|---|---|---|

**EDINBURGHSHIRE.**

| *Calder's Union* | James B. Smith | Cottage |  | 1 | 0 | 0 |
|---|---|---|---|---|---|---|
|  | Thomas Calder | do. |  | 0 | 10 | 0 |
|  | James B Smith | Garden | £1 and Minor Silver Medal | 1 | 6 | 0 |
|  | Thomas Calder | do. |  | 0 | 10 | 0 |
|  | John Calder | do. | Minor Silver Medal | 0 | 6 | 0 |
| *Currie and Balerno* | John Fraser | do. | £1 and Minor Silver Medal | 1 | 6 | 0 |
|  | Robert Paterson | do. |  | 0 | 10 | 0 |
|  | John Good | do. | Minor Silver Medal | 0 | 6 | 0 |

**FIFESHIRE.**

| *North of Fife* | Henry Balsillie | Cottage | £1 and Minor Silver Medal | 1 | 6 | 0 |
|---|---|---|---|---|---|---|
|  | Henry Lister | do. |  | 0 | 10 | 0 |
|  | Alex. Rolland | do. | Minor Silver Medal | 0 | 6 | 0 |
|  | James Kinnell | Garden | £1 and Minor Silver Medal | 1 | 6 | 0 |
|  | James Gillespie | do | | 0 | 10 | 0 |
|  | Thomas Archer | do. | Minor Silver Medal | 0 | 6 | 0 |
|  | James Maxwell | do. | Minor Silver Medal | 0 | 6 | 0 |
|  | (*1st Prize in 1880*) |  |  |  |  |  |

**KINCARDINESHIRE.**

| *Mearns.* | John Paterson | Cottage |  | 1 | 0 | 0 |
|---|---|---|---|---|---|---|
|  | William Eaton | do. |  | 0 | 10 | 0 |
|  | Mrs Alex. Bell | do. | Minor Silver Medal | 0 | 6 | 0 |
|  | John Ferguson | Garden | £1 and Minor Silver Medal | 1 | 6 | 0 |
|  | George Douglas | do. |  | 0 | 10 | 0 |
|  | James Taylor | do. | Minor Silver Medal | 0 | 6 | 0 |
|  | Alex. Stott | do. | Minor Silver Medal | 0 | 6 | 0 |
|  | (*1st Prize in 1880*) |  |  |  |  |  |

**LANARKSHIRE.**

| *Abington* | Matthew M'Kendrick | Cottage |  | 1 | 0 | 0 |
|---|---|---|---|---|---|---|
|  | David M'Kendrick | do. |  | 0 | 10 | 0 |
|  | William Clark | Garden | £1 and Minor Silver Medal | 1 | 6 | 0 |
|  | J. B. Forrest | do. |  | 0 | 10 | 0 |
|  | James Thomson | do. | Minor Silver Medal | 0 | 6 | 0 |

**LINLITHGOWSHIRE.**

| *Dalmeny & Queensferry* | Mrs Cochrane | Cottage | £1 and Minor Silver Medal | 1 | 6 | 0 |
|---|---|---|---|---|---|---|
|  | Mrs Younger | do. |  | 0 | 10 | 0 |
|  | Miss Wilson | do. | Minor Silver Medal | 0 | 6 | 0 |
|  | Mrs Morris | do. | Minor Silver Medal | 0 | 6 | 0 |
|  | (*1st Prize in 1879*) |  |  |  |  |  |
|  | Andrew Younger | Garden | £1 and Minor Silver Medal | 1 | 6 | 0 |
|  | John Russell | do |  | 0 | 10 | 0 |
|  | James Hunter | do. | Minor Silver Medal | 0 | 6 | 0 |
|  | Benjamin Miles | do. | Minor Silver Medal | 0 | 6 | 0 |
|  | (*1st Prize in 1879*) |  |  |  |  |  |

**PERTHSHIRE.**

| *Braco* | David Monteath | Cottage | £1 and Minor Silver Medal | 1 | 6 | 0 |
|---|---|---|---|---|---|---|
|  | John Stewart | do. |  | 0 | 10 | 0 |
|  | Richard Kirkwood | do. | Minor Silver Medal | 0 | 6 | 0 |
|  | William Bayne | do. | Minor Silver Medal | 0 | 6 | 0 |
|  | (*1st Prize in 1880*) |  |  |  |  |  |
|  | Robert Matthie | Garden | £1 and Minor Silver Medal | 1 | 6 | 0 |
|  | Richard Kirkwood | do. |  | 0 | 10 | 0 |
|  | John Stewart | do | Minor Silver Medal | 0 | 6 | 0 |
|  | John Dewar | do. | Minor Silver Medal | 0 | 6 | 0 |
|  | (*1st Prize in 1880*) |  |  |  |  |  |

|  |  |  |  | Carry forward, | £36 | 0 | 0 |
|---|---|---|---|---|---|---|---|

|  |  |  |  |  |  |  |
|---|---|---|---|---|---|---|
|  |  | Brought forward, | £36 | 0 | 0 |
| **PERTHSHIRE—*continued*.** | | | | | | |
| Dunning | A. M'Martin | Cottage | £1 and Minor Silver Medal | 1 | 6 | 0 |
|  | James Robertson | do. |  | 0 | 10 | 0 |
|  | Thos. Callum | do. | Minor Silver Medal | 0 | 6 | 0 |
|  | Arch. M'Martin | Garden | £1 and Minor Silver Medal | 1 | 6 | 0 |
|  | Henry M'Cathie | do. |  | 0 | 10 | 0 |
|  | Thos. Callum | do. | Minor Silver Medal | 0 | 6 | 0 |
|  | James Robertson | do. | Minor Silver Medal | 6 | 0 | 0 |
|  | (1st Prize in 188 ) | | | | | |
| Forgandenny | Mrs D. Stewart | Cottage | £1 and Minor Silver Medal | 1 | 6 | 0 |
|  | Mrs J. Ferguson | do. |  | 0 | 10 | 0 |
|  | Mrs R. Buchan | do. | Minor Silver Medal | 0 | 6 | 0 |
|  | Daniel Stewart | Garden | £1 and Minor Silver Medal | 1 | 6 | 0 |
|  | John Ferguson | do. |  | 0 | 10 | 0 |
|  | Robert Buchan | do. | Minor Silver Medal | 0 | 6 | 0 |
| Muthill | Mrs Jas. Graham | Cottage | £1 and Minor Silver Medal | 1 | 6 | 0 |
|  | Mrs Jas. Keron | do. |  | 0 | 10 | 0 |
|  | Mrs Daniel Jolly | do. | Minor Silver Medal | 0 | 6 | 0 |
|  | Mrs John Bayne | do. | Minor Silver Medal | 0 | 6 | 0 |
|  | (1st Prize in 1880) | | | | | |
|  | Jas. Keron | Garden | £1 and Minor Silver Medal | 1 | 6 | 0 |
|  | Jas. Richard | do. |  | 0 | 10 | 0 |
|  | David Buchanan | do. | Minor Silver Medal | 0 | 6 | 0 |
|  | A. Gowans | do. | Minor Silver Medal | 0 | 6 | 0 |
|  | (1st Prize in 1880) | | | | | |
| **ROSS-SHIRE.** | | | | | | |
| Wester Ross | Hector Crawford | Cottage | £1 and Minor Silver Medal | 1 | 6 | 0 |
|  | Dun. M'Kay | do. |  | 0 | 10 | 0 |
|  | Jas. M'Kenzie | do. | Minor Silver Medal | 0 | 6 | 0 |
|  | David Munro | Garden |  | 1 | 0 | 0 |
|  | Donald Denoon | do. |  | 0 | 10 | 0 |
|  | Hugh Morrison | do. | Minor Silver Medal | 0 | 6 | 0 |
| **STIRLINGSHIRE.** | | | | | | |
| Killearn | J. & W. M'Allan | Cottage |  | 1 | 0 | 0 |
|  | George Cameron | do. |  | 0 | 10 | 0 |
|  | J. & W. M'Allan | Garden | £1 and Minor Silver Medal | 1 | 6 | 0 |
|  | Mrs Robb | do. |  | 0 | 10 | 0 |
|  | William Gilfillan | do. | Minor Silver Medal | 0 | 6 | 0 |
|  | James M'Nicol | do. | Minor Silver Medal | 0 | 6 | 0 |
|  | (1st Prize in 1879) | | | | | |
|  | William Pearson | do | Minor Silver Medal | 0 | 6 | 0 |
|  | (1st Prize in 1880) | | | | | |
| **WIGTOWNSHIRE.** | | | | | | |
| Inch | Thomas Jess | Cottage | £1 and Minor Silver Medal | 1 | 6 | 0 |
|  | Peter M'Cracken | do. |  | 0 | 10 | 0 |
|  | Robert Crawford | do. | Minor Silver Medal | 0 | 6 | 0 |
|  | William Martin | do. | Minor Silver Medal | 0 | 6 | 0 |
|  | (1st Prize in 1879). | | | | | |
|  | William Rennie | Garden | £1 and Minor Silver Medal | 1 | 6 | 0 |
|  | Thomas Jess | do. |  | 0 | 10 | 0 |
|  | John Gibb | do. | Minor Silver Medal | 0 | 6 | 0 |
|  |  |  |  | £62 | 2 | 0 |

## 2. MEDALS FOR COTTAGES AND GARDENS AND GARDEN PRODUCE.

Medium Silver Medals were awarded to the following:—

**ABERDEENSHIRE.**

| Kinellar | George Taylor | Cottage Garden |
|---|---|---|
| Udny | Mrs Irvine | Cottage Garden |

**AYRSHIRE.**

| Galston | Abram Yendall | Vegetables |
|---|---|---|
|  | William Hendrie | Cut Blooms |

DUMBARTONSHIRE.

| | | |
|---|---|---|
| Vale of Leven and Dumbarton | James Stirling | Cottage Garden |
| | James Stirling | Flower Plot |

FIFESHIRE.

| | | |
|---|---|---|
| Dysart | William Saunders | Cottage Garden |
| | Joseph M'Kinney | Flower Plot |
| Kirkcaldy | Mrs Wilson | Flower Plot |
| | Robert Craig | Flower Plot |

LANARKSHIRE.

| | | |
|---|---|---|
| Albert Gardens | Alexander Muirhead | Best kept Plot |
| | Henry Winslow | Garden Produce |
| Carnwath | George C. Murray | Cottage Garden |
| | William Kay | Garden Produce |
| Gartsherrie | Robert Smith | Cottage |
| | John Jenkins | Cottage Garden |
| New Victoria Gardens | Mrs Charles M'Kenzie | Cottage Garden |
| | Wm. M'Haffie | Cottage Garden |
| Saracen Public Gardens | John Watson | Garden Produce |
| | John Muir | Best kept Plot |
| Shettleston | William Johnstone | Cottage Garden |
| | John Barclay | Cottage Garden |

NAIRNSHIRE.

| | | |
|---|---|---|
| Auldearn | Mrs Falconer | Cottage |
| | Mrs M'Kenzie | Cottage Garden |

PERTHSHIRE.

| | | |
|---|---|---|
| Blairgowrie and Rattray | Alexander Langlands | Cottage Garden |
| Breadalbane, Weem, &c. | James Fraser | Best Cropped Garden |
| | George Stewart | Best kept Garden |
| Dunkeld and Birnam | Charles Fletcher | Cottage Garden |
| | Charles Fletcher | Garden Produce |
| Logiealmond and Glenalmond | James M'Ainsh | Cottage |
| | Robert Wilson | Garden |

31 Medium Silver Medals, £16, 5s. 6d.

# V.—VETERINARY DEPARTMENT.

## ANNUAL EXAMINATION—APRIL 1881.

| | | | | |
|---|---|---|---|---|
| William Watt Dollar, London, | Best General Examination, | Med. Gold Medal, | £6 2 0 |
| William Woods, Wigan, | Second best do. | Silver Medal, | 0 16 0 |
| William Woods, Wigan, | Best Practical Examination | Med. Gold Medal, | 6 2 0 |
| John A. Thompson, County Down, | Second Best do. | Silver Medal, | 0 16 0 |

## CLASS EXAMINATIONS—APRIL 1881.

### EDINBURGH VETERINARY COLLEGE.

| | | | |
|---|---|---|---|
| Richard William Burke, | Materia Medica, | Silver Medal, | 0 16 0 |
| Richard William Burke, | Anatomy, | Silver Medal, | 0 16 0 |
| William Watt Dollar, | Botany, | Silver Medal, | 0 16 0 |
| Richard William Burke, | Physiology, | Silver Medal, | 0 16 0 |
| John J. Doyle, | Chemistry, | Silver Medal, | 0 16 0 |
| John Alex. Thompson, | Veterinary Med. and Surgery, | Silver Medal, | 0 16 0 |
| William James Powell, | Comparative Pathology, | Silver Medal, | 0 16 0 |
| Thomas A. Buttars, | Veterinary Med. and Surgery (Amateurs), | Silver Medal, | 0 16 0 |

Carry forward,    £20 4 0

### NEW VETERINARY COLLEGE, EDINBURGH.

| | | | Brought forward, | £30 | 4 | 0 |
|---|---|---|---|---|---|---|
| William Woods, Wigan, | Horse Pathology, | Silver Medal, | | 0 | 16 | 0 |
| William Woods, Wigan, | Cattle Pathology, | Silver Medal, | | 0 | 16 | 0 |
| Colin Gresty, Cheshire, | Chemistry, | Silver Medal, | | 0 | 16 | 0 |
| John Finlayson, Gourock, | Anatomy, | Silver Medal, | | 0 | 16 | 0 |
| W. F. Greenhalgh, Leeds, | Physiology, | Silver Medal. | | 0 | 16 | 0 |

#### SUMMER SESSION, 1881.

| | | | | | | |
|---|---|---|---|---|---|---|
| W. R. Davies, Isle of Man, | Materia Medica, | Silver Medal, | | 0 | 16 | 0 |
| W. R. Davies, Isle of Man, | Botany, | Silver Medal, | | 0 | 16 | 0 |
| Colin Gresty, Cheshire, | Botany, | Silver Medal, | | 0 | 16 | 0 |

#### GLASGOW VETERINARY COLLEGE.

| | | | | | | |
|---|---|---|---|---|---|---|
| Hugh Bradley, Hillhoun, | Horse Pathology, | Silver Medal, | | 0 | 16 | 0 |
| Henry Rogers, jun, Bombay, | Cattle Pathology, | Silver Medal, | | 0 | 16 | 0 |
| W. A. MacGregor, Pollokshields, | Histology and Physiology, | Silver Medal, | | 0 | 16 | 0 |
| John Renfrew, Hurlet, | Anatomy, | Silver Medal, | | 0 | 16 | 0 |

#### SUMMER SESSION, 1881.

| | | | | | | |
|---|---|---|---|---|---|---|
| Robert M'Nair, Helensburgh, | Botany, | Silver Medal, | | 0 | 16 | 0 |
| W. M. Williams, Port Madoc, | Materia Medica, | Silver Medal, | | 0 | 16 | 0 |
| James Laithwood, Congleton, | Chemistry, | Silver Medal, | | 0 | 16 | 0 |
| | | | | £39 | 4 | 0 |

## VI.—AGRICULTURAL CLASS, EDINBURGH UNIVERSITY.

| | | | | | | | |
|---|---|---|---|---|---|---|---|
| 1. | William Henderson, Northumberland, | . | . | . | £6 | 0 | 0 |
| 2. | { Daniel Bain, Caithness, James Craig, Fifeshire, } equal, | . | . | . | 4 | 0 | 0 |
| | | | | | £10 | 0 | 0 |

### ABSTRACT OF PREMIUMS.

| | | | | | | | |
|---|---|---|---|---|---|---|---|
| 1. ESSAYS AND REPORTS, | . | . | . | . | | £155 | 16 | 0 |
| 2. STIRLING SHOW, 1881, | . | . | . | . | | 2089 | 17 | 0 |
| 3. DISTRICT SHOWS:— | | | | | | | |
| Stock, | . | . | . | £549 | 17 | 6 | |
| Special Grants, | . | . | . | 91 | 0 | 0 | |
| Local Societies—Medals in aid of Premiums given by (192), | | | 100 | 16 | 0 | |
| Ploughing Associations—Medals to (111), | . | . | 33 | 6 | 0 | |
| | | | | | 774 | 19 | 6 |
| 4. COTTAGES AND GARDENS—Money Premiums and 62 Minor Silver Medals, £62, 2s.; 31 Medium Silver Medals, £16, 5s. 6d., | . | . | . | | 78 | 7 | 6 |
| 5. VETERINARY DEPARTMENT—Medals to Students, | . | . | . | | 32 | 4 | 0 |
| 6. AGRICULTURAL CHAIR, EDINBURGH UNIVERSITY—Prizes to Class, | . | . | | 10 | 0 | 0 |
| | | | | | £3141 | 4 | 0 |

# STATE OF THE FUNDS

OF

# THE HIGHLAND AND AGRICULTURAL SOCIETY
## OF SCOTLAND

### At 30th NOVEMBER 1881.

| | | | |
|---|---|---:|---:|
| I. BONDS— | | | |
| Heritable Bonds, | . . . . | £16,779 16 0 | |
| Debenture Bonds by Clyde Navigation Trustees, | . . | 3,450 0 0 | |
| Railway Debenture Bonds, | . . . . | 4,000 0 0 | |
| | | | £24,229 16 0 |
| II. DEBENTURE STOCK— | | | |
| £3,000 North British Railway Company, 4¼ per cent., at £109, 5s., | . . | £3,277 10 0 | |
| £1,000 London and North-Western Railway Company, 4 per cent., at £116, 10s. | . | 1,165 0 0 | |
| | | | 4,442 10 0 |
| III. BANK STOCKS— | | | |
| £6,407, 7s. 8d. Royal Bank of Scotland, at £211, | . | £13,519 11 7 | |
| 2,218, 6s. 5d. Bank of England, at £287, | . | 6,366 11 7 | |
| 2,000, 0s. 0d. British Linen Company Bank, at £282, | . . | 5,640 0 0 | |
| 1,250, 0s. 0d. National Bank of Scotland, at £284, | . . | 3,550 0 0 | |
| 1,062, 10s. 0d. Commercial Bank of Scotland, at £270, | . | 2,868 15 0 | |
| 1,091, 13s. 4d. Bank of Scotland, at £295, | . | 3,220 8 4 | |
| | | | 35,165 6 6 |
| £14,029, 17s. 5d. | | | |

*Note.*—The original cost of these Bank Stocks was £22,317, 18s. 6d., showing a profit, at present prices, of £12,847, 8s.

| | | | |
|---|---|---:|---:|
| IV. TEN SHARES (£500) OF THE BRITISH FISHERY SOCIETY, valued at | | 200 0 0 | |
| V. ARREARS OF MEMBERS' SUBSCRIPTIONS, considered recoverable, | . | 78 0 6 | |
| | | | £64,115 13 0 |
| DEDUCT BALANCE DUE TO ROYAL BANK ON CURRENT ACCOUNT, | . | 1,692 9 11 | |
| AMOUNT OF FUNDS, | . . | £62,423 3 1 | |
| VI. BUILDING FUND— | | | |
| 1. Estimated value of Building, No. 3 George IV. Bridge, | . | £3,100 0 0 | |
| 2. Sums Invested in Debenture Bonds— | | | |
| North British Railway Company, | . | £1,000 0 0 | |
| Clyde Navigation Trustees, | . | 1,000 0 0 | |
| | | 2,000 0 0 | |
| 3. Sum lent on Heritable Bond, | . . | 350 0 0 | |
| 4. Deposit with Royal Bank, of date 11th November 1881, | | 209 11 8 | |
| AMOUNT OF BUILDING FUND, | . | £5,659 11 8 | |
| VII. TWEEDDALE MEDAL FUND— | | | |
| Debenture Bond with Caledonian Railway Company, | . | £500 0 0 | |
| VIII. FURNITURE— | | | |
| Estimated Value of Furniture, Paintings, Books, &c., | . | £1,000 0 0 | |

W. S. WALKER, *Treasurer.*
ANTHONY MURRAY, *Convener of Finance Committee.*
J. TURNBULL SMITH, C.A., *Auditor.*

EDINBURGH, *4th January* 1882.

# VIEW OF THE INCOME AND EXPENDITURE
## For the Year 1880-81.

### INCOME.

| | | | | |
|---|---|---|---|---|
| 1. ANNUAL SUBSCRIPTIONS AND ARREARS received, | . | . | . | £764 6 6 |
| 2. LIFE SUBSCRIPTIONS received, | . | . | . | 938 11 6 |
| | | | | £1,702 18 0 |
| 3. INTERESTS AND DIVIDENDS received— | | | | |
| Interests, | . | . | £1,080 12 8 | |
| Dividends, | . | . | 1,549 16 9 | |
| | | | | 2,630 9 5 |
| 4. INCOME FROM BUILDING FUND, | . | . | . | 94 4 1 |
| 5. CHEMICAL DEPARTMENT— | | | | |
| Subscriptions, | . | . | £27 0 0 | |
| Experimental Stations, | . | . | 166 0 0 | |
| | | | | 193 0 0 |
| 6. ARREARS from former Shows, | . | . | . | 131 19 10 |
| 7. BALANCE OF RECEIPTS from Stirling Show 1881, excluding Premiums paid, | . | . | . | 1,133 1 9 |
| SUM OF INCOME, | . | . | . | £5,885 13 1 |

### EXPENDITURE.

| | | | | |
|---|---|---|---|---|
| 1. ESTABLISHMENT— | | | | |
| Salaries and Allowances, | . | . | £1,403 1 9 | |
| Feu Duty, Taxes, Coals, &c., | . | . | 121 16 2 | |
| | | | | £1,524 17 11 |
| 2. FEE TO AUDITORS for 1879-80, | . | . | 50 0 0 | |
| 3. FEE TO PRACTICAL ENGINEER, | . | . | 20 0 0 | |
| 4. AGRICULTURAL EDUCATION (including Bursaries and Fees to Examiners), | | | 325 1 0 | |
| 5. CHEMICAL DEPARTMENT, | . | . | 879 18 9 | |
| 6. VETERINARY DEPARTMENT, | . | . | 70 19 8 | |
| 7. TRANSACTIONS, | . | . | 765 10 6 | |
| 8. ORDINARY Printing, Advertising, Stationery, Stamps, Bank Charges, and Telegrams, | | | 204 1 4 | |
| 9. SUBSCRIPTIONS to Public Societies, | . | . | 25 0 0 | |
| 10. MISCELLANEOUS, | . | . | 10 14 0 | |
| 11. PREMIUMS— | | | | |
| Kelso Show | . | . | £361 10 0 | |
| Stirling Show, | . | . | 1,757 7 0 | |
| District Competitions, | . | . | 625 15 0 | |
| Medals in aid of Premiums given by Local Societies, | | 75 12 0 | | |
| Sums voted in aid of do., | . | . | 126 0 0 | |
| Cottages and Gardens, | . | . | 59 10 0 | |
| Ploughing Competitions, | . | . | 33 6 0 | |
| | | | 3,039 0 0 | |
| 12. EXPENSES incurred by the Secretary in visiting Norwich Fishery Exhibition, | | | 12 19 0 | |
| 13. INTEREST paid, | . | . | 17 12 9 | |
| SUM OF EXPENDITURE, | . | | | 6,945 14 11 |
| BALANCE OF EXPENDITURE, | . | . | | £1,060 1 10 |

Accounted for thus—

| | | | |
|---|---|---|---|
| BALANCE due to Royal Bank at 30th November 1881, | £1,692 9 11 | | |
| Less due at 30th November 1880, | . | 538 4 0 | |
| | | £1,154 5 11 | |
| DEDUCT— | | | |
| Sum in Deposit with Royal Bank, of date 11th November 1881, | £209 11 8 | | |
| Less Deposit with do. uplifted, | 115 7 7 | | |
| | | 94 4 1 | |
| | | | 1,060 1 10 |

## ABSTRACT of the ACCOUNTS of the HIGHLAND and

### CHARGE.

| | | | £ | s. | d. |
|---|---|---|---|---|---|
| 1. Sum lent to Clyde Navigation Trustees, | | | £450 | 0 | 0 |
| 2. Debenture Bond with Caledonian Railway Company in name of Tweeddale Medal Fund, | | | 500 | 0 | 0 |
| 3. Deposit with Royal Bank in name of Building Fund, of date 11th November 1880, | | | 115 | 7 | 7 |

4. Arrears of Annual Subscriptions at 30th Nov. 1880, £91 4 6
  Whereof due by Members who have now *compounded* for life, and thereby extinguished, . . £13 11 6
  Sum ordered to be written off as irrecoverable, . . . 32 1 0
  ———————
  45 12 6

  45 12 0

5. Arrears from former Shows :—
  (1) Kelso, . . . . . £128 19 10
  (2) Perth, . . . . . 3 0 0
  ———————
  131 19 10

6. Interest and Dividends—
  (1) Interest on Heritable Bonds, less Income-Tax, £631 3 9
  (2) Interest on Debenture Bonds—
    On £7,450 at 4 per cent., less tax, . 285 16 6
  (3) Interest on Debenture Stock—
    On £3,000 at 4½ per cent., less tax, £124 11 7
    On £1000 at 4 per cent., less tax, 39 0 10
    ———————
    163 12 5
  (4) Dividends on Bank Stock—
    £6,407, 7s. 8d. Royal Bank of Scotland, . £608 14 0
    2,218, 6s. 5d. Bank of England, 210 15 8
    2,000, 0s. 0d. British Linen Co. Bank, . 260 0 0
    1,250, 0s. 0d. National Bank of Scotland, 175 0 0
    1,062, 10s. 0d. Commercial Bank, 143 8 9
    1,091, 13s. 4d. Bank of Scotland, 141 18 4
    ———————
    1,539 16 9
    £14,029, 17s. 5d.
  (5) Dividend on 10 Shares British Fishery Society, 10 0 0
  ———————
  2,630 9 5

7. Income from Building Fund—
  Interest on Heritable Bond, £350, . £12 16 8
  Interest on Debenture Bonds, £2,000 at 4 per cent., less tax, . . . 78 3 4
  Interest on Deposits with Royal Bank, £2, 13s. and 11s. 1d. . . . 3 4 1
  ———————
  94 4 1

8. Subscriptions—
  Annual Subscriptions, . . . £832 13 6
  Life Subscriptions, . . . 938 11 6
  ———————
  1,771 5 0

9. Chemical Department—
  Subscriptions, . . . £27 0 0
  Experimental Stations—Proceeds from Oats sold from Harelaw, £153 ; and from Hay sold from Pumpherston, £13, . . . 166 0 0
  ———————
  193 0 0

10. Balance of Receipts from Stirling Show (exclusive of Premiums paid), *as shown in separate States,* 1,133 1 9

11. Balance due on current account, with Royal Bank at 30th November 1881, . . . . . 1,692 9 11

  Sum of Charge, . . . £8,757 9 7

Edinburgh, *4th January* 1882.

# AGRICULTURAL SOCIETY of SCOTLAND for the YEAR 1880-81.

## DISCHARGE.

| | | | |
|---|---|---|---|
| 1. Sum due to Royal Bank on current account at 30th November 1880, | | | £538 4 0 |
| 2. Establishment Expenses— | | | |
| Salary to Secretary, | | 850 0 0 | |
| Salary to Clerk, £300, and Second Clerk, £150, | | 450 0 0 | |
| Messenger, £72; Allowance and Burial Expenses of former Messenger's Widow, &c., £31, 1s. 9d., | | 103 1 9 | |
| Feu-Duty, £28; Water Duty, £2, 3s. 4d.; Taxes, £31, 19s. 4d., | | 62 2 8 | |
| Coals, £11, 4s.; Gas, £5, 13s. 3d.; Insurance, £3, 17s. 6d., | | 20 14 9 | |
| Repairs and Furnishings, | | 38 18 9 | |
| | | | 1,524 17 11 |
| 3. Fee to Auditors for 1880 Accounts, | | | 50 0 0 |
| 4. Allowance to Practical Engineer, | | | 20 0 0 |
| 5. Education— | | | |
| Grant to Professor of Agriculture, £150; Prizes, £10; Bursaries, £130; Fees to Examiners and Expenses, £35, 1s., | | | 825 1 0 |
| 6. Chemical— | | | |
| Salary to Chemist, | £600 0 0 | | |
| Repairs, &c., for Laboratory, | 75 12 0 | | |
| Experimental Stations— | | | |
| Harelaw—Rent, £30; Taxes, 15s. 7d.; Superintendent's Allowance, £15, 15s.; Labour, £42, 1s. 2d., | £88 11 9 | | |
| Pumpherston—Rent, £13; Superintendent's Allowance, £15, 15s., | 28 15 0 | | |
| Manures, &c., for Stations, | 87 0 0 | | |
| | | 204 6 9 | |
| | | | 879 18 9 |
| 7. Veterinary—Allowance to Professor Williams, £26, 5s.; Medals to Students, £32, 4s.; Balance of Fees to Examiners, £12, 10s. 8d., | | | 70 19 8 |
| 8. Society's Transactions—Printing, Binding, and Delivering, £539, 5s.; Essays and Reports, £226, 5s. 6d., | | | 765 10 6 |
| 9. Ordinary Printing and Lithographing, £58; Advertising, £49, 10s. 10d.; Stationery and Books, £35, 18s.; Postages, &c., £52; Bank Charges and Telegrams, £8, 12s. 6d., | | | 204 1 4 |
| 10. Subscriptions to Public Societies—Meteorological, £20; Society for Prevention of Cruelty to Animals, £5, | | | 25 0 0 |
| 11. Miscellaneous—Reporting General Meeting, £3, 3s.; Proof Slips of Meetings, £1, 1s.; Luncheons for Directors, £3, 16s.; Hand-sels, £1, 4s. 6d.; Sundries, £1, 9s. 6d., | | | 10 14 0 |
| 12. Premiums— | | | |
| Kelso Show, 1880, | £361 10 0 | | |
| Stirling Show, 1881, | 1,757 7 0 | | |
| District Competitions, | 625 15 0 | | |
| Medals in aid of Premiums given by Local Societies, | 75 12 0 | | |
| Sums voted in aid of Premiums given by do., | 126 0 0 | | |
| Cottages and Gardens, | 59 10 0 | | |
| Ploughing Competitions, | 33 6 0 | | |
| | | | 3,039 0 0 |
| 13. Expenses incurred by Mr. Menzies, the Secretary, in visiting Fishery Exhibition at Norwich, | | | 12 19 0 |
| 14. Interest paid on Current Account with Royal Bank for year to 30th November 1881, | | | 17 12 9 |
| 15. Arrears of Subscriptions to be struck off as irrecoverable, | | | 35 18 6 |
| 16. Arrears considered recoverable, | | | 78 0 6 |
| 17. Capital Sum lent on Debenture Bond, | | | 450 0 0 |
| 18. Debenture Bond with Caledonian Railway Company for "Tweeddale Medal," | | | 500 0 0 |
| 19. Deposit with Royal Bank in name of Building Fund, | | | 209 11 8 |
| SUM OF DISCHARGE, | | | £8,757 9 7 |

W. S. WALKER, *Treasurer.*
ANTHONY MURRAY, *Convener of Finance Committee.*
J. TURNBULL SMITH, C.A., *Auditor.*

## ABSTRACT OF ACCOUNTS—

### CHARGE.

1. LOCAL SUBSCRIPTIONS—
   | | | |
   |---|---:|---|
   | (1) Stirlingshire—Voluntary Assessment on Proprietors, . | £349 0 1 | |
   | (2) Dumbartonshire—General Subscription, . | 285 17 0 | |
   | (3) Clackmannanshire—Voluntary Assessment on Proprietors, | 70 5 9 | |
   | (4) Western Division of Perthshire, do. do. . | 74 14 9 | |
   | | £779 17 7 | |

2. AMOUNT COLLECTED DURING SHOW—

   | | | |
   |---|---:|---:|
   | Drawn at Gates, . . . | £2,089 8 0 | |
   | Drawn at Horse Ring and Cattle Parade, . | 224 4 0 | |
   | Season Tickets, . . | 10 0 0 | |
   | Catalogues and Awards sold, . | 243 9 0 | |
   | Drawn at Gentlemen's Room, . | 9 19 6 | |
   | | | 2,577 0 6 |
   | 3. RENT OF STALLS, . . . . | | 1,319 11 3 |
   | 4. RENT OF REFRESHMENT BOOTHS, . | | 200 0 0 |
   | 5. FORFEITED DEPOSIT MONEY FOR RETURN OF HORSES, | | 4 0 0 |
   | 6. DRAWN FOR ADMISSION OF PUBLIC TO FISH PONDS, | | 2 5 0 |
   | 7. INTEREST FROM ROYAL BANK, . . | | 1 13 6 |
   | 8. INTEREST FROM TWEEDDALE MEDAL FUND, . | | 19 10 10 |
   | 9. DRAWN AT TRIAL OF IMPLEMENTS, . | | 1 4 0 |
   | | | £4,905 2 8 |
   | BALANCE OF PAYMENTS, . | | 624 5 3 |
   | | | £5,529 7 11 |

NOTE.—To the above Balance of . . . £624 5 3
There must be added the Premiums undrawn at
30th November, amounting to £332 10 0
And Damage done to Potatoes at Trial, 15 0 0
                                     347 10 0

Making the probable Loss, . . £971 15 3

## ABSTRACT of the ACCOUNTS of the

### CHARGE

1. FUNDS as at 30th November 1880—

   | | | |
   |---|---:|---:|
   | Debenture Bond by Caledonian Railway Company, . | . £1,000 0 0 | |
   | Debenture Stock of the North British Railway Company, | 1,200 0 0 | |
   | Funded Debt of the Clyde Navigation Trustees, £3000, purchased at | 2,970 0 0 | |
   | Stock of the Royal Bank, £305, purchased at . . | 671 0 0 | |
   | | £5,841 0 0 | |
   | BALANCE in Bank at 30th November 1880, . | 265 19 10 | |
   | | | £6,106 19 10 |

2. INCOME received—

   | | | |
   |---|---:|---:|
   | On £1000 Caledonian Railway Company Debenture Bond at 3½ per cent. £37, 10s., less tax, 17s. 3d. | £36 12 9 | |
   | On £1200 North British Railway Company Debenture, Stock at 4½ per cent., £51, less tax, £1, 3s. 5d., | 49 16 7 | |
   | On £3000 Funded Debt Clyde Navigation Trustees at 4 per cent., £120, less tax, £2, 15s., | 117 5 0 | |
   | | £203 14 4 | |
   | On £305 Royal Bank Stock for year, . | 28 19 6 | |
   | On Bank Account, . . . | 2 8 5 | |
   | | | 235 2 3 |
   | SUM OF CHARGE . . | | £6,342 2 1 |

## STIRLING SHOW, 1881.

### DISCHARGE.

| | | |
|---|---|---|
| 1. SHOW-YARD EXPENDITURE—<br>Fitting up, £2104; Rent of King's Park, £100; Turnstiles, £86; Miscellaneous, £6, 15s. 1d., | | £2,296 15 1 |
| 2. FORAGE AND BEDDING FOR STOCK, | | 243 19 3 |
| 3. POLICE FORCE, | | 53 15 6 |
| 4. TRAVELLING EXPENSES of Judges, &c., | | 190 11 11 |
| 5. HOTEL and other Bills for Directors, Judges, Secretary, &c., | | 275 16 10 |
| 6. TICKETS for President's Dinner for do., | | 91 1 6 |
| 7. MUSIC in Show-Yard, &c., | | 68 2 0 |
| 8. PRINTING Catalogues and Awards, and Lithographing Tickets, &c., | | 228 0 0 |
| 9. ADVERTISING and Posting Bills, | | 57 17 10 |
| 10. ALLOWANCE to Local Secretary, | | 20 0 0 |
| 11. ALLOWANCE to Practical Engineer, | | 31 10 0 |
| 12. ALLOWANCE to Local Veterinary Inspector, | | 10 0 0 |
| 13. ASSISTANTS, Porters, and Attendants, | | 128 2 0 |
| 14. ATTENDANTS on Turnstiles and Ticket Gates, | | 28 8 0 |
| 15. EXPENSES in connection with Trials of Implements, | | 26 17 6 |
| 16. POSTAGES, | | 25 6 0 |
| 17. MISCELLANEOUS OUTLAYS—Telegrams, Bank Charges, &c., | | 0 17 6 |
| AMOUNT OF GENERAL EXPENSES, | | £3,772 0 11 |
| 18. PREMIUMS drawn at 30th November 1881, | | 1,757 7 0 |
| | | £5,529 7 11 |

W. S. WALKER, *Treasurer.*
ANTHONY MURRAY, *Convener of Finance Committee.*
J. TURNBULL SMITH, C.A., *Auditor.*

EDINBURGH, *4th January* 1882.

## ARGYLL NAVAL FUND for 1880-81.

### DISCHARGE.

| | | | | |
|---|---|---|---|---|
| 1. ALLOWANCES to the five following Recipients—<br>Norman Godfrey Macalister, seventh year, | | | £40 | 0 0 |
| Charles Hope Dundas, third year, | | | 40 | 0 0 |
| Edward Walrond de Wally Bruce, second year, | | | 40 | 0 0 |
| Edward W. Elphinstone Womyss, second year, | | | 40 | 0 0 |
| Louis Wentworth Chetwynd, second year, | | | 40 | 0 0 |
| | | | £200 | 0 0 |
| 2. FUNDS as at 30th November 1881—<br>Debenture Bond by Caledonian Railway Company, | £1,000 0 0 | | | |
| Debenture Stock of the North British Railway Company, | 1,200 0 0 | | | |
| Funded Debt of the Clyde Navigation Trustees, £3000, purchased at | 2,970 0 0 | | | |
| Stock of the Royal Bank, £305, purchased at | 671 0 0 | | | |
| | £5,841 0 0 | | | |
| BALANCE in Bank at 30th November 1881, | 301 2 1 | | | |
| | | | 6,142 | 2 1 |
| SUM OF DISCHARGE, | | | £6,342 | 2 1 |

W. S. WALKER, *Treasurer.*
ANTHONY MURRAY, *Convener of Finance Committee.*
J. TURNBULL SMITH, C.A., *Auditor.*

EDINBURGH, *4th January* 1882.

# APPENDIX (B).

# PREMIUMS

OFFERED BY

## THE HIGHLAND AND AGRICULTURAL SOCIETY OF SCOTLAND IN 1882.

## CONTENTS.

# GENERAL NOTICE.

THE HIGHLAND SOCIETY was instituted in the year 1784, and incorporated by Royal Charter in 1787. Its operation was at first limited to matters connected with the improvement of the Highlands of Scotland ; but the supervision of certain departments, proper to that part of the country, having been subsequently committed to special Boards of Management, several of the earlier objects contemplated by the Society were abandoned, while the progress of agriculture led to the adoption of others of a more general character. The exertions of the Society were thus early extended to the whole of Scotland, and have, for the greater part of a century, been directed to the promotion of the science and practice of agriculture in all its branches.

In accordance with this more enlarged sphere of action, the original title of the Society was altered, under a Royal Charter, in 1834, to THE HIGHLAND AND AGRICULTURAL SOCIETY OF SCOTLAND.

The leading purposes of the Institution are set forth in the following pages, where it will be found that Premiums are offered for Reports on almost every subject connected with the cultivation of the soil ; the rearing and feeding of stock ; the management of the dairy ; the improvement of agricultural machinery and implements ; the growth of timber ; the extension of cottage accommodation ; the application of chemical science ; and the dissemination of veterinary information.

Among the more important measures which have been effected by the Society are—

1. Agricultural Meetings and General Shows of Stock, Implements, &c., held in the principal towns of Scotland, at which exhibitors from all parts of the United Kingdom are allowed to compete.

2. A system of District Shows instituted for the purpose of improving the breeds of Stock most suitable for different parts of the country, and of aiding and directing the efforts of Local Agricultural Associations.

3. The encouragement of Agricultural Education, under powers conferred by a supplementary Royal Charter, granted in 1856, and authorising "The COUNCIL of the HIGHLAND AND AGRICULTURAL SOCIETY ON EDUCATION" to grant Diplomas to Students of Agriculture ; and by the establishment of Bursaries.

4. The establishment of Agricultural Stations for the purpose of promoting the application of science to agriculture, and the appointment of a chemist to superintend all experiments conducted at these Stations, and prepare a Report of the same to be published in the Transactions. Also to subsidise, under certain conditions, Local Analytical Associations.

5. The advancement of the Veterinary Art, by conferring Certificates on Students who have passed through a prescribed curriculum, and who are found, by public examination, qualified to practise. Now terminated in accordance with arrangements with the Royal College of Veterinary Surgeons.

6. The appointment of a Board of Examiners, and the granting of First and Second Class Certificates in Forestry.

7. The annual publication of the Transactions, which comprehend the Prize-Reports, and reports of experiments, also an abstract of the business at Board and General Meetings, and other communications.

8. The management of a fund left by John, 5th Duke of Argyll (the original President of the Society), to assist young natives of the Highlands who enter Her Majesty's Navy.

## CONSTITUTION AND MANAGEMENT.

The general business of THE HIGHLAND AND AGRICULTURAL SOCIETY is conducted under the sanction and control of a Royal Charter, which authorises the enactment of Bye-Laws. Business connected with Agricultural Education is conducted under the authority of a supplementary Royal Charter, also authorising the enactment of Bye-Laws.

The Office-Bearers consist of a President, Four Vice-Presidents, Thirty Ordinary and Twenty Extraordinary Directors, a Treasurer, an Honorary and an Acting Secretary, an Auditor, and other Officers.

The Directors meet on the first Wednesday of each month from November to June ; seven being a quorum. The proceedings of the Directors are reported to General Meetings of the Society, held in January and in June or July.

With reference to motions at General Meetings, Bye-Law No. 10 provides—"That at General Meetings of the Society no motion or proposal (except of mere form or courtesy) shall be submitted or entertained for immediate decision unless notice thereof has been given a week previously to the Board of Directors, without prejudice, however, to the competency of making such motion or proposal to the effect of its being remitted to the Directors for consideration, and thereafter being disposed of at a future General Meeting."

The Council on Education, under the Supplementary Charter, consists of Sixteen Members—Nine nominated by the Charter, and Seven elected by the Society. The Board of Examiners consists of Ten Members.

Candidates for admission to the Society must be proposed by a Member, and are elected at the half-yearly General Meetings in January and June or July. The ordinary subscription is £1, 3s. 6d. annually, which may be redeemed by one payment, varying, according to the number of previous annual payments, from £12, 12s. to £7, 1s. Proprietors farming the whole of their own lands, whose assessment on the Valuation Roll does not exceed £500 per annum, and all Tenant-Farmers, Office-Bearers of Local Agricultural Associations, Resident Agricultural Factors, Land Stewards, Foresters, Agricultural Implement Makers, and Veterinary Surgeons, none of them being also owners of land to an extent exceeding £500 per annum, are admitted on a subscription of 10s. annually, which may be redeemed by one payment, varying, according to the number of previous annual payments, from £5, 5s. to £3. According to the Charter, a Member who homologates his Election by paying his first subscription cannot retire until he has paid in annual subscriptions, or otherwise, an amount equivalent to a life composition. Members having candidates to propose are requested to state whether the candidate should be on the £1, 3s. 6d. or 10s. list.

Members of the Society receive the Transactions free on application to the Secretary, and are entitled to apply for District Premiums—to report Ploughing Matches for the Medal—to attend Shows free of charge, and to exhibit Stock at reduced rates.

Orders, payable at the Royal Bank of Scotland, Edinburgh, are issued by the Directors, in name of the persons in whose favour Premiums have been awarded.

All communications must be addressed to "FLETCHER NORTON MENZIES, Esq., Secretary of the Highland and Agricultural Society of Scotland, No. 3 George IV. Bridge, Edinburgh."

# ESTABLISHMENT FOR 1882.

---

## President.

HIS GRACE THE DUKE OF RICHMOND AND GORDON, K.G.,
49 Belgrave Square, London.

## Vice-Presidents.

His Grace The DUKE of ARGYLL, K.T., Inveraray Castle, Inveraray.
The Right Hon. The EARL of GLASGOW, Crawford Priory, Cupar-Fife.
The Right Hon. The EARL of STAIR, Lochinch, Castle Kennedy.
The Right Hon. LORD POLWARTH, Mertoun House, St. Boswells.

## Ordinary Directors.

ANDREW RALSTON, Glamis House, Glamis.
Sir M. R. SHAW STEWART of Greenock and Blackhall, Bart., Ardgowan, Greenock.
Sir ALEXANDER MUIR MACKENZIE of Delvine, Bart., Dunkeld.
WILLIAM DINGWALL, Ramornie, Ladybank.
JOHN HENDRIE of Larbert, Stirlingshire.
THOMAS ROSS, Bachilton, Perth.
The Right Hon. Lord ARTHUR CECIL, Orchard Mains, Innerleithen.
Sir HEW DALRYMPLE of North Berwick, Bart., Luchie, North Berwick.
JAMES CUNNINGHAM, Tarbreoch, Dalbeattie.
JOHN SCOTT DUDGEON, Longnewton, St. Boswells.
JOHN FORMAN, Duncrahill, 51 Great King Street, Edinburgh.
R. H. HARRIS, Earnhill, Forres.
WILLIAM ELIOTT LOCKHART of Borthwickbrae, Branxholme, Hawick.
DAVID R. WILLIAMSON of Lawers, Crieff.
Sir W. C. ANSTRUTHER of Anstruther, Bart., Carmichael House, Thankerton.
Sir JAMES H. GIBSON-CRAIG of Riccarton, Bart., Currie.
DAVID AINSLIE of Costerton, Blackshiels.
JOHN BALFOUR of Balbirnie, Markinch.
THOMAS ELLIOT, Blackhaugh, Galashiels.
Rev. JOHN GILLESPIE, Mouswald Manse, Dumfries.
Lieut.-Colonel HARE of Calder Hall, Philpston House, Winchburgh.
GIDEON POTT of Dod, Knowesouth, Jedburgh.
WALTER SCOTT, Glendronach, Huntly.
ANDREW ALLAN, Munnoch, Dalry, Ayrshire.
ARTHUR H. JOHNSTONE DOUGLAS of Lockerbie, Glen Stuart, Annan.
ALEXANDER DUDGEON, Easter Dalmeny, Queensferry.
THOMAS GORDON DUFF, Park House, Banff.
JAMES MOLLISON, Dochgarroch Lodge, Inverness.
THOMAS MUNRO NICOLL, Littleton, Kirriemuir.
GEORGE J. WALKER, Portlethen, Aberdeen.

## Extraordinary Directors.

The Right Hon. Lord BALFOUR OF BURLEIGH, Kennet, Alloa.
Vice-Admiral Sir WILLIAM EDMONSTONE of Duntreath, Bart., Strathblane.
Sir HENRY JAMES SETON STEUART of Allanton, Bart., Touch, Stirling.
Sir JAMES R. GIBSON-MAITLAND of Barnton, Bart., Craigend, Stirling.
ROBERT ANDERSON, Provost of Stirling.
HENRY DAVID ERSKINE of Cardross, Stirling.
WILLIAM FORBES of Callendar, Falkirk.
Lieut.-Col. JOHN MURRAY of Polmaise, Polmaise Castle, Stirling.
WILLIAM SMYTHE of Methven, Methven Castle, Perth.
The Hon. GREVILLE R. VERNON, Auchans House, Kilmarnock.
The Hon. JOHN URE, Lord Provost of Glasgow.
Sir ROBERT J. MILLIKEN NAPIER of Milliken, Bart., Johnstone
Sir THOMAS EDWARD COLEBROOKE of Crawford, Bart., M.P., Abington.
Sir SIMON MACDONALD LOCKHART of Lee and Carnwath, Bart., Lanark.
Sir ARCHIBALD C. CAMPBELL of Blythswood, Bart., Renfrew.
Captain DAVID BOYLE, R.N., of Shewalton, Dreghorn, Ayrshire.
COLIN G. CAMPBELL of Stonefield, Tarbert, Argyllshire.
CHARLES DALRYMPLE of Newhailes, M.P., Ardencraig, Rothesay.
Colonel W. W. HOZIER of Newlands, Mauldslie Castle, Carluke.
FREDERICK E. VILLIERS, Closeburn Hall, Thornhill, N.B.

## Office-Bearers.

WILLIAM STUART WALKER of Bowland, C.B., *Treasurer.*
Sir G. GRAHAM MONTGOMERY of Stanhope, Bart., *Honorary Secretary.*
FLETCHER NORTON MENZIES, *Secretary.*
Rev. JAMES GRANT, D.C.L., D.D., *Chaplain.*
ANDREW P. AITKEN, Sc.D., *Chemist.*
J. TURNBULL SMITH, C.A., *Auditor.*
MURRAY & FALCONER, W.S., *Law Agents.*
JOHN WILSON, University of Edinburgh, *Professor of Agriculture.*
JOHN HUTTON BALFOUR, M.D., F.R.S., *Professor of Botany.*
DAVID STEVENSON, F.R.S.E., M.I.C.E., *Consulting Engineer.*
JAMES D. PARK, *Practical Engineer.*
THOMAS DUNCAN, *Recorder and Clerk.*
JOHN MACDIARMID, *Second Clerk.*
GOURLAY STEELL, R.S.A., *Animal Portrait Painter.*
WILLIAM WILLIAMS, F.R.C.V.S., *Professor of Veterinary Surgery.*
THOMAS WALLEY, M.R.C.V.S., *Professor of Cattle Pathology.*
WILLIAM BLACKWOOD & SONS, *Publishers.*
NEILL & COMPANY, *Printers.*
G. WATERSTON & SONS, *Stationers.*
HAMILTON, CRICHTON, & Co., *Silversmiths.*
ALEXANDER KIRKWOOD & SON, *Medallists.*
JOHN WATHERSTON & SONS, *Inspectors of Works.*
WILLIAM SIMPSON, *Messenger.*

## Chairman of Committees.

| | | |
|---|---|---|
| 1. *Argyll Naval Fund,* | | Admiral MAITLAND DOUGALL of Scotscraig, Tayport |
| 2. *Chemical Department,* | | COLIN J. MACKENZIE of Portmore, Eddleston. |
| 3. *Cottages and Gardens,* | | The Hon. G. R. VERNON, Auchans House. |
| 4. *District Shows,* | | A. CAMPBELL SWINTON of Kimmerghame, Dunse. |
| 5. *Finance,* | | ANTHONY MURRAY of Dollerie. |
| 6. *General Shows,* | | Colonel GILLON of Wallhouse, Bathgate. |
| 7. *Hall and Chambers,* | | JOHN ORD MACKENZIE of Dolphinton. |
| 8. *Highland Industries and Fisheries,* | | Sir JAMES H. GIBSON-CRAIG of Riccarton, Bart. |
| 9. *Law,* | | GRAHAM BINNY, W.S., 9 Hart Street, Edinburgh. |
| 10. *Machinery,* | | THOMAS MYLNE, Niddrie Mains, Liberton. |
| 11. *Ordnance Survey,* | | ROBERT DUNDAS of Arniston, Gorebridge. |
| 12. *Publications and Premiums for Reports,* | | ALEXANDER FORBES IRVINE of Drum. |
| 13. *Veterinary Department,* | | JAMES HOPE, Duddingston, Portobello. |

# COMMITTEES FOR 1882.

### 1. ARGYLL NAVAL FUND.

Admiral MAITLAND DOUGALL of Scotscraig, R.N., Tayport, *Convener*.
GRAHAM BINNY, W.S., 9 Hart Street, Edinburgh.
HEW CRICHTON, S.S.C., 13 Nelson Street, Edinburgh.

### 2. CHEMICAL DEPARTMENT.

C. J. MACKENZIE of Portmore, Eddleston, *Convener*.
Professor DOUGLAS MACLAGAN, 28 Heriot Row, Edinburgh.
   ,,    BALFOUR, Inverleith House, Edinburgh.
   ,,    WILSON, University, Edinburgh.
P. B. SWINTON, Holyn Bank, Gifford.
JOHN MUNRO, Fairnington, Kelso.
ADAM SMITH, Stevenson Mains, Haddington.
CHARLES SMITH, Whittinghame, Prestonkirk.
JOHN SCOTT DUDGEON, Longnewton, St. Boswells.
GEORGE R. GLENDINNING, Hatton Mains, Ratho.
ALEX. R. MELVIN, Bonnington, Wilkieston.
DAVID AINSLIE of Costerton, Blackshiels.
Lieut.-Col. HARE of Calder Hall.
HUGH LINDSAY, Meadowflatt, Thankerton.
Dr. ANDREW P. AITKEN, 3 George IV. Bridge, Edinburgh, *Chemist*.

### 3. COTTAGES AND GARDENS.

The Hon. G. R. VERNON, Auchans House, Kilmarnock, *Convener*.
JOHN ORD MACKENZIE of Dolphinton.
ARCHIBALD CAMPBELL SWINTON of Kimmerghame, Dunse.
C. J. MACKENZIE of Portmore, Eddleston.
JAMES HOPE, Duddingston, Edinburgh.

### 4. DISTRICT SHOWS.

ARCHIBALD CAMPBELL SWINTON of Kimmerghame, *Convener*.
Sir JAMES R. GIBSON-MAITLAND of Barnton, Bart., Craigend, Stirling.
Sir JAMES H. GIBSON-CRAIG of Riccarton, Bart., Currie.
THOMAS MYLNE, Niddrie Mains, Liberton.
ANDREW MITCHELL, Alloa.
ADAM SMITH, Stevenson Mains, Haddington.
JAMES HOPE, Duddingston, Edinburgh.
THOMAS ELLIOT, Blackhaugh, Galashiels.
Lieut.-Col. Hare of Calder Hall, Philpston House, Winchburgh.
JAMES MAXTONE GRAHAM of Cultoquhey.
F. E. VILLIERS, Closeburn Hall, Thornhall.
Capt. BOYLE of Shewalton, Dreghorn, Ayrshire.

### 5. FINANCE.

ANTHONY MURRAY of Dollerie, *Convener*.
WILLIAM S. WALKER of Bowland, C.B., *Treasurer*.
Sir G. GRAHAM MONTGOMERY of Stanhope, Bart.
HEW CRICHTON, S.S.C., 13 Nelson Street, Edinburgh.
THOMAS A. HOG of Newliston, Kirkliston.
GRAHAM BINNY, W.S., 9 Hart Street, Edinburgh.
GEORGE AULDJO JAMIESON, C.A., Edinburgh.

## 6. GENERAL SHOWS.

Colonel GILLON of Wallhouse, Bathgate, *Convener*.
Lord ARTHUR CECIL, Orchard Mains, Innerleithen.
Lord POLWARTH, Mertoun House, St. Boswells.
The Hon. G. R. VERNON, Auchans House, Kilmarnock.
Sir MICHAEL R. SHAW STEWART of Greenock and Blackhall, Bart.
Sir JAMES H. GIBSON-CRAIG of Riccarton, Bart.
DAVID STEVENSON, C.E., 84 George Street, Edinburgh.
THOMAS MYLNE, Niddrie Mains, Liberton.
ALEXANDER YOUNG, Keir Mains, Dunblane.
WILLIAM FORD, Fentonbarns, Drem.
ANDREW MITCHELL, Alloa.
ALEXANDER FORBES IRVINE of Drum.
CHARLES SMITH, Whittinghame, Prestonkirk.
DAVID R. WILLIAMSON of Lawers, Crieff.
JOHN H. DICKSON of Corstorphine, Saughton Mains, Edinburgh.
WALTER SCOTT, Glendronach, Huntly.
Rev. JOHN GILLESPIE, Mouswald Manse, Dumfries.
JAMES HOPE, Duddingston, Edinburgh.
ANDREW RALSTON, Glamis House, Glamis.
GIDEON POTT of Dod, Knowesouth, Jedburgh.
C. J. MACKENZIE of Portmore, Eddleston.
JAMES CUNNINGHAM, Tarbreoch, Dalbeattie.
ANDREW ALLAN, Munnoch, Dalry, Ayrshire.
FRED. E. VILLIERS, Closeburn Hall, Thornhill.
A. H. JOHNSTONE DOUGLAS of Lockerbie, Glen Stuart, Annan.
R. H. HARRIS, Earnhill, Forres.

## 7. HALL AND CHAMBERS.

JOHN ORD MACKENZIE of Dolphinton, *Convener*.
Sir JAMES GARDINER BAIRD of Saughton Hall, Bart.
ANTHONY MURRAY of Dolleria. 141 George Street, Edinburgh.
GRAHAM BINNY, W.S., 9 Hart Street, Edinburgh.
DAVID STEVENSON, C.E., 84 George Street, Edinburgh.
WILLIAM S. WALKER of Bowland, C.B.

## 8. HIGHLAND INDUSTRIES AND FISHERIES.

Sir JAMES H. GIBSON-CRAIG of Riccarton, Bart., *Convener*.
Sir MICHAEL R. SHAW STEWART of Greenock and Blackhall, Bart.
Sir JAMES RAMSAY GIBSON-MAITLAND of Barnton. Bart.
Major-General BURROUGHS of Rousay, C.B., Orkney.
ALEXANDER FORBES IRVINE of Drum.
Professor WILSON, University, Edinburgh.
ARCHIBALD YOUNG, 22 Royal Circus, Edinburgh.

## 9. LAW.

GRAHAM BINNY, W.S., Edinburgh, *Convener*.
JOHN ORD MACKENZIE of Dolphinton, W.S., Edinburgh.
WILLIAM S. WALKER of Bowland, C.B.
ANTHONY MURRAY of Dollerie, W.S., Edinburgh.
HEW CRICHTON, S.S.C., 13 Nelson Street, Edinburgh.
GEORGE AULDJO JAMIESON, C.A., Edinburgh.
THOMAS GRAHAM MURRAY, W.S., 11 Randolph Crescent, Edinburgh.

## 10. MACHINERY.

THOMAS MYLNE, Niddrie Mains, *Convener*.
The EARL of STAIR, Lochinch, Castle Kennedy, Wigtownshire.
Lord ARTHUR CECIL, Orchard Mains, Innerleithen.
The Hon. GEORGE WALDEGRAVE LESLIE, Leslie House, Leslie.
Sir JAMES R. GIBSON-MAITLAND of Barnton, Bart.

DAVID STEVENSON, C.E., 84 George Street, Edinburgh.
Professor WILSON, University, Edinburgh.
JOHN MUNRO, Fairnington, Kelso.
P. B. Swinton, Holyn Bank, Gifford.
C. J. MACKENZIE of Portmore, Eddleston.
BRYDEN MONTEITH, Tower Mains, Liberton.
JAMES ROSS, Newtonlees, Kelso.
JOHN KEMP, Stirling.
G. W. MURRAY, Bauff Foundry, Banff.
JAMES A. R. MAIN, Clydesdale Iron Works, Possil Park, Glasgow.
JOHN MARSHALL, Maybole.
JOHN YOUNG, jun., Ayr.
A. H. JOHNSTONE DOUGLAS of Lockerbie, Glen Stuart, Annan.
T. M. NICOLL, Littleton, Kirriemuir.
ALEXANDER DUDGEON, Easter Dalmeny, Queensferry.
JAMES D. PARK, Greenside Lane, Edinburgh, *Practical Engineer.*

## 11 ORDNANCE SURVEY.

ROBERT DUNDAS of Arniston, *Convener.*
C. J. MACKENZIE of Portmore, Eddleston.
WILLIAM S. WALKER of Bowland, C.B.

## 12. PUBLICATIONS AND PREMIUMS FOR REPORTS.

ALEXANDER FORBES IRVINE of Drum, *Convener.*
Sir ALEX MUIR MACKENZIE of Delvine, Bart., Dunkeld.
Sir JAMES R. GIBSON-MAITLAND of Barnton, Bart.
WILLIAM S. WALKER of Bowland, C.B.
Professor BALFOUR, Inverleith House, Edinburgh.
    ,,     WILSON, University, Edinburgh.
ROBERT SCOT SKIRVING, 29 Drummond Place, Edinburgh.
P. B. SWINTON, Holyn Bank, Gifford.
ROBERT HUTCHISON of Carlowrie, 29 Chester Street, Edinburgh
THOMAS MYLNE, Niddrie Mains, Liberton.
DAVID STEVENSON, C.E. 84 George Street, Edinburgh.
Dr. CLEGHORN of Stravithie, St. Andrews.
WILLIAM ELIOTT LOCKHART of Borthwickbrae, Branxholme, Hawick.
ROBERT P. NEWTON of Castlandhill, Polmont Bank, Falkirk.
C. J. MACKENZIE of Portmore, Eddleston.
Rev. JOHN GILLESPIE, Mouswald Manse, Dumfries.
WILLIAM MACDONALD, Editor, *North British Agriculturist*, Edinburgh.

## 13. VETERINARY DEPARTMENT.

JAMES HOPE, Duddingston, Edinburgh, *Convener.*
Lord ARTHUR CECIL, Orchard Mains, Innerleithen.
The Hon. G. R. VERNON, Auchans House, Kilmarnock.
Sir ALEXANDER KINLOCH of Gilmerton, Bart., Drem.
Col. GILLON of Wallhouse, Bathgate.
WILLIAM S. WALKER of Bowland, C.B.
THOMAS MYLNE, Niddrie Mains, Liberton.
ADAM SMITH, Stevenson Mains, Haddington.
DAVID R. WILLIAMSON of Lawers, Crieff.

--------

The President, Vice-Presidents, and Honorary Secretary, are members *ex officio* of all Committees.

# AGRICULTURAL EDUCATION.
## CERTIFICATES AND DIPLOMA IN AGRICULTURE.

### COUNCIL ON EDUCATION.

By a Supplementary Charter under the Great Seal, granted in 1856, the Society is empowered to grant Diplomas.

### Members of Council named by Charter.

The PRESIDENT of the HIGHLAND AND AGRICULTURAL SOCIETY—*President.*
The LORD JUSTICE-GENERAL—*Vice-President.*

| | |
|---|---|
| The LORD ADVOCATE. | The PROFESSOR OF BOTANY. |
| The DEAN OF FACULTY. | The PROFESSOR OF CHEMISTRY. |
| The PROFESSOR OF AGRICULTURE. | The PROFESSOR OF NATURAL |
| The PROFESSOR OF ANATOMY. | HISTORY. |

### Members of Council nominated by Society.

| | |
|---|---|
| The DUKE OF BUCCLEUCH, K.G. | THOMAS MYLNE, Niddrie Mains. |
| WILLIAM S. WALKER of Bowland, C.B. | ROBERT DUNDAS of Arniston. |
| JOHN WILSON, Wellnage. | JOHN MUNRO, Fairnington. |

A. CAMPBELL SWINTON of Kimmerghame.

### Board of Examiners.

1. *Science and Practice of Agriculture.*—Professor WILSON ; JOHN WILSON, Wellnage, Dunse ; THOMAS MYLNE, Niddrie Mains, Liberton ; and JOHN MUNRO, Fairnington, Kelso.
2. *Botany.*—Professor BALFOUR.
3. *Chemistry.*—Dr A. P. AITKIN.
4. *Natural History.*—Professor Sir C. WYVILLE THOMSON.
5. *Veterinary Science.*—Professor WILLIAMS.
6. *Field Engineering.*—DAVID STEVENSON, M. Inst. C.E.
7. *Book-keeping.*—JOHN TURNBULL SMITH, C.A.

### Standing Acting Committee.

The LORD JUSTICE-GENERAL—*Convener.*

| | |
|---|---|
| The PROFESSOR OF AGRICULTURE. | THOMAS MYLNE, Niddrie Mains. |
| The PROFESSOR OF BOTANY. | JOHN MUNRO, Fairnington. |
| The PROFESSOR OF CHEMISTRY. | A. CAMPBELL SWINTON of Kimmerghame. |

### BYE-LAWS.

I. That, in terms of the Charter, the Society shall nominate seven members to act on the Council on Education.

II. That the Council shall appoint a Board of Examiners on the following subjects :—Science and Practice of Agriculture ; Botany ; Chemistry ; Natural History ; Veterinary Science ; Field Engineering ; and Book-keeping.

III. That the examinations shall be both written and oral, that the value of the answers shall be determined by numbers, and that the oral examinations shall be public.

IV. That there shall be three examinations,* to be styled respectively the "Second Class Certificate Examination," the "First Class Certificate Examination," and the "Diploma Examination."

V. That to pass the "Second Class Certificate Examination," a candidate must be acquainted with the science and practice of agriculture, elemen-

---

* It has been resolved that, under ordinary circumstances, the examinations shall be held annually in the end of March or beginning of April, candidates being required to lodge intimation before the 15th of March.

tary chemistry, field engineering, and book-keeping ; and that a certificate in the following terms, bearing the corporate seal and arms of the Society, signed by the President or Vice-President of the Council on Education, the Examiners, and by the Secretary, shall be granted to a candidate passing this examination :—

"These are to certify that on the          A. B. was examined, and has been found to possess a knowledge of the science and practice of agriculture, elementary chemistry, field engineering, and book-keeping."

VI. That to pass the "First Class Certificate Examination" a candidate must be acquainted with the science and practice of agriculture, botany, chemistry, natural history, veterinary science, field engineering, and book-keeping ; and that a certificate in the following terms, bearing the corporate seal and arms of the Society, signed by the President or Vice-President of the Council on Education, the Examiners, and by the Secretary, shall be granted to candidates passing this examination :—

"These are to certify that on the          A. B. was examined, and has been found to possess a knowledge of the science and practice of agriculture, botany, chemistry, natural history, veterinary science, field engineering, and book-keeping."

VII. That to pass the "Diploma Examination" a candidate must possess a *thorough knowledge* of the science and practice of agriculture, botany, chemistry, natural history, veterinary science, field engineering, and book-keeping ; and that a diploma in the following terms, bearing the corporate seal and arms of the Society, and signed by the President or Vice-President of the Council on Education, the Examiners, and by the Secretary, shall be granted to candidates passing this examination :—

"These are to certify that, on the          A. B. was examined, and has been found to be proficient in the science and practice of agriculture, botany, chemistry, natural history, veterinary science, field engineering, and book-keeping."

VIII. That each successful candidate for the Society's Agricultural Diploma shall thereby become eligible to be elected a free life member of the Society.

IX. That the Society shall grant annually ten bursaries of £20 each ; and five of £10 each, to be competed for by pupils of schools to be approved of by the Directors, which include or are willing to introduce the teaching of chemistry, and the following branches of natural science—physical geography, botany, and geology, into their curriculum.

X. That the £20 bursaries* shall be tenable for one year at the University of Edinburgh, for the purpose of enabling the holders to take the classes necessary to qualify for the Society's certificate or diploma ; and the £10 bursaries to be tenable for the same period to enable the holders to receive another year's preparation at the schools.

XI. That the bursaries shall be determined by examination held in Edinburgh by the Society's Examiners.

XII. That a Standing Acting Committee of the Council on Agricultural Education shall be appointed by the Directors.

## SYLLABUS OF EXAMINATION
### FOR CERTIFICATES AND DIPLOMA.

### I.—SCIENCE AND PRACTICE OF AGRICULTURE.

1. Geological strata—surface geology—formation of soils—their classification—chemical and physical characters and composition—suitability for cultivation. 2. The principle of rotations—rotations suitable for different

* The £20 bursaries are not due till the holder presents himself for examination for the certificate or diploma.

soils—systems of farming. 3. The composition of (a) manures—farmyard and artificial—period and mode of application. The composition of (b) feeding substances—their suitability for different classes of farm stock—considerations affecting their use. 4. "How crops grow"—our farm crops—their cultivation—diseases—insect injuries and remedies—their chemical composition. The formation and management of plantations. 5. The principles on which drainage, irrigation, and warping operations should be based and carried out. The application of lime—marl—clay, &c. 6 Meteorology, or the laws of climate as affecting plant life—the influence of light and heat on cultivation—of absorption and retention of heat and moisture—of porosity and capillarity in soils. 8. The breeding, rearing, feeding, and general treatment of farm stock—the different breeds of cattle and sheep—their characteristics—the districts where they are generally met with. 9. The machines and implements used in farming—their uses—and the principal points to be attended to in their construction. The "prime movers," or sources of power used in agriculture—man—horse—wind—water—steam,—their relative values and advantages. *Text-books*—Morton's "Cyclopedia of Agriculture," Blackie & Son ; "Our Farm Crops," Blackie and Son ; "How Crops Grow," Macmillan & Co. ; Roscoe's "Elementary Chemistry," Macmillan & Co. ; Lindley's, Henfrey's, or Balfour's "Botany;" Page's "Geological Text-Book," Blackwood & Sons.

## II.—BOTANY.

1. Nutritive Organs of Plants—root, stem, leaves. Functions of roots. Various kinds of stems, with examples. Use of the stem. Structure of leaves. Different kinds of leaves. Arrangement and functions of leaves. 2. Reproductive Organs—Flower and its parts. Arrangements of the whorls of the flower—calyx, corolla, stamens, pistil. Ovule. Mature pistil or fruit. Pruning and grafting. Seed. Young plant or embryo. Sprouting of the seed, or germination. 3. General Principles of Classification—meaning of the terms Class, Order, Genus, Species. Illustrations of natural orders taken from plants used in agriculture, such as grain-crops, grasses, clovers, vetches, turnips, mangold-wurzel, peas, beans, &c. Practical examination in fresh specimens and models ; some of the latter may be seen in the Museum, at the Royal Botanic Garden, which is open daily to the public, free. *Text-book*—Balfour's "Elements of Botany," A. & C. Black, 1876 ; price 3s. 6d.

## III.—CHEMISTRY.

The general principles of chemical combination. The chemistry of the more commonly occurring elements, and their more important compounds. The chemical processes concerned in agriculture generally. The changes which take place in the germination, growth, and maturation of plants, in the weathering and manuring of soils, &c. The composition and chemical character of the common mineral manures. *Text-books*—Roscoe's "Lessons in Elementary Chemistry," Macmillan & Co., London ; price 4s. 6d. Anderson's "Elements of Agricultural Chemistry," A. & C. Black, Edinburgh ; price 6s. 6d. Johnson's "How Crops Grow," Macmillan & Co., London.

## IV.—NATURAL HISTORY.

### 1. Zoology.

1. The Primary Divisions of the Animal Kingdom, with examples of each. 2. The Vertebrate Kingdom. The peculiarities and functions of the alimentary canal, distinguishing the Ruminants. 3. The orders—Hymenoptera, Diptera, and Coleoptera—with examples of insects injurious to farm crops belonging to each of the Orders—the preservation of birds which prey upon these insects, drawing a distinction between those which are beneficial and those which are destructive to crops. *Text-book*—Nicholson's "Introductory Text-Book of Zoology," William Blackwood & Sons, Edinburgh and London.

## 2. GEOLOGY.

4. The various strata forming the earth's crust in their order of deposition. 5. Their influences on the surface soils of the country. 6. The meaning and application of Disintegration, Drift, Alluvium, Dip, Strike, Fault. Page's "Introductory Text-Book of Geology," and Lyell's "Students' Elements of Geology."

## V.—VETERINARY SCIENCE.

1. Anatomy of the digestive organs of horse and ox, describing their structural differences. 2. The process of digestion in the above animals, and food most proper for each in quantity and quality. 3. The management of stock before, at, and after parturition. The time of utero-gestation in the domesticated animals. 4. The general principles to be followed in the treatment of very acute disease, before assistance of the veterinary surgeon can be procured.

## VI.—FIELD ENGINEERING.

1. Land-Surveying with the Chain. 2. Mensuration of Areas of Land, in Imperial and Scotch acres, from a Chain Survey or from a Plan. 3. Levelling with the ordinary levelling instrument and staff, and calculating levels and gradients. *Text-books*—Any one of the following:—Butler Williams' "Practical Geodesy," J. W. Parker, London; price 8s. 6d.; pages 1 to 19, 30 to 33, 56 to 59, 118 to 120. "Cassell on Land-Surveying," Cassell, Petter & Galpin. London; or "Bruff on Land-Surveying," Simpkin and Marshall, London; the parts which relate to chain-surveying and ordinary levelling only.

## VII.—BOOK-KEEPING.

1. Questions in Practice and Proportion. 2. Book-keeping—Describe books to be kept; give examples—taking of stock. *Text-book*—Stephen's "Practical System of Farm Book-keeping," Wm. Blackwood & Sons, Edinburgh; price 2s. 6d.

### EXAMINATION FOR BURSARIES.

Candidates are examined in the Elements of Botany, Chemistry, Physical Geography, and Geology. *Text-books*—Balfour's "Elements of Botany;" Roscoe's "Lessons in Elementary Chemistry;" Page's "Introductory Text-Book of Geology;" and Geikie's "Primer of Physical Geography;" Lyell's "Students' Elements of Geology."

It has been resolved that, under ordinary circumstances, the examinations shall be held annually in the end of October, and candidates must enter their names with the Secretary before the 10th of that month, and produce the necessary certificates from the teachers of the schools they have attended.

The bursaries are open to candidates not less than fourteen years of age.

---

# VETERINARY DEPARMTENT.

The Society established a Veterinary Department in 1823, but by an arrangement made with the Royal College of Veterinary Surgeons, the Society's examinations ceased in 1881. Holders of the Society's Veterinary Certificate are entitled to become Members of the Royal College of Veterinary Surgeons on payment of certain fees, without being required to undergo any further examination. The number of students who have passed for the Society's Certificate is 1183

# FORESTRY DEPARTMENT.

The Society grants FIRST and SECOND CLASS CERTIFICATES in FORESTRY.

### BOARD OF EXAMINERS.

1. *Science of Forestry and Practical Management of Woods.*—Dr CLEG-HORN of Stravithie, St. Andrews ; JOHN MACGREGOR, Ladywell, Dunkeld ; WILLIAM M'CORQUODALE, Scone Palace, Perth ; J. GRANT THOMSON, Grantown, Strathspey.
2. *Elements of Botany.*—Professor BALFOUR.
3. *Nature and Properties of Soils, Drainage, and Effects of Climate.*—Professor WILSON.
4. *Land and Timber Measuring and Surveying ; Mechanics and Construction, as applied to Fencing, Drainage, Bridging, and Road-Making ; Implements of Forestry.*—A. W. BELFRAGE, C.E.
5. —*Book-keeping and Accounts.*—JOHN TURNBULL SMITH, C.A.

Candidates must possess—1st, A thorough acquaintance with the details of practical forestry. 2d, a general knowledge of the following branches of study, so far as these apply to forestry :—The Outlines of Botany ; the Nature and Properties of Soils, Drainage and Effects of Climate ; Land and Timber Measuring and Surveying ; Mechanics and Construction, as applied to fencing, draining, bridging, and road-making ; Implements of Forestry ; Book-keeping and Accounts. The examinations are open to candidates of any age.

## SYLLABUS OF EXAMINATION.

### 1.—SCIENCE OF FORESTRY AND PRACTICAL MANAGEMENT OF WOODS.

1. Formation and ripening of Wood. Predisposing causes of decay. 2. Restoration of Wood-lands :—(1) Natural reproduction ; (2) Artificial planting. 3. General management of plantations. Cropping by rotation. Trees recommended for different situations. 4. Season and methods of pruning, thinning, and felling. 5. Circumstances unfavourable to the growth of trees. 6. Mechanical appliances for conveying and converting timber. Construction of saw-mills. 7. Qualities and uses of chief indigenous timbers. Processes of preserving timber. 8. Management of nurseries. Seed-sowing. 9. Collection of forest produce. 10. Manufacture of tar and charcoal. 11. Insects injurious to trees—preservation of birds which prey upon them, drawing a distinction between birds which are beneficial and those which are destructive to trees.

### II.—ELEMENTS OF BOTANY.

1. Nutritive Organs of Plants.—Root, stem, leaves. Functions of roots. Various kinds of stems, with examples. Use of the stem. Structure of leaves. Different kinds of leaves. Arrangement and functions of leaves. 2. Reproductive Organs.—Flower and its parts. Arrangement of the whorls of the flower—calyx, corolla, stamens, pistil. Ovule. Mature pistil or fruit. Pruning and grafting. Seed. Young plant or embryo. Sprouting of the seed or germination. 3. General Principles of Classification—Meaning of the terms Class, Order, Genus, Species. Illustrations taken from common forest trees and shrubs. Practical examination on fresh specimens and models ;

some of the latter may be seen in the Museum at the Royal Botanic Garden, which is open daily to the public free. Candidates may consult Professor Balfour's "Elements of Botany," published by A. & C. Black, Edinburgh, 1869, price 3s. 6d.

## III.—NATURE AND PROPERTIES OF SOILS, DRAINAGE AND EFFECTS OF CLIMATE.

1. The different descriptions of soils, their classification, and suitability to growth of different descriptions of timber trees. 2. The composition and constituents of soils. The relations between the soil and trees growing on it. 3. The effects of drainage on soils and on climate. 4. The mode of drainage for plantations. 5. The influence of temperature, rainfall, aspect, shelter, and prevailing winds on tree life. 6. The methods of registering and recording observations, and the instruments used.

## IV.—LAND AND TIMBER MEASURING AND SURVEYING; MECHANICS AND CONSTRUCTION as applied to Fencing, Bridging, and Road-Making; IMPLEMENTS OF FORESTRY.

1.—The Use of the Level and Measuring Chain. Measuring and mapping surface areas. 2. The measurement of solid bodies—as timber, stacked bark, faggots, &c., earthwork. 3. The different modes of fencing and enclosing plantations; their relative advantages, durability, cost of construction, and repairs. 4. The setting out and formation of roads for temporary or permanent use. 5. The construction of bridges over streams and gullies; of gates or other entrances. 6. The different implements and tools used in planting, pruning, felling, barking, and working up timber trees, or preparing them for sale. Ewart's "Agricultural Assistant," Blackie & Son, Glasgow and Edinburgh, price 3s. 6d. Strachan's "Agricultural Tables," Oliver & Boyd, Edinburgh, price 2s. 6d.

## V.—BOOK-KEEPING AND ACCOUNTS.

1. Questions in Practice and Proportion. 2. Book-keeping—describe books to be kept; give examples. Taking of stock.

# CHEMICAL DEPARTMENT.

*Chemist to the Society*—Dr A. P. AITKEN, Chemical Laboratory,

11 St. Andrew's Lane, Edinburgh.

The object of the Chemical Department is to carry on the Experiments at the Society's Agricultural Stations, and to consider all matters coming before the Society's notice in connection with the chemistry of agriculture.

The practical chemical work of the Society is under the charge of its Chemist, whose duties are—

1. To superintend the experiments being carried on at the experimental stations of the Society, to make all necessary analyses and investigations in connection therewith, and to prepare an annual report of these for publication in the *Transactions*.

2. To perform the requisite analyses in connection with such other experiments as are conducted under the sanction and direction of the Chemical Committee, and report on the same if desired.

3. To prepare a summary of all analyses for which the Society has contributed payment, and full details of such as appear to the Chemical Committee worthy of notice for publication in the *Transactions*.

4. To attend all meetings of the Chemical Committee of the Society.

5. To have a laboratory in Edinburgh, where he may be consulted by members of the Society, and to be in attendance there every Wednesday for that purpose.

6. To maintain a sufficient staff of assistants, one of whom at least is specially engaged in, and acquainted with, both the chemical and experimental work of the Society.

7. To prepare annually for publication in the Society's *Transactions* a report on the more important investigations and experiments being conducted in this country and elsewhere on the application of chemistry to agriculture.

8. To deliver lectures at such places and on such subjects connected with the chemistry of agriculture as are approved of by the Chemical Committee, and for which the chemist is permitted to receive remuneration from those applying for his services.

The chemist and his assistants are paid their travelling expenses when on the Society's work.

He receives a fee of £1, 1s. for each analysis made by him when employed as referee in connection with Local Associations.

He is entitled to charge for analyses made for members of the Society according to the following scale of fees :—

| | | | | | | | | |
|---|---|---|---|---|---|---|---|---|
| Manures, | . | | . | | . | £1 | 0 | 0 |
| Feeding Stuffs, | . | | . | | . | 1 | 0 | 0 |
| Water, Sanitary Analysis, | . | | . | | . | 1 | 0 | 0 |
| „ Full Analysis, | . | | . | | . | 5 | 0 | 0 |
| Soil, Analytical Examination and Recommendation of Manures, | . | | . | | . | 1 | 10 | 0 |
| „ Full Analysis, | . | | . | | . | 5 | 0 | 0 |
| Vegetable Products, such as Hay, Turnips, Grain, &c., | | | | | . | 1 | 10 | 0 |
| Partial Analysis, each constituent, | . | | . | | . | 0 | 10 | 0 |
| Testing for Gross Adulteration, | . | | . | | . | 0 | 5 | 0 |
| Advice, | . | | . | | . | 0 | 5 | 0 |

# INSTRUCTIONS FOR SELECTING SAMPLES FOR ANALYSIS.

## MANURES.

Four or more bags are to be selected for sampling. Each bag is to be emptied out separately on a clean floor, worked through with the spade, and one spadeful taken out and set aside. The four or more spadefuls thus set aside are to be mixed together until a uniform mixture is obtained. Of this mixture one spadeful is to be taken, spread on paper, and still more thoroughly mixed, any lumps which it may contain being broken down with the hand. Of this mixture two samples of about a pound each shall be taken by the purchaser or his agent, in the presence of the seller or his agent or two witnesses, and these samples shall be taken as quickly as possible and put into bottles or tin cases to prevent loss of moisture, and having been labelled, shall be sealed by the samplers—one sample to be retained by the association, and the other to be sent to the chemist for analysis.

## FEEDING STUFFS.

Samples of feeding compounds are to be taken in a similar manner.

Samples of cake are to be taken by selecting three cakes, breaking each across the middle, and from the broken part breaking a small segment across the entire breadth of the cake. The three pieces thus obtained shall be wrapped up and sealed by the samplers, and sent for analysis as in the case of manures, and three duplicate pieces similarly sealed shall be retained by the association.

## SOILS.

Dig a little trench about two feet deep, exposing the soil and subsoil. Cut from the side of this trench a perpendicular section of the soil down to the top of the subsoil, and about four inches wide. Extract it carefully, and do not allow the subsoil to mix with it. A similar section of subsoil immediately below this sample should be taken and preserved separately. Five or six similarly drawn samples should be taken from different parts of the field, and kept separate while being sent to the chemist, that he may examine them individually before mixing in the laboratory.

## VEGETABLE PRODUCTS.

*Turnips, &c.,* 20 to 30 carefully selected as fair average bulbs.

*Hay and straw* must be sampled from a thin section cut across the whole stack, and carefully mixed about; about 20 lbs. weight is required for analysis.

*Grain* should be sampled like feeding stuffs.

## WATERS.

The bottles or jars in which samples of water are sent should be thoroughly cleaned. This is done by first rinsing them with water, then with a little oil of vitriol. After pouring this out the bottle should be rinsed six times with water, filled, corked with a new washed cork, sealed, and sent *without delay.* (Chemically clean bottles may be sent from the laboratory.)

Well water may be collected at any time, but it should be allowed to run for some time before the sample is taken.

Spring or stream water should be collected when the weather is dry.

In the analysis of a mineral water it may sometimes be desirable to determine the amount of gases held in solution, in which case certain precautions must be observed which require the presence of the chemist at the spring.

## LOCAL ANALYTICAL ASSOCIATIONS.

At the General Meeting of the Society held on 19th January 1881, the following resolutions were passed :—

I. With the view of encouraging, as well as regulating the conduct of, Local Analytical Associations, the Society shall contribute from its funds towards their expenses a sum for the present not exceeding £250 annually.

II. That the amount of such contribution shall be to each association at the rate of 5s. for each full analysis, and 2s. 6d. for each partial analysis of manures or feeding stuffs effected, or such proportion thereof as the above annual contribution may permit of, the pecuniary assistance thus contemplated to be subject to the following conditions being complied with to the satisfaction of the Chemical Committee :—

1. That the rules of the association be submitted to and approved of by the Chemical Committee.

2. That it be a condition of participating in the grant that the association make analyses for members of the Highland and Agricultural Society being farmers and not members of the local association, charging them the cost price to the association, less the amount recovered from the Society.

3. That the association is managed by a committee of practical farmers owning or occupying land in the district.

4. That the analyst employed is of acknowledged standing.

5. That the benefits of the grant shall apply only to analyses made for farmers, and that they subscribe towards the expenses of the association, subject to the exception in No. 2.

6. That each analysis represents at least 2 tons of bulk actually purchased under guarantee, or at a specified price per unit of valuable ingredients, and delivered to one or more members, and that the analysis has been made from a sample drawn in accordance with the published instructions of the Society, and that a sealed duplicate sample has been retained.

7. That with each analysis is furnished the names and addresses of the seller and of the buyer or buyers, the guarantee given, the cash or credit price at which bought, the place of delivery, and the result as determined by the analyst of the association.

8. That in the case of any manufactured manure reported upon, the seller shall be obliged to supply members of the association with a further quantity at the same price and terms, provided the order is given not later than one month after the parcel reported upon has been delivered and the quantity in all does not exceed 20 tons.

9. That all analyses be reported according to forms to be furnished by the Highland and Agricultural Society, and valuations of manures, if any are made, to be calculated on a uniform standard to be issued periodically by the Society, and at least once a year.

III. That a summary of all analyses for which the Society has contributed payment, and full details of such as shall appear to the Chemical Committee worthy of notice, shall be published each year in the *Transactions*. But before such publication is made, in the case of all which show an inferiority in the whole valuable constituents of 8 per cent. or upwards between the guarantee given and the analysis obtained, there may be at the option of the seller, to whom due notice will be given, a further analysis made by an independent chemist to be chosen by the Society.

The report of each analysis for which a grant is claimed must be sent to the Secretary of the Highland and Agricultural Society on or before the 1st November of each year, written on a schedule containing the following particulars:—

Name and Address of Seller and of Buyer.

Kind of Manure or Feeding Stuff and quantity purchased.

Price per ton, or prices per unit of ingredients.

Guaranteed and found analyses, date when sample was drawn, and in whose presence.

Copies of schedules to be filled up by the associations may be had on application to the Secretary of the Society, and no grants can be given for any analysis whose schedules are not accurately filled up.

The actual analytical reports of the association's analyst must accompany the schedules as vouchers, and these will be returned.

In the case of all analyses which show an inferiority in the whole valuable constituents of 8 per cent. or upwards, it is necessary that no time be lost in communicating with the seller, in order that no deterioration may take place in the reserved sample, which, along with any explanation received from the seller, shall be forthwith forwarded to the Secretary of the Highland and Agricultural Society.

The following are the forms in which analyses of *ordinary genuine* manures and feeding stuffs must be reported :—

I. Reports of Analyses of *MANURES.*

(*On the one side are the analytical details, and on the other the valuable constituents, which alone are considered in estimating the value of manure*).

1. Form of Analysis for SUPERPHOSPHATES, DISSOLVED BONES, and the like.

Capable of yielding as valuable constituents.

Phosphoric Acid, in a soluble state, . . . }

Do., in an insoluble state,

Lime, .

Sulphuric Acid, Organic Matter, &c.,.

Sand and insoluble matter, .

hosphate of Lime, dissolved, . . } ...... }......

Do. undissolved, . ......

Ammonia,

2. Form of Analysis for BONES, BONE MEAL, FISH GUANO, and the like.

Capable of yielding as valuable constituents.

Phosphoric Acid, . .

Lime, . . .

Alkalies, &c., . .

Organic matter, . .

Moisture, . . .

Sand and insoluble matter,

} Phosphate of Lime, .

Ammonia,

3. Form of Analysis for MIXED MANURES, PERUVIAN and ICHABOE GUANOS, and the like.

Capable of yielding as valuable constituents.

Phosphoric Acid, in a soluble state, . . }

Do., in an insoluble state, .

Lime,

Alkalies, &c.,

Organic matter and Ammonia Salts, }

Moisture, . . .

Sand and insoluble matter,

Phosphate of Lime, dissolved, . } ...... }......

Do., undissolved, . ......

Potash, .

Nitrates = Ammonia

Ammonia . .

II. REPORTS OF ANALYSES OF *FEEDING STUFFS*.

*Valuable constituents* $\begin{cases} \text{Albuminoid compounds,} \\ \text{Oil,} \\ \text{Mucilage, Sugar, Starch, &c.,} \\ \text{Woody Fibre,} \\ \text{Moisture,} \\ \text{Ash,} \end{cases}$

Nitrogen, . . . . . . . ......

## NOTES REGARDING ANALYSES.

### I. MANURES.

The three items of greatest importance in manures are phosphoric acid, nitrogen, and potash.

1. PHOSPHORIC ACID is present in manures as such, and also as phosphates of lime, magnesia, iron, and alumina.
*Phosphate of Lime* is most important, and exists in two states, insoluble and soluble.

*Insoluble—*

Insoluble phosphate of lime, called also $\left.\begin{array}{l} \text{Tricalcic phosphate, and} \\ \text{Tribasic phosphate of lime.} \end{array}\right\}$ contains about 46% phosphoric acid.

*Soluble—*

Soluble phosphate of lime, called also
Acid phosphate of lime, and *erroneously* $\left.\right\}$ contains about 61%
Monobasic phosphate of lime, $\phantom{xx}$ phosphoric acid.

Some analysts prefer to state the soluble phosphate as
Biphosphate of Lime, called also $\left.\right\}$ contains about 72%
Monobasic phosphate, $\phantom{xx}$ phosphoric acid.

The soluble phosphates are usually stated as equivalent to so much tricalcic phosphate.

Soluble phosphate, multiplied by $1\frac{1}{3}$ $\left.\right\}$ gives the equivalent of
Biphosphate,     "   " $1\frac{1}{2}$ $\phantom{x}$ tricalcic phosphate nearly.

The term "*soluble phosphate*" is generally used in place of *phosphate of lime rendered soluble.*

Phosphate of magnesia occurs in small quantity in bones, &c., and is usually reckoned as tricalcic phosphate.

Phosphates of iron and alumina when occurring in *small quantity* are usually reckoned as tricalcic phosphate, but if the quantity is considerable it should be separately estimated.

*N.B.*—To save ambiguity all phosphates should be described as containing so much anhydrous phosphoric acid ($P_2O_5$) in a soluble or in an insoluble state.

This amount multiplied by 2·183 would then give the equivalent of tricalcic phosphate.

2. NITROGEN occurs in manures mostly in three forms—Ammonia salts, nitrates, and albuminoid matter.

Ammonia sulphate (pure), contains $25\frac{3}{4}\%$ ammonia.
Ammonia chloride (pure),    $31\frac{4}{}$ " "
Nitrate of soda (pure), contains 16·47 % nitrogen, equal to 20 % ammonia.

Albuminoid matter contains about 16 % nitrogen, equal to about 19 % ammonia, most of which sooner or later becomes available as plant food.

3. POTASH is found in small amount in most manures, and should be reckoned as anhydrous potash ($K_2O$).

Sulphate of potash (pure), contains potassium = 50 % anhydrous potash.

Muriate of potash (pure), contains potassium = fully 63 % anhydrous potash.

## II. FEEDING STUFFS.

These are chiefly concentrated forms of food whose value depends on the amounts they contain of albuminoids, oil, and carbohydrates.

*Albuminoids* are compounds containing nitrogen, and more or less resemble dry flesh in their composition. They are sometimes called *flesh formers*. They are the most valuable constituents of feeding stuffs. The percentage of nitrogen contained in a cake multiplied by $6\frac{1}{4}$ gives the percentage of albuminoids.

*Carbohydrates* are compounds such as sugar, starch, gum, and cellulose.

*Woody fibre* is the name given to that part of the cellulose which is insoluble when boiled in weak solutions (5%) of acids and alkalies, and is therefore considered indigestible.

Good linseed, cotton, and rape cakes should contain from 4% to 5 % nitrogen, about 10 % oil, and about 6 % ash.

USEFUL FACTORS.

| Amount of | Multiplied by | Gives corresponding amount of |
|---|---|---|
| Nitrogen | 1·214 | Ammonia. |
| " | 6·3 | Albuminoid matter. |
| Ammonia | 3·882 | Sulphate of Ammonia. |
| " | 3·147 | Muriate of Ammonia. |
| " | 3·706 | Nitric Acid. |
| " | 5·0 | Nitrate of Soda. |
| Potash (anhydrous) | 1·85 | Sulphate of Potash. |
| " | 1·585 | Muriate of Potash. |
| Phosphoric Acid (anhydrous) | 2·183 | *Phosphate of Lime. |
| " " | 1·4 | Biphosphate. |
| " " | 1·648 | Soluble Phosphate (monocalcic tribasic). |
| Soluble Phosphate | 1·325 | Phosphate of Lime. |
| Biphosphate | 1·566 | Phosphate of Lime. |
| Lime | 1·845 | Phosphate of Lime. |
| " | 1·786 | Carbonate of Lime. |

By phosphate of lime is meant tricalcic phosphate ($Ca_3 P_2O_8$).

# PREMIUMS.

---

## GENERAL REGULATIONS FOR COMPETITORS.

All reports must be legibly written, and on one side of the paper only; they must specify the number and subject of the Premium for which they are in competition; they must bear a distinguishing motto, and be accompanied by a sealed letter similary marked, containing the name and address of the Reporter—initials must not be used.

No sealed letter, unless belonging to a Report found entitled to at least one-half of the premium offered, will be opened without the author's consent.

Reports for which a Premium, or one-half of it, has been awarded, become the property of the Society, and cannot be published in whole or in part, nor circulated in any manner, without the consent of the Directors. All other papers will be returned to the authors, if applied for within twelve months.

When a Report is unsatisfactory, the Society is not bound to award the whole or any part of a premium.

All Reports must be of a practical character, containing the results of the writer's own observation or experiment, and the special conditions attached to each Premium must be strictly fulfilled. General essays, and papers compiled from books, will not be rewarded. Weights and measurements must be indicated by the Imperial standards.

The Directors, before awarding a Premium, shall have power to require the writer of any report to verify the statements made in it.

The decisions of the Board of Directors are final and conclusive as to all Premiums, whether for Reports or at General or District Shows; and it shall not be competent to raise any question or appeal touching such decisions before any other tribunal.

The Directors will welcome papers from any Contributor on any suitable subject not included in the Premium List; and if the topic and the treatment of it are both approved, the Writer will be remunerated, and his paper published.

# CLASS I.

## REPORTS.

### SECTION 1.—THE SCIENCE AND PRACTICE OF AGRICULTURE.

#### FOR APPROVED REPORTS.

1. On the Agriculture of the Counties of Clackmannan and Kinross—Twenty Sovereigns. To be lodged by 1st November 1882.

> The Report should embrace full details of the different systems of Farm Management observed in the Counties, and of the progress which Agriculture and other industries have made within the last 25 years.

2. On the Agriculture of the County of Lanark—Forty Sovereigns. To be lodged by 1st November 1882.

> The Report should embrace full details of the different systems of Farm Management observed in the County, and of the progress which Agriculture and other industries have made within the last 25 years.

3. On the Agriculture of the County of Stirling—Twenty Sovereigns. To be lodged by 1st November 1882.

> The Report should embrace full details of the different systems of Farm Management observed in the County, and of the progress which Agriculture and other industries have made within the last 25 years.

4. On the Agriculture of the Counties of Elgin and Nairn—Thirty Sovereigns to be lodged by 1st November 1882.

> The Report should embrace full details of the different systems of Farm Management observed in the Counties, and of the progress which Agriculture and other industries have made within the last 25 years.

5. On the results of experiments for fixing and retaining the volatile and soluble ingredients in farm-yard manure—Twenty Sovereigns. To be lodged by 1st November 1882.

> The Report must detail the treatment adopted to fix and retain these ingredients—the materials used for that purpose—and the quantity and cost thereof—comparative analyses of the manure with and without the treatment, and also a statement of the crops grown with manure with and without such treatment, must be given by the Reporter. The experiments to have extended over at least two years and crops.

6. On the results of experiments for ascertaining the comparative value of farm-yard manure obtained from cattle fed upon different varieties of food, by the application of such manures to farm crops—Twenty Sovereigns. To be lodged by 1st November in any year.

> The Report must state the effects produced on two successive crops by the application of manure obtained from cattle fed on different sorts of food, such as turnips and straw alone ; and turnips and straw, with an addition of oil-cake, linseed, bean-meal, grain or other substances. The animals should be as nearly as possible of the same age, weight, condition, and maturity, and each lot should receive daily the same quantity of litter ; and, except as to the difference of food, they must be treated alike.
>
> The preparation of the manure, by fermentation or otherwise, should be in every respect the same ; and it is desirable that not less than two several experiments be made with each kind, and that the ground to which it is to be applied be as equal as possible in quality and condition.

7. On the means successfully employed for obtaining new Agricultural Plants, or new and superior varieties, or improved sub-varieties, of any of the cereal grains, grasses, roots, or other agricultural plants at present cultivated in this country—Medals, or sums of Money not exceeding Fifty Sovereigns. To be lodged by 1st November in any year.

> It is necessary that the varieties and sub-varieties reported upon shall have been proved capable of reproduction from seed, and also that the relation they bear to others, or well-known sorts, should be stated. The Reporter is further requested to mention the effects that he may have observed produced by different soils, manures, &c., on the plants forming the subject of report, and how far he may have ascertained such effects to be lasting.
>
> Should any improved variety reported upon be the result of direct experiment by cross impregnation, involving expense and long-continued attention, a higher premium will be awarded.

8. On the hardy and useful Herbaceous Plants of any country where such climate exists as to induce the belief that the plants may be beneficially introduced into the cultivation of Scotland —The Gold Medal, or Ten Sovereigns. To be lodged by 1st November in any year.

> Attention is particularly directed to the Grains and Grasses of China, Japan, the Islands of the Eastern Archipelago, the Himalaya country, the Falkland and South Sea Islands, California, and the high north-western district of America.
>
> Reporters are required to give the generic and specific names of the plants treated of, with the authority for the same—together with the native names, so far as known ; and to state the elevation of the locality and nature of the soil in which they are cultivated, or which they naturally inhabit, with their qualities or uses ; and it is further requested that the descriptions be accompanied, in so far as possible, with specimens of the plants, and their fruit, seed, and other products.

9. On the adulteration of Agricultural Seeds, whether by colouring, mixing, or otherwise, and the best means of detecting the same, and preventing their sale—Ten Sovereigns. To be lodged by 1st November 1882.

10. On the comparative advantages of fattening Cattle in stalls, in loose houses or boxes, and in sheds or hammels—Twenty Sovereigns. To be lodged by 1st November in any year.

> The Report must detail the comparative result of actual experiments. The same quantities and kinds of food must be used. Information is required as to the comparative expense of attendance, the cost of erecting the buildings, and any other circumstance deserving of attention. The state of the weather during the experiment, in point of temperature and wetness, and the advantages or disadvantages of clipping cattle put up to feed, must be particularly noted and reported.

11. On experiments for ascertaining the actual addition of weight to growing or fattening Stock, by the use of different kinds of food—Twenty Sovereigns. To be lodged by 1st November in any year.

> The attention of the Experimenter is directed to turnips, carrots, beet, mangold-wurzel, potatoes, cabbage, as well as to beans, oats, barley, Indian corn, linseed, oil-cake or rape-cake, and to the effect of warmth and proper ventilation, and the difference between food cooked and raw. The above roots and other kinds of food are merely suggested ; competitors are neither restricted to them nor obliged to experiment on all of them.
> When experiments are made with linseed and cake, attention should be paid to the comparative advantages, economically and otherwise, of the substance in these two states.
> Before commencing the comparative experiments, the animals must be fed alike for some time previously.
> The progress of different breeds may be compared. This will form an interesting experiment of itself, for Reports of which encouragement will be given.
>
> N.B.—The experiments specified in the two previous subjects must be conducted over a period of not less than three months. No lot shall consist of fewer than four Cattle or ten Sheep. The animals selected should be of the same age, sex, and breed, and, as nearly as possible, of the same weight, condition, and maturity. The live weight before and after the experiment must be stated, and, if killed, their dead weight and quantity of tallow.

12. On the Blackfaced Breed of Sheep, and the means that have been or might be used for its improvement—The Gold Medal, or Ten Sovereigns. To be lodged by 1st November 1882.

13. On the influence of Soil and Geological Formation in the production of Disease in Animals—Ten Sovereigns.  To be lodged by 1st November 1882.

14. On the effect of Sewage upon the Animal System, introduced either with drinking water or with herbage when sewage has been used as a top-dressing—Ten Sovereigns.  To be lodged by 1st November 1882.

15. On a description of any scheme whereby Town Sewage has been successfully utilised for irrigation in Agriculture—Twenty Sovereigns.  To be lodged by 1st November in any year.

> The scheme described must have been in operation for at least two years—the description to include (1) the manner in which the land was drained and prepared for irrigation, and the cost of preparing it per acre ; (2) the quantity of sewage used per acre, and the mode in which it is applied to the fields ; (3) the annual cost per acre of wages, &c., in working the process ; (4) the kind, amount, and value of the crops obtained per acre.

16. On any useful practice in Rural Economy adopted in other countries, and susceptible of being introduced with advantage into Scotland—The Gold Medal.  To be lodged by 1st November in any year.

> The purpose chiefly contemplated by the offer of this premium is to induce travellers to notice and record such particular practices as may seem calculated to benefit Scotland.  The Report to be founded on personal observation.

## Section 2.—ESTATE IMPROVEMENTS.

### FOR APPROVED REPORTS.

1. By the Proprietor in Scotland who shall have executed the most judicious, successful, and extensive improvement—The Gold Medal, or Ten Sovereigns.  To be lodged by 1st November in any year.

> Should the successful Report be written for the Proprietor by his resident factor or farm manager, a Minor Gold Medal will be awarded to the writer in addition to the Gold Medal to the Proprietor.
> The merits of the Report will not be determined so much by the mere extent of the improvements, as by their character and relation to the size of the property.  The improvements may comprise reclaiming, draining, enclosing, planting, road-making, building, and all other operations proper to landed estates.  The period within which the operations may have been conducted is not limited, except that it must not exceed the term of the Reporter's proprietorship.

2. By the Proprietor in Scotland who shall have erected on his estate the most approved Farm-buildings—The Gold Medal. Reports, Plans, and Specifications to be lodged by 1st November in any year.

3. By the Proprietor or Tenant in Scotland who shall have reclaimed within the ten preceding years not less than forty acres of waste land—The Gold Medal, or Ten Sovereigns. To be lodged by 1st November in any year.

4. By the Tenant in Scotland who shall have reclaimed within the ten preceding years not less than twenty acres of waste land—The Gold Medal, or Ten Sovereigns. To be lodged by 1st November in any year.

5. By the Tenant in Scotland who shall have reclaimed not less than ten acres within a similar period—The Medium Gold Medal, or Five Sovereigns. To be lodged by 1st November in any year.

> The Reports in competition for Nos. 3, 4, and 5 may comprehend such general observations on the improvement of waste lands as the writer's experience may lead him to make, but must refer especially to the lands reclaimed—to the nature of the soil—the previous state and probable value of the subject—the obstacles opposed to its improvement—the details of the various operations—the mode of cultivation adopted—and the produce and value of the crops produced. As the required extent cannot be made up of different patches of land, the improvement must have relation to one subject; it must be of a profitable character, and a rotation of crops must have been concluded before the date of the Report. *A detailed statement of the expenditure and return* and a certified measurement of the ground are requisite.

6. By the Proprietor or Tenant in Scotland who shall have improved within the ten preceding years the pasturage of not less than thirty acres, by means of top-dressing, draining, or otherwise, without tillage, in situations where tillage may be inexpedient—The Gold Medal, or Ten Sovereigns. To be lodged by 1st November in any year.

7. By the Tenant in Scotland who shall have improved not less than ten acres within a similar period—The Minor Gold Medal. To be lodged by 1st November in any year.

> Reports in competition for Nos. 6 and 7 must state the particular mode of management adopted, the substances applied, the elevation and nature of the soil, its previous natural products, and the changes produced.

## SECTION 3.—MACHINERY.

### FOR APPROVED REPORTS.

1. On such inventions or improvements, by the Reporters, of any implement or machine as shall be deemed by the Society of public utility—Medals, or sums of money not exceeding Fifty Sovereigns.   To be lodged at any time.

> Reports should be accompanied by drawings and descriptions of the implement or machine, and, if necessary, by a model.

2. On the best and most improved Cattle Truck for feeding and watering the animals in transit—Twenty Sovereigns.   To be lodged by 1st November 1882.

> Reports must be accompanied with drawings and description, or, if necessary, by a model.

## SECTION 4.—FORESTRY DEPARTMENT.

### FOR APPROVED REPORTS.

1. By the Proprietor in Scotland who shall, within the five preceding years, have planted not less than 150 acres—The Gold Medal.   To be lodged by 1st November in any year.

> The whole planting operations which may have been conducted by the Reporter within the five years, whether completed or not, must be embraced, and he must state the expense—description of soils—age, kind, and number of trees planted per acre—mode of planting, draining, and fencing—general state of the plantation—and any other observations of interest.

2. On Plantations of not less than eight years standing, formed on deep peat bog—The Medium Gold Medal, or Five Sovereigns.   To be lodged by 1st November 1882.

> The premium is strictly applicable to deep peat or flow moss; the condition of the moss previous to planting, as well as at the date of the Report, should, if possible, be stated.
> The Report must describe the mode and extent of the drainage, and the effect it has had in subsiding the moss—the trenching, levelling, or other preliminary operations that may have been performed on the surface—the mode of planting—kinds, sizes, and numbers of trees planted per acre—and their relative progress and value, as compared with plantations of a similar age and description grown on other soils in the vicinity.

3. On the more extended introduction of hardy, useful, or ornamental Trees, which have not hitherto been generally cultivated in Scotland—The Medium Gold Medal, or Five Sovereigns. To be lodged by 1st November in any year.

The Report should specify as distinctly as possible the kind of trees introduced. The adaptation of the trees for use or ornament, and their comparative progress should be mentioned. Attention is directed to the introduction of any tree as a nurse in young plantations, which by growing rapidly for several years, and attaining maturity when at the height of 20 or 25 feet, might realise the advantage and avoid the evils of thick planting.

4. On the *Picea Pectinata* (Silver Fir)—The Medium Gold Medal, or Five Sovereigns. To be lodged by 1st November 1882.

5. On the varieties of Trees best adapted for planting as shelter in the Islands of Scotland—The Medium Gold Medal, or Five Sovereigns. To be lodged by 1st November 1882.

6. On the old and remarkable Walnut Trees in Scotland— The Gold Medal, or Ten Sovereigns. To be lodged by 1st November 1883.

Details of their growth, measurements, and condition, and any particulars of their history, must be given. The measurements to be taken by the Reporter himself, and at 5 feet from the ground, if possible. Photographs and drawings are desirable.

7. On the old and remarkable Horse Chestnut Trees in Scotland—The Gold Medal, or Ten Sovereigns. To be lodged by 1st November 1883.

Details of their growth, measurements, and condition, and any particulars of their history, must be given. The measurements to be taken by the Reporter himself, and at 5 feet from the ground, if possible. Photographs and drawings are desirable.

8. On the most suitable varieties of Trees, adapted to various soils and altitudes, to be left as standards in cutting down plantations, with a view to the encouragement of a healthy undergrowth of herbage and grasses for the purpose of grazing cattle and sheep, with a list of those grasses and forage plants best adapted for growth in the locality under such conditions—Ten Sovereigns. Reports to be lodged by 1st November 1882.

Reports need not be confined to Scotland. Information is desired from such countries as India.

9. On the deterioration in quality and durability of Home-Grown Timber at the present day, especially regarding Scotch Fir, as compared with the timber of the old Scotch forests, and suggestions for a remedy—The Medium Gold Medal, or Five Sovereigns. To be lodged by 1st November 1882.

10. On the cutting and transport of Firewood (soft and hard wood), with detailed statement of charges—The Medium Gold Medal, or Five Sovereigns. To be lodged by 1st November 1882.

In many districts large branches and tops of trees are burned up, which in England, and much more on the Continent, are sold at a profit. The Report should state the system pursued, and contain practical suggestions for utilising fragments now destroyed.

11. On the more extended cultivation in Scotland of Charcoal-producing Plants, for gunpowder or commercial purposes—The Medium Gold Medal, or Five Sovereigns. To be lodged by 1st November 1882.

Reference to be made to suitable varieties of plants not generally grown in this country for that purpose, such as *Rhamnus Frangula*, prices realisable, and suggestions for their more general introduction, treatment, &c.

12. On the Woods, Forests, and Forestry in the county of Perth—The Gold Medal, or Ten Sovereigns. To be lodged by 1st November 1882.

13. On the Woods, Forests, and Forestry in the county of Ross—The Gold Medal, or Ten Sovereigns. To be lodged by 1st November 1882.

14. On the Woods, Forests, and Forestry in the county of Inverness—The Gold Medal, or Ten Sovereigns. To be lodged by 1st November 1882.

15. On the comparative advantages of High Forest with Coppice, or Coppice with a limited number of Standard Trees—The Medium Gold Medal, or Five Sovereigns. To be lodged by 1st November 1882.

16. On the utilisation of waste produce of Forests and Woodlands, as matter for making, either separately or in combination with other substances, an Artificial Fuel—The Gold Medal, or Ten Sovereigns. To be lodged by 1st November 1882.

17. On the Insects most injurious to Forest Trees, and the diseases occasioned by them, and the best means of prevention—Twenty Sovereigns. To be lodged by 1st November 1882.

The Report to be accompanied, where practicable, by specimens of the insects.

18. On the disastrous Gales of Season 1881-82, and their destruction to Trees in different localities in Scotland, with detailed statistics of losses—The Medium Gold Medal, or Five Sovereigns. To be lodged by 1st November 1882.

19. On the best mode of preparing Wood for Fencing with a view to its preservation—The Medium Gold Medal, or Five Sovereigns. To be lodged by 1st November 1882.

# CLASS II.

## DISTRICT COMPETITIONS.

*The Money Premiums and Medals awarded at District Competitions will be issued in January next. No payments must, therefore, be made by the Secretary or Treasurer of any local Association.*

*Grants in aid of DISTRICT COMPETITIONS for 1883 must be applied for before 1st NOVEMBER 1882, on Forms to be obtained from the Secretary.*

*When a Grant has expired, the District cannot apply again for aid for two years.*

### SECTION 1.—CATTLE.

*Note.*—The Society's Cattle Premiums are granted to each District for three alternate years, on condition that the District shall, in the two intermediate years, continue the Competitions by offering for the same description of Stock a sum not less than one-half of that given by the Society. At the intermediate Competitions, a Silver Medal will be placed at the disposal of the Committee, to be awarded for the Best Bull which has gained a first money prize at a previous District or General Show of the Highland and Agricultural Society, and of the Class for which the District receives Premiums ; also three Medium Silver Medals to be given along with the first prize in the three Classes of Cattle, provided there are not fewer than two lots exhibited in each Class.
The selection of the Breed is left to the local Committee. See Rule 6.

#### DISTRICTS.

1. DISTRICT OF FORMARTINE.—*Convener*, The Earl of Aberdeen, Haddo House, Methlick ; *Secretary*, Alex. Davidson, Mains of Cairnbrogie, Old Meldrum. Granted 1878.
2. DISTRICT OF THE KINGLASSIE SOCIETY.—*Convener*, R. Sinclair Aytoun of Inchdairnie, Kirkcaldy ; *Secretary*, David Beath, Auchmuir, Leslie. Granted 1878.
3. COUNTY OF AYR.—*Convener*, Hon. G. R. Vernon, Auchans House, Kilmarnock ; *Secretary*, James M'Murtrie, Ayr. Granted 1878.
4. CENTRAL BANFFSHIRE.—*Convener*, William Longmore, Keith ; *Secretary*, J. Geddes Brown, Keith. Granted 1880.
5. STIRLINGSHIRE.—*Convener*, Sir James R. Gibson-Maitland of Barnton, Bart., Craigend, Stirling ; *Secretary*, Robert Taylor, 22 Barnton Place, Stirling. Granted 1880.
6. ISLANDS OF MULL, COLL, AND TIREE.—*Convener*, James Noel Forsyth of Quinish, Tobermory ; *Secretary*, Robert Lang, Aros Mains, Aros, Mull. Granted 1880.
7. RENFREWSHIRE.—*Convener*, Lieut-Colonel Sir Archibald C. Campbell of Blythswood, Bart., Renfrew ; *Secretary*, William Bartlemore, County Buildings, Paisley. Granted 1880.
8. DISTRICT OF BUCHAN.—*Convener*, John Sleigh, Strichen ; *Secretary*, James Smith, Strichen. Granted 1882.

9. DISTRICT OF THE DEESIDE UNION.—*Convener*, Colonel Innes of Learney, Torphins; *Secretary*, James Shaw, Tillyching, Lumphanan. Granted 1879.

10. DISTRICT OF LORN.—*Convener*, Colonel M'Dougall of Dunollie, Oban; *Secretary*, Donald Macgregor, Solicitor, Oban. Granted 1879.

11. DISTRICT OF INVERARAY.—*Convener* and *Secretary*, John Macarthur, Inveraray. Granted 1881.

### PREMIUMS.

1. Best Bull, of any pure breed, having gained a previous Highland and Agricultural Society's First Money Prize, . The Silver Medal.

2. Best Bull, 3-year old and upwards, of any pure breed,
Medium Silver Medal and £4

Second Best, . . . . . . . . . £3
Third best, . . . . . . . . . £1

3. Best Bull, 2-year old and under, of any pure breed,
Medium Silver Medal and £3

Second best, . . . . . . . . . £2
Third best, . . . . . . . . . £1

4. Best 2-year old Heifer (if Highland breed, 3 years), of any pure breed,
Medium Silver Medal and £3

Second best, . . . . . . . . . £2
Third best, . . . . . . . . . £1

The dates of calving of cattle will be counted as from on and after January 1, except Polled Angus and Aberdeen, which will be counted as from on and after December 1. ___

In 1882,

Nos. 1, 2, and 3 are in competition for the last year;
Nos. 4, 5, 6, and 7 for the second year;
No. 8 for the first year;
Nos. 9, 10, and 11 compete for Local Premiums.

## SECTION 2.—HORSES.

#### FOR AGRICULTURAL PURPOSES.

*Nota.*—The Society's Stallion Premiums are granted to each District for two years, and are followed by Premiums for other two years for Brood Mares, and again for a similar period by Premiums for Entire Colts and Fillies.

#### 1. STALLIONS.

1. DISTRICT OF ESKDALE AND LIDDESDALE.—*Convener*, William Little of Whithaugh, Burnfoot, Ewes, Langholm; *Secretary*, Thos. Stevenson, Langholm. Granted 1881.

2. MORAYSHIRE.—*Convener*, Robert M'Kessack, of Ardgye and Roseisle, Forres; *Secretary*, William Macdonald, Caledonian Bank Buildings, Elgin. Granted 1881.

3. LOWER WARD OF RENFREWSHIRE.—*Convener*, Horatio R. R. Peile, Mansion House, Greenock; *Secretary*, John Crawford, 26 Hamilton Street, Greenock. Granted 1882.

4. VALE OF ALFORD.—*Convener*, R. O. Farquharson of Haughton, Alford, N.B.; *Secretary*, George Bruce, Farniton, Alford. Granted 1882.

5. LOWER ANNANDALE.—*Convener*, A. H. Johnstone Douglas of Lockerbie, Glen Stuart, Annan ; *Secretary*, William Roddick, Annan. Granted 1882.

PREMIUM.

Best Stallion, not under 3 years, and not above 12 years old,   .   £25

In 1882,

Nos. 1 and 2 are in competition for the last year ;
Nos. 3, 4, and 5 for the first year.

2. BROOD MARES.

1. DISTRICT OF THE LESMAHAGOW SOCIETY.—*Convener*, Gavin Hamilton of Auldtown, Lesmahagow ; *Secretary*, John Hamilton, British Linen Co. Bank, Lesmahagow. Granted 1881.
2. DISTRICT OF CARRICK.—*Convener*, John Rankine of Beoch, Lochlands, Maybole ; *Secretary*, David Brown, Maybole. Granted 1881.
3. DISTRICT OF CUPAR AND ST. ANDREWS.—*Convener*, David Bayne Meldrum of Kincaple, St. Andrews ; *Secretary*, William Dingwall, Ramornie, Ladybank. Granted 1882.
4. DUMFRIES HORSE ASSOCIATION.—*Convener*, John M'Tier of Ladyfield, Dumfries ; *Secretary*, D. Robison, 48 Irish Street, Dumfries. Granted 1882.
5. NAIRNSHIRE.—*Convener*, Robert Anderson of Lochdhu, Nairn ; *Secretary*, John Ross, Budgate, Cawdor. Granted 1882.
6. EARL OF SELKIRK'S TENANTRY AND DISTRICT.—*Convener*, Andrew Lusk, Howell, Kirkcudbright ; *Secretaries*, D. G. Williamson, Bombie, Kirkcudbright ; and James Muir, Lochfergus, Kirkcudbright. Granted 1882.
7. DISTRICT OF CENTRAL STRATHEARN.—*Convener*, John Kerr, Rossie Ochil, Bridge of Earn ; *Secretary*, Robert Gardiner, Chapel Bank, Auchterarder. Granted 1882.

PREMIUMS.

1. Best Brood Mare,   . .  .  .  . Medium Silver Medal an £4
2. Second best,  .  .  .  .  .  .  .  . £3
3. Third best,  .  .  .  .  .  .  .  . £1

In 1882,

Nos. 1 and 2 are in competition for the last year ;
Nos. 3, 4, 5, 6, and 7 for the first year.

3. ENTIRE COLTS AND FILLIES.

1. COUNTY OF CLACKMANNAN.—*Convener*, James Johnstone of Alva ; *Secretaries*, D. & T. Fisher, Jellyholm, Alloa. Granted 1881.
2. DISTRICT OF LOCKERBIE.—*Convener*, Sir Alexander Jardine of Applegarth, Bart., Jardine Hall, Lockerbie ; *Secretary*, David Dobie, Banker, Lockerbie. Granted 1881.
3. EASTERN DISTRICT OF BERWICKSHIRE.—*Convener*, John Allan, Redheugh, Cockburnspath ; *Secretary*, James Gibson, Gunsgreen, Ayton. Granted 1882.
4. DISTRICT OF LAUDERDALE.—*Convener*, George M'Dougal, Blythe, Lauder ; *Secretary*, Thomas Broomfield, Lauder. Granted 1882.
5. MACHARS DISTRICT OF WIGTOWNSHIRE.—*Convener*, Sir Herbert E. Maxwell of Monreith, Bart., M.P., Port-William ; *Secretary*, Charles M. Routledge, Banker, Port-William. Granted 1882.

6. COUNTY OF PEEBLES.—*Convener*, Lord Arthur Cecil, Orchard Mains, Innerleithen; *Secretaries*, William Riddell, Howford, Peebles; and A. Alexander, West Linton. Granted 1882.

7. EASTERN DISTRICT OF STIRLINGSHIRE.—*Convener*, Ralph Stark of Summerford, Falkirk; *Secretary*, Thomas Binnie, Falkirk. Granted 1882.

### PREMIUMS.

1. Best Entire Colt, foaled after 1st January 1880,

|  |  |
|---|---|
| | Medium Silver Medal and £3 |
| Second best, . . . . . . . . . . | £2 |
| Third best, . . . . . . . . . . | £1 |

2. Best Entire Colt, foaled after 1st January 1881,

|  |  |
|---|---|
| | Medium Silver Medal and £2 |
| Second best, . . . . . . . . . . | £1 |
| Third best, . . . . . . . . . . | 10s. |

3. Best Filly, foaled after 1st January 1880, Medium Silver Medal and £3

|  |  |
|---|---|
| Second best, . . . . . . . . . . | £2 |
| Third best, . . . . . . . . . . | £1 |

4. Best Filly, foaled after 1st January 1881, Medium Silver Medal and £2

|  |  |
|---|---|
| Second best, . . . . . . . . . . | £1 |
| Third best, . . . . . . . . . . | 10s. |

In 1882,

Nos. 1 and 2 are in competition for the last year;
Nos. 3, 4, 5, 6, and 7 for the first year.

### SECTION 3.—SHEEP.

*Note.*—The Society's Sheep Premiums are granted to each District for three alternate years, on condition that the District shall, in the two intermediate years, continue the Competitions by offering for the same description of stock a sum not less than one-half of that given by the Society.

At the intermediate Competitions, a Silver Medal will be placed at the disposal of the Committee, to be awarded for the best Tup which has gained a First Money Prize at a previous District or General Show of the Highland and Agricultural Society, and of the class for which the District receives Premiums; also four Medium Silver Medals, to be given along with the first prize in the four Classes of Sheep, provided there are not less than two lots in each class.

The selection of the Breed is left to the local Committee. See Rule 6

### DISTRICTS.

1. ISLANDS OF ISLAY, JURA, AND COLONSAY.—*Convener*, Kirkman Finlay of Dunlossait, Portnakaig, Islay; *Secretary*, John M'Taggart, Kilchearan, Islay. Granted 1878.

2. DISTRICT OF DUNOON.—*Convener*, A. S. Finlay of Castle Toward, Greenock; *Secretary*, Archibald Mitchell, junior, Clydesdale Bank, Dunoon. Granted 1880.

3. DISTRICT OF DALKEITH.—*Convener*, Sir James Gardiner Baird of Saughton Hall, Bart., Inch House, Liberton; *Secretary*, William Harper, Sheriffhall Mains, Dalkeith. Granted 1880.

4. UPPER WARD OF LANARKSHIRE.—*Convener*, John Ord Mackenzie of Dolphinton; *Secretary*, David Oswald, Abington, N.B. Granted 1880.

5. DISTRICT OF LOCHABER.—*Convener*, D. P. M'Donald, Invernevis, Fort-William; *Secretary*, N. B. Mackenzie, British Linen Co. Bank, Fort-William. Granted 1880.

6. COUNTY OF FORFAR.—*Convener*, Charles Lyall, Old Montrose, Montrose; *Secretary*, Alexander M. Thomson, Accountant, Arbroath. Granted 1882.

7. COUNTY OF CAITHNESS.—*Convener*, Alexander Henderson of Stemster, Thurso; *Secretary*, James Brims, Solicitor, Thurso. Granted 1882.

8. DISTRICT OF THE BORDER UNION SOCIETY.—*Convener*, Lord Polwarth, Mertoun House, St. Boswells; *Secretary*, John Usher, 25 Bridge Street, Kelso. Granted 1878. (In abeyance in 1880.)

9. DISTRICT OF ATHOLE AND WEEM.—*Convener*, Archibald Butter of Faskally, Pitlochry; *Secretary*, James Mitchell, Solicitor, Pitlochry. Granted 1879.

10. DISTRICT OF THE UNITED EAST LOTHIAN SOCIETY.—*Convener*, Sir Hew Dalrymple of North Berwick, Bart., Luchie, North Berwick; *Secretaries*, Richardson & Gemmell, Haddington. Granted 1879.

11. DISTRICT OF NETHER LORN.—*Convener*, Donald Johnston, Kilbride, Easdale, Oban; *Secretary*, Angus Whyte, Easdale, Oban. Granted 1879.

12. DISTRICT OF ARGYLL.—*Convener*, Sir John W. P. Campbell Orde of Kilmory, Bart., Lochgilphead; *Secretary*, A. M'Nair, Ri-Cruin, Lochgilphead. Granted 1879.

### PREMIUMS.

1. Best Tup having gained a previous Highland and Agricultural Society's First Money Prize, . . . . The Silver Medal
2. Best Tup above One-Shear, . Medium Silver Medal and £3
   Second best, . . . . . . £1
   Third best, . . . . . . 10s.
3. Best Shearling Tup, . . Medium Silver Medal and £3
   Second best, . . . . . . £1
   Third best, . . . , . . 10s.
4. Best 3 Ewes above One Shear, . Medium Silver Medal and £3
   Second best, . . . . . . £1
   Third best, . . . . . . 10s.
5. Best 3 Gimmers or Shearling Ewes, . Medium Silver Medal and £3
   Second best, . . . . . . £1
   Third best, . . . . . . 10s.

In 1882,
No. 1 is in competition for the last year;
Nos. 2, 3, 4, and 5 for the second year;
Nos. 6 and 7 for the first year;
Nos. 8, 9, 10, 11, and 12 compete for local Premiums.

## SECTION 4.—SWINE.

The Society's Swine Premiums are given for three consecutive years.

### PREMIUMS.

1. Best Boar having gained a previous Highland and Agricultural Society's First Money Prize, . . . . The Silver Medal
2. Best Boar, . . . . Medium Silver Medal and £3
   Second best, . . . . . . £1
   Third best, . . . . . . 10s.
3. Best Brood Sow, . . . Medium Silver Medal and £2
   Second best, . . . . . . £1
   Third best, . . . . . . 10s.

In 1882,
No application has been received.

## Section 5.—DAIRY PRODUCE.

The Society's Dairy Premiums are given for three consecutive years.

### Premiums.

1. Best Couple of Sweet Milk Cheeses belonging to a Proprietor,
   The Silver Medal.
2. Best Couple of Sweet Milk Cheeses,    Medium Silver Medal and £2
   Second best, . . . . . . . . . . £1
   Third best, . . . . . . . . . . 10s.
3. Best Cured Butter (not less than 14 lbs.), belonging to a Proprietor,
   The Silver Medal.
4. Best Cured Butter (not less than 14 lbs.), Medium Silver Medal and £2
   Second best, . . . . . . . . . . £1
   Third best, . . . . . . . . . . 10s.

In 1882,
No application has been received.

### RULES OF COMPETITION.

1. The Members of the Highland and Agricultural Society connected with the respective districts are appointed Committees for arranging the Competitions, the Convener being appointed by the Directors : five members to be a quorum.

2. The Convener of each District shall summon a meeting of Committee for the purpose of determining the time and place of Competition, the nomination of Judges, and other preliminary arrangements. The time and place (which must be within the bounds of the District, unless in reference to Stallions) shall be publicly intimated by Conveners.

3. The Money Premiums and Medals awarded at District Competitions will be paid in January next, by precepts issued by the Directors. No payments must, therefore, be paid by the Secretary or Treasurer of any local Association. Medals will be issued at same time.

4. Stock must be the property of the Exhibitor at the date of Entry. *No entry shall be received later than one week previous to the Show.* Entry-Money shall not exceed 2½ per cent. on the amount of the Premium to be competed for.

5. The Competitions (except for Stallions to serve in the District) must take place between the 1st of April and the 26th of October, and are open to general competition to all parties within the boundaries of the District of the local Society, whether members of the local Association or not. The Stallion Premiums are open to all comers, or the Horses may be selected at the Glasgow Stallion Show on permission to that effect being obtained.

6. The Committee shall select the breed, and specify it in the returns. In Cattle the animals exhibited must belong to one of the following pure breeds—Short-horn, Ayrshire, Polled (Galloway, Angus, or Aberdeen), Highland. The Bulls may be of one breed, and the Heifers of another. In Sheep, the breeds must be Leicester, Cheviot, or Blackfaced.

7. Stock of an inferior description, or which does not fall within the proscribed regulations, shall not be placed for competition.

8. The Premiums shall not be divided. In Cattle, Horses (except Stallions to serve in the district), Sheep, and Swine, five lots in each Class will warrant the award of full, and three lots of half, Premiums. In Dairy Produce, eight Exhibitors in any one Class will warrant an award of full, and four of half, Premiums. A Competitor may exhibit two lots in each class, except in Dairy Produce, where only one lot is allowed from the same farm. For the Silver Medal to former first prize animals two lots are required. No animal to be allowed to compete in more than one section.

9. To authorise the award of the Medals in the intermediate year, there

must be not less than two lots in each Class, and the Society's Regulations must be adhered to.

10. An animal which has gained the Highland and Agricultural Society's first Money Premium at a previous District or General Show is inadmissible in the same Class (except in the case of Stallions and in that of Bulls and Tups for the Silver Medal, under section I.) ; and one which has gained a second Money Premium can only thereafter compete in that Class for the first.

11. A Bull the property of two or more Tenants may compete, although the Exhibitors may not be Joint-Tenants.

12. Bulls for which Money Premiums are awarded may be required to serve in the District at least one season ; the rate of service to be fixed by the Committee, and the prizes may be withheld till the conditions are fulfilled. Premiums for the Heifers may be retained till the animals are certified to have calved.

13. Evidence must be produced that the Prize Stallions have had produce.

14. Mares must have foals at foot (except when death of foal is certified), or be entered as being in foal ; in the latter case payment of the Premiums will be deferred till certificate of birth, which must be within 11 months from the date of the Show.

15. All Prize Tups must serve within the District during the season following the Competition. Ewes and Gimmers must be taken from the Exhibitor's stock, and must have been bred by him in the District ; and Ewes must have reared Lambs during the ordinary season of the District.

16. Sheep must have been clipped bare during the season, and the Judges are instructed to examine the fleeces of the sheep selected for prizes, and to cast those on which they find any of the former fleece. Fleeces must not be artificially coloured.

17. Should it be proved to the satisfaction of the Committee that an animal has been entered under a false name, pedigree, or description, for the purpose of misleading the Committee or Judges as to its qualifications or properties, the case shall be reported to the Directors, and submitted by them to the first General Meeting, in order that the Exhibitor may be disqualified from again competing for the Society's Premiums, and his name, if he is a member, struck from the roll, or his case otherwise disposed of as the Directors may determine.

18. When an animal has previously been disqualified by the decision of any Agricultural Association in Great Britain or Ireland, such disqualification shall attach, if the Exhibitor, being aware of the disqualification, fail to state it and the grounds thereof, in his entry, to enable the Committee to judge of its validity.

19. Competitors must certify that the Butter and Cheese exhibited by them are average specimens of the produce of their dairies in 1882, and that the quantity produced during the season has not been less than 1 cwt. of Butter, or 2 cwt. of Cheese.

20. It is to be distinctly understood that in no instance does any claim lie against the Highland and Agricultural Society for expenses attending a show of stock beyond the amount of the Premiums offered.

21. Blank reports will be furnished to the Conveners and Secretaries of the different Districts. These must, in all details, be completed, and lodged with the Secretary *on or before the 1st of November next*, for the approval of the Directors, against whose decisions there shall be no appeal.

22. A report of the Competitions and Premiums awarded at the *intermediate* local shows in the several Districts for Cattle and Sheep, signed by a member of the Society, must be transmitted to the Secretary *on or before the 1st of November in each year*, otherwise the Society's grants shall terminate.

23. When a grant has expired, the District cannot apply again for aid for two years.

## Section 6.—SPECIAL GRANTS.

£50 to Glasgow Agricultural Society.—*Secretary*, Mark Marshall, 145 St. Vincent Street, Glasgow.

£20 to the Ayrshire Agricultural Association, to be competed for at the Dairy Produce Show at Kilmarnock.—*Convener*, The Hon. G. R. Vernon, Auchans House, Kilmarnock ; *Secretary*, James M'Murtrie, Ayr. Granted 1872.

£3 to Unst Society for five consecutive years.—*Convener* and *Secretary*, Alex. Sandison, Uyasound, Unst. Granted 1679.

## Section 7.—MEDALS IN AID OF PREMIUMS GIVEN BY LOCAL SOCIETIES.

The Society, being anxious to co-operate with local Associations, will give a limited number of Medium Silver Medals annually to Societies, not on the list of Cattle or Sheep Premiums, in addition to the Money Premiums awarded in the Districts for—

1. Best Bull, Cow, Heifer of any pure breed, or Ox.
2. Best Stallion, Mare, or Gelding.
3. Best Tup, or Pen of Ewes or Wethers.
4. Best Boar, Sow, or Pig.
5. Best Coops of Poultry.
6. Best sample of any variety of Wool.
7. Best sample of any variety of Seeds.
8. Best managed Farm.
9. Best managed Green Crop.
10. Best managed Hay Crop.
11. Best managed Dairy.
12. Best Sweet Milk Cheese.
13. Best Cured Butter.
14. Best sample of Honey, not less than 5 lbs., taken without destroying the bees.
15. Best collection of Roots.
16. Best kept Fences.
17. Male Farm Servant who has been longest in the same service, and who has proved himself most efficient in his duties, and to have invariably treated the animals under his charge with kindness.
18. Female Servant in charge of Dairy and Poultry who has been longest in the same service, and who has proved herself most efficient in her duties, and to have invariably treated the animals under her charge with kindness.
19. Best Sheep Shearer.
20. Most expert Hedge Cutter.
21. Most expert Labourer at Draining.
22. Most expert Farm-Servant at trial of Reaping Machines.
23. Best Maker of Oat Cakes.

It is left to the local Society to choose out of the foregoing list the classes for which the Medals are to be competed.

The Medals are given for five consecutive years.

### Aberdeenshire.

1. AUCHINDOIR, KILDRUMMIE, AND TOWIE ASSOCIATION. — *Convener*, Carlos P. Gordon of Wardhouse, Insch ; *Secretary*, William Walker, Ardhuncart, Mossat. 4 Medals. Granted 1881.

2. CLUNY, MONYMUSK, AND MIDMAR ASSOCIATION.—*Convener*, Ranald Macdonald, Cluny Castle, Aberdeen ; *Secretary*, James Christie, Backhill of Castle Fraser, Kemnay, Aberdeen. 2 Medals. Granted 1881.

3. CROMAR, UPPER DEE, AND DONSIDE ASSOCIATION.—*Convener*, Sir John Forbes Clark, Bart., Tillypronie, Tarland ; *Secretary*, William Thomson, Tarland. 4 Medals. Granted 1881.

4. EBRIESIDE ASSOCIATION.—*Convener*, Wm. Leask, Skilmafilly, Ellon ; *Secretary*, William Hetherwick, Knoxhill, Ellon. 5 Medals. Granted 1881.

5. FORMARTINE ROOT ASSOCIATION.—*Convener*, Captain Alexander C. Hunter of Tillery, Aberdeen ; *Secretary*, Thomas Duguid, Mosshead, Udny, Aberdeen. 2 Medals. Granted 1879.

6. FYVIE ASSOCIATION.—*Convener*, James Mackie, Lewes, Fyvie ; *Secretary*, James Ironside, Stoinmanhill, Fyvie. 2 Medals. Granted 1880.

7. GARIOCH TURNIP GROWING ASSOCIATION.—*Convener*, Henry Gordon of Manar, Inverurie ; *Secretary*, James Stephen, Conglass, Inverurie. 2 Medals. Granted 1878. (In abeyance in 1881.)

8. INVERURIE ASSOCIATION.—*Convener*, Henry Lumsden of Pitcaple, Pitcaple ; *Secretary*, James Stephen, Conglass, Inverurie. 2 Medals. Granted 1878.

9. KINELLAR HORTICULTURAL AND POULTRY ASSOCIATION.—*Convener*, Colonel William Ross King of Tertowie, Kinellar, Aberdeen ; *Secretary*, Alexander Taylor, Fichnie, Kinellar, Aberdeen. 2 Medals. Granted 1879.

10. KINNETHMONT ASSOCIATION.—*Convener*, Col. Leith Hay of Rannes, C.B., Leith Hall, Kinnethmont ; *Secretary*, James R. Moir, 25 South Mount Street, Aberdeen. 5 Medals. Granted 1881.

11. LEOCHEL-CUSHNIE SOCIETY.—*Convener*, Sir William Forbes of Craigievar, Bart., Fintray House, Aberdeen ; *Secretary*, James Strachan, Wester Fowlis, Alford. 3 Medals. Granted 1879.

12. MAR ASSOCIATION.—*Convener*, William Wishart, Cairntradlyn, Kinellar, Blackburn, N.B. ; *Secretary*, Silvester Campbell, jun., Tofthills, Kintore. 2 Medals. Granted 1882.

13. NEW ABERDOUR SOCIETY.—*Convener*, James Cruickshank, Ladysford, Fraserburgh ; *Secretary*, William Chapman, Woodhead, New Aberdour, Fraserburgh. 5 Medals. Granted 1878.

14. NORTH-EAST ABERDEENSHIRE SOCIETY.—*Convener*, Sir Alexander Anderson, Aberdeen ; *Secretary*, G. A. Cruickshank, Nether Cortes, Lonmay. 6 Medals. Granted 1880.

15. NORTH OF SCOTLAND ROOT, VEGETABLE, AND FRUIT ASSOCIATION.—*Convener*, A. F. Nares, Brucktor, Old Meldrum ; *Secretary*, James Smith, Agent, Inverurie. 2 Medals. Granted 1881.

16. STRICHEN SOCIETY.—*Convener* and *Secretary*, John Sleigh, Strichen. 2 Medals. Granted 1882.

### Argyllshire.

17. KINTYRE SOCIETY.—*Convener*, Colonel Mackay of Carskey, Campbeltown ; *Secretary*, James Lothian, Campbeltown. 4 Medals. Granted 1882.

18. LISMORE SOCIETY.—*Convener*, Major James Robertson, Glackeriaky, Appin; *Secretary*, Dugald M'Intyre, Frackersaig, Lismore, Oban. 2 Medals. Granted 1878.

19. MULL, COLL, AND TIREE.—*Convener*, James Noel Forsyth of Quinish, Tobermory; *Secretary*, Robert Lang, Aros Mains, Aros, Mull. 4 Medals. Granted 1880.

20. BEITH SOCIETY.—*Convener*, William Bartlemore, County Buildings, Paisley; *Secretary*, William Fulton Love, Writer, Beith, Ayrshire. 2 Medals. Granted 1881.

21. COYLTON AND STAIR SOCIETY.—*Convener*, Major-General Burnett of Gadgirth, Tarbolton; *Secretary*, Robert Caldwell, Knockshoggle, Stair. 2 Medals. Granted 1882.

22. CRAIGIE SOCIETY.—*Convener*, R. Drummond, Pocknave, Craigie, Kilmarnock; *Secretary*, Andrew M'Farlane, Schoolhouse, Craigie. 3 Medals. Granted 1881.

23. DALRY SOCIETY.—*Convener*, Andrew Allan, Munnoch, Dalry, Ayr; *Secretary*, Robert Craig, Flashwood, Dalry. 4 Medals. Granted 1879.

24. DUNDONALD SOCIETY.—*Convener*, The Hon. G. R. Vernon, Auchans House, Kilmarnock; *Secretary*, John Caldwell, Bogside, Dundonald. 3 Medals. Granted 1878.

25. GALSTON HORTICULTURAL SOCIETY.—*Convener*, Robert Mackie, Loudoun Cottage, Galston; *Secretary*, Thomas Paterson, Galston. 3 Medals. Granted 1880.

26. KILMARNOCK SOCIETY.—*Convener*, Robert Guthrie, Crossburn, Troon; *Secretary*, James Wilson, Banker, Kilmarnock. 4 Medals. Granted 1882.

27. LOUDOUN AND LANFINE SOCIETY.—*Convener*, Robert Mackie, Draffen House, Stewarton; *Secretary*, Andrew Cameron, Solicitor, Newmilns, Kilmarnock. 4 Medals. Granted 1879.

28. MUIRKIRK SOCIETY.—*Convener*, Robert Millar, Alloway Cottage, Ayr; *Secretary*, Alexander Donald, The Schoolhouse, Muirkirk. 6 Medals. Granted 1881.

29. NEW CUMNOCK.—*Convener*, John Picken, Mansfield Mains, New Cumnock; *Secretary*, William F. Haddow, Riggfoot, New Cumnock. 4 Medals. Granted 1881.

30. SORN AND DALGAIN SOCIETY.—*Convener*, James Somervell of Sorn, Mauchline; *Secretary*, Robert Brown, Dalgain, Sorn, Mauchline. 5 Medals. Granted 1879.

31. TARBOLTON SOCIETY.—*Convener*, W. S. Cooper of Failford, New Club, Edinburgh; *Secretary*, Wm. Candlish, Middlemuir, Tarbolton. 2 Medals. Granted 1878.

32. WEST KILBRIDE SOCIETY.—*Convener*, John Crawford, Milstonford, West Kilbride; *Secretary*, Malcolm Logan, Kirkland, West Kilbride. 5 Medals. Granted 1879.

*Buteshire.*

33. BUTE SOCIETY.—*Convener*, William Barr, Kerrylamont, Rothesay; *Secretary*, John M'Ewen, 9 Victoria Street, Rothesay. 3 Medals. Granted 1878.

*Dumbartonshire.*

34. KIRKINTILLOCH SOCIETY.—*Convener*, William Burt Wright, Auchinvole Castle, Croy; *Secretary*, Andrew Matson, National Bank of Scotland, Kirkintilloch. 4 Medals. Granted 1882.

35. WESTERN DISTRICT OF DUMBARTONSHIRE.—*Convener*, Sir James Colquhoun of Luss, Bart., Ross-dhu, Luss; *Secretary*, Colonel James Colquhoun, Ben Cruagh Lodge, Arroquhar. 2 Medals. Granted 1879.

### Dumfriesshire.

36. MOFFAT AND UPPER ANNANDALE SOCIETY.—*Convener*, Walter Johnstone, Alton, Moffat; *Secretary*, Alexander Scott, Annandale Estates Office, Moffat. 4 Medals. Granted 1881.
37. SANQUHAR SOCIETY.—*Convener*, James Kennedy of Sundaywell, Brandleys, Sanquhar; *Secretary*, Joseph Carruthers, Sanquhar. 5 Medals. Granted 1878.

### Edinburghshire.

38. WESTERN DISTRICT OF MID-LOTHIAN ASSOCIATION.—*Convener*, James Paterson of Bankton, Mid-Calder; *Secretary*, James H. Steuart, Selms, Kirknewton. 4 Medals. Granted 1878.

### Elginshire.

39. FORRES AND NORTHERN FAT CATTLE CLUB.—*Convener*, Richard H. Harris, Earnhill, Forres; *Secretary*, Robert Urquhart, jun., Forres. 6 Medals. Granted 1881.

### Fifeshire.

40. WINDYGATES SOCIETY.—*Convener*, John Gilmour of Lundin, Leven; *Secretary*, J. F. Thom, Wellgreen, East Wemyss. 2 Medals. Granted 1882.

### Inverness-shire.

41. NORTHERN COUNTIES FAT SHOW CLUB.—*Convener*, Duncan Forbes of Culloden, Inverness; *Secretary*, D. Cameron, Fettes, Inverness. 6 Medals. Granted 1878.
42. STRATHSPEY CLUB.—*Convener*, Earl of Seafield, Castle Grant, Grantown; *Secretary*, F. Macbean, Writer, Grantown. 5 Medals. Granted 1881.

### Kincardineshire.

43. FETTERCAIRN CLUB.—*Convener*, Col. M'Inroy of The Burn, Brechin; *Secretary*, William Crighton, Castleton of Kincardine, Laurencekirk. 3 Medals. Granted 1878.

### Lanarkshire.

44. CALDERWATERHEAD SOCIETY.—*Convener*, Peter Forrest, Shotts; *Secretary*, James Ferguson, Fairnieshaw, Holytown. 2 Medals. Granted 1881.
45. CARNWATH SOCIETY.—*Convener*, Hector F. M'Lean, Carnwath House; *Secretary*, George Russell, Carnwath. 4 Medals. Granted 1878. (In abeyance in 1881.)
46. STONEHOUSE ASSOCIATION,—*Convener*, J. P. Alston of Muirburn, Glassford; *Secretary*, William Stevenson, Stonehouse, Lanark. 2 Medals. Granted 1878.

### Orkney.

47. ROUSAY SOCIETY.—*Convener*, General Burroughs of Rousay, C.B., Orkney; *Secretary*, Wm. Seatter, Saviskaill, Rousay. 2 Medals. Granted 1878.

*Perthshire.*

48. CULROSS SOCIETY.—*Convener*, John J. Dalgleish of West Grange ; *Secretary*, James Thomson, Middle Grange, Bogside, Culross.  3 Medals. Granted 1879.
49. MIDDLE DISTRICT OF ATHOLE AND TULLYMET.—*Convener*, Wm. Dick of Tullymet, Ballinluig ; *Secretary*, John S. Grant, Tullymet, Ballinluig. 1 Medal.  Granted 1878.
50. MOULIN ASSOCIATION.—*Convener*, Alexander Forbes, Pitfourie, Pitlochry ; *Secretary*, R. M'Gillewie, Balnadrum, Pitlochry. 1 Medal. Granted 1881.
51. STORMONT UNION SOCIETY.—*Convener*, Sir Alex. Muir Mackenzie of Delvine, Bart. ; *Secretary*, Robert Grant, The Pleasance, Coupar Angus. 5 Medals. Granted 1880.
52. STRATHEARN ORNITHOLOGICAL SOCIETY.—*Convener*, C. H. Dundas, Gerrichrew, Dunira, Crieff ; *Secretary*, James M'Laren, jun., Crieff. 2 Medals. Granted 1880.

*Renfrewshire.*

53. EAGLESHAM SOCIETY.—*Convener*, William Gillies, Writer, Pollokshaws ; *Secretary*, Wm. Dykes, Polnoon Mains, Eaglesham. 1 Medal. Granted 1878.
54. LOCHWINNOCH SOCIETY.—*Convener*, William Bartlemore, County Buildings, Paisley ; *Secretary*, William Logan of Cloak, Writer, Lochwinnoch. 2 Medals. Granted 1881.

*Ross-shire.*

55. BLACK ISLE SOCIETY.—*Convener*, James Fletcher of Rosehaugh, Avoch ; *Secretary*, James R. Mitchell, Drynie, Inverness. 6 Medals.  Granted 1879 and 1881.

*Stirlingshire.*

56. CAMPSIE, STRATHBLANE, AND BALDERNOCK SOCIETY.—*Convener*, Sir Charles E. F. Stirling of Glorat, Bart., Milton of Campsie ; *Secretary*, William Horne, Newmill, Milton of Campsie.  2 Medals.  Granted 1879.
57. KILSYTH SOCIETY.—*Convener*, James Patrick, Queenzieburn, Milton of Campsie ; *Secretary*, R. M. Lennox, Writer, Kilsyth. 2 Medals. Granted 1880.

The Medals are given for five consecutive years.

Applications from other Districts must be lodged with the Secretary of the Society by *1st November next.*

### RULES OF COMPETITION.

1. All Competitions must be at the instance of a local Society.
2. The classes for which Medals are granted must be in accordance with the list at page 38.  The Committee shall select the classes, and specify them in the return.
3. In each District the Convener (who must be a member of the Society appointed by the Directors) shall fix the time and place of Competition, appoint the Judges, and make all other necessary arrangements, in concurrence with the other Members of the Society, and the local Association of the District.

4. The Money Premiums given in the District must be £2 for each Medal claimed.

5. The Medal for Sheep Shearing shall not be awarded unless there are three competitors, and it shall always accompany the highest Money Premium. There must not be fewer than two competitors in all the classes.

6. Blank reports will be furnished to all the Conveners of the different Districts. These must, in all details, be completed and lodged with the Secretary *on or before the 1st of November next*, with the exception of green crop reports, which must be forwarded on or before the 20th of December, for the approval of the Directors, against whose decisions there shall be no appeal.

7. When a grant has expired, the District cannot apply again for aid for two years.

## Section 8.—PLOUGHING COMPETITIONS.

The Minor Silver Medal will be given to the winner of the first or highest Premium at Ploughing Competitions, provided a Report in the following terms is made to the Secretary, within one month of the Competition, by a Member of the Society:—

### FORM OF REPORT.

I            of            Member of the Highland and Agricultural Society, hereby certify that I attended the Ploughing Match of the            Association at            in the county of            on the            when            ploughs competed;            of land was assigned to each, and            hours were allowed for the execution of the work. The sum of £            was awarded in the following proportions, viz. :—

[Here enumerate the names and designations of successful Competitors.]

### RULES OF COMPETITION.

1. All Matches must be at the instance of a local Society or Ploughing Association, and no Match at the instance of an individual, or confined to the tenants of one estate, will be recognised.

2. The title of such Society or Association, together with the name and address of the Secretary, must be registered with the Secretary of the Highland and Agricultural Society, 3 George IV. Bridge, Edinburgh.

3. Not more than one Match in the same season can take place within the bounds of the same Society or Association.

4. All reports must be lodged within one month of the date of the Match, and certified by a Member of the Highland and Agricultural Society who was present at it.

5. A Member can only report one Match, and a Ploughman cannot carry more than three Medals in the same season.

6. To warrant the grant of the Medal there must have been twelve ploughs in Competition, and Three Pounds awarded in Premiums by the local Society. The Medal to be given to the winner of the first or highest prize.

7. Ploughmen shall not be allowed any assistance, and their work must not be set up nor touched by others; on land of average tenacity the ploughing should be at the rate of an imperial acre in ten hours, and attention should be given to the firmness and sufficiency of the work below, more than to its neatness above the surface.

# CLASS III.

## COTTAGES AND GARDENS.

The following Premiums are offered for Competition in the Parishes after mentioned.

The Premiums for Cottages and Gardens are given for five consecutive years.

### SECTION I.—PREMIUMS FOR BEST KEPT COTTAGES AND GARDENS.

1. Best kept Cottage—One Pound ; and where there are four Competitors—Minor Silver Medal.
    Second best—Ten Shillings.
    Third best—Minor Silver Medal.
2. Best kept Cottage Garden—One Pound ; and where there are four Competitors—Minor Silver Medal.
    Second best—Ten Shillings.
    Third best—Minor Silver Medal.

*Argyllshire.*

1. OBAN.—*Secretary*, Donald Macgregor, Solicitor, Oban. Granted 1880.
2. COLL.—*Convener*, John Lorne Stewart of Coll ; *Secretary*, J. A. Hain, Coll. Granted 1882.

*Dumbartonshire.*

3. CARDROSS.—*Secretary*, Mrs Murray, Moore Park, Cardross. Granted 1881.

*Edinburghshire.*

4. CALDERS UNION HORTICULTURAL SOCIETY.—*Convener*, R. G. Smith, Georgeville, Mid-Calder ; *Secretary*, James B. Smith, Greenloan Cottage, Kirknewton. Granted 1878.
5. CURRIE AND BALERNO.—*Convener*, Sir James H. Gibson-Craig of Riccarton, Bart., Currie ; *Secretary*, Alexander Maltman, Rosebank, Currie. Granted 1881.

*Fifeshire.*

6. NEWBURGH DISTRICT GARDENING SOCIETY.—*Convener*, John Lyall, Newburgh ; *Secretaries*, George Anderson and Angus Cameron, Newburgh. Granted 1882.
7. NORTH OF FIFE HORTICULTURAL SOCIETY.—*Convener*, John Mitchell Fliskmillan, Cupar Fife ; *Secretary*, George Leslie, Luthrie, Cupar Fife. Granted 1878.

*Kincardineshire.*

8. MEARNS AMATEUR HORTICULTURAL SOCIETY.—*Convener*, D. A. Pearson of Johnston, Laurencekirk ; *Secretary*, James Burgess, Laurencekirk. Granted 1878.

### Lanarkshire.

9. ABINGTON FLORAL AND HORTICULTURAL SOCIETY.—*Convener*, John Morton, Nether Abington, Abington; *Secretary*, Matthew M'Kendrick, Abington. Granted 1881.

### Linlithgowshire.

10. DALMENY AND QUEENSFERRY HORTICULTURAL SOCIETY.—*Convener*, Peter Glendinning, Leuchold, Dalmeny Park, Edinburgh; *Secretary*, John Allan, Dalmeny Park, Edinburgh. Granted 1879.
11. TORPHICHEN HORTICULTURAL SOCIETY.—*Convener*, Colonel Gillon of Wallhouse, Bathgate; *Secretary*, James Roberts, Torphichen. Granted 1882.

### Perthshire.

12. BRACO HORTICULTURAL SOCIETY.—*Convener*, John Kinross, Gannochan, Braco; *Secretary*, George Dingwall, Ardoch Gardens, Braco. Granted 1878.
13. BRIDGE OF EARN HORTICULTURAL SOCIETY.—*Convener*, Thomas Richmond, Hilton, Perth; *Secretary*, John Ellis, Bridge of Earn. Granted 1882.
14. DUNNING HORTICULTURAL SOCIETY.—*Convener*, Robert Gardiner, Chapelbank, Auchterarder. *Secretary*, Johnstone Wright, Dunning. Granted 1880.

### Ross-shire.

15. EDDERTON SOCIETY.—*Convener*, W. E. Catley of Edderton, Ross-shire; *Secretary*, James Ross, Balblair, Edderton, Ross-shire. Granted 1882.
16. WESTER ROSS HORTICULTURAL SOCIETY.—*Convener*, Sir Kenneth S. Mackenzie of Gairloch, Bart.; *Secretary*, David Munro, 65 High Street, Dingwall. Granted 1881.

### Stirlingshire.

17. KILLEARN SOCIETY.—*Convener*, David Edmond of Ballochruin, Balfron; *Secretary*, John MacIntyre, Kirkhouse, Killearn. Granted 1879.

### Sutherlandshire.

18. SKIBO ASSOCIATION.—*Convener*, Evan C. Sutherland Walker of Skibo, Skibo Castle, Sutherland. Granted 1879 (one year in abeyance).

### Wigtownshire.

19. INCH.—*Convener*, The Earl of Stair, K.T., Lochinch, Castle Kennedy, Wigtownshire; *Secretary*, Thomas C. Greig, Rephad, Stranraer. Granted 1879.

### RULES OF COMPETITION.

1. Competitions may take place in the different parishes for Cottages and Gardens, or for either separately.
2. The occupiers of Lodges at Gentlemen's Approach Gates and Gardener's Houses are excluded, as well as others whom the Committee consider, from their position, not to be entitled to compete. The inspection must be completed by the 1st of October. In making the inspection, the Conveners may take the assistance of any competent judges.
3. It is left to the Committee of the district to regulate the maximum annual rent of the Cottages, which may, with the garden, be from £5 to £7.

4. A person who has gained the highest Premium cannot compete again, but will be entitled to a Medal if certified by the Committee to be equal in merit to the first on the list of Competitors.

5. If the Cottage is occupied by the proprietor, the roof must be in good repair; if the roof is thatch, it must be in good repair, though in the occupation of a tenant. The interior and external conveniences must be clean and orderly—the windows must be free of broken glass, clean, and affording the means of ventilation. Dunghills, and all other nuisances, must be removed from the front and gables. In awarding the Cottage Premiums, preference will be given to Competitors who, in addition to the above requisites, have displayed the greatest taste in ornamenting the exterior of their houses, and the ground in front and at the gables.

6. In estimating the claims for the Garden Premiums, the judges should have in view :—The sufficiency and neatness of the fences and walks ; the cleanness of the ground ; the quality and choice of the crops ; and the general productiveness of the garden.

7. Reports, stating the number of Competitors, the names of successful parties, and the nature of the exertions which have been made by them, must be transmitted by the Conveners to the Secretary *on or before the 1st November next.*

8. When a grant has expired, the District cannot apply again for aid for two years.

Parishes desirous of these Premiums must lodge applications with the Secretary *on or before the 1st November next.*

## Section 2.—MEDALS FOR COTTAGES AND GARDENS OR GARDEN PRODUCE.

The Society will issue annually two Medium Silver Medals to a limited number of local Associations or individuals, who at their own expense establish Premiums for Cottages or Gardens under £15 of Rent. The Medals may be awarded for best kept Cottage, and best kept Garden or Flower Plot, or Garden Produce.

Local Associations or individuals desirous of these Medals, must lodge applications with the Secretary *on or before the 1st November next.* The Medals are given for five consecutive years.

1. UDNY HORTICULTURAL SOCIETY.—*Convener*, Alexander Keith, Chapelton, Ellon ; *Secretary*, Thomas Duguid, Mosshead, Udny.  2 Medals. Granted 1881.

*Ayrshire.*

2. GALSTON HORTICULTURAL SOCIETY.—*Convener*, Robert Mackie Draffen House, Stewarton ; *Secretary*, Thomas Paterson, Galston.  2 Medals. Granted 1881.

*Dumbartonshire.*

3. VALE OF LEVEN AND DUMBARTON HORTICULTURAL SOCIETY.—*Convener*, J. M. Martin, yr. of Auchendennan, Bloomhill, Cardross ; *Secretary*, Arch. M'Dougall, 13 North Street, Alexandria, N.B.  Granted 1879.

*Edinburghshire.*

4. LIBERTON AND NEWTON HORTICULTURAL SOCIETY.—*Convener*, Robert Black, Liberton Mains, Liberton; *Secretary*, James Anderson, Schoolhouse, Gilmerton. Granted 1882.

*Elginshire.*

5. DYKE HORTICULTURAL SOCIETY.—*Convener*, Hugh Brodie of Brodie, Brodie Castle, Forres; *Secretary*, J. Clark, Brodie Gardens, Forres Granted 1882.

*Fifeshire.*

6. KIRKCALDY HORTICULTURAL SOCIETY.—*Convener*, William Drysdale of Kilrie, Kinghorn; *Secretary*, John Leslie, West Mills, Kirkcaldy. Granted 1880.

*Lanarkshire.*

7. BOTHWELL HORTICULTURAL SOCIETY.—*Convener*, Dr. Bruce Goff, Woodlea, Bothwell; *Secretary*, Thomas Donald, Springbank, Bothwell. Granted 1876. (In abeyance in 1880 and 1881.)
8. CARNWATH HORTICULTURAL SOCIETY.— *Convener*, George Russell, Carnwath; *Secretary*, David Aitken, Carnwath. Granted 1880.
9. GARTSHERRIE WORKS HORTICULTURAL SOCIETY.—*Convener*, Dr. Bruce Goff, Woodlea, Bothwell; *Secretary*, James Findlay, Bothwell Collieries, Bothwell. Granted 1881.
10. MAULDSLIE AND ROSEBANK HORTICULTURAL SOCIETY. — *Convener* Colonel Hozier of Newlands, Mauldalie Castle, Carluke; *Secretary*, Edward Waddell, Dalserf. Granted 1882.
11. NEW VICTORIA GARDENS, LILY BANK ROAD, GLASGOW.—*Secretary*, James Walker, 86 Ardgowan Street, Glasgow. Granted 1878. (One year in abeyance.)
12. SARACEN PUBLIC GARDENS, POSSIL PARK, GLASGOW.—*Convener*, Walter Macfarlane, 22 Park Circus, Glasgow; *Secretary*, William Manson, 348 Saracen Street, Possil Park, Glasgow. Granted 1879.
13. SHETTLESTON HORTICULTURAL SOCIETY.—*Secretary*, James Mitchell, 12 East Muir Street, Shettleston. 2 Medals. Granted 1881.

*Linlithgowshire.*

14. KIRKLISTON HORTICULTURAL SOCIETY.—*Convener*, Peter Glendinning, The Leuchold, Dalmeny Park, Edinburgh; *Secretary*, George Innes, Ratho Station. Granted 1882.

*Nairnshire.*

15. AULDEARN FLOWER SHOW.—*Convener*, Hugh Brodie of Brodie, Brodie Castle, Forres; *Secretary*, James Carson, Auldearn, Nairn. Granted 1880.

*Perthshire.*

16. BLAIRGOWRIE AND RATTRAY HORTICULTURAL SOCIETY.—*Convener*, John Anderson, Royal Hotel, Blairgowrie; *Secretary*, Henry Dryerre, Croft House, Blairgowrie. Granted 1880.
17. BREADALBANE, WEEM, STRATHTAY, AND GRANDTULLY HORTICULTURAL SOCIETY—*Convener*, E. O. Douglas of Killiechassie, Aberfeldy; *Joint-Secretaries*, D. Macdiarmid, Bank of Scotland, Aberfeldy, and Peter Haggart, Keltneyburn; Aberfeldy. Granted 1879.

18. CHERRYBANK HORTICULTURAL SOCIETY.—*Convener*, William Macdonald, Woodlands, Perth; *Secretary*, W. M. Law, Cherrybank, Perth. Granted 1882.
19. DUNKELD AND BIRNAM HORTICULTURAL AND POULTRY ASSOCIATION.— *Convener*, John Macgregor, Ladywell, Dunkeld; *Secretary*, Robert Robertson, Ladywell, Dunkeld. Granted 1880.
20. LOGIEALMOND AND GLENALMOND HORTICULTURAL SOCIETY.—*Convener*, Graeme R. Mercer of Gorthie, Glen Tulchan House, Perth; *Secretary*, Daniel Paton, Harrietfield, Perth. Granted 1878.

### REGULATIONS.

1. Competitions may take place in the different districts for Cottages and Gardens, or for either separately.
2. The annual value of each Cottage, with the ground occupied in the parish by a Competitor, must not exceed £15.
3. If Competition takes place for Garden Produce in place of the best kept Garden, such produce must be *bona fide* grown in the Exhibitor's Garden, and he will not be allowed to make up a collection from any other Garden.
4. Blank reports will be furnished to the Conveners and Secretaries of the different Districts. These must, in all details, be completed and lodged with the Secretary *on or before the 1st November next*, for the approval of the Directors, against whose decisions there shall be no appeal.
5. When a grant has expired, the District cannot apply again for aid for two years.

## SECTION 3.—IMPROVING EXISTING COTTAGES.

To the Proprietor in Scotland who shall report the Improvement of the greatest number of Cottages during the years 1879, 1880, and 1881—The Gold Medal.

## SECTION 4.—BUILDING NEW COTTAGES.

To the Proprietor in Scotland who shall report the Erection of the greatest number of approved Cottages during the years 1878, 1879, 1880, and 1881— The Gold Medal.

### RULES OF COMPETITION.

1. Claims for the Premiums Nos. 3 and 4 must be lodged with the Secretary on or before the 1st of October next, to allow an inspection to be made of the different Cottages. The inspection will be conducted by a Committee of the Society's Members, and Reports must be transmitted to the Secretary *on or before the 1st November next.*
2. The annual value of the Cottage or Cottages separately, with the garden ground, must not exceed £5.
3. In estimating the claims of the Competitors, the following points will be kept in view:—The external appearance of the Cottages; their internal accommodation; the arrangements of the out-houses; the means of drainage and ventilation; and the expense of the building or of the alteration, compared with its durability and accommodation. When the Cottages of one Competitor are superior in style and comfort to those of another, though not so numerous, the Inspectors will give them preference, provided they amount at least to three, and have been erected at a moderate expense.
4. Parties competing will forward to the Society Plans, Specifications, and Estimates, of which, and of all information sent therewith, copies may be taken for publication, if the Society shall see fit, and the originals returned to the parties within six months, if desired.

# GENERAL SHOW OF STOCK AND IMPLEMENTS

AT

# GLASGOW

ON 25TH, 26TH, 27TH, AND 28TH JULY 1882.

---

President of the Society.

HIS GRACE THE DUKE OF RICHMOND AND GORDON, K.G.

Chairman of the Local Committee.

SIR MICHAEL R. SHAW STEWART OF GREENOCK AND BLACKHALL, BART.

---

The District connected with the Show comprises the Counties of Lanark, Ayr, Argyll, Renfrew, and Bute.

---

## REGULATIONS.

---

### GENERAL CONDITIONS.

1. The Competition is open to Exhibitors from all parts of the United Kingdom.

2. Every Lot must be intimated by a Certificate of Entry, lodged with the Secretary *not later than the 1st June for Implements, and 14th June for Stock and other Entries.* Printed forms will be issued on application to the Secretary, No. 3 George IV. Bridge, Edinburgh. Admission Orders will be forwarded to Exhibitors, by post, previous to the Show.

3. Protests against the awards of the Judges must be lodged with the Secretary not later than 9 A.M. on Wednesday, 26th July, and parties must be in attendance at the Committee-Room, in the Show-Yard, at 10 A.M. that day, when protests will be disposed of.

4. Protests lodged for causes which the protestor produces no good evidence to substantiate, will render him liable to be reported to the Board of Directors, with the view, if they see reason, to his being prohibited from again entering stock for a General Show.

5. The Society shall not be liable for any loss or damage which Stock, Poultry, Implements, or other articles may sustain at the Show, or in transit.

6. The decisions of the Board of Directors are final in all questions respecting Premiums and all other matters connected with the Show, and it shall not be competent for any Exhibitor to appeal against such decisions to, nor seek redress in respect of them from, any other tribunal.

7. Covered Booths for Offices (9 feet by 9 feet), purely for business, not for exhibition of goods, can be had for £3, 10s. to Members, and £5 to Non-Members. Intimation to be made to the Secretary before the 1st of July.

8. No lights allowed in the Yard at night, and Smoking is strictly prohibited within the sheds. Those infringing this Rule will be fined 10s.

9. As the command of water in the Yard is limited, it is particularly requested that waste be avoided.

10. When the ground requires to be broken, the turf must be carefully lifted and laid aside, and the surface must be restored to the satisfaction of the Society, and at the expense of the Exhibitor.

11. All persons admitted into the Show-Yard shall be subject to the Rules and Orders of the Directors.

12. The violation by an Exhibitor of any one of the Regulations will involve

the forfeiture of all Premiums awarded to him, or of such a portion as the Directors may ordain.

13. Railway Passes for unsold stock and implements must be applied for at the Committee Room in the Yard between 9 and 11 o'clock on the forenoon of Thursday and Friday.

14. The Show terminates at 5 P.M. on Friday, 28th July, and no animals or article can be withdrawn before that hour. Stock and Implements may remain in the Yard till Saturday afternoon.

15. The Premiums awarded will be paid in November 1882, and, with the exception of the Tweeddale Gold Medal and the Silver Medals, may be taken either in money or in plate

## STOCK AND POULTRY.

16. Stock and Poultry to be entered with the Secretary on or before the 14th day of June. Received in the Yard on Monday, 24th, and till 10 A.M. on Tuesday, 25th July. Judged at 11 A.M. on Tuesday. Exhibited on Tuesday, Wednesday, Thursday, and Friday, 25th, 26th, 27th, and 28th July.

17. All animals must be entered in the sections applicable to their ages, and cannot be withdrawn after entry.

18. No animal to be allowed to compete in more than one section, except horses in sections 10 and 11, which may be also entered in the sections applicable to their ages.

19. Shorthorn, Polled Angus or Aberdeen, and Galloway animals must be entered in the herd books, or the exhibitor must produce evidence that his animal is eligible to be entered therein.

20. Stock must be *bona fide the property and in the possession of* the Exhibitor from the 14th June (the last day of Entry).

21. The schedule of Entry must be filled up so far as within the knowledge of the Exhibitor.

22. The name of the Breeder, if known, must be given, and if the Breeder is not known a declaration to that effect, signed by the Exhibitor, must be sent along with the Schedule, and no pedigree will be entered in the Catalogue when the Breeder is unknown.

23. Should it be proved to the satisfaction of the Directors that an animal has been entered under a false name, pedigree, or description, for the purpose of misleading the Directors or Judges as to its qualification or properties, the case shall be reported to the first General Meeting, in order that the Exhibitor shall be disqualified from again competing at the Society's Shows, and his name, if he be a Member, struck from the roll, or his case otherwise disposed of as the Directors may determine.

24. An animal which has gained a first premium at a General Show of the Society cannot again compete in the same section.

25. When an animal has previously been disqualified by the decision of any Agricultural Association in Great Britain or Ireland, such disqualification shall attach, if the Exhibitor, being aware of the disqualification, fail to state it, and the grounds thereof, in his entry, to enable the Directors to judge of its validity.

26. Breeding Stock must not be shown in an improper state of fatness, and the Judges will be prohibited from awarding Premiums to overfed animals.

27. No animal shall bear on its rug, harness, pail, or other fittings, any initial, crest, or mark of ownership, nor be distinguished otherwise than by the number indicating its place in the Catalogue.

28. Any artificial contrivance or device of any description found on an animal either for preventing the flow of milk or for any other purpose, will disqualify that animal from being awarded a Premium, and the Owner of said animal will be prohibited from again entering stock for any of the Society's General Shows, or for such a period as the Directors may see fit.

29. Exhibitors shall be answerable for all acts, whether committed by themselves, their servants, or others, and shall be responsible for the condition of their animals during the whole time they remain in the Show-Yard.

30. No animal to be taken out of its stall after 10 A.M. during the Show, except by order of the Judges, or with permission of the Secretary. Those infringing this Rule will be fined 10s.

31. Aged Bulls and Stallions must have had produce, and, along with Two-year-old Bulls, Three-year-old Colts, and aged Tups have served within the year of the Show.

32. All Cows must have had calves previous to the Show, and when exhibited, they must either be in milk or in calf; if in milk, birth must have been within 9 months of the Show; if in calf, birth must be certified within 9 months after the Show. In the case of Ayrshire Cows in Calf, calved before 1st January 1879, and Ayrshire Heifers in Calf, calved on or after 1st January 1879, birth must be certified within 9 months after the Show.

33. All Milch Cows must have been milked dry the evening previous to being judged, and they must, while within the Show-Yard, be milked morning and evening. The Judges will be instructed to withhold the prizes from any animals overstrained or suffering from want of being milked.

34. Ayrshire Cows in milk will be inspected by Veterinary Surgeons appointed by the Directors before the judging commences, and those Cows found over strained from excess of milk will be prevented from being placed before the Judges.

35. Two-year-old Heifers—of the Short-horn and Polled Breeds—must be in calf when exhibited, and the premiums will be withheld till birth be certified, which must be within 9 months after the Show. Animals of any age that have had a calf must be shown as Cows.

36. Mares in Sections 5 and 14 must have produced foals after 1st January 1882, and foals must be at foot, except when death can be proved. Mares in Section 6 must be in foal, and awards will be suspended till birth is certified, which must be within 11 months from the date of the Show.

37. With reference to regulations 33 and 35, birth of at least a seven months' calf must be certified; and in regard to regulation 36, birth of at least a nine months' foal.

38. Horses entered as suitable for Field are expected to be jumped in the Horse Ring, but this is not compulsory except when the animals are being judged, and then only if required by the Judges.

39. The inspection of Horses as to soundness is left entirely to the Judges, who may consult the Society's Veterinary Surgeon if they deem it expedient.

40. No protests on veterinary grounds will be received.

41. All Ewes must have reared Lambs in 1882; and Ewes in Sections 3 and 8 (Blackfaced and Cheviot) must be in milk, and have their Lambs at foot.

42. Sheep must have been clipped bare during the season, and the Judges are instructed to examine the fleeces of the Sheep selected for prizes, and to cast those on which they find any of the former fleece. Fleeces must not be artificially coloured.

43. Sows must have reared pigs in 1882, or be in pig; and Pigs must belong to the same litter, and be uncut.

44. In Poultry the Aged Birds must have been hatched previous to, and Cockerels and Pullets in, 1882. No dubbing is allowed in the male birds of the Game Breeds. In the sections for Ducks, Turkeys, Geese, and Hens and Pullets of the Game and Malay Breeds, the lots to consist of one bird only.

45. The Yard will be open for Stock on Monday, 24th July, and between Six and Ten o'clock on the morning of Tuesday, 25th, after which hour no Stock can be admitted.

46. Bulls must be secured by nose rings, with chains or ropes attached, or with strong halters and double ropes. All cattle must be tied in their stalls.

47. Servants in charge of Stock must bring their own buckets or pails, and a piece of rope to carry their forage.

48. Strong loose boxes will be provided for Stallions and three and two-year old Entire Colts, in which they can remain all night, and loose boxes for Mares with foal at foot; closed-in stables for all the other horses, and covered

accommodation for the whole of the other stock. Night accommodation will be provided for Attendants on Stock, and those requiring the same must make application when they return their Entry Schedules, and remit the charge along with their stall rent.

49. Straw, hay, grass, and tares will be provided free by the Society during the four days of the Show; other kinds of food will be supplied at fixed prices in the forage yard. Any Servant removing bedding from an adjoining stall will be fined in double the amount taken. Exhibitors may fetch their own cake or corn to the Yard, but not grass, tares, hay, nor straw. Coops, food, and attendance for Poultry will be found by the Society.

50. Cattle, Sheep, Swine, or Poultry cannot be removed from the Yard till 5 P.M. on Friday, 28th July, except on certificate by the Veterinary Surgeon employed by the Directors.

51. Horses may be withdrawn at 6 o'clock each evening on a deposit of £2 for each animal, which shall be forfeited if the animal is not brought back. They must return at half-past 7 o'clock the following morning, and those not in before 8 will forfeit 10s. Horse passes to be applied for at the Committee Room between 5 and 6 P.M. on Tuesday, and the deposit will be returned between 12.30 and 2.30 on Friday.

52. When the Stock is leaving the Yard, no animal is to be moved till ordered by those in charge of clearing the Yard. Those transgressing this Rule will be detained till all the other Stock is removed.

### JUDGING STOCK AND POULTRY.

53. On Tuesday, 25th July, Exhibitors, and all others except Servants in charge of Stock, must leave the Yard at 10 A.M.

54. The Judges will commence their inspection at 11 A.M., when the public will be admitted. The space reserved for the Judges will be enclosed by ropes, and no encroachment will be permitted. In no case shall a Premium be awarded unless the Judges deem the animals to have sufficient merit; and where only one or two lots are presented in a section, and the Judges consider them unworthy of the premiums offered, it shall be in their power to award a lower prize, or to suggest the removal of any lot which appears to them unworthy of being placed in the Yard.

55. In addition to the Premiums, the Judges are authorised to award three Commendations in each section (except Poultry, where only two prizes are to be awarded) if the entries are numerous and the animals of sufficient merit. These Commendations to consist of—Very Highly Commended, Highly Commended, and Commended.

56. The animals in Sections 10 and 11 (Ayrshire Breed) which have not calved before the Show will be judged along with Cows and Heifers in Calf, and those in Sections 13 and 14 which have calved before the Show will be judged along with Cows and Heifers in Milk.

57. Two Members of Committee will attend each Section of the Judges. It will be their duty to see that no obstruction is offered to them, and that the space reserved for them is not encroached on; to communicate to the Secretary any question that may arise for the consideration of the Committee; to complete their reports; and to ticket the prize animals.

58. It shall not be competent for any Exhibitor, nor for his Factor or Land-Steward, to act as a Judge or Attending Member in any class in which he is competing; and no Exhibitor shall remain in charge of any lot, whether belonging to himself or another, while the Judges are at work in the Yard.

### DAIRY PRODUCE.

59. Dairy Produce to be entered with the Secretary on or before 14th June. Received in the Showyard on Monday 24th July, and till 10 A.M. on Tuesday 25th July. Judged at 11 A.M. on Tuesday. Exhibited Tuesday, Wednesday, Thursday, and Friday, 25th, 26th, 27th and 28th July.

60. Dairy Produce must have been made on the Exhibitor's farm in 1882. At least 1 cwt. of the variety of Butter, and 2 cwt. of that of the Cheese exhibited, must have been made during the season. The lots must be fair samples, and untasted. No lot can be removed from the Yard till 5 P.M. on Friday, 28th July.

## STALL RENT.

61. The following rates shall be paid by Exhibitors when making their Entries :—

|  | Members. | | Non-Members. | |
|---|---|---|---|---|
|  | s. | d. | s. | d. |
| Cattle, each, . . . . . | 15 | 0 | 25 | 0 |
| Loose boxes for Stallions—3 and 2 year old entire Colts, and Mares with Foals at foot, | 30 | 0 | 40 | 0 |
| All other Horses, each, . . . | 20 | 0 | 30 | 0 |
| Sheep, per pen, . . . . | 10 | 0 | 15 | 0 |
| Swine, per pen, . . . | 15 | 0 | 20 | 0 |
| Poultry, each entry, . . . | 3 | 0 | 5 | 0 |
| Dairy Produce, each entry, . . . | 4 | 0 | 6 | 0 |
| Night accommodation for Attendants, each, . | 10 | 0 | 12 | 0 |
| Covered Booths for offices, 9 feet by 9 feet, . | 70 | 0 | 100 | 0 |
| Newspaper offices, . . £2, 10s. | | | | |

## IMPLEMENTS AND OTHER ARTICLES.

62. Implements to be entered with the Secretary on or before 1st June. Received in the Yard on Tuesday, 18th July, and till ten o'clock on the morning of Tuesday, 25th July. Exhibited Tuesday, Wednesday, Thursday, and Friday, 25th, 26th, 27th, and 28th July.

63. No Money Prizes or Medals will be given for Implements of any kind, and no inspection of them by Judges will take place, except those specified at p. 15.

64. Agricultural Implements, and Implements and collections of articles not Agricultural, will be received for Exhibition, but the Secretary will be entitled to refuse Entries from dealers in articles not deemed worthy of Exhibition.

65. Implements will be placed in the following sections, the Exhibitors' names being in alphabetical order, viz. :—1st, Under cover ; 2nd, Open ; 3rd, Motion yard ; 4th, For Exhibits not Implements of Husbandry, which will be placed apart from the Agricultural Implements, either under cover or open. Exhibitors must specify the space they require.

66. The articles of each Exhibitor will be all placed in one stand, except implements in motion, and must not on any account extend beyond the width allowed. No article to be moved out of its stand, or the stand dismantled, till the termination of the Show, at 5 P.M. on Friday, 28th July. Those infringing this rule will be reported to the Directors.

67. Exhibitors must arrange their own articles *within* the space allotted to them before 11 o'clock on Tuesday the 25th July, and to the satisfaction of those in charge of the Implement Yard.

68. Exhibitors must on no account leave their stands during the judging of Stock, and if found in the Stock Yard they will be fined 10s.

69. All Machines requiring steam or fire must be entered as such in the Certificate, and will be placed in the Motion Yard. Coke must be used in all cases where fire is required.

70. No Steam Engine shall be driven in the Yard at a greater speed than 4 miles an hour.

71. Locomotive and Traction Engines and other Machines must not be moved from their places without permission of the Secretary, and must not leave their stands till 5.30 P.M. on Friday.

72. There must be attached to each Implement, when forwarded to the Show, a label bearing the Exhibitor's name, and that of the implement.

73. The carriage of all Implements must be prepaid.

### STALL RENT.

74. No smaller space than 6 feet frontage, 20 feet deep (in Motion Yard 50 feet deep), can be allowed for Implements, and, except for exhibits not agricultural, no boarding shall exceed 4 feet in height.

75. Implement Exhibitors who are Members of the Society are entitled to either 20 feet by 30 feet of open space free; or in Motion Yard 8 feet by 50 feet of open space free; for additional space the charge is as follows :—

|  | Members. | Non-Members. |
|---|---|---|
|  | 3 0 | £0 4 0 |
|  | 1 0 | 0 2 0 |
| 30 feet open space behind, per foot, | 0 4 6 | 0 7 0 |
| Implements in Motion Yard, without shedding, 50 feet deep, per foot, | 0 2 6 | 0 5 0 |
| Covered Booths for offices, 9 feet by 9 feet, each, | 3 10 0 | 5 0 0 |
| Newspaper offices, each, . . . . £2, 10s. | | |

### ADMISSION TO YARD.

The public will be admitted on Tuesday, 25th July, at 11 A.M., when the inspection by the Judges commences. The charges will be—Tuesday, from 11 A.M. till 5 P.M., 5s.; Wednesday, from 6 A.M. till 5 P.M., 2s. 6d.; Thursday, from 6 A.M. till 5 P.M., 1s.; Friday, from 8 A.M. till 5 P.M. 6d.

Members of the Society are admitted to the Show-Yard without payment, on exhibiting a "*Member's Ticket,*" which is strictly not transferable. Tickets will be sent to all Members residing in the Counties connected with the Show. Members residing in other localities must apply for Tickets at the Secretary's Office, 3 George IV. Bridge, Edinburgh, *before the 15th of July.*

Exhibitors of Stock (not Members) will be charged 5s. for admission to the judging on Tuesday; on Wednesday at 8 A.M., and throughout the Show they will be admitted free.

Exhibitors of Implements and their attendants will be entitled to free entry during the Show, but must remain at their stalls during the judging of the Stock on Tuesday.

Tickets for attendants on Stock and Implements are not available to admit to the Yard between 11 A.M. and 5 P.M.; and any attendant requiring to leave the Yard during the day, cannot be again admitted except by a special pass (to be applied for at the Committee Room), which must be given up on his return.

---

Placards are prohibited both inside the Show-Yard and on the outside of the Boundary Fence, with the exception of those belonging to Exhibitors, whose right is confined to their own stalls. No newspapers or any other article allowed to be carried about the Yard for sale. No strolling bands admitted.

*No Carriages or Equestrians admitted without special leave from the Directors, and then only for Invalids. Bath chairs may be brought in.*

Premium Lists, Regulations, and Certificates of Entry, may be obtained by applying at the Secretary's Office, No. 3 George IV. Bridge, Edinburgh.

---

*All Communications should be addressed to* FLETCHER NORTON MENZIES, *Esq., Secretary of the Highland and Agricultural Society of Scotland, No. 3 George IV. Bridge, Edinburgh.*

---

### LAST DAYS OF ENTRY.

IMPLEMENTS—THURSDAY, 1st JUNE.
STOCK AND ALL OTHER ENTRIES—WEDNESDAY, 14TH JUNE.

## RAILWAY ARRANGEMENTS.

The Caledonian, North British, and Glasgow and South-Western Railway Companies have adopted the following regulations:—

1. Stock and Implements to the Show to be charged full rates.
2. From the Show, if sold, full rates.
3. From the Show, if unsold, to be conveyed back at one-half the ordinary charge to the station whence they were sent, on production of a certificate from the Secretary of the Show, to the effect that they are really unsold. *This Regulation applies only if the Traffic is conveyed by Goods Trains, there being no reduction in the rates when it is conveyed by Passenger Trains.*

4. HORSES—By Passenger or Special Train.
    (a) A Stallion to be charged the rate for one Horse, plus 50 per cent.
    (b) Any other Horse, for which the exclusive use of a horse-box is ordered, to be charged the rate for one Horse, plus 50 per cent.
    (c) Other Horses to be charged at ordinary rates.
5. BULLS, COWS, AND OTHER ANIMALS—
    (a) A Bull, Cow, or other animal sent in a horse-box, and for which the exclusive use of the box has been ordered, to be charged the rate for three Horses.
    (b) Bulls, Cows, or other animals sent in horse-boxes, but for which the exclusive use of the box has not been ordered, to be charged each the rate for one Horse, plus 50 per cent.
6. Poultry.—The Companies give notice that they are not common carriers of poultry; they will, however, to accommodate the public, carry such by special agreement only, and at special rates, to be obtained at the Companies' stations.
7. Dogs to be charged full rates both ways.
8. All the above to be carried at owners' risk.
9. Collection and Delivery to be performed in all cases by the owners.

The Highland and Great North of Scotland Railway Companies have adopted the following Clearing-House Regulations:—

1. Stock and implements to the Show to be charged full rates.
2. From the Show, if sold, full rates.
3. From the Show, if unsold, to be conveyed at *half rates* back to the station whence they were sent, on production of a certificate from the Secretary of the Agricultural Show to the effect that they are really unsold.
4. All the above to be carried at owners' risk.
5. When agricultural machines and implements are carried under these regulations to and from Shows, they must be invoiced station to station at the ordinary rates. Collection and delivery at sending station, and delivery to, or collection from, the Show-Yard to be performed by, or at the expense of the owners.
6. Regulations Nos. 1, 2, and 3, as to Cattle and Horses, to apply only if the traffic be conveyed in Cattle Waggons and by Goods Trains.
7. Poultry and Dogs to be charged full rates both ways.
8. No reduction in the ordinary rates for Horses or Cattle when conveyed in Horse-boxes.
9. Parties requiring the exclusive use of a Horse-box for only one animal to be charged one fare and a half.

The North-Eastern Railway Company has adopted the above Clearing-House Regulations, except No. 9, which they have altered as follows:—
"If three stalls be occupied, or if the exclusive use of a box be ordered, 25 per cent. beyond the ordinary charge for three horses."

## PREMIUMS.

THE TWEEDDALE GOLD MEDAL, *value £20, will be given for the best Border Leicester Tup in the Yard. All former Prize Animals are eligible to compete.*

*In addition to the Premiums, the Judges are authorised to award three Commendations in each section (except Poultry, where only two prizes are to be awarded) if the entries are numerous, and the animals of sufficient merit. These Commendations to consist of —Very Highly Commended, Highly Commended, and Commended.*

# CLASS I.—CATTLE.

| | Premiums. | | |
|---|---|---|---|
| SHORTHORN. | 1st. | 2d. | 3d. |
| Section | £ | £ | £ |
| 1. Bull calved before 1st Jan. 1880, . | 25 | 15 | 10 |
|    Breeder of best Bull, The Silver Medal. | | | |
| 2. Bull calved on or after 1st Jan. 1880, . | 25 | 15 | 10 |
| 3. Bull calved on or after 1st Jan. 1881, . | 15 | 10 | 5 |
| 4. Cow of any age, . . . | 20 | 10 | 5 |
| 5. Heifer calved on or after 1st Jan. 1880, | 15 | 10 | 5 |
| 6. Heifer calved on or after 1st Jan. 1881, | 10 | 8 | 4 |

£217

| | | | |
|---|---|---|---|
| AYRSHIRE. | | | |
| 7. Bull calved before 1st Jan 1880, . | 20 | 10 | 5 |
|    Breeder of best Bull,—The Silver Medal. | | | |
| 8. Bull calved on or after 1st Jan. 1880, . | 20 | 10 | 5 |
| 9. Bull calved on or after 1st Jan. 1881, . | 10 | 5 | 3 |
| 10. Cow in Milk, calved before 1st Jan. 1879, | 20 | 10 | 5 |
| 11. Cow in Milk calved on or after 1st Jan. 1879, | 20 | 10 | 5 |
| 12. Cow in Milk or in Calf, of any age, bred by Exhibitor, . . . . | 20 | 10 | 5 |
| 13. Cow in Calf, calved before 1st Jan. 1879, | 15 | 10 | 5 |
| 14. Heifer in Calf, calved on or after 1st Jan. 1879, . . . . | 12 | 8 | 4 |
| 15. Heifer calved on or after 1st Jan. 1880, | 10 | 6 | 4 |
| 16. Heifer calved on or after 1st Jan. 1881, . | 8 | 5 | 3 |

283

Carry forward, . . . £500

Brought forward, . . . £500

### POLLED ANGUS OR ABERDEEN.

|  | Premiums. | | |
|---|---|---|---|
|  | 1st. | 2d. | 3d. |
| Section | £ | £ | £ |
| 17. Bull calved before 1st Dec. 1879, . | 20 | 10 | 5 |
| Breeder of best Bull, The Silver Medal. | | | |
| 18. Bull calved on or after 1st Dec. 1879, . | 20 | 10 | 5 |
| 19. Bull calved on or after 1st Dec. 1880, . | 10 | 5 | 3 |
| 20. Cow of any age, . . | 15 | 8 | 4 |
| 21. Heifer calved on or after 1st Dec. 1879, . | 10 | 6 | 4 |
| 22. Heifer calved on or after 1st Dec 1880, . | 8 | 5 | 3 |

151

### GALLOWAY.

| 23. Bull calved before 1st Jan. 1880, . | 20 | 10 | 5 |
|---|---|---|---|
| Breeder of best Bull,—The Silver Medal. | | | |
| 24. Bull calved on or after 1st Jan. 1880, . | 20 | 10 | 5 |
| 25. Bull calved on or after 1st Jan. 1881, . | 10 | 5 | 3 |
| 26. Cow of any age, . . . | 15 | 8 | 4 |
| 27. Heifer calved on or after 1st Jan. 1880, | 10 | 6 | 4 |
| 28. Heifer calved on or after 1st Jan. 1881, | 8 | 5 | 3 |

151

### HIGHLAND.

| 29. Bull calved before 1st Jan. 1879, . | 20 | 10 | 5 |
|---|---|---|---|
| Broeder of best Bull,—The Silver Medal. | | | |
| 30. Bull calved on or after 1st Jan. 1879, . | 20 | 10 | 5 |
| 31. Bull calved on or after 1st Jan. 1880, . | 10 | 5 | 3 |
| 32. Cow of any age, . . | 15 | 8 | 4 |
| 33. Hoifer calved on or after 1st Jan. 1879, | 10 | 6 | 4 |
| 34. Heifer calved on or after 1st Jan. 1880, | 8 | 5 | 3 |

151

### FAT STOCK.

| Section | | |
|---|---|---|
| 35. Highland Ox calved before 1st Jan. 1879, | 6 | 3 |
| 36. Highland Ox calved on or after 1st Jan. 1879, | 5 | 2 |
| 37. Polled Ox calved before 1st Jan. 1880, . | 6 | 3 |
| 38. Polled Ox calved on or after 1st Jan. 1880, | 5 | 2 |
| 39. Ox, of any other Pure or Cross Breed, calved | | |
| before 1st Jan. 1880, . . . | 6 | 3 |
| 40. Ditto, calved on or after 1st Jan. 1880, . | 5 | 2 |
| 41. Cross-bred Heifer calved before 1st Jan. 1880, | 6 | 3 |
| 42. Cross-bred Heifer calved on or after 1st | | |
| Jan. 1880, . . . . | 5 | 2 |

64

£1017

# CLASS II.—HORSES.

| | Premiums. | | | |
| FOR AGRICULTURAL PURPOSES. | 1st. | 2d. | 3d. | 4th. |
| | £ | £ | £ | £ |
|---|---|---|---|---|
| Section | | | | |
| 1. Stallion foaled before 1st Jan. 1879, Breeder of best Stallion,—The Silver Metal. | 30 | 20 | 10 | 5 |
| 2. Entire Colt foaled on or after 1st Jan. 1879, . . . | 20 | 15 | 10 | 5 |
| 3. Entire Colt foaled on or after 1st Jan. 1880, . . . | 15 | 8 | 4 | 2 |
| 4. Entire Colt foaled on or after 1st Jan. 1881, . . . | 10 | 6 | 4 | 2 |
| 5. Mare (with Foal at foot) foaled before 1st Jan. 1879, | 25 | 15 | 10 | 5 |
| 6. Mare (in Foal) foaled before 1st Jan. 1879, . . . | 20 | 10 | 5 | 3 |
| 7. Filly foaled on or after 1st Jan. 1879, | 15 | 8 | 4 | 2 |
| 8. Filly foaled on or after 1st Jan. 1880, | 10 | 5 | 3 | 2 |
| 9. Filly foaled on or after 1st Jan. 1881, | 8 | 4 | 2 | 1 |
| 10) Family Prize.—The family to consist of five animals, foaled before 1st Jan. 1880 (male or female, the offspring of one sire), not necessarily the property of one person,* . | 20 | 15 | 10 | — |
| 11. Do. Do., foaled on or after 1st Jan. 1880, do. do.,* . . . | 20 | 15 | 10 | — |
| 12. Draught Gelding foaled before 1st Jan. 1879, . . . | 8 | 4 | 2 | — |
| 13. Draught Gelding foaled on or after 1st Jan. 1879, . . . | 6 | 3 | 1 | — |

437

### HUNTERS AND ROADSTERS.

| | | | | |
|---|---|---|---|---|
| 14. Brood Mare, with Foal at foot, suitable for Field, foaled before 1st Jan. 1878, | 20 | 10 | 5 | — |
| 15. Yeld Mare or Gelding, suitable for Field, foaled before 1st Jan. 1878, | 20 | 10 | 5 | — |
| 16. Filly or Gelding, suitable for Field, foaled on or after 1st Jan. 1878, | 15 | 8 | 4 | — |
| 17. Filly or Gelding, suitable for Field, foaled on or after 1st Jan. 1879, | 10 | 5 | 3 | — |
| 18. Mare or Gelding, suitable for carriage, foaled before 1st Jan. 1879, | 20 | 10 | 5 | — |
| 19. Mare or Gelding, suitable as Hackney or Roadster, between 14 and 15 hands, | 10 | 5 | 3 | — |
| 20. Mare or Gelding, not exceeding 15 hands, for milk cart of heavy draught, | 10 | 5 | 3 | — |
| 21. Mare or Gelding, not exceeding 14½ hands, for milk cart of light draught, | 10 | 5 | 3 | — |

204

Carry forward, . . . £641

* In Sections 10 and 11 the prizes to go to the owner of the sire.

Brought forward, . . . £611

| | Premiums | | |
|---|---|---|---|
| | 1st. | 2d. | 3d. |

**PONILS.**

| | £ | £ | £ |
|---|---|---|---|
| 22. Highland Stallion, 14¼ hands and under, . . . . | 6 | 3 | 1 |
| 23. Highland Mare or Gelding, between 13 and 14¼ hands, . . . | 6 | 3 | 1 |
| 24. Mare or Gelding, between 12¼ and 14 hands, . . . . | 6 | 3 | 1 |
| 25 Mare or Gelding, under 12¼ hands, | 6 | 3 | 1 |

40

**STALLIONS FOR AGRICULTURAL PURPOSES.**

Stallion for Agricultural Purposes to serve in the District of the Show in season 1882, Competition to take place in spring, . . . . 100

£781

# CLASS III.—SHEEP.

| | Premiums | | |
|---|---|---|---|
| **BLACKFACED.** | 1st. | 2d | 3d. |
| Section | £ | £ | £ |
| 1 Tup above one shear, . . . | 12 | 8 | 4 |
| 2 Shearling Tup, . . . . | 12 | 8 | 4 |
| 3. Three Ewes above one shear, . | 10 | 5 | 2 |
| Lambs shown with Ewes, . . | 2 | 1 | — |
| 4. Three Shearling Ewes or Gimmers, . | 10 | 5 | 2 |
| 5. Aged Tup, 2 Ewes, 2 Shearlings, and 2 Lambs. The Ewes to have Lambs in Season 1882, and all bred by Exhibitor except aged Tup, . . . | 8 | 4 | 2 |

99

Carry forward, . . . £99

|  | Brought forward, . . . | | | | £99 |
|---|---|---|---|---|---|

|  | | Premiums. | | | |
|---|---|---|---|---|---|
|  | | 1st. | 2d. | 3d. | |
| **CHEVIOT.** | | £ | £ | £ | |
| Section | | | | | |
| 6. Tup above one shear, | . . . | 12 | 8 | 4 | |
| 7. Shearling Tup, | . . . | 12 | 8 | 4 | |
| 8. Three Ewes above one shear, | . . | 10 | 5 | 2 | |
| Lambs shown with Ewes, | . . | 2 | 1 | — | |
| 9. Three Shearling Ewes or Gimmers, | . | 10 | 5 | 2 | 85 |
| **BORDER LEICESTER.** * | | | | | |
| 10. Tup above one shear, | . . | 12 | 8 | 4 | |
| 11. Shearling Tup, | . . . | 12 | 8 | 4 | |
| 12. Three Ewes above one shear, | . . | 10 | 5 | 2 | |
| 13. Three Shearling Ewes or Gimmers, | . | 10 | 5 | 2 | 82 |
| **LONG-WOOLLED OTHER THAN BORDER LEICESTER.** | | | | | |
| 14. Tup above one shear, | . . | 3 | 2 | — | |
| 15. Shearling Tup, | . . . | 3 | 2 | — | |
| 16. Three Ewes above one shear, | . . | 3 | 2 | — | |
| 17. Three Shearling Ewes or Gimmers, | . | 3 | 2 | — | 20 |
| **SHROPSHIRE.** | | | | | |
| 18. Tup above one shear, | . . | 8 | 4 | 2 | |
| 19. Shearling Tup, | . . . | 8 | 4 | 2 | |
| 20. Three Ewes above one shear, | . . | 6 | 3 | 1 | |
| 21. Three Shearling Ewes or Gimmers, | . | 6 | 3 | 1 | 48 |
| **SHORT WOOLLED OTHER THAN SHROPSHIRE.** | | | | | |
| 22. Tup above one shear, | . . | 3 | 2 | 1 | |
| 23. Shearling Tup, | . . . | 3 | 2 | 1 | |
| 24. Three Ewes above one shear, | . . | 3 | 2 | 1 | |
| 25. Three Shearling Ewes or Gimmers, | . | 3 | 2 | 1 | 24 |
| **EXTRA SECTIONS.** | | | | | |
| 26. Five Blackfaced Wethers, not above 4 shear, | | 4 | 2 | — | |
| 27. Five Cheviot Wethers, not above 3 shear, | | 4 | 2 | — | |
| 28. Five Half-bred† Wethers, not above 2 shear, | | 4 | 2 | — | |
| 29. Five Cross-bred‡ Wethers, not above 2 shear, | | 4 | 2 | — | |
| 30. Five Half-bred Wether Hoggs, | . . | 4 | 2 | — | |
| 31. Five Cross-bred Wether Hoggs, | . . | 4 | 2 | — | 36 |
|  | | | | | £394 |

\* The Tweeddale Gold Medal, value £20, will be given for the best Border Leicester Tup in the Yard. All former Prize Animals are eligible to compete.

† Half-breds must be the progeny of any kind of Long-Woolled or Short-Woolled (except Blackfaced) with Cheviot Ewes.

‡ Cross-breds must be the offspring of any Whitefaced or Short-Woolled Tup with Blackfaced Ewes, or the progeny of Blackfaced Tups with Whitefaced or Short-Woolled Ewes.

# CLASS IV.—WOOL.

| | Premiums. | |
|---|---|---|
| | 1st | 2d. |
| | £ | £ |
| 1. Woolled Tup, Blackfaced Breed, | 3 | 2 |
| 2. Woolled Tup, Cheviot Breed, | 3 | 2 |
| 3. Woolled Tup, Leicester Breed, | 3 | 2 |

£15

*Note.*—Exhibitors do not require to make separate Entries for Wool, as all the Tups entered in the Breeds where Wool Prizes are offered are judged, and Tups exhibited for Wool only must be entered in the sections applicable to their breed and age in the class for Sheep.

---

# CLASS V.—SWINE.

|  | Premiums. | | |
|---|---|---|---|
| **LARGE BREED.** | 1st. | 2d. | 3d. |
|  | £ | £ | £ |
| 1. Boar, | 8 | 4 | 2 |
| 2. Sow, | 6 | 3 | 1 |
| 3. Three Pigs, not above 8 months old, | 4 | 2 | 1 |

31

| **BLACK OR BERKSHIRE.** | | | |
|---|---|---|---|
| 4. Boar, | 8 | 4 | 2 |
| 5. Sow, | 6 | 3 | 1 |
| 6. Three Pigs, not above 8 months old, | 4 | 2 | 1 |

31

| **SMALL BREED.** | | | |
|---|---|---|---|
| 7. Boar, | 8 | 4 | 2 |
| 8. Sow, | 6 | 3 | 1 |
| 9. Three Pigs, not above 8 months old, | 4 | 2 | 1 |

31

£93

## EXTRA STOCK.

Animals not included in the Sections for Competition may be exhibited as Extra Stock, and will receive Honorary Premiums when specially commended, as follows :—

### CATTLE AND HORSES.

| Very highly commended, | Medium Gold Medal. |
|---|---|
| Highly commended, | Minor Gold Medal. |
| Commended, | The Silver Medal. |

SHEEP AND SWINE.

| | | | |
|---|---|---|---|
| Very highly commended, | | . | Minor Gold Medal. |
| Highly commended, | . | . | The Silver Medal. |
| Commended, | . | . | Medium Silver Medal. |

---

# CLASS VI.—POULTRY.

FIRST PREMIUM—ONE SOVEREIGN; SECOND PREMIUM—TEN SHILLINGS —in all the Sections of Poultry.

Aged Birds must have been hatched previous to, and Cockerels and Pullets in, 1882.

| | Section | Section |
|---|---|---|
| DORKING—*Silver Grey*, . | 1. Cock. | 2. 2 Hens. |
| | 3. Cockerel. | 4. 2 Pullets. |
| DORKING—*Coloured*, . | 5. Cock. | 6. 2 Hens. |
| | 7. Cockerel. | 8. 2 Pullets. |
| COCHIN-CHINA, . | 9. Cock. | 10. 2 Hens. |
| | 11. Cockerel. | 12. 2 Pullets. |
| BRAMAHPOOTRA, . . | 13. Cock. | 14. 2 Hens. |
| | 15. Cockerel. | 16. 2 Pullets. |
| SPANISH, . . . | 17. Cock. | 18. 2 Hens. |
| | 19. Cockerel. | 20. 2 Pullets. |
| SCOTCH GREY. . . | 21. Cock. | 22. 2 Hens. |
| | 23. Cockerel. | 24. 2 Pullets. |
| HAMBURG. . . . | 25. Cock. | 26. 2 Hens. |
| | 27. Cockerel | 28. 2 Pullets |
| ANY OTHER PURE BREED, { | 29. Cock. | 30. 2 Hens. |
| | 31. Cockerel. | 32. 2 Pullets. |
| GAME—*Black or Brown* { | 33. Cock. | 34. 1 Hen. |
| *Reds*, . . . { | 35. Cockerel. | 36. 1 Pullet. |
| GAME — *Any other* { | 37. Cock. | 38. 1 Hen. |
| *Pure Breed*, . . { | 39. Cockerel. | 40. 1 Pullet. |
| BANTAMS — *Any Pure* { | 41. Cock. | 42. 2 Hens. |
| *Breed*, . . . { | 43. Cockerel. | 44. 2 Pullets. |
| DUCKS—*White Aylesbury*, | 45. Drake. | 46. 1 Duck. |
| | 47. Drake (Young). | 48. 1 Duckling. |
| DUCKS—*Rouen*, . . | 49. Drake. | 50. 1 Duck. |
| | 51. Drake (Young). | 52. 1 Duckling |
| DUCKS—*Any other Pure* { | 53. Drake. | 54. 1 Duck. |
| *Breed*, . . . { | 55. Drake (Young). | 56. 1 Duckling. |
| TURKEYS—*Any Pure Breed*, | 57. Cock. | 58. 1 Hen. |
| | 59. Cock (Poult). | 60. 1 Hen (Poult). |
| GEESE—*Any Pure Breed*, | 61. Gander. | 62. 1 Goose. |
| | 63. Gander (Young). | 64. 1 Gosling. |

Amount of Poultry Premiums, £96.

# CLASS VII.—DAIRY PRODUCE.

|  | Premiums. | | |
|---|---|---|---|
|  | 1st. | 2d. | 3d. |
|  | £ | £ | £ |
| 1. Cured Butter, not less than 7 lbs., . | 6 | 4 | 2 |
| 2. Powdered Butter, not less than 7 lbs, . | 6 | 4 | 2 |
| 3 Fresh Butter, three ¹ lb. rolls, . | 6 | 4 | 2 |
| 4. Cheddar Cheese, 56 lbs. and upwards, . | 8 | 6 | 3 |
| 5. Cheddar Cheese, 14 lbs. and under, . | 4 | 2 | 1 |
| 6. Dunlop Cheese, 30 lbs. and upwards, . | 6 | 4 | 2 |
| 7. Cheese, any other variety 30 lbs. and upwards, . | 6 | 4 | 2 |
| 8. Cheese, any variety, 15 lbs. and under, . | 4 | 2 | 1 |

£91

# CLASS VIII.—IMPLEMENTS.

The following Implements, being yet in a comparatively undeveloped state, will be dealt with as new inventions, and Premiums will be offered, as follows:—

|  | Premiums. | | |
|---|---|---|---|
|  | 1st. | 2d. | 3d. |
| Section | £ | £ | £ |
| 1. Combined Reaper and Binder, or Lifting and Binding Machine, . . | 100 | 50 | 25 |
| 2. Seed Cleaner, . . . . | 15 | 10 | 5 |

£205

## REGULATIONS FOR COMPETITIVE TRIALS.

1. Implements to be entered with the Secretary on or before 1st June. Received in the Yard on Tuesday, 18th July, and till ten o'clock on the morning of Tuesday, 25th July. Exhibited Tuesday, Wednesday, Thursday, and Friday, 25th, 26th, 27th, and 28th July.

2. The Society will provide ground near Glasgow at a suitable season (probably in August), and make arrangements for the proper trial of the Implements.

3. Implements must remain in possession of the Society from the Show till the trials are over.

4. The price as entered in the catalogue must be held the same till after the trials are over.

5. Implements must be *bona fide* the manufacture of the exhibitor, and fitted together by him, but portions of the machine or other article exhibited for competition may be purchased from other works.

6. The Premiums will not be awarded without thorough and exhaustive open and competitive trials.

7. The Committee shall have power to withhold the Prizes where there is not sufficient merit, or to apportion them as they think best.

## REGULATIONS FOR EXHIBITION OF IMPLEMENTS AT WORK.

8. At the time of the competitive trials the Society will provide ground suitable for the exhibition at work of Mowers, Horse Rakes, and Hay Collectors.

9. The Implements must be entered and exhibited as specified in Rule 1.

10. Exhibitors must, when making their entries, specify on the Entry Schedule the quantity of ground required at the time of the trials, which will probably be in August.

11. Exhibitors must bind themselves at the time of entry to pay their proportion of the land required at such rate as the Committee may determine, whether they bring their Implements forward or not.

Reference is made to the General Regulations for the terms on which other Implements and Machines may be exhibited at the Show.

# CLASS IX.—BEE HUSBANDRY.

£20 and 2 Silver Medals have been granted to the Caledonian Apiarian and Entomological Society. Information to be obtained from, and Entries made with, Mr. R. J. Bennett, 50 Gordon Street, Glasgow.

## ABSTRACT OF PREMIUMS.

| | | | | |
|---|---|---:|---:|---:|
| 1. Cattle, | . . . . | £1017 | 0 | 0 |
| 2. Horses, | . . . | 781 | 0 | 0 |
| 3. Sheep, | . . . | 394 | 0 | 0 |
| 4. Wool, | . . . | 15 | 0 | 0 |
| 5. Swine, | . . . | 93 | 0 | 0 |
| 6. Poultry, | . . . | 96 | 0 | 0 |
| 7. Dairy Produce, | . . . | 91 | 0 | 0 |
| 8. Implements, | . . . . | 205 | 0 | 0 |
| 9. Bee Husbandry, | . . . | 21 | 12 | 0 |
| 10. Tweeddale Gold Medal, | . . | 20 | 0 | 0 |
| 11. Six Silver Medals to Breeders of best Aged Bulls and best Stallion, | . | 4 | 16 | 0 |
| 12. Extra Stock, say | . . . | 80 | 0 | 0 |
| | | £2818 | 8 | 0 |

# GENERAL SHOW OF STOCK AND IMPLEMENTS
## At INVERNESS, 1883.

The District connected with the Show comprises the Counties of Inverness, Elgin, Nairn, Ross and Cromarty, Caithness, Sutherland, and Orkney (including Shetland).

*Premiums will be offered for the following Classes :—*

## CATTLE.

### SHORTHORN.
Bull calved before 1st January ........ ................................1881
Bull calved on or after 1st January . ..............................1881
Bull calved on or after 1st January... ............................1882
Cow of any age.
Heifer calved on or after 1st January ...........................1881
Heifer calved on or after 1st January ...........................1882

### AYRSHIRE.
Bull calved before 1st January ..................................... 1882
Cow in milk of any age.
Cow in calf of any age or Heifer in calf calved before 1st
    January .................. ........... ...............................1881
Heifer calved on or after 1st January .............................1881
Heifer calved on or after 1st January ..............................1882

### POLLED ANGUS OR ABERDEEN.
Bull calved before 1st December .................................1880
Bull calved on or after 1st December .............................1880
Bull calved on or after 1st December .............................1881
Cow of any age.
Heifer calved on or after 1st December ..........................1880
Heifer calved on or after 1st December ..........................1881

### GALLOWAY.
Bull calved before 1st January ...................................1882
Cow of any age.
Heifer calved on or after 1st January ............................1881
Heifer calved on or after 1st January ............................1882

### HIGHLAND.

Bull calved before 1st January ........................................1880
Bull calved on or after 1st January ................................1880
Bull calved on or after 1st January ................................1881
Bull calved on or after 1st January................................1882
Cow of any age.
Heifer calved on or after 1st January ..............................1880
Heifer calved on or after 1st January ..............................1881
Heifer calved on or after 1st January ..............................1882
Cow of any age, and three or more of her descendants, male or female.

### FAT STOCK.

Highland Ox calved before 1st January ........ ....................1880
Highland Ox calved on or after 1st January ......................1880
Shorthorn Ox calved before 1st January ..........................1881
Shorthorn Ox calved on or after 1st January ....................1881
Polled Ox calved before 1st January ..............................1881
Polled Ox calved on or after 1st January ........................1881
Ox of any other pure or cross breed calved before 1st January...1881
Ox of any other pure or cross breed calved on or after 1st Jan....1881
Cross-bred Heifer calved before 1st January ....................1881
Cross-bred Heifer calved on or after 1st January ................1881

# HORSES

### For Agricultural Purposes.

Stallion foaled before 1st January ..................................1880
Entire Colt foaled on or after 1st January ........................1880
Entire Colt foaled on or after 1st January ........................1881
Entire Colt foaled on or after 1st January ........................1882
Mare with foal at foot, foaled before 1st January ................1880
Mare in foal, foaled before 1st January ..........................1880
Filly foaled on or after 1st January................................1880
Filly foaled on or after 1st January................................1881
Filly foaled on or after 1st January................................1882
Draught Gelding foaled before 1st January ......................1880
Draught Gelding foaled on or after 1st January..................1880

Stallion to serve in the district of the Show, season 1883.

### ROADSTERS.

Mare or Gelding, suitable for carriage, foaled before 1st January 1880
Mare or Gelding, suitable for carriage, foaled on or after 1st
   January ..................................................................1839
Mare or Gelding, suitable as Hackney or Roadster, between 14 and
   15 hands.

### PONIES.

Highland Stallion, 15 hands and under.
Highland Mare or Gelding, between 13 and 14½ hands.
Mare or Gelding, between 12½ and 14 hands.
Mare or Gelding, under 12½ hands.

# SHEEP.

*Ewes and Gimmers to be exhibited in pens of three ; Wethers and Hoggs in pens of five.*

### BLACKFACED.

Tup above one shear.
Shearling Tup.
Ewes above one shear.
Shearling Ewes or Gimmers.

### CHEVIOT.

Tup above one shear.
Shearling Tup.
Ewes above one shear.
Shearling Ewes or Gimmers.

### BORDER LEICESTER.

Tup above one shear.
Shearling Tup.
Ewes above one shear.
Shearling Ewes or Gimmers.

### LONG-WOOLLED OTHER THAN BORDER LEICESTER.

Tup above one shear.
Shearling Tup.
Ewes above one shear.
Shearling Ewes or Gimmers.

### SHROPSHIRE.

Tup above one shear.
Shearling Tup.
Ewes above one shear.
Shearling Ewes or Gimmers.

### SHORT-WOOLLED OTHER THAN SHROPSHIRE.

Tup above one shear.
Shearling Tup.
Ewes above one shear.
Shearling Ewes or Gimmers.

### EXTRA SECTIONS.

Blackfaced Wethers not above four shear.
Cheviot Wethers not above three shear.
* Half-bred Wethers not above two shear.
† Cross-bred Wethers not above two shear.

*Sheep not included in the above Classes must be entered as Extra Stock.*

---

* Half-breds must be the progeny of any kind of Long-woolled or Short-woolled Tup (except Blackfaced) with Cheviot Ewes.
† Cross-breds must be the offspring of any Whitefaced or Short-woolled Tup with Blackfaced Ewes, or the progeny of Blackfaced Tups with Whitefaced or Short-woolled Ewes.

# SWINE.

*Pigs to be exhibited in pens of three.*

**BLACK OR BERKSHIRE.**

Boar.
Sow.
Pigs not above 8 months old.

**SMALL BREED.**

Boar.
Sow.
Pigs not above 8 months old.

# COLLIE DOGS.

Dogs—Long haired, not exceeding 6 years old.
Bitches—Long haired, not exceeding 6 years old.
Dogs—Short haired, not exceeding 6 years old.
Bitches—Short haired, not exceeding 6 years old.

# POULTRY.

To be shown in Pens of One Cock or Cockerel and Two Hens or Pullets of each of the following breeds, except in the sections for Ducks, Turkeys, Geese, and Hens and Pullets of the Game and Malay Breeds, where only one bird is required :—

Dorking—Silver-Grey.
Dorking—coloured.
Cochin-China.
Bramahpootra.
Spanish
Scotch Grey.
Hamburg.
Any other pure Breed.

Game Black or Brown Reds.
Game—Any other pure Breed.
Bantams—Any pure Breed.
Ducks—White Aylesbury.
Ducks—Rouen.
Ducks—Any other pure Breed.
Turkeys—Any pure Breed.
Geese—Any pure Breed.

# IMPLEMENTS.

The following special Premiums will be offered for competition :—

Turnip Thinners—Three Premiums of £15, £10, and £5.
Potato Planters—Three Premiums of £15, £10, and £5.
Weed Eradicators—Three Premiums of £15, £10, and £5.

At the time of the trials the Society will provide ground suitable for the exhibition at work of Ploughs, Grubbers, Diggers, and Cultivators.

---

# GENERAL SHOW OF STOCK AND IMPLEMENTS

## AT EDINBURGH IN 1884.

The CENTENARY of the SOCIETY being in 1884, it has been resolved to hold the GENERAL SHOW of STOCK and IMPLEMENTS at Edinburgh that year.

The district in connection with the Show will, as on former occasions, embrace the Counties of Edinburgh, Haddington, Linlithgow, and Peebles.

The Classes of Stock will be afterwards notified.

# MEMBERS ADMITTED SINCE THE LIST WAS PUBLISHED IN MARCH 1881.

## 15th June 1881.

Portland, The Duke of, 18 Grosvenor Place, London

Seafield, The Earl of, Cullen House, Cullen

Middleton, Lord, Birdsall House, York

Innes, Sir J., of Balveny and Edengight, Bart., Keith

Allan, Alexander, of Aros, Tobermory

Anderson, William Malcolm, Pirntaton, Stow

Archibald, Francis, Blackfaulds, Alloa

Auld, R. C., Bridgend, Whitehouse, Aberdeen

Baird, Alexander, of Urie, Stonehaven

Balfour, Douglas, Letham, Leven

Ballingal, J. Smith Ronaldson, Ellabus, Islay, Greenock

Bell, John B., Cauldcoats, Arbroath

Beveridge, William, jun., East Grange, Culross

Blyth, Arthur Howard, Corston, Coupar-Angus

Brechin, Robert Miller, 44 Inverleith Row, Edinburgh

Buchanan, Angus, Auchinrair, Barcaldine, Ledaig

Burt-Wright, W., Auchinvole Castle, Croy, Dumbartonshire

Cairns, James, 67 South Methven Street, Perth

Chirnside, John, Auchinrair, Ledaig

Christie, Gilbert, Auchlyne, Killin

Clark, W. A., Crossbasket, High Blantyre, Lanarkshire

Cowan, Walter, Clathick House, Crieff

Crawford, James, Brydekirk Mains, Annan

Crerar, Alexander, Innerhadden, Rannoch

Cross, David, jun., East Bank House, Langbank, Renfrewshire

Cullen, William, Barbeggs, Croy

Curror, Peter, Leuchats Beath, Cowdenbeath

Daish, John, 5 South St. Andrew Street, Edinburgh

Dawson, John Muirhead, Elcho House, Balfron

Duke, William, Newbarns, Kirriemuir

Duncan, James, yr. of Auchandavie, Kirkintilloch

Duncan, John, Auchenbee, Croy

Duncan, Thomas, Dullatur, Cumbernauld

Dyer, John, wood merchant, Peebles

Finlayson, Matthew, Poppletrees, Stirling

Fleming, Rev. A., of Inchyra, Hamilton House, Perth

Fleming, Hugh, Lower Ballaird, Balfron, Stirling

Forbes, Alexander M., 6 St. Andrew Square, Edinburgh

Galbraith, Wm. W., Croftfoot, Gartcosh, Lanarkshire

Gilmour, William E., Croftengea, Alexandria, N.B.

Gordon, John P., yr. of Cairnfield, Cairnfield House, Fochabers

Graham, George, jun., Easter Board, Gartshore, Croy

Graham, T. D. Cunningham, of Dunlop, Stewarton

Hamilton, Alexander, Commercial Bank, 63 Wallace Street, Stirling

Hamilton, James E., of Whiteshawgate, Strathaven

Hamilton, Zachray Macaulay, Garth, Shetland

Hardie, James, seedsman, 73 Nethergate, Dundee

Hart, Andrew, Aberdalgie, Perth

Hood, David M., Gedhall, Barry, Carnoustie

Jaffray, William, Broomridge, St. Ninians, Stirling

Jardine, James, Killunan, Fintry

Johnston, Walter, Whitfield, West Linton

Kay, Robert, Mains Farm, Gargunnock, Stirling

Kerr, Thomas, Forehill, Caputh

Lang, Hugh, Glengorm, Tobermory

Lang, Robert, Aros Mains, Aros, Mull

M'Corquodale, David, banker, Carnoustie

Macdonald, James, Vallay, North Uist, Lochmaddy

Macdonald, John Macdonald Stewart, Monachyle, Lochearnhead

MacIntire, William, grieve, Mount Stuart, Rothesay

M'Kay, Allan, Cross Arthurlee, Barrhead

M'Keich, John, Upper Ballaird, Balfron, Stirling

M'Laren, Alexander, 11 Assembly Street, Leith

M'Leish, Daniel, Wester Keillor, Methven, Perthshire

Mack, Joseph, of Berrybank, Beston

Maxwell, William, Baraskomel, Campbeltown

Menzies, R. Stewart, of Pitcur, Hallyburton House, Coupar-Angus

Millar, David, coachbuilder, Crieff

Moffat, William, general manager, Great North of Scotland Railway, Aberdeen

Moir, Alexander, Nether Carse, Gargunnock, Stirling

Morton, James S., secretary, Scottish Provident Institution, 6 St. Andrew Square, Edinburgh

Murray, Captain A. B., Gartur, Stirling

Nisbet, Hugh Craig, Barnton Dairy, Stirling.

Ogilvie, David, jun., Nether Kelly, Arbroath

Paterson, J. Jardine, of Balgray, Lockerbie

Pollock, A., agricultural engineer, Mauchline

Pollock, J. J., of Auchineden, Strathblane

Rennie, James, Ironshill, Inverkeillor, Arbroath

Ritchie, G. Deans, Cloverhill, Biggar

Roberts, William, auctioneer, Bathgate

Robertson, Alexander, forester, Shaw Park, Alloa

Rodger, George, Arden House, Altrincham, Cheshire

Scott, Rev. John, Camelon Manse, Falkirk

Scott, John, Hillhead, Kingsbarns

Scott, John Corse, of Sinton, Hawick

Scott, Ronald, Renmure, Arbroath

Sharp, James, Viewfield, Blackford, Perthshire

Sleasor, Rev. Alexander, The Manse, Balfron

Smith, Ralph Colley, Corston, Coupar-Angus

Smith, William Anderson, Ledaig, Argyllshire

Somerville, William, Cormiston, Biggar

Sproat, George B., writer, Tobermory

Stenart, Alan Henry Seton, Touch, Stirling

Stenart, Charles Edward, Gilchristland, Thornhill

Stewart, Charles, Gateside of Arngomery, Kippen

Stewart, Duncan, Monachyle, Callander

Stewart, Duncan Douglas, land steward, Rossie Priory, Inchture

Stewart, George Mercer Falconar, of Binny, Uphall

Stewart, James, Donovan House, Denny

Stewart, John Lorne, of Coll, Argyllshire

Stewart, Robert King, of Murdostoun, New Mains, Lanarkshire

Stirling, Robert, Pendreich, Bridge of Allan

Stodart, John, jun., factor, Whitehill, Rosewell

Stuart, J. Windsor, Bute Estates Office, Rothesay

Swinton, Alan, Swinton House, Coldstream

Tennant, James, Vitriol Works, Carnoustie

Tervit, John, Boat, Thankerton

Thomson, Thomas, Gordon, Abernethy, Perthshire

Turnbull, James, Carnock Smithy, Larbert

Wallace, John, Hailes, Haddington

Webster, James, Mungall Mill, Larbert

Weir, James, Hole Farm, Campsie

Williams, W. O., New Veterinary College, Edinburgh

Wilson, David, jun., of Carbeth, Killearn

Wilson, James, Burnetland, Biggar

Woodroffe, D. (Albion Iron Works Co.), Chase View, Rugeley, Staffordshire

Young, Arch., advocate (Commissioner of Scotch Salmon Fisheries), 22 Royal Circus, Edinburgh

Young, James, Mungall Farm, Larbert

18TH JANUARY 1882.

Ainslie, John, jun., Hillend, Loanhead
Aiton, John, Milnwood Iron Works, Holytown
Alston, George, Loudoun Hill, Darvel
Argo, James, Cairdseat, Udny, Aberdeen

Barclay, William, Dorsincilly, Ballater
Baxter, Frederick, seedsman, Inverness
Belfrage, A. J., Cairdinnes, Haddington
Bell, William, Muirloch, Fowlis Easter, Lochee, Dundee
Beresford, John George Massy, younger of Macbiehill, Peebles
Bertram, William, Lieutenant 96th Regiment, younger of Kersewell, Carnwath
Bigg, Thomas, Leicester House, Great Dover Street, London
Blair, Robert, Inversnaid Hotel, Lochlomond
Borland, William, Townfoot, Closeburn, Thornhill
Bowick, T., Bedford
Boyle, Captain David, of Shewalton, R.N., Dreghorn, Ayrshire
Brown, John Alexr. Harvie, of Quarter, Duntpace, Larbert
Bryce, J. H., M.R.C.V.S., 69 Port Street, Stirling
Buchanan, George, of Ardan, Bridge of Allan
Buntine, J. R., Sheriff-Substitute, Stirling
Burton, Matthew Bernard, Rosewell Mains, Rosewell

Cameron, Donald, Inversanda, Fort-William
Campbell, Farquhar, Ormsary, Ardrishaig
Campbell, Captain Henry John Fletcher, R.N., Boquhan, Stirling
Carruthers, Joseph, B. L. Co. Bank, Sanquhar
Chapman, William, Meadowhead, Airdrie
Couper, James, chemical manufacturer, Craigforth, Stirling
Cox, George Addison, of Invertrossachs, Callander
Cox, George Methven, Beechwood, Dundee
Cox, James C., Invertrossachs, Callander
Craw, James, Whitsome Hill, Chirnside

Dewar, Alexander, Bothlen, Cluny, Aberdeen
Dundas, Commander Colin M., R.N., of Ochtertyre, Stirling
Dundas, David, advocate, 46 Heriot Row, Edinburgh

Ewing, Archibald Ernest Orr, Auchintorlie, Bowling

Ferguson, Alexander Robertson, writer, Neilston
Ferguson, John, Bornish, South Uist, Lochmaddy
Ferguson, J., Dunse Castle Estate Office, Dunse

Ferguson, Ronald C. Munro, of Raith and Novar, Raith House, Kirkcaldy
Finlayson, John, Harperstone, Braco, Perthshire
Finlayson, William, Kersie Mains, South Alloa
Fleming, James S., Cashier, Royal Bank of Scotland, Edinburgh
Forrester, John, builder, 39 Broughton Place, Edinburgh

Garioch, Peter, 1 Stirling Street, Aberdeen
Graham, Thomas, Glandhall, Chryston
Gunn, Alex., V.S., Balloan, Muir of Ord

Hay, John Adam, younger of Haystoun, Eshiels, Peebles
Henry, Major-General Charles Stuart, C.B., The Pavilion, Melrose
Hislop, William (John Hislop & Son), coachbuilder, Edinburgh and Haddington
Holm, Alexander, Balliemore, Kilmichael, Lochgilphead

Keyden, James, cattle salesman, Stirling

Learmont, Robert, Westness, Rousay, Orkney

M'Alister, Ebenezer, of Corbeth Guthrie, Strathblane
M'Cowan, Robert William, accountant, 87 St. Vincent Street, Glasgow
Macdonald, Angus, Bellfield, Campbelltown
M'Gregor, Alexander, Easter Culmore, Gargunnock, Stirling
M'Gregor, Athole, Her Majesty's Indian Civil Service, Dunsinnane, Perth
Mackay, John, of Herriesdale, Dalbeattie
Mackenzie, Donald, Glengloy, Fort-William
M'Kie, John, of Auchencairn, Castle-Douglas
Macleish, John, Sunnylaw, Bridge of Allan
M'Nab, Robert, farmer, and innkeeper, Luss
M'Pherson, Professor Norman, LL.D., 2 Randolph Cliff, Edinburgh
Mann, Robert J., Cliff House, Seaham Harbour, Co. Durham
Mann, William, S.S.C., 119 Princes St., Edinburgh
Marr, Thomas, land steward, Kennet, Alloa
Marshall, Francis, of Park, Girvan, Ayrshire
Maxwell, Joseph, farmer, Thornhill Dumfries
Maxwell, Sir William, of Calderwood, Bart., Blantyre
Mill, George, 5 Thistle Street, Edinburgh
Mollison, James, agricultural implement maker, Ruthven, Meigle
Montgomary, Henry James, of Hattonburn, Milnathort

Morries-Stirling, John Morries, Gogar House Blairlogie
Mowbray, John James, of Naemoor, Dollar
Muir, John Gardner (Anderston Foundry Company, Glasgow), Cunningham-head House, Kilmarnock
Muir, Matthew Andrew (Anderston Foundry Company, Glasgow), Ardenvohr House, Row, Helensburgh
Munro, Patrick, 180 West Regent Street, Glasgow

Ord, Thomas Roberts, F.C.S., 52 Lime Street, London

Parr, Thomas P., of Killichronan, Aros, Mull
Paterson, George Frederick, of Castle Huntley, Longforgan
Paterson, Robert, Stock o' Broom, Kincardine, Thornhill, Stirling
Perman, Thomas Frederick, 2 W. Regent Street, Glasgow

Rae, John, jun., corn merchant, Ellon
Rae, William, advocate, Aberdeen
Reid, Robert, writer, Lochwinnoch
Rennie, David, 16 James Morrison Street, Glasgow
Rennie, James, Corrie, Kilsyth
Risk, James, Drumbrae, Bridge of Allan
Robertson, Donald, of Mayfield, Cupar-Fife
Rodger, Hugh, Cleland Estate Office, Townhead, Motherwell
Russel, James, Dundas Castle, Queensferry

Scott, Hugh James Elibank, Gala House, Galashiels

Scott, James B., Ryacacs Farm, Linwood
Sheppard, Rev. H. A. G., of Rednock, Port of Monteith, Stirling
Somervell, James, of Sorn, Sorn Castle, Mauchline
Sommerville, John, Belloch, Campbell-town
Stevenson, D., 85 Constitution St., Leith
Stevenson, John, Gateside, Kilsyth
Strachan, John, Mains of Montcoffer, Banff

Taylor, John, Drimore, South Uist, Lochmaddy
Thomson, James, H., Knocknahaw, Campbelltown
Thomson, Seton, Kinnaird House, Larbert
Thorneycroft, James Baird, Portland Iron Works, Kilmarnock

Ure, The Hon. John, Lord Provost of Glasgow
Urquhart, Robert, jun., Forres

Wallace, John, of Glassangall, Dunblane
Wallace, John, Stonelaw, Rutherglen
Wallace, Robert H., Rosa, N.-W.P., India
Watson, Adam, 23 Union Street, Edinburgh
Watson, Graham Gilbert, W.S., 45 Charlotte Square, Edinburgh
Watt, William, seed merchant, Cupar-Fife
Whitelaw, Alexander, of Woodhall and Gartshore, Leckie House, Stirling
Wilson, Dr. Alexander, Ivy Bank, Mid-Calder
Wilson, Thomas, Murrayshall Lime Works, Stirling
Wyse, Dr., Bridge of Allan

## DIPLOMA-HOLDERS—ELECTED FREE LIFE MEMBERS, 15TH JUNE 1881.

Gover, Lawford D., Findon, Worthing
Henderson, William, East Elrington, Haydon Bridge

Sandison, Marcus, Hempriggs, Wick
Weber, Frederick Herman, Estate Office, Escrick, York

| | |
|---|---|
| Number of Members in List published March 1881, | 4812 |
| Number of Members admitted in June 1881, | 118 |
| Number of Members admitted in January 1882, | 114 |
| Number of Holders of Agricultural Diploma admitted Free Life Members in June 1881, | 4 |
| | 5048 |
| Deduct estimated deaths, &c., | 148 |
| Total, | 4900 |

EDINBURGH, 1st March 1882.

F. N. MENZIES, Secretary.

# INDEX.

6

PRINTED BY NEILL AND COMPANY, EDINBURGH.